RESEARCH AND MANAGEMENT OF THE BROWN-HEADED COWBIRD IN WESTERN LANDSCAPES

Michael L. Morrison, Linnea S. Hall, Scott K. Robinson, Stephen I. Rothstein, D. Caldwell Hahn, and Terrell D. Rich, Editors

Proceedings of a Symposium of
PARTNERS IN FLIGHT-RESEARCH WORKING GROUP,
U.S. BUREAU OF LAND MANAGEMENT,
U.S.G.S.-BIOLOGICAL RESOURCES DIVISION
and
CALIFORNIA STATE UNIVERSITY, SACRAMENTO
Sacramento, California,
23–25 October 1997

Sponsors:

Partners in Flight-Research Working Group, U.S. Bureau of
Land Management, U.S.G.S.-Biological Resources Division
California State University, Sacramento
U.S. Forest Service, Pacific Southwest Research Station, Fresno
U.S. Forest Service, Rocky Mountain Research Station, Albuquerque
U.S. Fish and Wildlife Service, Ecological Services, Sacramento
U.S. Forest Service, Rocky Mountain Research Station, Flagstaff
U.S.G.S.-Biological Resources Division, Patuxent Wildlife Research Center
Western Section, The Wildlife Society
Cooper Ornithological Society

Studies in Avian Biology No. 18
A PUBLICATION OF THE COOPER ORNITHOLOGICAL SOCIETY

Cover drawing of a female Brown-headed Cowbird and Bell's Vireo by Jason Meigs

STUDIES IN AVIAN BIOLOGY

Edited by

John T. Rotenberry
Department of Biology
University of California
Riverside, California 92521

Studies in Avian Biology is a series of works too long for *The Condor,* published at irregular intervals by the Cooper Ornithological Society. Manuscripts for consideration should be submitted to the editor. Style and format should follow those of previous issues.

Price $18.00 including postage and handling. All orders cash in advance; make checks payable to Cooper Ornithological Society. Send orders to Cooper Ornithological Society, % Western Foundation of Vertebrate Zoology, 439 Calle San Pablo, Camarillo, CA 93010.

ISBN: 1-891276-06-9

Library of Congress Catalog Card Number: 99-74167
Printed at Allen Press, Inc., Lawrence, Kansas 66044
Issued: 18 May 1999

CONTENTS

LIST OF AUTHORS

SARAH ALLEN
Point Reyes National Seashore
Point Reyes, CA 94956-9799

D. E. ANDERSEN
Minnesota Cooperative Fish and Wildlife Research
  Unit
Department of Fisheries and Wildlife
1980 Folwell Ave.
St. Paul, MN 55108

V. ARTMAN
Ohio Cooperative Fish and Wildlife Research Unit
Ohio State University
1735 Neil Ave.
Columbus, OH 43210

ANNALAURA AVERILL-MURRAY
Wildlife and Fisheries Science
School of Renewable Natural Resources
University of Arizona
Tucson, AZ 85721
(present address: Nongame Branch, Arizona Game
  and Fish Department
2221 W. Greenway Rd.
Phoenix, AZ 85023)

JAMES C. BEDNARZ
Department of Biological Sciences
Arkansas State University
State University, AR 72467

JEFFREY D. BRAWN
Illinois Natural History Survey
607 E. Peabody Drive
Champaign, IL 61820
Champaign, IL 61820
  and
Department of Ecology, Ethology, and Evolution
University of Illinois
606 E. Healey
Champaign, IL 61820

NANCY J. CASNA
Therion Corporation
Renssalaer Technology Park
185 Jordan Road
Troy, NY 12180

JAMESON F. CHACE
Department of Environmental, Population, and
  Organismic Biology
University of Colorado
Boulder, CO 80309-0334

JOHN J. CITTA
Wildlife Biology Program
University of Montana
Missoula, MT 59812

ETHAN D. CLOTFELTER
Department of Zoology
University of Wisconsin
Madison, WI 53706

J. A. COLLAZO
North Carolina Cooperative Fish and Wildlife
  Research Unit
North Carolina State University
Raleigh, NC 27695

ALEXANDER CRUZ
Department of Environmental, Population, and
  Organismic Biology
University of Colorado
Boulder, CO 80309-0334

C. CURSON
Department of Wildlife Ecology
University of Wisconsin
1630 Linden Dr.
Madison, WI 53706

KRISTA L. DE GROOT
Department of Zoology and Centre for Biodiversity
  Research
University of British Columbia
6270 University Blvd.
Vancouver, BC V6T 1Z4

R. DETTMERS
Department of Forestry, Wildlife, and Fisheries
Plant Sciences Building
University of Tennessee
Knoxville, TN 37901

T. DONOVAN
College of Environmental Science and Forestry
State University of New York
Syracuse, NY 13210

J. P. DUGUAY
West Virginia Cooperative Fish and Wildlife
  Research Unit
West Virginia University
Box 6125
Morgantown, WV 26506

GILBERT H. ECKRICH
The Nature Conservancy
P.O. Box 5190
Fort Hood, Texas 76544-0190

KEVIN ELLISON
Department of Biology
University of California
Riverside, CA 92521
(present address: 8717 Bull Run Trail,
Woodstock, IL 60098)

KRISTEN M. ENOS
Kern River Research Center
P.O. Box 990
Weldon, CA 93283

D. M. EVANS
Forestry Sciences Laboratory
3625 93rd Ave. SW
Olympia, WA 98512

JOHN FAABORG
Department of Biological Sciences
110 Tucker Hall
University of Missouri
Columbia, MO 65211

CHRIS FARMER
Department of Ecology, Evolution and Marine
  Biology
University of California
Santa Barbara, CA 93106

L. GARNER
Montana Cooperative Wildlife Research Unit
University of Montana
Missoula, MT 59812

S. GARNER
Montana Cooperative Wildlife Research Unit
University of Montana
Missoula, MT 59812

GEOFF GEUPEL
Point Reyes Bird Observatory
4990 Shoreline Highway
Stinson Beach, CA 94970

M. D. GOERING
The Nature Conservancy
P.O. Box 5190
Fort Hood, Texas 76544-0190

CHRISTOPHER B. GOGUEN
Department of Wildlife Ecology
University of Wisconsin
1630 Linden Dr.
Madison, WI 53706

ERICK GREENE
Division of Biological Sciences
University of Montana
Missoula, MT 59812-1002

D. CALDWELL HAHN
Patuxent Wildlife Research Center
US Geological Survey
Laurel, MD 20708-4015

LINNEA HALL
Department of Biological Sciences
California State University
Sacramento, CA 95819

MARY D. HALTERMAN
Kern River Research Center
P.O. Box 1316
Weldon, CA 93283

JONATHAN B. HAUFLER
Boise Cascade Corporation
P.O. Box 50
Boise, ID 83728

SALLIE J. HEJL
USDA Forest Service
Rocky Mountain Research Station
P.O. Box 8089
Missoula, MT 59807

JAMES R. HERKERT
Illinois Endangered Species Protection Board
524 South Second Street
Springfield, IL 62701-1787

WESLEY M. HOCHACHKA
Montana Cooperative Wildlife Research Unit
University of Montana
Missoula, MT 59812
(present address: Cornell Laboratory of Ornithology
159 Sapsucker Woods Road
Ithaca, NY 14850-1999)

RICHARD L. HUTTO
Division of Biological Sciences
University of Montana
Missoula, MT 59812

WILLIAM M. IKO
USGS Biological Resources Division
Midcontinent Ecological Science Center
4512 McMurry Avenue
Fort Collins, CO 80525-3400

JENNIFER JOLIVETTE
Wildlife Program
University of Montana
Missoula, MT 59812-1002

E. E. KLAAS
Iowa Cooperative Wildlife Research Unit
Iowa State University
Ames, IA 50011

M. KNUTSON
USGS Biological Resources Division
Upper Mississippi Science Center
LaCrosse, WI 54602

T. E. KOLOSZAR
The Nature Conservancy
P.O. Box 5190
Fort Hood, Texas 76544-0190

BARBARA E. KUS
USGS Biological Resources Division
Department of Biology
San Diego State University
San Diego, CA 92182

STEPHEN A. LAYMON
P.O. Box 1236
Weldon, CA 93283

JANICE C. LORENZANA
Department of Zoology
University of Manitoba
Winnipeg, MB R3T 2N2

SUELLEN LYNN
Wildlife and Fisheries Science
School of Renewable Natural Resources
University of Arizona
Tucson, AZ 85721
(present address: SCE, NRO, NALF, SCI
P.O. Box 357054
San Diego, CA 92135)

J. C. MANOLIS
Minnesota Cooperative Fish and Wildlife Research
  Unit
Department of Fisheries and Wildlife
1980 Folwell Ave.
St. Paul, MN 55108

THOMAS E. MARTIN
USGS Biological Resources Division
Montana Cooperative Wildlife Research Unit
Avian Studies Program
University of Montana
Missoula, MT 59812

NANCY E. MATHEWS
Department of Wildlife Ecology
University of Wisconsin
1630 Linden Dr.
Madison, WI 53706

K. P. MCFARLAND
Vermont Institute of Natural Science
RR 2, Box 532
Woodstock, VT 05091

SHARON D. MCKELVEY
Cleveland National Forest
10845 Rancho Bernardo Road #200
San Diego, CA 92127

L. SCOTT MILLS
Wildlife Biology Program
University of Montana
Missoula, MT 59812

MICHAEL L. MORRISON
Wildlife and Fisheries Science
School of Renewable Natural Resources
University of Arizona
Tucson, AZ 85721
(present address: Department of Biological Sciences
California State University
Sacramento, CA 95819)

SOLON MORSE
Illinois Natural History Survey
607 E. Peabody Drive
Champaign, IL 61820
    and
Department of Ecology, Ethology, and Evolution
University of Illinois
606 E. Healey
Champaign, IL 61820

RICHARD D. NEWSOME
Department of Biology
Beloit College
Beloit, WI 53511

J. V. NICHOLS
West Virginia Cooperative Fish and Wildlife
    Research Unit
West Virginia University
Box 6125
Morgantown, WV 26506

IAN PAINTER
North Carolina State University
Department of Statistical Genetics
Raleigh, NC 27695-8023
(present address: TalariaInc
909 NE 43rd Street, Suite #206
Seattle, WA 98105)

BRIAN D. PEER
Department of Zoology
University of Manitoba
Winnipeg, MB R3T 2N2

LISA PETIT
Smithsonian Migratory Bird Center
National Zoological Park
Washington, DC 20008

KATHRYN L. PURCELL
Pacific Southwest Research Station
USDA Forest Service
2081 E. Sierra Avenue
Fresno, CA 93710

TIMOTHY S. REDMAN
VINS Research
Route 2, Box 532
Woodstock, VT 05091

ROLAND REDMOND
Montana Cooperative Wildlife Research Unit
University of Montana
Missoula, MT 59812-1002

TERRELL D. RICH
1387 S. Vinnell Way
Fish, Wildlife, and Forest Group
U.S. Bureau of Land Management
Boise, ID 83709

C. RIMMER
Vermont Institute of Natural Science
RR 2, Box 532
Woodstock, VT 05091

SCOTT K. ROBINSON
Illinois Natural History Survey
607 East Peabody Drive
Champaign, IL 61820
    and
Department of Ecology, Ethology, and Evolution
University of Illinois
515 Morrill Hall
Urbana, IL 61801

STEPHEN I. ROTHSTEIN
Department of Ecology, Evolution and Marine
    Biology
University of California
Santa Barbara, CA 93106

SEAN P. ROWE
Kern River Research Center
P.O. Box 990
Weldon, CA 93283
(present address: Archbold Biological Station
P.O. Box 2057
Lake Placid, FL 33862)

SPENCER G. SEALY
Department of Zoology
University of Manitoba
Winnipeg, MB R3T 2N2

JAMES A. SEDGWICK
USGS Biological Resources Division
Midcontinent Ecological Science Center
4512 McMurry Avenue
Fort Collins, CO 80525-3400

C. R. SMITH
Department of Natural Resources
Cornell University
Ithaca, NY 14853

JAMES N. M. SMITH
Department of Zoology and Centre for Biodiversity
    Research
University of British Columbia
6270 University Blvd.
Vancouver, BC V6T 1Z4

MARK K. SOGGE
USGS Forest and Rangeland Ecosystem Science
    Center
Colorado Plateau Field Station
P.O. Box 5614
Northern Arizona University
Flagstaff, AZ 86011

HILDIE SPAUTZ
San Francisco State University
Department of Biology
1600 Holloway Ave.
San Francisco, CA 97132
(present address: Point Reyes Bird Observatory,
4990 Shoreline Hwy.,
Stinson Beach, CA 94924)

CARA A. STAAB
USDA Forest Service
Prescott National Forest
P.O. Box 485
Chino Valley, AZ 86323

JOHN M. STRIBLEY
Department of Zoology
University of Maryland
College Park, MD 20742-4415

MARY J. TAITT
Department of Zoology and Centre for Biodiversity
   Research
University of British Columbia
6270 University Blvd.
Vancouver, BC V6T 1Z4

KRISTIN K. TERPENING
Travis County Transportation and Natural Resources
P.O. Box 1748
Austin, TX 78767

JOSHUA J. TEWKSBURY
Montana Cooperative Wildlife Research Unit
University of Montana
Missoula, MT 59812

W. MATTHEW VANDER HAEGEN
Washington Department of Fish and Wildlife
Wildlife Research Division
600 Capitol Way North
Olympia, WA 98501

JARED VERNER
Pacific Southwest Research Station
USDA Forest Service
2081 E. Sierra Avenue
Fresno, CA 93710

BRETT WALKER
Department of Biological Sciences
University of Montana
Missoula, MT 59812

F. JEREMY WHEELER
Mattole Restoration Council
P.O. Box 160
Petrolia, CA 95558

D. WHITEHEAD
Department of Biology
Indiana University
Bloomington, IN 47405

MARY J. WHITFIELD
Kern River Research Center
P.O. Box 990
Weldon, CA 93283

KIRSTEN J. WINTER
Cleveland National Forest
10845 Rancho Bernardo Road #200
San Diego, CA 92127

P. B. WOOD
West Virginia Cooperative Fish and Wildlife
   Research Unit
West Virginia University
Box 6125
Morgantown, WV 26506

ANTHONY L. WRIGHT
Hornocker Wildlife Institute
P.O. Box 3246
University of Idaho
Moscow, ID 83843-1908

KEN YASUKAWA
Department of Biology
Beloit College
Beloit, WI 53511

JOCK S. YOUNG
USDA Forest Service
Rocky Mountain Research Station
P.O. Box 8089
Missoula, MT 59807
(present address: Division of Biological Sciences
University of Montana
Missoula, MT 59812)

Studies in Avian Biology No. 18:1, 1999.

PREFACE

Terrell D. Rich

In August 1996, the Research Working Group of Partners In Flight, Ben Wigley and Peter Vickery, chairs, decided to sponsor a series of conferences across the U. S. that would focus discussion on topics of particular importance in bird conservation and identify high priority research needs. Using all available communication and funding mechanisms, Partners In Flight working groups would then assist in seeing that the needed research actually was carried out. Each of the four Partners In Flight regional working groups was asked to identify a high priority topic and the Western Working Group chose Brown-headed Cowbird parasitism.

Cowbirds were selected because research on their ecology and impacts on host species has been conducted primarily in landscapes and vegetation communities from the Great Plains east. As a result, there is a reasonable understanding of cowbird ecology in those regions and of management actions that will help conserve host species.

However, in the expansive landscapes of the West, where many vegetation communities are naturally fragmented and cattle grazing is nearly ubiquitous, relatively little research has been conducted. Most of the West is public land—over 175 million ha are managed by the U.S. Bureau of Land Management and the U.S. Forest Service. About two-thirds of this land is grazed, suggesting that cowbirds may have ready access to hosts across this broad region.

Evidence that the relationship between livestock and cowbird parasitism is poorly researched comes from the array of papers presented at an earlier conference, the North American Research Workshop on the Ecology and Management of Cowbirds, held 4–5 November 1993 in Austin, Texas. Of the 57 papers presented at that conference, only a single paper addressed the relationship between cowbirds and cattle.

This is unfortunate because little is known about what impacts cowbirds are having on western host species. It seems reasonable to assume that the productivity of some hosts is being reduced, perhaps significantly so. Certainly some western species have declining population trends for which currently there are no explanations.

Resource managers in the West have yet to be provided with information on most aspects of cowbird ecology. These include: (1) the temporal and spatial relationships between cowbirds and livestock; (2) cowbird densities in different geographic areas and vegetation types; (3) factors attracting cowbirds to a given area; (4) cowbird movements and lengths of stay; (5) distances cowbirds are traveling to obtain hosts; (6) impacts on host productivity; (7) host reaction to the presence of cowbirds and cowbird eggs; and (8) how all of the previous factors are affected by topography and landscape characteristics.

If cowbirds are found to impact populations of high priority bird species, management options are available. The dates on which cattle are allowed into a given area and the dates on which they are removed are both flexible. The amount of time they remain and their numbers can be adjusted. Features that attract livestock and cause concentrations that might attract cowbirds, such as water, salt, and shade, can be managed. Because birds nest over a relatively short time period, it is easy to imagine how grazing regimes can be changed to reduce or even eliminate cowbird impacts.

The conference upon which these proceedings are based had at least six presentations on this topic, suggesting an increasing attention to cowbird ecology in western landscapes. I hope that this volume will help stimulate further interest and assure the reader that Partners In Flight, through the Research Working Group and the Western Working Group in particular, will be eager to help support research on this most interesting and important topic.

Studies in Avian Biology No. 18:2–3, 1999.

INTRODUCTION

MICHAEL L. MORRISON, LINNEA S. HALL, SCOTT K. ROBINSON, STEPHEN I. ROTHSTEIN, D. CALDWELL HAHN, AND TERRELL D. RICH

This volume represents the culmination of the efforts of numerous individuals to synthesize current research on and management activities for the Brown-headed Cowbird (*Molothrus ater*). Intense interest in cowbirds is due to the potential negative impacts that their expanding populations may have on some host populations. The actual impact that cowbird parasitism has on host population size, however, remains controversial. That is, whereas there is little debate that cowbird parasitism can lower the productivity of individual host nests, it is not clear that such reductions have major effects on the overall productivity of host populations. It is also not clear that populations of hosts are declining and endangered species are limited by recruitment. It is also worth considering the possibility that host recruitment is impacted by factors that outweigh the influence of parasitism (e.g., predation). In addition, the efficacy of various remedies, especially cowbird control programs, has been questioned.

As outlined by Terrell D. Rich in the *Preface* to this volume, much research on these topics has been accomplished, especially in midwestern and eastern localities of North America. However, much less research has been conducted in the West. In response to the situation in the West, a symposium was organized by the Research Working Group of Partners in Flight, and California State University, Sacramento, with the goal of concentrating on cowbird research and management in western environments. Presentations from other geographic regions that could be used to guide efforts in the West were also encouraged. The result was a meeting held 23–25 October 1997 in Sacramento, California, at which about 200 individuals assembled to discuss cowbird biology. Of the 67 presentations (40 talks and 27 posters), 36 were subsequently submitted as manuscripts. Each submission was assigned to an editor, who obtained an additional 1–2 peer reviews. The 33 papers published in this volume are the result of that review process.

This volume is organized into three sections, each of which begins with a review of the state-of-the-knowledge, and a summary of the contribution that each paper makes to our knowledge of cowbirds. The three sections are:

I. *Cowbird ecology: factors affecting the abundance and distribution of cowbirds.*

II. *The basis for cowbird management: host selection, impacts on hosts, and criteria for taking management action.*

III. *Cowbird control: the efficacy of long-term control and proposed alternatives to standard control practices.*

Section I, introduced and reviewed by Scott K. Robinson, contains 13 papers that consider the factors determining cowbird abundance such as habitat characteristics, the presence of livestock, and general land-use practices. Section II, summarized by James N. M. Smith, presents 15 papers on the demographics of cowbirds and their hosts, the cost of parasitism to hosts, and the basis for taking different management actions. Finally, Section III, summarized by Linnea S. Hall and Stephen I. Rothstein, contains five papers that discuss the rationale for controlling cowbirds and propose alternatives to removal practices. The paucity of papers in the final section is indicative of the lack of research into the efficacy of cowbird control methods, including alternatives to lethal control.

Simply implementing a management action, be it habitat modification, removal of livestock, or killing of cowbirds, without a rigorous study design that includes monitoring of results, is unwarranted. Similarly, it is unwarranted to even implement cowbird management actions without baseline data showing significant cowbird impacts on host species of special concern. We view this volume, and the results of the 1993 Austin meeting (see *Preface*), as building blocks towards a more comprehensive understanding of cowbird ecology, and the development of more effective management tools.

NEED FOR NATIONAL PERSPECTIVE ON COWBIRD MANAGEMENT

The 1997 Sacramento symposium culminated in a closing workshop that recommended continuing the dialog to achieve a national perspective on cowbird populations as well as improving protocols for cowbird management as gleaned from control programs. Discussion sessions at the Conference began to synthesize a national perspective on cowbird ecology and management as participants contributed diverse regional and local perspectives. To participants, the Austin and Sacramento conferences illustrated the value of an on-going forum and focal point for integrating insights, methods, and effective practices related to cowbird management as part of endangered species recovery efforts, and more broadly as part of efforts to enhance overall passerine diversity and conservation. Scientists and managers expressed growing recognition that lessons and insights from longstanding programs should now be distilled into national policies on cowbird management. Driving the debate on such national policies is the major program being launched in the southwest by the U.S. Bureau of Reclamation to protect riparian habitat of the southwestern Willow Flycatcher (*Empidonax traillii extimus*) and to institute wider cowbird control programs. In particular, meeting participants recognized that new control programs should reflect the insights and experience of other cowbird management programs.

However, the lack of regular exchange of procedures or results among cowbird control programs and the lack of a centralized authority or designated lead agency has meant that we still have no standard procedures for optimal trapping protocol: evaluations of whether and when to initiate new trapping programs; evaluations of the effects of trapping on non-target species; reviews of trapping efficacy; or summaries of cost accounting, or cost:benefit analyses.

NATIONAL SCIENTIFIC ADVISORY COUNCIL AND CENTRALIZED DATABASE ON COWBIRD MANAGEMENT PROGRAMS

To capitalize on the emerging national perspective on methods and practices in cowbird management, a group of scientists and managers has formed the *Cowbird Scientific Advisory Council* whose goal is to provide a logistic center for cowbird information, dedicated to providing a national perspective on the need for control, and also to provide a centralized database on current control programs and practices. The council's objective is to maintain high professional standards in initiating, managing, and reviewing cowbird control programs and to facilitate effective information exchange among regional and local programs and between scientific, management, and conservation communities.

The Cowbird Scientific Advisory Council will establish a central database at Patuxent Wildlife Research Center (U.S. Geological Survey, Biological Resources Division), in Laurel, Maryland, where all cowbird management programs will be registered by name, geographic location, name of the responsible agency or organization, program manager, and annual cost. The council will coordinate efforts to define (1) the criteria and data that need to be addressed prior to initiation of any control program, and (2) the criteria and data necessary to evaluate the success of control programs. The resources of the database and the advice of the Council will be available to all state and federal offices considering the initiation of cowbird management programs as part of endangered species recovery efforts, or more broadly as part of efforts to enhance overall passerine diversity and conservation. The best procedures and evaluation techniques should be recognized and made available to maintain high and cost effective professional standards in all new and continuing programs. The Council can be reached by contacting either D. Caldwell Hahn or Stephen I. Rothstein (addresses within this volume).

ACKNOWLEDGMENTS

Many individuals made this volume, and the October, 1997, symposium, possible. The individuals responsible for obtaining funding for the meeting and for reducing the costs of publishing this volume are: T. Rich and J. Ruth, U.S. Bureau of Land Management and U.S. Geological Survey Biological Resources Division; R. Brown, California State University, Sacramento, Foundation; W. Laudenslayer and J. Verner, U.S. Forest Service, Pacific Southwest Research Station, Fresno; D. Finch, U.S. Forest Service, Rocky Mountain Research Station, Albuquerque; D. Harlow and K. Miller, Ecological Services, U.S. Fish and Wildlife Service, Sacramento; W. Block, U.S. Forest Service, Rocky Mountain Research Station, Flagstaff; D. C. Hahn, U.S. Geological Survey Biological Resources Division, Patuxent Wildlife Research Center; R. Barrett, Western Section, The Wildlife Society; and the Cooper Ornithological Society, E. Campbell, Treasurer.

The symposium would not have been successful without the assistance of the following individuals who volunteered their time to help with registration, audiovisual assistance, being session chairs, or with any number of other logistical needs: B. Kus, H. Bombay, N. Tuatoo-Bartley, J. Holloway, L. Kenner, C. Geisler, S. Estrella, C. Bailey, S. Hejl, P. Stackpole, D. Beck, T. Hopper, R. Holmes, R. Wall, E. Stitt, J. Kernohan, K. Christopherson, G. Grunder, L. Ochikubo-Chan, P. Mosley, S. Mungia, S. Hoover, John Lovelady, and D. Kwong. We also thank the staff of the Red Lion's Sacramento Inn for providing meeting services.

Studies in Avian Biology No. 18:4–9, 1999.

SECTION I: COWBIRD ECOLOGY: FACTORS AFFECTING THE ABUNDANCE AND DISTRIBUTION OF COWBIRDS

SCOTT K. ROBINSON

Over the last decade, a great deal has been written about the distribution and abundance of Brown-headed Cowbirds (*Molothrus ater*) (e.g., Lowther 1993, Robinson et al. 1993, 1995a; Rothstein and Robinson 1994, 1998; Thompson 1994, Donovan et al. in press, Smith et al. in press). The intense interest in this subject has arisen mainly because cowbirds are a major conservation problem in some areas. Studying cowbird abundance and distribution is a logical first step in developing management plans to reduce brood parasitization. But, cowbirds are also of interest as one of the best case history studies demonstrating the need to consider multiple spatial scales. A common conclusion of most reviews of cowbird ecology is that continental, regional, and landscape scales influence the abundance and distribution of cowbirds as much as local factors such as distances from edges.

THE ORTHODOX VIEW

To some extent, an orthodox view has arisen from the studies and reviews published to date. This orthodoxy has recently been dominated by a series of studies from the American Midwest, a landscape dominated by row-crop agriculture in which landscape composition can easily be characterized (Robinson 1992, Donovan et al. 1995a,b, Robinson et al. 1995b, Brawn and Robinson 1996, Thompson et al. in press). This orthodox view can be summarized as follows (Robinson and Smith in press).

1. At the continental scale, cowbirds are extremely widespread, but are most abundant in the northern Great Plains; abundance declines with distance from this region (Lowther 1993, Peterjohn et al. in press, Thompson et al. in press, Wiedenfeld in press). For many widespread host species, parasitization also declines with distance from this center of abundance (Hoover and Brittingham 1993, Smith and Myers-Smith 1998). Presumably, the Great Plains forms the historical center of cowbird abundance (Mayfield 1965) and cowbirds are still relatively less abundant in newly invaded areas in the West, East, and South.

2. At the regional scale (e.g., the American Midwest), cowbird abundance is determined by the composition of landscapes within the region (e.g., percent of forest cover; Robinson et al. 1995b). The presumed mechanism underlying this pattern is that in mostly forested landscapes, cowbird populations are limited by feeding sites (e.g., for northern New England; Coker and Capen in press, Yamasaki et al. in press), whereas in mostly agricultural landscapes, cowbird populations are limited by the availability of hosts (Robinson et al. 1995a).

3. At the landscape scale (operationally defined as a 10-km radius around a study site; Robinson et al. 1995b), cowbird abundance is strongly dictated by distance to feeding sites. A common result of many studies using radiotelemetry is that cowbirds commute up to 7 km between breeding and feeding sites, but that most flights are less than 2 km (e.g., Rothstein et al. 1984, Thompson 1994). As a result, cowbird abundance declines with distance from known feeding areas. In mostly agricultural landscapes in which feeding habitat is widespread, cowbirds may saturate all available breeding habitats (e.g., Thompson et al. in press), in which case parasitization does not decline as a function of distance from feeding areas. Recent studies from a saturated midwestern U.S. landscape, however, show that parasitization levels for some less-preferred hosts decline dramatically with increased distance (up to 1.5 km) from a particularly favored cowbird feeding site (a pig feedlot; Morse and Robinson, in press).

4. At the local scale (within a reserve or tract), patterns affecting the abundance and distribution of cowbirds are far less clear. Local edge effects may be pronounced (e.g., Temple and Cary 1988, Johnson and Temple 1990, Rich et al. 1994,) or absent (e.g., Robinson and Wilcove 1994), and may depend upon landscape context (Donovan et al. 1997). Thompson et al. (in press) argued that edge effects would be most pronounced in landscapes in which cowbird populations were low. Cowbird parasitization levels also may differ profoundly among habitats within a landscape (Hahn and Hatfield 1995), but it is not clear if cowbirds are more abundant in some habitats than they are in others. Cowbird parasitization can be related to tract size (Petit and Petit in press, Robinson et al. in press), but cowbirds can be abundant in large tracts (e.g., Trine, 1998, in press; Trine et al. 1998) and rare in small tracts (e.g., Roth and Johnson 1993, Hoover et al. 1996). Cowbirds appear to prefer sites and habitats where hosts

are more abundant, at least in landscapes in which cowbirds appear to saturate available habitat (Robinson et al. in press).

5. Other conclusions of note from previous studies include the following: (1) Cowbird populations are generally stable or declining in many regions (Lowther 1993, Peterjohn et al. in press, Wiedenfeld in press) with the exception of the northern Great Plains, in which populations continue to increase, and in the Southeast, where several species of cowbirds are still invading new areas such as Florida (Cruz et al. 1998). (2) Cowbird presence may be affected by such features as local availability of perches in grasslands or marshes, cover around nest sites, and vertical strata within forested habitats. In general, however, there are few consistent patterns of cowbird abundance in relation to these microhabitat features (Robinson et al. 1995a). (3) Cowbirds may use certain natural edges such as streams as travel corridors (Gates and Giffen 1991). (4) Winter food availability may strongly determine cowbird populations, although evidence for this remains speculative (Brittingham and Temple 1983).

Now that the orthodox view has been established, I will examine how the papers in this volume, most of which are from western landscapes, fit the established pattern. Specifically, I will use the results presented in volume to check for consistency with the following predictions derived from research in the midwestern U.S.:

(a) Cowbird abundance and parasitization levels should decrease as distance from the Great Plains increases (Hoover and Brittingham 1983, Lowther 1993, Smith and Myers-Smith 1998, Thompson et al. in press).

(b) Cowbird abundance and parasitization levels should be much lower in mostly forested landscapes in which foraging opportunities are limited (Robinson et al. 1995a, Donovan et al. 1997). In landscapes with unlimited foraging habitat, cowbird abundance should be correlated with host abundance (Robinson et al. in press, Thompson et al. in press).

(c) Cowbird abundance should decrease with distance from feeding areas, and should be absent 7 km or further from feeding areas (Rothstein et al. 1984, Thompson 1994, Thompson and Dijak in press).

(d) Cowbirds should be less abundant in habitats with lower parasitization levels (Robinson et al. in press).

(e) At local spatial scales, cowbirds should be most abundant near edges and where hosts are more abundant, but these relationships are likely to vary with landscape context (Donovan et al. 1997).

FIT OF PAPERS TO THE ORTHODOX VIEW

CONTINENTAL SCALE

Most papers in this section support the prediction that cowbird abundance and parasitization levels are greatest in or near their historical center of abundance in the Great Plains. Cowbird abundance or levels of parasitization are generally higher in the midwestern U.S. (Robinson et al., Stribley and Haufler) and central Texas (T. E. Koloszar et al., pers. comm.) than in the Rocky Mountains (Chase and Cruz, Hejl and Young, Tewksbury et al., Wright, and Young and Hutto; C. P. Ortega et al., pers. comm.), California (Farmer, Purcell and Verner, Staab), and Washington (Vander Haegen and Walker). In heavily grazed riparian corridors in Colorado (C. P. Ortega et al., pers. comm.) and fragmented shrubsteppe habitats in Washington (Vander Haegen and Walker), levels of parasitization were generally much lower than in comparably fragmented habitats in Illinois (Robinson et al.). Nevertheless, within each region, cowbirds can be locally abundant in the vicinity of livestock and agriculture (Rocky Mountains; Goguen and Mathews, Hejl and Young, Tewksbury et al., Young and Hutto). Even in the Midwest, cowbirds may be largely absent from large forest tracts (Stribley and Haufler). Cowbird abundance and levels of parasitization in some western communities are at least comparable to those in the Midwest (Farmer, Hochachka et al., Staab and Morrison; see also Averill et al., Chace and Cruz, Greene et al., Kus, Sedgwick and Iko, Whitfield and Sogge from other sections in this volume). Cowbird abundance, therefore, is not solely determined by distance from the cowbird's historical range and conservation problems associated with cowbird parasitization are not confined to the Midwest.

Another challenge to the orthodox view comes from Chace and Cruz's analysis of historical patterns of American bison (*Bison bison*) distribution. Chace and Cruz argue that bison, and therefore cowbirds, may have been much more widely distributed, especially at high elevations, than previously thought. This result suggests the intriguing possibility that cowbirds and their western hosts may have been in contact for a much longer time than previously supposed (see also Rothstein 1994).

REGIONAL SCALE

Hochachka et al. provide strong evidence that the relationship between forest cover at the landscape scale and parasitization levels holds across all regions of the U.S. At least at the scale of a 10-km radius around study sites, parasitization decreases within increasing percent forest cover within all regions of the U.S. for which there are data. The relationship weakens substantially (and may even be reversed) at a 50-km radius, which suggests a strong scale dependence when operationally defining a landscape. Nevertheless, Hochachka et al. provide strong support for the hypothesis that cowbirds may be limited by the availability of feeding sites within mostly forested landscapes (see Goguen and Mathews, Hejl and Young, Stribley and Haufler, Tewksbury et al., Wright, and Young and Hutto for additional evidence of the absence of cowbirds far from feeding sites in mostly forested landscapes).

LANDSCAPE SCALE

The overwhelming conclusion of most papers in this section is that cowbird distribution and abundance within landscapes is limited by the availability and proximity of feeding sites (reviewed in Goguen and Mathews). Cowbirds were abundant in virtually all study sites in Illinois (with the notable exception of grasslands, see below) in which there are no areas more than 7 km from extensive cowbird feeding habitat. In Michigan, Stribley and Haufler only found cowbirds to be abundant within 3 km of agriculture. In Texas, cowbirds were strongly associated with recently grazed areas on Fort Hood (T. E. Koloszar et al., pers. comm.). In the northern Rockies, Young and Hutto's huge census data set showed that a landscape variable, distance to agricultural land, was by far the strongest correlate of cowbird abundance in multivariate models. Hejl and Young's census data from the same general areas also show that distance to agriculture is the key variable explaining cowbird abundance. In the Idaho wilderness, Wright also found cowbirds only in the vicinity of livestock and park stations. In another area of the northern Rockies, the Bitterroot Valley, Tewksbury et al. found that cowbirds were only found within 4 km of agriculture and that distance to large agricultural areas was the strongest predictor of cowbird occurrence. In a general overview, Goguen and Mathews found a strong association between cattle and cowbird abundance throughout much of the West. Chace and Cruz further argued that the restricted movements of cattle herds can create severe chronic local problems for hosts nesting nearby. Purcell and Verner came to similar conclusions for the southern Sierra Nevada; cowbirds are found mainly at lower elevations because of the proximity of cowbirds during the nesting season.

There were, however, some notable exceptions to this general pattern. Several papers found some evidence for breeding habitat preferences within landscapes (Hejl and Young, Robinson et al., Tewksbury et al., Young and Hutto), some of which may have been related to host density (see below). Farmer found that cowbirds were unaccountably rare at Vandenberg Air Force Base in central coastal California, even in areas where foraging habitat was present. Vander Haegen and Walker found very little parasitization in fragmented shrubsteppe even though there were extensive agricultural areas nearby and cowbirds occurred throughout most study areas. These data suggest that factors operating at a more local scale than the landscape may also be important (see below).

One of the most interesting results from several studies is the extent to which cowbirds may be more flexible in their home range use than generally thought. Many western breeding habitats also provide local foraging habitat as well, which reduces the need for long commutes (Goguen and Mathews 1998). Even more surprising was Goguen and Mathew's (1998) data showing that cowbirds in New Mexico routinely commute 12 km between breeding and feeding areas, a result that breaks the 7-km barrier of Rothstein et al. (1984) and Thompson (1994). The spatial scale at which we examine cowbird abundance and distribution, therefore, may need to be increased beyond the 10-km radius used previously (Robinson et al. 1995a, Hochachka et al. *this volume*). These results are somewhat discouraging for managers who want to eliminate cowbird parasitization by managing cattle herds (Goguen and Mathews *this volume*).

LOCAL SCALE

At the scale of the habitat tract or study area, cowbird abundance can be related to (1) habitat type, (2) host abundance, (3) distances from habitat edges, and (4) vegetation structure.

1. Several papers in this volume address the use of different vegetation types (hereafter referred to as habitats) by cowbirds. One of the most striking patterns throughout much of the West is the cowbird's tendency to be most abundant in riparian habitats (Farmer, Hejl and Young, Staab and Morrison, Tewksbury et al., Young and Hutto; see also Averill et al., Kus, Sedgwick and Iko, Spautz, Whitfield and Sogge from other sections of this volume). This result holds when controlling for distance to cowbird foraging habitat (Hejl and Young, Tewksbury et al., Young and Hutto), although many riparian corridors tend to be heavily grazed and therefore provide foraging habitat within them. Cowbird parasitization appears to be contributing to the population declines in and endangered status of Southwestern Willow Flycatchers (*Empidonax traillii extimus*) and Least Bell's Vireos (*Vireo*

bellii pusillus). It is unclear, however, whether cowbirds prefer riparian corridors because of some aspect of their vegetation structure (Staab and Morrison) or because hosts also tend to be most abundant in riparian corridors (Tewksbury et al.). Fortunately for conservation planners, there are riparian corridors in which cowbirds are rare (Farmer), and wider corridors with complex, multi-layered vegetation may be less heavily used by cowbirds (or at least may be more difficult for cowbirds to search; Farmer, and Staab and Morrison).

Another dramatic difference in cowbird use of habitats occurs in the Midwest in which cowbirds are less abundant in grasslands, even heavily grazed ones, than they are in other adjacent habitats, even when controlling for host density (Robinson et al.). The reasons for this apparent avoidance are unclear, although grasslands have few perches from which to search for hosts and many hosts may have effective defenses against parasitization (egg ejecting; Peer et al.; or mobbing cowbirds). The much lower community-wide levels of parasitization in midwestern shrublands and savannas (when compared with forests) does not appear to be a result of lower cowbird abundance in these habitats (Robinson et al.). Rather, these habitats appear to contain a much higher proportion of unsuitable hosts. A similar result was obtained by Vander Haegen and Walker, who found very low levels of parasitization in shrubsteppe habitats in which cowbirds were widespread and relatively common. A lack of suitable perches and the timing of cowbird versus host breeding may explain some of the enigmatically low parasitization levels in fragmented shrubsteppe and other shrublands (e.g., Ellison), but it is also possible that many hosts within these communities have defenses against parasitization. For these reasons, the cowbird:host ratio (Robinson et al. in press, Thompson et al. in press) may not be a good predictor of parasitization levels among habitats.

Otherwise, few consistent patterns of differential habitat use have been documented when controlling for distance to cowbird feeding habitat. Cowbirds avoided steep-sided canyons in the Bitterroot Valley of Montana (Tewksbury et al.). Hejl and Young and Young and Hutto found no consistent association between forest types and cowbird abundance in Montana where cowbirds were not more abundant in logged forests. Robinson et al. found no differences in cowbird abundance (controlling for host abundance) among upland, floodplain, and coniferous forests in Illinois. Purcell and Verner found that cowbirds were most abundant at lower-elevation forests, probably because of proximity to cowbird feeding habitats and host abundance rather than

preferences for particular vegetation types (see below).

2. When controlling for proximity to feeding habitat, cowbirds tend to be most abundant in habitats in which hosts are most abundant (Robinson et al., Tewksbury et al., Young and Hutto). Purcell and Verner, however, found that species richness (including non-hosts) was a better predictor of cowbird abundance than host population densities in the Sierra Nevada. The cues used by cowbirds to select habitat is a promising area for future study (see below).

3. Few studies in this volume address the issue of cowbird abundance in relation to edges. Farmer found cowbirds to be most abundant along edges, which is the basis of the recommendation that riparian corridors be as wide as possible. Hejl and Young and Young and Hutto found no evidence that cowbirds were more abundant near silvicultural openings. Many studies, however, showed cowbirds to be most abundant near large agricultural openings (Hejl and Young, Stribley and, Young and Hutto) and near openings in which cowbirds feed (Goguen and Mathews, Wright).

4. The effects of vegetation structure on parasitization is the subject of only one paper in this section. Staab and Morrison found that nests were less likely to be parasitized in riparian corridors with distinct canopy and shrub layers. It is not clear, however, if this difference results from reduced cowbird abundance, or greater difficulty of finding nests in multilayered vegetation (see also Spautz for a discussion of vegetation structure).

OTHER FACTORS

Many western hosts may escape parasitization because cowbirds arrive too late in the season (Ellison, Purcell and Verner, Vander Haegen and Walker). Breeding of many western species may be triggered by seasonal rains that occur before the cowbird breeding season, especially in California (Ellison). The timing of cattle movements may also keep cowbirds out of some areas during the host nesting season (Goguen and Mathews, Purcell and Verner).

Cowbirds do not necessarily feed equally in all pastures or other agricultural areas. Cowbird abundance therefore may depend additionally on the kinds of pastures available within a site (Goguen and Mathews; T. E. Koloszar, pers. comm.) and in some areas, row crops may provide suitable cowbird feeding habitat (Thompson 1994, Robinson et al.)

FUTURE RESEARCH QUESTIONS

1. What cues are used by cowbirds to select breeding habitat? There is some evidence that

both host density and overall species richness are used as cues in habitat selection, but definitive experimental studies are lacking. This question is particularly important because there is growing evidence that cowbirds are often attracted to poor habitats with few suitable hosts and high predation rates (e.g., in Illinois shrublands, Robinson et al. *this volume*; the Central Valley of California, Farmer *this volume*; and the northern Great Plains, Davis and Sealy in press, Wiedenfeld in press). Such regions and habitats may act as ecological traps (sensu Gates and Gysel 1978) for cowbirds and might help explain why cowbird populations nationwide are stable or even decreasing through negative feedback on overall populations, as suggested by Rodenhouse et al. (1997).

2. What agricultural lands (row crops, pasture, and open range) provide the best foraging conditions for cowbirds? Our understanding of what makes optimal foraging habitat for cowbirds is still in its infancy. If we are to reduce parasitization through managing cattle movements and agricultural practices, we need more studies such as those of T. E. Koloszar et al. (pers. comm.) and Morris and Thompson (1998). In some areas, row crops may provide high-quality feeding habitat (Thompson 1994, Thompson and Dijak in press).

3. To what extent do cowbirds use foraging sites other than open range, pastures, and row crops? During the symposium, participants listed a wide variety of foraging habitats that cowbirds used when not feeding with cattle or in row crops. Cowbirds may be able to increase their home ranges enormously if they can supplement their diet with food obtained on or near breeding areas.

4. Can cowbirds use human residential areas exclusively, even if there are no cattle or row crops nearby? Anecdotal observations from urban areas in the Midwest suggest that cowbirds spend the afternoon feeding in mowed grass (S. K. Robinson, unpubl. data). If this pattern is widespread, human habitations may be replacing cattle as a feeding habitat in many parts of the country where cattle ranches and farms are being replaced with suburban developments.

5. How flexible are commuting distances of cowbirds? With the results of papers in this section, we now know that there is no 7-km barrier beyond which cowbirds cannot commute (Goguen and Mathews 1998). Yet, many studies show that most cowbird breeding-feeding flights are less than 3 km. Even in the "saturated" Midwest, parasitization levels of some hosts drop to very low levels 1.5 km from cowbird feeding sites (Morse and Robinson in press). In contrast, parasitization levels in some sites in New Mex-

ico can be very high even far (>5 km) from the closest feeding area (Goguen and Mathews 1998). Cowbirds in different regions of the country may respond differently to landscape structure. Additional studies using telemetry to define cowbird home ranges would help determine how cowbirds modify their commuting patters in different landscapes.

6. Do cowbirds select habitats and hosts more efficiently in areas where cowbird abundance is low? Many studies showing less-than-optimal habitat selection and host selection come from regions in which cowbird populations may saturate the landscape (e.g., Robinson et al. *this volume*). In such landscapes, many cowbirds may be forced to use less optimal habitats and hosts. Experimental reduction of cowbird abundance might provide answers to this question.

7. Do cowbirds select breeding home ranges based on foraging habitat or on breeding habitat? The high abundance of cowbirds in many host-poor habitats (e.g., Farmer *this volume*) suggests that cowbirds may be selecting habitats based on foraging rather than breeding. If so, then cowbirds may be highly susceptible to ecological traps (sensu Gates and Gysel 1978).

8. Are there cryptic or as-yet unstudied defenses of many host species that confound our ability to calculate cowbird:host ratios and are such defenses more likely to occur in historical cowbird habitat? To address this question, we need more studies of the ways in which hosts defend their nests against parasitization.

9. Can cowbird parasitization be reduced by altering range management practices? Experimental manipulations of cattle may enable us to develop methods of reducing cowbird abundance in critical habitats during the breeding season (Goguen and Mathews *this volume*).

10. Can cowbird parasitization be reduced through local vegetation management? Removal of woody vegetation from grasslands, maintaining a dense shrub layer in riparian corridors, and promoting complex, shrubby edges have all been proposed as ways of reducing parasitization (e.g., Johnson and Temple 1990, Staab and Morrison *this volume*). Many of these variables can be manipulated as a test of vegetation-based management.

11. Are there enough cowbird-free areas of the West to balance losses in cowbird-dominated landscapes? In the midwestern and eastern U.S. there are huge forest tracts in which cowbird parasitization is not a problem (Robinson et al. 1995b, Coker and Capen in press, Yamasaki et al. in press). There are also areas in the West in which cowbirds are extremely rare, but cattle ranching is also pervasive in the West. Large-

scale spatial models of cowbird abundance may tell us a great deal about the potential balance of sources and sinks for sensitive hosts (Green et al. *this volume*).

12. At what spatial scale can cowbird abundance best be predicted? Hochachka et al.'s (*this volume*) analysis suggests that the scale at which a landscape is defined may be critical for predicting cowbird abundance and levels of parasitization.

13. To what extent are cowbird populations limited by winter food availability? This topic remains poorly studied.

14. To what extent are cowbird populations limited by nutrient (mainly calcium) availability? Some differences in cowbird abundance (and fecundity) may result from regional differences in nutrient availability, which may limit cowbird reproduction (Ankney and Scott 1980, Holford and Roby 1993).

Studies in Avian Biology No. 18:10–17, 1999.

REVIEW OF THE CAUSES AND IMPLICATIONS OF THE ASSOCIATION BETWEEN COWBIRDS AND LIVESTOCK

CHRISTOPHER B. GOGUEN AND NANCY E. MATHEWS

Abstract. The Brown-headed Cowbird (*Molothrus ater*) participates in a well-known association with livestock, yet the full nature of the benefits of this association for cowbirds remains unclear. Historically, cowbirds were associated with American bison (*Bison bison*) on the Great Plains, but are now found across most of the United States. Cowbirds may benefit from livestock because grazing, or the presence of livestock itself, facilitates foraging opportunities. Livestock may create cowbird feeding microhabitats, increase insect abundance, provide foods in their manure, and may make food more visible by flushing insects when grazing. Due to this close association, livestock can influence the number and distribution of cowbirds. The presence of livestock tends to increase densities of cowbirds locally and can create gradients of parasitism pressure within a landscape. Research in primarily undeveloped sites in the Sierra Nevada and the Front Range of New Mexico confirm the influence of livestock on cowbird distributions. Cowbirds are extremely adaptable and can exploit a variety of anthropogenic food sources. Still, in areas where other artificial food sources are absent, the presence of livestock may be essential for continued cowbird presence or prolonged egg production. The strong bond between cowbirds and livestock has led to the use of livestock removal (i.e., rotation of livestock away from host breeding habitat) as a management technique to reduce parasitization of host nests. The effectiveness of this technique, as well as other aspects of the commensalistic relationship between cowbirds and ungulates, requires further study.

Key Words: brood parasitism, Brown-headed Cowbird, commensalism, foraging, grazing ungulates, livestock grazing, livestock removal, *Molothrus ater,* songbirds.

The Brown-headed Cowbird (*Molothrus ater*) is an obligate brood parasite that often reduces the success and productivity of the nests it parasitizes (Robinson et al. 1995a). As its name implies, the cowbird participates in a well-known association with livestock and is often observed in large numbers among herds of these grazers (Friedmann 1929, Bent 1958, Mayfield 1965, Morris and Thompson 1998). Although cowbirds undoubtedly engage in foraging activities when with livestock, the full nature of the benefits they receive through this association remains unclear. Cowbirds were historically believed to have been primarily a grassland species, typically found in association with American bison (*Bison bison*; Mayfield 1965). As bison were eliminated and replaced by cattle and other domestic livestock, the cowbird has readily adjusted to the change. The "buffalo-bird" of the past has become the "cowbird" of the present (Friedmann 1929).

Historically, cowbirds were restricted to the Great Plains, probably due to the shortage of open, short-grass feeding areas elsewhere (Friedmann 1929, Mayfield 1965). It was not until the native forests of the eastern United States were opened up and interspersed with agriculture and livestock that cowbirds were able to invade (Mayfield 1965). In the western United States, agriculture, irrigation, human development, and widespread livestock grazing have probably all contributed to the cowbird's spread (Rothstein 1994). At present, the cowbird has become one of the most widespread bird species in the United States. In many regions, cowbirds now parasitize a large proportion of nests, often across many species within bird communities (see Robinson et al. 1995a for examples). As a result, cowbird parasitization is often implicated as a contributor in perceived declines of neotropical migrant songbirds (Brittingham and Temple 1983, Finch 1991).

In this paper, we examine the potential causes of the association between cowbirds and livestock and discuss the implications of this association in terms of its influence on the distribution of cowbirds and cowbird parasitization. We use case studies from two well-researched western sites to focus more closely on how this association influences cowbird movements and parasitization frequencies of hosts in primarily undeveloped regions. We examine the question of cowbird dependence on livestock during the breeding season, particularly as it applies to the potential effectiveness of livestock removals as management strategies to reduce cowbird parasitization. Finally, we discuss what we think are the important research needs on this topic. We emphasize western rangelands because livestock grazing is a dominant land-use in the West (Sabadell 1982), and we think that in many undeveloped regions of the West, the presence of livestock is a primary factor influencing cowbird distribution and abundance.

WHY DO COWBIRDS ASSOCIATE WITH LIVESTOCK?

Although the association between cowbirds and grazing ungulates is well-recognized, remarkably little research has been done on the causes of this association. Early accounts by Great Plains explorers (summarized in Friedmann 1929) recorded the common observation of cowbirds with bison. Cowbirds were also associated with other native ungulates and are still occasionally observed with herds of elk (*Cervus elaphus*; C. Goguen, pers. obs.). The destruction of millions of bison in the late nineteenth century was followed by the introduction of millions of domestic livestock (reviewed in Knopf 1994). Cowbirds have apparently adapted to this switch and, in addition to cattle, are also known to associate regularly with horses, sheep, and other domestic animals (Friedmann 1929, Lowther 1993).

Several not necessarily mutually exclusive hypotheses can be postulated as possible explanations for the current association between cowbirds and livestock:

1. Livestock may act as perches or protective cover (Morris and Thompson 1998). In grassland habitats where cowbirds often feed, perches and protective cover from predators are rare. Livestock may provide elevated sites for social interactions and displays, protective cover while birds forage, and possibly provide females with perches for nest searching.

2. Livestock, or livestock-holding facilities, may be used as obvious gathering points for social interactions (Rothstein et al. 1987). Cowbirds are often found in groups when among livestock, and some social displaying occurs (Rothstein et al. 1986b, 1987). Rothstein et al. (1986b) refuted this hypothesis as the primary explanation for cowbird aggregations with livestock based on two arguments: (1) Cowbirds are opportunistic in their use of space, and will stop commuting to sites where large groups normally aggregate if feeding opportunities arise closer to their breeding ranges. (2) Although some social interactions occur at the large aggregations, most time is spent either feeding or loafing.

3. Cowbirds associate with livestock because the presence of livestock, or livestock grazing itself, facilitates foraging opportunities (Friedmann 1929, Mayfield 1965). Under this hypothesis, aggregations of cowbirds with livestock are not necessarily the result of active social interactions but, rather, may be passive aggregations due to limited, prime feeding sites, or due to the general selection pressures that favor group foraging, such as predator detection (Rothstein et al. 1986b).

4. Cowbirds associate with livestock as a result of a hard-wired response to a cattle-like stimulus (i.e., bison) with which they evolved, even though this response does not generate the same, if any, benefits at present. When studying animal behavior in a human altered environment, it is necessary to consider that the behavior may simply be an artifact of superimposing a stimulus on an otherwise well-adapted response (Gavin 1991). The ultimate causes that led to this association may be unimportant under current human-altered conditions; however, the innate response of cowbirds to grazing mammals remains. If this hypothesis is true, then determination of the causes of this association must take place under natural conditions (e.g., with bison).

Currently, the third hypothesis, which we will refer to as the foraging site hypothesis, appears to have the most support (Friedmann 1929, Mayfield 1965, Morris and Thompson 1998). The primary evidence for the foraging site hypothesis is the fact that feeding is the main behavior cowbirds exhibit when with livestock (Rothstein et al. 1986b, Morris and Thompson 1998; C. Goguen, unpubl. data). Cowbirds are omnivorous, feeding on both seeds and arthropods, and forage primarily on the ground in areas of short vegetation (Lowther 1993). Once again, several, nonmutually exclusive hypotheses can be proposed to explain the manner in which livestock may provide or enhance cowbird foraging opportunities:

1. Grazing may create or enhance microhabitats for cowbird foraging. Livestock grazing, by creating areas of short vegetation, may provide sites where a cowbird can forage more easily. Cowbirds often feed on mowed lawns and highway berms, suggesting that a reduction in grass height alone creates cowbird foraging opportunities (Mayfield 1965). Grass height alone, however, does not appear to explain cowbird behavior as cowbirds will abandon customary prairie feeding sites immediately following cattle removal to move to other actively grazed sites to feed with cattle (See CASE STUDY 2—THE FRONT RANGE, NEW MEXICO, below).

2. Grazing may increase foraging habitat quality by increasing grassland invertebrate abundance. Many studies have shown that grasshopper densities tend to increase with livestock grazing (Smith 1940, Nerney 1958, Holmes et al. 1979, Jepson-Innes and Bock 1989). Further, densities of foraging female cowbirds appear to be positively related to invertebrate density (Morris and Thompson 1998). This suggests that cowbirds may be found with grazing mammals simply because grazed areas have more invertebrates. We question this hypothesis as the main

explanation of a cowbird-livestock association based on the observation that cowbirds in actively grazed pastures usually forage close to livestock (Morris and Thompson 1998; C. Goguen, unpubl. data). If cowbirds were selecting grazed areas only because of higher insect densities, then they should be able to select any region of the pasture in which to feed, regardless of the proximity to an ungulate.

3. The presence of livestock may increase food availability via livestock body parasites, insects attracted to livestock, or insects and seeds in manure. Early naturalists speculated that cowbirds fed upon intestinal worms of ungulates extracted from their manure, removed and ate body parasites such as ticks, or captured flying insects attracted to ungulates such as horseflies (Friedmann 1929). Although arthropods often make up a substantial proportion of a cowbird's diet, particularly during the breeding season, Beal (1900) found little evidence in cowbird stomachs of the ungulate-attracted arthropods described above. Still, manure often contains seeds and larval insects that may be eaten by cowbirds. In the Sierra Nevada, cowbirds foraging in horse corrals appear to obtain most food by probing and pecking into horse manure (Rothstein et al. 1980). Additionally, trampling actions of horses commonly expose for cowbird consumption insect larvae under hard manure cakes (Rothstein et al. 1987). Food obtained from manure may be particularly important at holding facilities (e.g., corrals) where livestock are concentrated.

4. Cowbirds may obtain food from the forage provided to domestic livestock by humans. Cowbirds are commonly found in large numbers at corrals or feedlots, sites with high densities of livestock that are maintained by human feeding (Rothstein et al. 1984, Coker and Capen 1995, Morris and Thompson 1998). Cowbirds likely benefit from these sites by feeding on seeds in hay or on waste grains. This does not explain the association of cowbirds with free-ranging cattle or wild ungulates, however.

5. Finally, livestock may make grassland insect foods more visible to cowbirds by flushing invertebrates from vegetation during their grazing activities. Friedmann (1929) proposed that grazing ungulates increase the cowbird's ability to detect invertebrates in grassland vegetation. These invertebrates are normally stationary and camouflaged, but can be readily located when flushed by ungulate feeding or footsteps. This explanation is supported by studies that demonstrate that "hide-and-flush" grassland insects, such as grasshoppers and leafhoppers, comprise the majority of animal food in cowbird diets (Beal 1900). Observations of foraging cowbirds also support this explanation. When in herds of cattle, cowbirds tend to group around foraging and moving cows rather than stationary, resting cows; as a cow forages, cowbirds move along behind the feet and mouth of the cow and dart after insects that are flushed with each footstep (C. Goguen, pers. obs.). This is similar to the benefit that the Cattle Egret (*Bubulcus ibis*) obtains from its association with grazing animals (Telfair 1994).

IMPLICATIONS OF A COWBIRD-LIVESTOCK ASSOCIATION

Based on the above, it appears that, at the least, cowbirds benefit in a commensalistic relationship with livestock because of the enhanced feeding opportunities provided. Cowbirds are well known for their ability to separate their egg-laying and feeding ranges due to their parasitic nature (Rothstein et al. 1986b). In fact, most studies of cowbird movements have shown that cowbirds spend their mornings in areas of high host densities engaged in breeding activities, then commute to afternoon feeding sites, often in association with livestock (Rothstein et al. 1984, Teather and Robertson 1985, Thompson 1994). Historically, the breeding range of the cowbird depended upon the distribution of large ungulates (Mayfield 1965). This suggests that the presence of domestic livestock may influence the numbers and distribution of cowbirds.

How Does the Presence of Livestock Influence Cowbird Density?

The close link of cowbirds to livestock leads to the general prediction that cowbird densities should be higher on actively grazed areas, and maybe grazed areas in general, than on ungrazed. Results of western studies evaluating the effects of livestock grazing on cowbird densities are varied, but some patterns, based on vegetation type, appear to exist (Saab et al. 1995). In western riparian and shrubsteppe systems, the patterns observed agree with the prediction; cowbird densities tended to be higher in actively grazed areas (Reynolds and Trost 1981, Mosconi and Hutto 1982, Knopf et al. 1988, Schulz and Leininger 1991). In studies of western grasslands, however, cowbird densities were high, but no difference was detected among different grazing intensities (Kantrud 1981, Kantrud and Kologowski 1982).

Two grazing studies that conflict with the predicted patterns of cowbird densities raise important points concerning the evaluation of livestock effects on cowbird density. Goguen and Mathews (1998) found no significant difference in cowbird abundance between actively grazed and ungrazed pinyon-juniper (*Pinus edulus—Ju-*

niperus spp.) woodlands. They attributed this result to the ability of cowbirds to commute far beyond the grazing fenceline to ungrazed areas (See CASE STUDY 2—THE FRONT RANGE, NEW MEXICO, below). Taylor (1986) studied riparian areas that were either ungrazed all year or winter-grazed at various intensities. Livestock were not present to provide feeding opportunities for cowbirds on any of the sites during the breeding season, but cowbird abundance was higher in ungrazed sites. Host densities were also higher on ungrazed sites, probably because winter grazing had reduced the vegetation density on the grazed sites. Cowbirds appear to select breeding habitats with high host densities (Thompson et al. in press). This suggests that cowbirds were commuting from feeding areas outside the study sites and selecting breeding habitats based on host densities. The important point raised by these two studies is that cowbird mobility and breeding behavior, as well as grazing effects on host habitats, can confound attempts to assess the influence of livestock on cowbird abundance.

DOES THE PRESENCE OF LIVESTOCK INFLUENCE COWBIRD BREEDING DISTRIBUTIONS AND PARASITISM RATES ON LOCAL AND LANDSCAPE SCALES?

Although cowbirds have the ability to commute substantial distances between breeding and feeding ranges, most commute <3 km (Rothstein et al. 1984, Thompson 1994). If livestock are essential for providing feeding sites, then we predict that cowbird densities and parasitization rates decrease with distance from livestock. In a general sense this prediction has substantial support. Numerous studies have shown that cowbird numbers and parasitization rates are highest in areas closest to cowbird feeding sites (Verner and Ritter 1983, Airola 1986, Young and Hutto *this volume*). In the Sierra Nevada, higher numbers of cowbirds and parasitized nests were found in areas near human developments, horse corrals, and free-ranging livestock (Verner and Ritter 1983, Airola 1986). In New Mexico, the probability of a Plumbeous Vireo (*Vireo plumbeus*) nest becoming parasitized decreased with increasing distance from cattle grazing (C. Goguen, unpubl. data). In Vermont, the probability of a forest disturbance patch being occupied by a cowbird was positively related to the number of livestock sites (e.g., pastures or corrals) within 7 km (Coker and Capen 1995). In the midwestern United States, levels of parasitization were negatively correlated with percent forest cover, probably because non-forested areas tended to contain cowbird feeding habitat, such as livestock pastures (Robinson et al. 1995b).

These studies, as a whole, suggest that livestock distributions can influence cowbird distributions at both local and landscape scales.

THE INFLUENCE OF LIVESTOCK ON COWBIRDS IN PRIMARILY UNDEVELOPED, WESTERN LANDSCAPES: CASE STUDIES

To examine further the link between cowbirds and livestock, we selected two well-studied sites in the West to examine in detail. These sites were primarily undeveloped, meaning that few human alterations beyond the introduction of domestic livestock were present. We focus on these sites because they present an opportunity to examine cowbird behavior when livestock are responsible for most feeding opportunities. They also represent conditions that are common in the western United States.

CASE 1—THE SIERRA NEVADA, CALIFORNIA

The Sierra Nevada runs in a northwest to southeast direction through eastern California, between California's Central Valley and the deserts and Great Basin of Nevada. Coniferous forest, riparian, and mountain meadow vegetation cover a wide range of elevations and, although human impacts (e.g., logging, grazing) are pervasive, human developments remain relatively rare (Verner and Ritter 1983; S. Rothstein, pers. comm.). Free-ranging cattle are locally common during the summer, and horse corrals at pack stations are widespread (Rothstein et al. 1987). The Sierra Nevada constitutes one of the last major regions in the continental United States to be colonized by the cowbird. Few cowbirds were present prior to the 1940s (Rothstein et al. 1980, Rothstein 1994). Since colonization, the spread of cowbirds has been well documented, and much research has investigated the causes of the invasion and the factors that currently influence the abundance and distribution of cowbirds (Rothstein et al. 1980, 1984, 1986b, 1987; Verner and Ritter 1983, Airola 1986).

These studies established anthropogenic food sources, including livestock, as a primary factor allowing invasion of the Sierras by cowbirds and suggested that current cowbird distributions, and perhaps even prolonged egg-production ability, depended on the presence of these food sources. On the eastern slope of the Sierra Nevada, where human developments were present, cowbirds aggregated at horse corrals, bird feeders, and campgrounds for afternoon feeding (Rothstein et al. 1980, 1984). In the moderately developed northern Sierra, parasitization frequencies of hosts were highest in areas closest to regularly occupied human and livestock sites (Airola 1986). In the semi-wilderness of the west slope, cowbird abundance was negatively correlated with distance from horse corrals, and even preferred breeding habitats (e.g., riparian) tended to have few or no cowbirds in regions >10 km from horse corrals (Verner and Ritter 1983). Summer cattle grazing also occurred, and although cowbirds arrived and laid some eggs before cattle or horses were introduced each spring, the peak cowbird egg-laying period was apparently delayed until after livestock arrival (Verner and Ritter 1983). This delay caused female cowbirds to miss the peak period of host clutch initiations and implies a pivotal importance of livestock for prolonged cowbird breeding in this undeveloped region.

Although no species is currently threatened due to parasitism within the Sierra Nevada, one management implication is clear: controlling the spread of cowbirds there will need to involve controlling the spread of human-created food sources (e.g., concentrating further development into areas already affected; Rothstein et al. 1980, Airola 1986). Livestock appear to be particularly important where other anthropogenic disturbances are lacking. In these regions, increasing the distribution and numbers of horse corrals or free-ranging livestock may increase the proportion of area susceptible to cowbird parasitism. Further, introduction of livestock earlier in the spring could result in a longer cowbird laying period with greater overlap between cowbirds and hosts (Verner and Ritter 1983).

CASE 2—THE FRONT RANGE, NEW MEXICO

The Front Range is a general term for the mountains and foothills at the western edge of the Great Plains in Colorado and northern New Mexico. Along this range, grasslands of the Plains are replaced by coniferous forests on the mountain slopes creating a natural prairie-forest interface. In northeastern New Mexico, the Front Range forms along the foothills of the Sangre de Cristo Mountains. Cattle grazing is the primary land-use of this sparsely inhabited region, particularly in lower-elevation shortgrass prairie and pinyon-juniper habitats. We have studied cowbird-livestock interactions on adjacent ungrazed and actively grazed rangelands in this region since 1992 (Goguen and Mathews 1998).

Our initial research examined grazing-induced differences in bird species composition and nesting success in pinyon-juniper woodlands (Goguen and Mathews 1998). We predicted that cowbird parasitism would be an important influence on nesting success, particularly in actively grazed woodlands where livestock provide cowbird feeding sites. Cowbird parasitism did prove to be important, but parasitization frequencies of most hosts did not differ between actively

TABLE 1. COWBIRD PARASITIZATION FREQUENCIES OF COMMON HOST SPECIES BREEDING IN GRAZED AND UNGRAZED PINYON-JUNIPER WOODLANDS IN NORTHEASTERN NEW MEXICO, 1992–1995 (ADAPTED FROM GOGUEN AND MATHEWS 1998)

Species	Percent nests parasitized (sample size)	
	Ungrazed	Grazed
Plumbeous Vireo (Vireo plumbeus)	86 (29)	86 (36)
Western Tanager (Piranga ludoviciana)	89 (19)	80 (20)
Blue-gray Gnatcatcher (Polioptila caerulea)	76 (41)	76 (41)
Spotted Towhee (Pipilo maculatus)	0 (30)[a]	26 (23)
Western Wood-Pewee (Contopus sordidulus)	12 (41)	24 (33)

[a] Spotted Towhee nests were parasitized significantly more frequently on grazed plots. Parasitization frequencies for all other species did not differ by treatment.

grazed and ungrazed sites (Table 1). We attributed our inability to detect an influence of livestock grazing to a problem of scale. All ungrazed study plots were 4 km or less from active cattle grazing. Given the high mobility of cowbirds, we hypothesized that female cowbirds breeding on ungrazed sites commuted to adjacent grazed areas to feed with livestock; in effect, the scale at which our study plots were distributed among grazing treatments was finer than the scale of cowbird movements.

To assess how the distribution of cattle influenced cowbird feeding behavior and movements, in 1994 we initiated an intensive study of cowbird behavior. We performed surveys of cowbird abundance and we radio-tracked female cowbirds in both actively grazed and ungrazed areas. Cowbird surveys consisted of a system of point counts performed weekly, mid-May through July, along fixed routes in actively grazed and ungrazed prairie and pinyon-juniper woodlands. Surveys were conducted in the morning and afternoon to evaluate daily patterns of behavior and habitat use. Results from these surveys (C. Goguen, unpubl. data) suggest that cowbirds tend to spend mornings engaged in breeding activities in pinyon-juniper woodlands of grazed and ungrazed sites (Fig. 1a) but move in the afternoons to common feeding sites in grazed prairies with cattle herds (Fig. 1b). The rarity of cowbirds on ungrazed prairies in the afternoon demonstrates the importance of cattle for foraging opportunities. Additional evidence for this is suggested by the precipitous decline in cowbird numbers in the grazed prairies during afternoons late in the summer (Fig. 1b). This drop in detections coincided with the removal of

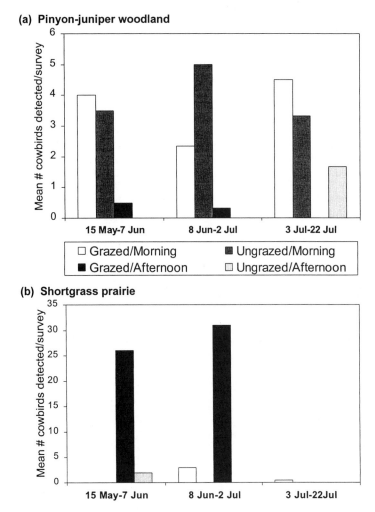

FIGURE 1. Mean numbers of cowbirds detected during point-count surveys of (a) pinyon-juniper and (b) shortgrass prairie vegetation, based on treatment and time of day (based on unpublished data of C. Goguen). Legend abbreviations refer to the treatment and time of survey, for instance "Grazed/Morning" means surveys were done on grazed sites in the morning. Note that the scale of the y-axes differs between (a) and (b).

cattle from the grazed pasture by 2 July. Radio-telemetry data corroborate these conclusions. Seventy-six percent of feeding locations of female cowbirds were with grazing livestock; an additional 22% occurred at livestock corrals (C. Goguen, unpubl. data). Further, when cattle were removed from the principal feeding pasture, female cowbirds immediately shifted to other pastures that remained actively grazed, even though these sites were 1 to 2 km farther away from their egg-laying ranges (C. Goguen, unpubl. data). These observations support our hypotheses of scale effects and cowbird movements between grazing treatments, and demonstrate the potential landscape-level influence of livestock grazing via commuting cowbirds.

DO COWBIRDS DEPEND ON GRAZING UNGULATES DURING THE BREEDING SEASON?

Results described in the case studies above introduce a question, the answer to which is likely to become increasingly important and controversial over the next several years: Do cowbirds depend on grazing ungulates during the breeding season? In both case studies, cowbird movements and distributions were linked closely to livestock, and, in fact, the physical presence of livestock appeared to be an important element of high-quality feeding sites for cowbirds. From a purely ecological perspective, this question is interesting because it provides insight into fundamental questions of ecology; that is, what controls the abundance and distribution of a species? From a management perspective, however, this question is potentially controversial because it raises the possibility that livestock removal could be used as a management strategy to reduce cowbird parasitism.

In a broad sense, the answer to the question of whether cowbirds depend on grazing ungulates during the breeding season is "no". Cowbirds are extremely adaptable and readily exploit a variety of anthropogenic food sources, ranging from recently tilled agricultural fields (Thompson 1994) to lawns, campgrounds, and bird feeders (Mayfield 1965, Verner and Ritter 1983, Rothstein et al. 1984). But what if the question is narrowed? Do cowbirds depend on livestock in regions where other anthropogenic food sources are absent or rare? This applies to many regions in the West. The answer to this question is less clear. In the undeveloped sites described in the case studies, cowbirds fed almost exclusively with livestock and bred in lower densities in areas distant from livestock. Without manipulative experiments, however, we have no way of knowing whether cowbirds depend on livestock in these regions, or if they can breed there regardless, but concentrate near livestock because food is easily obtained. In the western Sierra Nevada cowbirds survive several weeks without livestock in early spring (Verner and Ritter 1983). The evidence that females delayed most breeding until after livestock were introduced, however, has led to the hypothesis that even though cowbirds can survive without livestock, females may require the high rates of intake of invertebrate foods that livestock provide to maintain egg production (Rothstein et al. 1987). Low energetic costs of egg production argue against this hypothesis (Ankney and Scott 1980), but the foraging efficiency and diet of cowbirds with and without livestock remains unknown (Lowther 1993).

LIVESTOCK REMOVAL AS A TECHNIQUE TO MANAGE COWBIRD PARASITISM

The exclusion of livestock from sensitive habitats (e.g., riparian) is clearly important in creating and maintaining habitat structure for many bird species (Taylor 1986, Taylor and Littlefield 1986, Rothstein and Cook in press). The close association between livestock and cowbirds has also led to the proposal for, and implementation of, livestock removal as a management tool to protect some endangered songbird species from cowbird parasitism (J. Agyagos, pers. comm.; D. Ahlers, pers. comm.). Livestock removal entails the rotation of livestock away from host breeding habitat, at least during the critical spring and summer breeding months, in an effort to reduce parasitization. Often this technique involves removing or minimizing livestock presence within a certain radius of the critical habitat to act as an impediment to cowbird commuting.

In the Southwest, two endangered subspecies, the Least Bell's Vireo (*Vireo bellii pusillus*) and the Southwestern Willow Flycatcher (*Empidonax traillii extimus*), currently experience high parasitization rates (Franzeb 1989, Harris 1991). Livestock removal has been proposed as a management technique for both of these riparian breeding subspecies, and has been recently initiated to protect flycatchers in Arizona and New Mexico (J. Agyagos, pers. comm.; D. Ahlers, pers. comm.). As an example of its application, on the Coconino National Forest in Arizona, livestock are rotated out of public lands in a 6.8-km-radius area around an occupied flycatcher site from April through July (J. Agyagos, pers. comm.). This radius is based on maximum commuting distances observed by Rothstein et al. (1984).

Although the idea of livestock removal to reduce parasitization is intuitively appealing, the effectiveness of this technique remains unknown. Additionally, many factors, such as the availability of alternate cowbird food sources or the size of the livestock removal radius used, may influence its success. Still, under many circumstances livestock removal techniques may provide effective management of cowbirds, and offer an interesting opportunity to do "adaptive management" (Walters 1986). To assess their effectiveness, workers initiating livestock removal programs should incorporate baseline monitoring of cowbird abundance and nests of all host species, post-treatment monitoring, and the use of experimental controls when possible. Experimental removals comparing developed and undeveloped regions would also be useful.

RESEARCH NEEDS

Although the Brown-headed Cowbird is rapidly becoming one of the most studied bird species in North America, surprisingly little is understood about the relationship with livestock that earned this species its name. To conclude, we have summarized several of the main aspects of this association that we feel require further research:

(1) Basic understanding of the causes and benefits of the cowbird-livestock association.— Although feeding is undoubtedly a primary reason for cowbirds to associate with livestock, the importance of social interactions at these feeding groups, and the mechanics of food facilitation by livestock remain unclear.

(2) The dependence of cowbirds on grazing

ungulates, and livestock removals.—The effectiveness of a livestock removal program probably hinges on the degree of dependence of cowbirds on livestock in the region of concern. Given the potential costs of livestock removals (e.g., public relations, manager's and rancher's time and money, lost opportunities to protect the species with alternative techniques), manipulative experiments are needed to evaluate the many unknowns: Do livestock removals reduce parasitization rates in developed regions where other anthropogenic feeding sites exist? Do livestock removals reduce parasitism rates in undeveloped regions? What is the proper scale for removals, i.e., how far must livestock be withdrawn to prevent cowbird commuting?

(3) Effects of grazing management strategies.—A variety of grazing systems exist, yet little is known about how different systems affect cowbirds. For example, do increased stocking densities lead to higher cowbird densities? Can seasonal grazing strategies be used over large regions to move cowbirds away from sensitive areas during the breeding season?

(4) Necessity of livestock or other anthropogenic sources for prolonged cowbird reproduction.—It has been hypothesized that cowbirds need access to high-quality feeding sites, such as livestock, to sustain a high egg-laying rate throughout the breeding season. Studies comparing cowbird foraging efficiency and egg production rates with and without livestock would be useful to assess the validity of this hypothesis.

(5) Role of native ungulates.—Today, because of the prevalence of livestock, native ungulates play a much smaller role in cowbird ecology than they have historically. Bison grazing, however, is becoming popular as an alternative grassland management tool to cattle grazing (Plumb and Dodd 1993). Although from an ecological perspective, bison foraging behavior and food preferences differ from cattle (Plumb and Dodd 1993), bison provide feeding opportunities for cowbirds, just as cattle do. Comparisons of cowbird behavior and parasitism effects with bison versus cattle would be useful. From an evolutionary perspective, these comparisons may also provide insight into the ultimate causes of the cowbird-livestock association.

ACKNOWLEDGMENTS

We thank J. Agyagos, D. Ahlers, J. Record, and M. Sogge for information concerning the management of Willow Flycatchers. This manuscript benefited from discussion and comments from D. R. Curson, M. L. Morrison, R. L. Hutto, S. I. Rothstein, and J. Verner. Our research on cowbird-livestock interactions has been supported by the NRA Whittington Center, the Breeding Biology, Research, and Monitoring Database (BBIRD), the Caeser Kleberg Foundation at Texas Tech University Department of Range and Wildlife, USFWS Region 2, National Fish and Wildlife Foundation, Max McGraw Wildlife Foundation, Texas Cooperative Fish and Wildlife Research Unit, and the Department of Wildlife Ecology at the University of Wisconsin, Madison.

Studies in Avian Biology No. 18:18–22, 1999.

MANAGING RIPARIAN VEGETATION TO CONTROL COWBIRDS

CARA A. STAAB AND MICHAEL L. MORRISON

Abstract. Management strategies are needed to reduce the rate at which Brown-headed Cowbirds (*Molothrus ater*) parasitize their hosts. We investigated whether vegetation management could be used to reduce parasitism by seeking differences in nest-site microhabitats of hosts in a riparian area of central Arizona. During 1993 and 1994, we quantified vegetation characteristics in 0.04 ha plots centered on 128 nests of four commonly parasitized species and four infrequently parasitized species. We compared characteristics between parasitized and unparasitized nests of common hosts, and between nests of common and infrequent hosts. Factors associated with likelihood of parasitization were vegetation volume at nest, size of nest substrate, distance from nest to visual obstruction below nest, and presence of large trees near the nest. Whether nests belonged to common hosts or infrequent hosts was best predicted by nest height. Our results indicate riparian areas can be managed for large trees and numerous shrubs when the goal is to reduce parasitization.

Key Words: Arizona, avian reproduction, brood parasitism, Brown-headed Cowbird, host selection, microhabitat, *Molothrus ater,* nest selection, riparian.

It is well documented that brood parasitism by Brown-headed Cowbirds (*Molothrus ater*) causes many species of birds to fledge significantly fewer of their own young (e.g., Elliot 1978, Marvil and Cruz 1989). Consequently, some host species have undergone population declines that are at least partly due to parasitization (Mayfield 1977, Franzreb 1990). A few management strategies have been developed to minimize the potential impact of cowbirds on their hosts. Trapping and shooting can be done on or near host breeding grounds to reduce the number of cowbirds (Kelly and DeCapita 1982, Robinson et al. 1993). Host nests also can be located, allowing managers to monitor and remove cowbird eggs from the nests, or place artificial cowbird eggs in them, which act as a deterrent to subsequent parasitization (Ortega et al. 1994). These programs have the greatest potential when used to aid the recovery of threatened or endangered species (Robinson et al. 1993, Ortega et al. 1994). Because these strategies need to be repeated annually, have high costs, are labor-intensive, and have a restricted area of effectiveness, they may not be feasible for widespread use.

One way to control the effects of cowbirds on hosts would be to reduce the quality of cowbird breeding habitat, as measured by the proportion of nests that are vulnerable to parasitization. If a link existed between the vegetation surrounding available nests (i.e., nest-site microhabitat) and rates of parasitization, vegetation could be manipulated to reduce the number of nests being parasitized.

Within their breeding habitat, cowbirds appear to prefer edges (e.g., forest-meadow interfaces and perimeters of clearcuts; Brittingham and Temple 1983, Coker and Capen 1995). Managers can try to minimize the extent, rate, or lo-

cation of further fragmentation to minimize the risk that new areas will experience an increase in parasitization. However, this strategy will not work in areas that are, by nature, edges. Riparian zones of the southwestern United States are one example. These areas consist of narrow strips of vegetation that are characterized by a more diverse structure and assemblage of plant species than the surrounding, more xeric, environments. Because southwestern riparian areas support very high densities of breeding birds (Carothers 1974, Mills et al. 1991), and because parasitism rates have been positively correlated with density, many of these areas should be evaluated in regard to cowbird management needs.

We examined nest-site microhabitat characteristics of four common host species and four infrequent host species to determine if vegetative composition and structure influenced the susceptibility of a nest to parasitism by Brown-headed Cowbirds. Our specific objectives were to: (1) determine if differences existed between nest-site microhabitat of parasitized and unparasitized nests of common hosts, and (2) determine if differences existed between nest-site microhabitat of common hosts and infrequent hosts. From these data, we developed recommendations for habitat management that could minimize the impact cowbirds have on avian communities in southwestern riparian vegetation.

STUDY AREA

We worked along Walnut and Apache creeks, Yavapai County, Arizona, on about 50 ha of public (Prescott National Forest) and private lands at 1530–1580 m elevation. Vegetation consisted of 0.5–5.0 ha patches of riparian woodlands separated by grassy openings or strips of willow (*Salix* spp.). Following Szaro's

(1989) classification scheme, most patches were community type (1) *Acer negundo*-mixed broadleaf, (2) *Populus fremontii*, or (3) *Juglans major*; *Acer negundo*-mixed broadleaf was the most extensive type present. Mean annual precipitation was 40 cm, and mean annual temperature was 11.2 C (National Oceanic and Atmospheric Administration 1994).

METHODS

SPECIES STUDIED

Parasitization rates among species that accept cowbird eggs are highly variable, and indicate that factors other than egg rejection can influence the impact cowbirds have on a species. We used the natural patterns of variations in parasitization rates to divide the accepters into two groups: common hosts and infrequent hosts. Common hosts are those species that are frequently parasitized ($\geq 25\%$) in most of their range. Infrequent hosts are species that are rarely parasitized ($<25\%$) in large portions of their range, despite their apparent suitability or tolerance as hosts. By these definitions, infrequent hosts in Arizona can include species that are rarely parasitized in the western US, even if they are more commonly parasitized in the east (or vice versa). By studying these two groups, researchers might gain additional insight into what features make a potential host susceptible to parasitization, which would lead to ways to lessen the impact cowbirds have on common hosts.

In 1993 and 1994, we searched for nests of four common host species and four infrequent host species that (1) are known Brown-headed Cowbird hosts (Friedmann and Kiff 1985), (2) are not known to reject cowbird eggs, (3) are open-cup nesters, and (4) breed during the same period that cowbirds do. The common hosts were Plumbeous Vireo (*Vireo plumbeus*), Yellow Warbler (*Dendroica petechia*), Yellow-breasted Chat (*Icteria virens*), and Blue Grosbeak (*Guiraca caerulea*). The infrequent hosts were Western Wood-Pewee (*Contopus sordidulus*), Black-headed Grosbeak (*Pheucticus melanocephalus*), House Finch (*Carpodacus mexicanus*), and Spotted Towhee (*Pipilo maculatus*). Staab (1995) presented details on classification of these species as common or infrequent host, and as acceptor or rejector.

NEST SEARCHES

We located nests by watching potential hosts (Ralph et al. 1993) and by conducting intensive searches through vegetation. We identified distinct stands of vegetation to serve as relocatable units to be searched. Nest searches were conducted from May through July to correspond with the egg-laying period of cowbirds (Best 1978). We revisited each stand every 10–12 d, yielding 5–7 visits per stand. We usually began searching for nests within 1 hr of sunrise, and concluded within 1 hr of sunset.

To determine if microhabitats differed between parasitized and unparasitized nests of common hosts, we included nests in our sample only if they could be classified with a high degree of certainty as parasitized or unparasitized. Nests were classified as unparasitized only if they contained a complete clutch of host eggs and no cowbird eggs, or a full brood of host young and no cowbird young or eggs. We classified nests as parasitized if they contained at least one cowbird egg or chick, regardless of what stage the nest was in when discovered, or whether the nest had been abandoned by the host (see Staab 1995 for further details). All nests were used in our analysis of common versus infrequent hosts regardless of parasitization status.

HABITAT CHARACTERISTICS

We established a 0.04 ha circular plot centered on each nest by stretching a tape measure out to 11.3 m in each of the cardinal directions. By defining the plot in this fashion, there were four transects (along the tape measure) and four quadrants (between the transects). We estimated the following variables modified from Noon (1981) and Mills et al. (1991) within each plot: (1) A vertical profile of vegetation volume was measured at 9 sampling points per nest by holding a pole perpendicular to the ground at each of the sampling points (1 at the nest, and 2 per transect [1 at the mid-point, and 1 at the edge of the plot]). For each m of the pole, we recorded the number of dm intervals that had woody vegetation (i.e., number of hits by species) within a radius of 1 dm from the pole; measurements above 8 m were visually estimated. (2) Distance to and height of the nearest shrub (woody vegetation >1 m tall and <3 cm dbh [diameter at breast height]), sapling (woody vegetation >1 m tall and 3 cm $\leq$ dbh <8 cm) and tree (woody vegetation >1 m tall and ≥ 8 cm dbh) in each of the four quadrants. (3) Dbh size class of all standing trees (3–23 cm, 23–69 cm, and >69 cm). (4) We estimated shrub density at breast height by counting the number of woody stems <3 cm dbh that intersected our bodies and outstretched arms at breast height as we walked along each transect. (5) We estimated percent ground cover and live canopy cover by sighting through an ocular tube at five equidistant points along each of the four transects. (6) We used a clinometer or visual estimation to obtain average, minimum, and maximum canopy height within the plot. (7) Nest substrate type (i.e., tree, shrub, or ground), species, and dbh size class (if tree). (8) Distance to and size of nearest opening (<10% canopy cover and <10% ground cover of shrubs). We estimated size of opening by visually estimating the length and width by size class (≤10, 11–25, 26–50, 51–100, or >100 m). (9) Percentage class (0%, 1–25%, 26–50%, 51–75%, and 76–100%) of nest visible from the nearest tree and shrub in each quadrant, and from the end of each transect (visually estimated). (10) Position of the nest within the nest substrate. For each nest, we measured its height above the ground, distance to trunk (if in tree; distance was 0 if nest was in a shrub), distance to the edge of the substrate along the 4 transects, and total height of the nest substrate. We also recorded the distance to where ≥50% of the nest was visually obstructed by vegetation directly above and below the nest.

DATA ANALYSIS

We used the logistic regression procedure of the SPSS statistical program to test for differences in parasitization status (within common hosts only) and between host types (SPSS 1992). All data were analyzed without regard to year of collection, because sample sizes were too small in 1993 to permit statistically valid analyses. To test for differences in parasitization status, we used presence or absence of parasitization as the dependent variable ("parasitization model"). To test for differences between host types, we used host type (common or infrequent) as the dependent variable ("host type model").

We used forward stepwise variable selection, with identical independent variables, to build both models. The score statistic was used to determine variable entry, and the likelihood ratio statistic to determine variable removal. The host type model was built with an entry P-value of 0.05, and a removal P-value of 0.10. The same set of P-values did not identify any significant variables when they were applied to the parasitization model; therefore, this model was built with an entry P-value of 0.10, and a removal P-value of 0.11. We used these sets of P-values because they resulted in models with an overall classification rate >70%, no outlying cases with studentized residuals >2.00, and a small number of variables. Models with few variables are more likely to be numerically stable, and are more easily generalized, than models with many variables (Hosmer and Lemeshow 1989:83).

We assessed the fit of our final models by examining the model chi-square (SPSS 1992). This tests the null hypothesis that the coefficients for all of the terms in a model, except the constant, are 0. To interpret the final models, we examined the odds ratio of each variable, which indicates how much more (or less) likely it is for the outcome (i.e., parasitization or common host type) to be present for a 1 unit change in the independent variable.

The variable "distance to obstruction below nest" required further analysis, as was partly indicated by the large confidence interval of the estimated odds ratios. From each nest, the distance was measured to the point where vegetation provided ≥50% obscurement. Where there was not enough vegetation to meet this criterion, we recorded the distance from the nest to the ground, even though there was <50% concealment. Our purpose was to minimize the number of cases excluded from analysis due to missing values in the covariate. To clarify the relationship between parasitism and the distance to obstruction below nests, we performed a 2 × 2 contingency table analysis with the obstruction amount coded as ≥50% or <50%.

RESULTS

PARASITIZATION RATES

Minimum parasitization rates for common hosts were 32–50%, and no infrequent hosts were known to be parasitized (Table 1). No nests of either host type were known to contain buried cowbird eggs, nor showed evidence that cowbird eggs had been removed (e.g., broken eggs on ground).

PARASITIZED VS. UNPARASITIZED NESTS OF COMMON HOSTS

Four variables were included in the final logistic regression model of the parasitism data set (Table 2). The odds ratio for the variable dis-

TABLE 1. NUMBER OF PARASITIZED, UNPARASITIZED, AND UNKNOWN PARASITIZED NESTS, AND TOTAL SAMPLE SIZE FOR ALL COMMON AND INFREQUENT HOST SPECIES IN ARIZONA, 1993–94

Species (N)	% Para- sitized	% Unpara- sitized	% Unknown
Common hosts			
Plumbeous Vireo (29)	45	31	24
Yellow Warbler (12)	33	50	17
Yellow-breasted Chat (31)	32	48	19
Blue Grosbeak (12)	50	33	17
Total (84)	39	40	20
Infrequent hosts			
Western Wood-Pewee (21)	0	57	43
Black-headed Grosbeak (6)	0	100	0
House Finch (10)	0	40	60
Spotted Towhee (7)	0	57	43
Total (44)	0	59	41

TABLE 2. LOGISTIC COEFFICIENT (β), STANDARD ERROR (SE), ODDS RATIO (Y), AND 95% CONFIDENCE INTERVAL OF ODDS RATIO (CI Y) FOR VARIABLES IN PARASITIZATION MODEL

Variable	β	SE	Y	95% CI Y
Distance to obstruction below nest (m)	0.426	0.332	1.53	0.80, 2.93
Volume at nest (m³)	−0.648	0.263	0.52	0.31, 0.88
Trees >69 cm dbh present	−1.768	0.872	0.17	0.03, 0.94
Nest substrate dbh (3–23 cm)[a]				
24–69 cm	−2.716	1.005	0.07	0.01, 0.47
<3 cm	−1.614	0.720	0.20	0.05, 0.82
Constant	2.143	0.912		

[a] Reference category.

tance to obstruction below nest indicates that parasitization was 1.5 times more likely to occur with each 1 m increase to vegetation below the nest (Table 2). The odds ratio of vegetation volume at nest was <1, reflecting that as the volume increased, chances of parasitization decreased (Table 2). For each 1 m³ increase of vegetation in a vertical cylinder around the nest, parasitization was half as likely to occur.

Interpretation of the categorical variables is slightly modified, because a reference category is involved. The odds ratio for the presence of large trees was 0.17, the inverse of which indicates that nests with at least one large dbh tree within 11.3 m from them were 6 times less likely to be parasitized than nests where no large trees were nearby (Table 2). The variable nest substrate dbh had a reference category of small trees (3–23 cm dbh). Therefore, the effect of nests in shrubs and mid-sized trees were compared to the effect of nests in small trees. Nests in shrubs and mid-sized dbh trees were 5 and 15 times less likely to be parasitized than nests in small trees, respectively (Table 2). There was no category for large trees because no common host nests were in large trees. The model chi-square indicated that the model fit the data well; all of the coefficients in the model were significantly different from zero (P < 0.001, χ^2 = 20.034, df = 5). The largest correlation coefficient had an absolute value of r = 0.37.

In our additional analysis on the variable distance to obstruction below nest, we found an association between parasitization and the amount of obscurement below the nests (P = 0.048, χ^2 = 3.91, df = 1). Parasitized nests had ≥50% obscurement less frequently than was expected, and unparasitized nests had ≥50% obscurement more frequently than expected.

COMMON VS. INFREQUENT HOSTS

The best fitting model of the host type data set involved only one variable, the height of nest above ground level. Nests <3 m above ground were 7.7 times more likely to belong to a com-

mon host than nests >3 m above ground (coeff = −2.074, SE = 0.426). The coefficient of the nest height variable was different from zero (P < 0.001, χ^2 = 27.34, df = 1).

DISCUSSION

PARASITIZED VS. UNPARASITIZED NESTS

The amount and arrangement of vegetation in a vertical profile above and below nests were associated with likelihood of parasitization. Unparasitized nests had greater vegetation volume and shorter distance to concealing vegetation below the nest. A large vegetation volume could reduce a cowbird's line-of-site as she follows a host during nest-building activities, camouflage a nest, or swamp appropriate search cues with numerous inappropriate images. A short distance to cover below a nest would conceal the nest from more angles that originate below it than a longer distance would. This would be most effective in preventing discovery if cowbirds were searching from the ground or relatively low perches.

The third variable associated large-diameter trees on plots with reduced likelihood of parasitization. On our study site, these trees were always tall cottonwoods, which provided few perch sites in the canopy range from which we sampled nests. Although low perches provided by smaller trees and shrubs generally did not appear to be limited within our study area, they may have been less abundant where large trees dominated plots.

Nests in small dbh trees were at far greater risk of parasitization than those in shrubs or mid-sized trees. Small trees may increase the likelihood of parasitization not only by providing search perches as discussed above, but also by providing less vegetation to conceal a nest. Curson (1996) reported decreased parasitization in trees with a large dbh when he examined Plumbeous Vireos in a pinyon-juniper woodland, although he did not relate it to concealment.

Although we did not investigate any mechanisms as to why vegetation immediately around a nest would affect the likelihood of parasitization, it could be that vegetation may influence a cowbird's ability to locate a nest by providing concealment, camouflage, or search perches. These ideas have also been hypothesized in other studies. In a different Southwestern riparian area, Averill (1996) showed that parasitized Yellow-breasted Chat nests were less concealed from below than unparasitized nests were. When she analyzed four common host species together (including two species common to our study), she found that parasitized nests had less ground cover immediately below them, and that shrubs were farther away when compared to unparasitized nests. Nice (1937) found that parasitized Song Sparrow (*Melospiza melodia*) nests were less concealed from human view than those that were not parasitized. Brittingham and Temple (1996) combined 12 species and found that parasitized nests had a more open canopy and subcanopy. Although they did not relate this to concealment per se, they did suggest it could reflect nest-searching strategies or local variations in host densities.

In contrast to these supportive studies, Anderson and Storer (1976) reported no relationship to concealment at parasitized Kirtland's Warbler (*Dendroica kirtlandii*) nests, although they did not specify how they measured concealment. However, they did report that availability of appropriate perch sites was associated with parasitized nests, as did Freeman et al. (1990). Curson (1996) examined relationships between vegetation and parasitization for several host species, but concluded that differential parasitization was more likely a response to host behavior than vegetation attributes.

COMMON VS. INFREQUENT HOSTS

The host type model indicated that nest height was the key microhabitat feature that distinguished nests of common and infrequent hosts.

Briskie et al. (1990) observed the same phenomenon in their study of Least Flycatchers (*Empidonax minimus,* an infrequent host) and Yellow Warblers. They suggested that nest height constituted a nest-detection curve for cowbirds. This was supported by Norman and Robertson (1975), who observed that cowbirds often searched for nests from the ground.

Our results indicate that management for mid-sized and large trees, along with a well-developed shrub layer, might effectively reduce parasitization rates in Southwestern riparian areas. The plant density and species composition required is a location-specific decision. In general, however, these goals can be achieved by planting seedlings in areas where regeneration is not occurring naturally, prohibiting overgrazing by livestock, restricting the area trampled by humans in high-use recreation zones, and eliminating the cutting of trees for development and fuelwood. Watershed management is also important, because properly functioning watersheds can lessen the severity of floods, which can result in fewer losses of large trees during high volume flood events (Groeneveld and Griepentrog 1985).

Although we can alter vegetation, we cannot control nest-site selection processes. The challenge is to alter structure so that conditions are less favorable for cowbirds, yet they are still within the range of habitat characteristics that are acceptable to most hosts. This range must be defined location-specific for the hosts in question as well as for cowbirds. Achieving these characteristics would maximize breeding habitat quality for hosts by providing them with options for suitable nest sites that are less susceptible to brood parasitism by Brown-headed Cowbirds.

ACKNOWLEDGMENTS

We thank A. Rogers, J. Cornell, and T. Riede for field assistance, and the Box L and K-4 ranches for access to their lands. R. W. Mannan and C. Schwalbe reviewed earlier drafts. Funding was provided by the USDA Forest Service, Prescott National Forest.

Studies in Avian Biology No. 18:23–33, 1999.

COWBIRDS IN A WESTERN VALLEY: EFFECTS OF LANDSCAPE STRUCTURE, VEGETATION, AND HOST DENSITY

JOSHUA J. TEWKSBURY, THOMAS E. MARTIN, SALLIE J. HEJL, TIMOTHY S. REDMAN, AND F. JEREMY WHEELER

Abstract. Brown-headed Cowbird (*Molothrus ater*) abundance varies dramatically over both large and small spatial scales, causing extreme heterogeneity in parasitism pressure. Understanding the factors responsible for the occurrence and relative abundance of cowbirds is thus essential for properly predicting the regional impact of cowbirds on different host species. We studied the occurrence and relative abundance of Brown-headed Cowbirds across three vegetation types in the foothills and valley floor of the Bitterroot Valley in western Montana. Using multiple logistic regression and univariate analyses, we examined the potential impacts of landscape structure, habitat type, distance to agricultural areas, and the density of the cowbird host community on the occurrence and relative abundance of cowbirds. We never encountered cowbirds more than 4 km from agricultural areas, and the distance to large agricultural areas was the strongest predictor of cowbird occurrence and relative abundance. Topographic location of survey points was also important in predicting cowbird occurrence, as cowbirds were almost never encountered within steep-sided canyons. Outside of canyons, both host density and vegetation type appear to influence cowbird abundance, with more cowbirds in deciduous riparian areas and areas of higher host density. Cowbird occurrence and abundance may be mediated by multiple features of the landscape and host community, but in the Bitterroot Valley, cowbird abundance appears greatest in deciduous riparian communities within 2 km of agricultural areas. Intensive research into the demographic impact of cowbirds and the effectiveness of different management options should be directed at species that are confined to these areas for breeding.

Key Words: Brown-headed Cowbirds, fragmentation, host density, landscape ecology, *Molothrus ater*, parasitism pressure.

Numerous studies have demonstrated the detrimental impacts of Brown-headed Cowbirds (*Molothrus ater*) on a wide variety of hosts (Nolan 1978, Sedgwick and Knopf 1988, Marvil and Cruz 1989, Trail and Baptista 1993, Greene *this volume,* Whitfield and Sogge *this volume*) and the potential for cowbirds to precipitate the decline and extirpation of some species (Mayfield 1960, 1977; Gaines 1974, Goldwasser et al. 1980, Harris et al. 1987, Franzreb 1989b). Given the large impact cowbirds can have on host populations, and the continental range of cowbirds, understanding the landscape features correlated with the distribution of cowbirds is important in identifying habitats and species that are potentially at risk from parasitism (Verner and Ritter 1983; Donovan et al. 1997, in press; Thompson et al. in press).

Due to their parasitic nature and lack of parental care, cowbirds can decouple breeding and feeding behaviors and choose breeding habitats that have the highest density of nests available for parasitism regardless of food availability (Rothstein et al. 1984, Robinson et al. 1995a, Thompson 1994). Cowbirds are constrained to some extent, however, by the distance between breeding and feeding areas (Verner and Ritter 1983, Rothstein et al. 1984, Thompson 1994), and thus the distribution of cowbirds may be strongly dependent on the distribution of breeding and feeding areas on the landscape. Cow-

birds have been reported to move as far as 7 to 12 km from breeding areas to feeding locations (Rothstein et al. 1980, 1984, 1987; Thompson 1994; Goguen and Mathews *this volume*), but whereas a few cowbirds may move long distances, the majority of cowbirds appear to move less than 1.5 km between these areas (Thompson 1994), and the proximity and abundance of feeding habitat are the most often cited variables explaining the presence and abundance of cowbirds on the landscape (Rothstein et al. 1980, 1984; Robinson 1992, Rothstein 1994, Thompson 1994, Robinson et al 1995b; Donovan et al. 1995a, 1997, in press; Hejl and Young *this volume,* Young and Hutto *this volume*). However, the presence and abundance of cowbirds may also be influenced by a variety of other variables affecting the quality and quantity of breeding habitat. Vegetation (Rothstein et al. 1984, Rosenburg et al. 1991, Robinson et al. *this volume*), topography (Curson and Mathews *this volume*), and host abundance (Barber and Martin 1997, Tewksbury et al. 1998, Robinson et al. *this volume*) may all affect cowbird distribution and abundance. While these variables have been examined separately, few studies have included all these variables to predict the occurrence or relative abundance of cowbirds (but see Young and Hutto *this volume*).

We develop a model for predicting cowbird occurrence in the Bitterroot Valley of western

Montana using relative abundance point-count sampling and logistic regression. We examine how cowbirds are distributed in relation to agriculture, vegetation, topography, and the density of hosts in this western landscape, compare these relations with eastern and midwestern landscapes, and discuss the implications for the management of western forests.

METHODS

STUDY AREA AND STUDY SITES

The study was conducted in the Bitterroot Valley of western Montana. Primary point count locations were originally established in 1994 in conjunction with 16 nest-monitoring sites (Martin et al. 1996) in deciduous riparian communities. These sites were set in local landscapes that ranged from highly fragmented by agriculture to predominantly forested and unfragmented (Fig. 1). Within each nest monitoring site, we established 2–7 point counts for a total of 73 point locations. We stratified these points within each site so that all points were greater than 200m from all other points on the site. All points were located in habitats dominated by deciduous trees and shrubs typical of either the black cottonwood (*Populus trichocarpa*)/red-osier dogwood (*Cornus stolonifera*) community type, the quaking aspen (*Populus tremuloides*)/red-osier dogwood community type, or the mountain alder (*Alnus incana*) community type (Hansen et al. 1995).

To understand the features affecting cowbird abundance at a landscape scale in multiple vegetation types, we established an additional 117 point locations in 14 transects extending from the forest-farmland interface into the Selway-Bitterroot Wilderness Area (Fig. 1). This area is predominantly Douglas-fir (*Pseudotsuga menziesii*) and ponderosa pine (*Pinus ponderosa*) forest with numerous streams flowing east from the wilderness area to join the Bitterroot River in the valley floor. Stream-side vegetation ranges from coniferous riparian areas dominated by Engelmann spruce (*Picea engelmannii*) and grand fir (*Abies grandis*), to deciduous riparian areas dominated by aspen, alder and willow (*Salix spp.*) We established points in three vegetation types: conifer forest (referred to as xeric conifer), conifer riparian, and deciduous riparian. All points were a minimum of 500 m from neighboring points, and we chose locations within vegetation types at least 50 m from the edge of the vegetation type whenever possible (many deciduous riparian areas sampled were too narrow to meet this criterion). We positioned points in an attempt to census all three vegetation types over the full range of distances from agriculture.

Deciduous riparian vegetation, however, was concentrated near the valley floor where virtually all of the agriculture is located, and our original points (all in deciduous riparian) were on average closer to agriculture than the points established in transects. This prevented us from establishing a completely balanced design (Fig 1). Census locations varied from 40 to 7,700 m from agriculture, with a mean distance of 2,080 m from agricultural development. The Bitterroot Mountains are dissected by steep-sided canyons, and thus some transect points were located within canyons, while others were on much more open terrain. Because of the large differences in topography between these locations, we noted topographic location (canyon or open topography) and included this in our analysis of cowbird distribution. We identified agricultural land use throughout the Bitterroot Valley using existing Landsat satellite data (Redmond and Prather 1996) and determined the distance of all point-count locations to agricultural areas defined by this data set. This agricultural delineation has a minimum mapping unit of 2 ha and thus depicts only large agricultural areas. While cowbirds may also respond to smaller agricultural units and the presence of farm buildings and bird feeders (Tewksbury et al. 1998), if reliable associations between cowbird abundance and distance to agricultural areas can be found at this resolution of landscape structure, it will allow managers to use existing information to predict and manage cowbird populations.

ASSESSING COWBIRD AND HOST ABUNDANCE

For this paper, we use point-count data from 1996 only, as this is the only year in which all points were sampled. Point count locations were censused three times during the season, each count was 10 minutes long, and all birds seen or heard were recorded. We standardized detection effort by using only birds seen or heard within 50 m of the observer (Hutto et al. 1986, Ralph et al. 1995). We recorded vocalizations of males and females separately where possible. Two experienced observers (T.S.R. and F.J.W.) conducted all surveys, switching off transects so that all locations were surveyed by both observers. We recorded noise level at each point (mostly from streams), determined the level at which noise caused a decline in detections, and excluded results from all high noise censuses. All censuses analyzed were conducted at least one-half hr after sunrise and before 11:00.

To examine the effect of relative host density on cowbird abundance, we calculated the average abundance of all hosts at each survey location based on all censuses. A species was considered a host if it was parasitized greater than

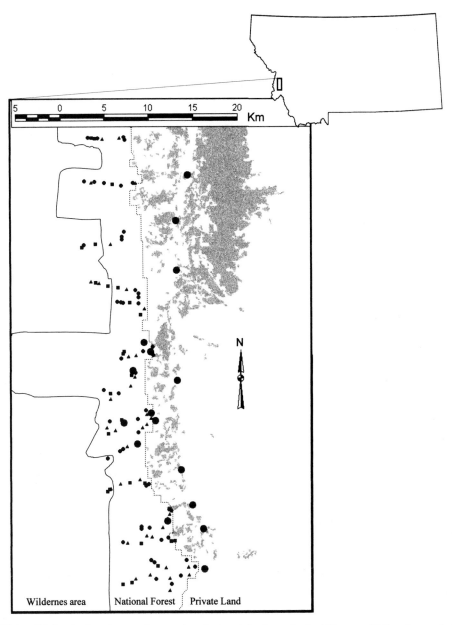

FIGURE 1.   Study site locations and general agricultural land use in the Bitterroot Valley. Large dark gray points are nest searching plots where parasitism rates were monitored, smaller points are census locations in the three habitat types: deciduous riparian areas (triangles), coniferous riparian areas (squares) and xeric conifer forest (circles). Agricultural land (light gray) is from Landsat image data.

15% of the time on our nest-monitoring sites (See Tewksbury et al. 1998 for parasitism rates and nest monitoring methods) or known to be regularly parasitized by cowbirds elsewhere (Table 1). We included this latter category because we have not determined parasitism rates across species in xeric conifer or mesic conifer forests, but we wanted to include all potential hosts in our calculation of host density across all three habitat types. The complete list of hosts (Table 1) includes two species that were not often parasitized on our deciduous riparian nest-monitoring sites, the Chipping Sparrow (see Table 1 for scientific names of bird species) and Dark-eyed

TABLE 1. RELATIVE ABUNDANCE (DETECTIONS ≤ 50 M PER 10 MIN CENSUS PERIOD) OF BROWN-HEADED COWBIRDS AND ALL SPECIES INCLUDED AS COWBIRD HOSTS IN THREE HABITATS AND TWO TOPOGRAPHIC LOCATIONS, BITTER-ROOT VALLEY, MT, 1996

		Coniferous Riparian		Xeric Conifer		Deciduous Riparian	
	Topography: # of census locations:	Open 9	Canyon 18	Open 33	Canyon 19	Open 98	Canyon 13
Brown-headed Cowbird	*Molothrus ater*	0.037	0	0.283	0.035	0.862	0.026
Willow Flycatcher	*Empidonax traillii*	0	0	0	0	0.061	0
Least Flycatcher	*Empidonax minimus*	0	0	0	0	0.003	0
Hammond's Flycatcher	*Empidonax hammondii*	0.148	0.056	0.293	0.105	0.122	0.231
Dusky Flycatcher	*Empidonax wrightii*	0.074	0	0.061	0.017	0.264	0.115
Veery	*Catharus fuscescens*	0	0	0	0	0.124	0
Swainson's Thrush	*Catharus ustulatus*	0.259	0.398	0.167	0.158	0.151	0.385
Hermit Thrush	*Catharus guttatus*	0	0	0	0.017	0	0
Cassin's Vireo	*Vireo cassinii*	0	0	0.212	0.035	0.092	0.09
Red-eyed Vireo	*Vireo olivaceus*	0	0	0	0	0.032	0
Warbling Vireo	*Vireo gilvus*	0.185	0.139	0.05	0.053	0.541	0.410
Orange-crowned Warbler	*Vermivora celata*	0	0	0.03	0	0.121	0.064
Nashville Warbler	*Vermivora ruficapilla*	0	0	0	0.017	0.012	0
Yellow Warbler	*Dendroica petechia*	0	0	0.010	0	0.599	0.026
Yellow-rumped Warbler	*Dendroica coronata*	0.037	0.102	0.263	0.184	0.08	0.051
Townsend's Warbler	*Dendroica townsendi*	0.741	0.62	0.227	0.263	0.056	0.731
American Redstart	*Setophaga ruticilla*	0	0	0	0	0.179	0
Northern Waterthrush	*Seiurus noveboracensis*	0	0	0	0	0.107	0
MacGillivray's Warbler	*Oporornis tolmiei*	0.333	0.083	0.071	0.07	0.360	0.538
Common Yellowthroat	*Geothlypis trichas*	0	0	0	0	0.059	0
Chipping Sparrow	*Spizella passerina*	0.037	0	0.328	0.228	0.095	0.026
Song Sparrow	*Melospiza melodia*	0	0	0	0	0.124	0
Dark-eyed Junco	*Junco hyemalis*	0.148	0.028	0.359	0.105	0.082	0.064
Lazuli Bunting	*Passerina amoena*	0	0	0	0	0.005	0

Junco, but neither of these species are very abundant in deciduous riparian areas, and both of these species known to be parasitized elsewhere (Buech 1982, Wolf 1987, Graham 1988, Scott and Lemon 1996). These species were included because they may be parasitized more often in coniferous areas where their abundance relative to other hosts is greater. Though we were unable to find data addressing parasitism rates in the Townsend's Warbler, we included this species in our list of hosts because we have seen adults feeding cowbird fledglings, and virtually all other open-cup nesting *Dendroica* species are common cowbird hosts.

DATA ANALYSIS

We examined the importance of landscapes, vegetation and host communities on cowbird occurrence using multiple logistic regression. On the subset of locations where cowbirds were detected, we examined the importance of these same factors on the relative abundance of cowbirds. This approach has statistical advantages because it avoids the difficulties of properly characterizing relative abundance when a large percentage of sampling points have zero detections, and may be more biologically meaningful if the factors that influence the presence of a species are different than those that influence density.

We included distance to agriculture, vegetation type, host abundance, and topographic location to predict cowbird occurrence through logistic regression. Our a priori hypothesis considered all of these variables important predictors of cowbird occurrence, and we made no predictions regarding interactions; therefore our primary model includes all variables entered without interactions. We also used a forward stepwise model selection procedure to compare with our a priori model. For forward stepwise selection, we used the likelihood ratio method in SPSS v7.5 (SPSS 1996), which calculates P-values using the likelihood-ratio Chi-square test. Variables are entered into the model based on their improvement to the likelihood of obtaining the observed results. The variable that most significantly improves the probability of obtaining the observed results is added to the model first, and all variables are reevaluated after each step. The entry criteria was $P = 0.05$.

Stepwise procedures have been criticized as unreliable at properly ranking the importance of variables or finding the most parsimonious model (James and McCulloch 1990). Moreover, the predictive power of any logistic model cannot be assessed without validation using data independent of those used to build the model (Hosmer and Lemeshow 1989). To address these problems and compare the predictive ability of our models, we used a jackknife procedure to predict the occurrence of cowbirds at locations excluded from data used to create the models. We surveyed 190 locations for the occurrence of cowbirds. Our jackknife procedure was to run 190 logistic regressions for each model (our primary model, the model chosen by forward stepwise selection, and a full model including all two-way interactions for comparison). In each regression, we left a single location out of the data used to create the model and asked the model created with 189 locations to predict the occurrence of cowbirds on the location left out. The case left out was changed each run, so that in 190 runs we made independent predictions for each location under the model being jackknifed. We then compared the predictive ability of our model with that of the forward stepwise model and the full model by comparing the percent of points correctly classified with and without cowbirds using McNemar's test, which tests for differences in response (0 or 1) of individuals or locations tested twice (Sokal and Rohlf 1995). If our a priori model classifies independent cases as well as the forward stepwise and full models, we consider it the best working model to use in predicting cowbirds, as it is simpler than the full model, and avoids the uncertainties of stepwise procedures (James and McCulloch 1990). If the other models are significantly better at classifying cases, we have shown that our a priori model is not sufficient to predict cowbird occurrence accurately, and alternative models will need to be developed.

In all logistic regressions, cowbird occurrence at a location was coded as 1 if any cowbirds were detected within 50m of the observer during any of the censuses at the location, and 0 if no cowbirds were detected. As we excluded surveys where noise at a location prevented accurate detection, some locations include data for less than three visits. To correct for this unequal effort, we weighted logistic regression by the number of visits to each location. We also analyzed the occurrence of female cowbirds separately, but as this metric was correlated with the occurrence of all cowbirds (Spearman's rank correlation coefficient = 0.412, P < 0.001), and as results from logistic regression were similar, we only present the results from all cowbirds. We used distance to agriculture, topography, vegetation type, host density, and all two-way interactions as potential predictive variables. We checked for correlations between the two continuous variables, distance to agriculture and

host density, and found no significant correlations in any combination of habitat type and topographic location (bivariate correlations, all P's > 0.7, except within xeric conifer forests, where P = 0.112 in open topography, and P = 0.186 in canyon habitats).

To examine the factors affecting cowbird occurrence further, we also present the proportion of locations in which cowbirds were detected by distance from agriculture (1 km categories), host density (< 1 host per point, 1–2 hosts, 2–3 hosts, etc.), and vegetation type. These data were analyzed using Kruskal-Wallis H-tests for two sample tests and Mann-Whitney U for multiway tests.

Analysis of relative abundance of cowbirds was confined to points where cowbirds were detected and thus is not confounded with the logistic analysis of occurrence. Relative abundance is defined as the number of cowbirds detected per 10-min survey period averaged over all surveys at a given location. To examine the influence of distance from agriculture on cowbird abundance, we used nonlinear regression though the Curvefit function in Sigmaplot version 4 (SPSS 1997). We also analyzed the effect of host density, vegetation type, and topographic location on cowbird abundance using Kruskal-Wallis and Mann-Whitney U-tests. Test statistics reported are for Kruskal-Wallis tests unless otherwise noted.

RESULTS

The distance from the census location to the nearest agricultural area was the strongest, most consistent predictor of cowbird occurrence in all logistic models (Table 2). In open topography cowbirds were detected at more than 80% of all points located within 1 km of agricultural areas, but declined rapidly, with less than 40% occurrence in points 2–3 km from agriculture and no cowbirds detected in any points farther than 4 km from agriculture (Fig. 2A). On points where cowbirds were present, relative abundance also declined with increasing distance to agriculture (Fig. 2B). This relationship was fit best by an exponential curve ($R^2 = 0.166$; df = 1, 94; P < 0.001).

The topographic location was also a strong predictor of cowbird occurrence; cowbirds were detected in a total of 68% of the 140 open topography locations, and only two of the 50 canyon locations (4%). Some of this difference in occurrence is a function of the location of canyon points, which are rarely close to agriculture due to the topography of the Bitterroot Mountains. Additionally, canyon points had lower host density in all habitat types (Fig. 3). However, topographic location was significant in our

TABLE 2. LOGISTIC REGRESSION MODELS: RESULTS OF THE PRIMARY MODEL, WHICH INCLUDED ALL MAIN EFFECTS BUT NO INTERACTIONS, THE MODEL GENERATED THROUGH FORWARD STEPWISE SELECTION, AND THE FULL MODEL WITH INTERACTIONS

	B^b	SE	Exp $(B)^b$	r^c	P
Primary model: $\chi^2 = 125$, P < 0.001[a]					
Distance to agriculture (m)	−0.0008	0.0002	0.999	−0.2448	<0.001
Topographic location[d]	2.0865	0.7946	8.057	0.1365	0.009
Vegetation type[e]				0.0374	0.113
Deciduous riparian[e]	2.2094	1.1038	9.110	0.0874	0.045
Xeric conifer[e]	1.6760	1.1068	5.344	0.0334	0.130
Host density	0.2911	0.1766	1.338	0.0522	0.099
Constant	−2.7848	1.3549			0.040
Forward step-wise model: $\chi^2 = 119$, P < 0.001[a]					
Distance to agriculture (m)	−0.0008	0.0002	0.999	−0.2414	<0.001
Vegetation type[e] × Topographic location[d]				0.2381	<0.001
Deciduous riparian × Topographic location[d]	2.9549	0.6860	19.201	0.2510	<0.001
Xeric conifer forest × Topographic location[d]	2.0705	0.7198	7.929	0.1545	0.004
Constant	−0.5784	0.7229			0.423
Full model: $\chi^2 = 127$, P < 0.001[a]					
Distance to agriculture	−0.0016	0.0018	0.998	0.0000	0.375
Topographic location[d]	5.9436	18.4935	381.292	0.0000	0.748
Vegetation type[e]				0.0000	0.925
Deciduous riparian[e]	7.3160	18.5851	1504.178	0.0000	0.694
Xeric conifer[e]	7.2171	18.4377	1362.466	0.0000	0.696
Host density	−0.2946	1.8471	0.745	0.0000	0.873
Vegetation type[e] × Host density				0.0000	0.554
Deciduous riparian[e] × Host density	0.0020	1.4145	1.002	0.0000	0.999
Xeric conifer[e] × Host density	−0.4829	1.4488	0.617	0.0000	0.739
Topographic location[d] × Host density	0.6527	1.0136	1.921	0.0000	0.520
Distance to agriculture × Host density	5.57 E-05	0.0002	1.000	0.0000	0.928
Vegetation type[e] × Topographic location[d]				0.0000	0.824
Deciduous riparian[e] × Topographic location[d]	−6.4737	18.8693	0.002	0.0000	0.729
Xeric conifer[e] × Topographic location[d]	−5.1432	18.5290	0.006	0.0000	0.781
Distance to agriculture × Vegetation type[e]				0.0000	0.732
Distance to agriculture × Deciduous riparian[e]	0.0005	0.0016	1.001	0.0000	0.739
Distance to agriculture × Xeric conifer[e]	0.0001	0.0017	1.000	0.0000	0.933
Distance to agriculture × Topographic location[d]	0.0003	0.0008	1.000	0.0000	0.717

[a] Model χ^2 measures the difference between the likelihood of obtaining the observed results under the final model and the null model without any variables included.

[b] B is the regression coefficient for each effect, representing the change in the log odds of cowbird detection with a one unit change in the independent variable. Exp (B) represents the change in actual odds of cowbird occurrence with a one unit change in the independent variable. Odds are defined as the ratio of the probability that an event will occur to the probability that it will not (SPSS 1996).

[c] Correlation between the independent variable and the probability of cowbird occurrence.

[d] Canyon topography is the reference category. Coefficient (B) and Exp (B) for topographic location refers to the increase in the probability of encountering a cowbird in open topography over canyons

[e] Coniferous riparian is the reference category. All coefficients for deciduous riparian and xeric conifer represent the change in probability of encountering a cowbird in these vegetation types when compared to coniferous riparian areas.

primary logistic model without interaction terms, and had a larger influence on cowbird occurrence than host density (Table 2), suggesting a strong independent affect of topographic location on cowbird occurrence. Cowbirds occurred at only two canyon locations, precluding a comparison of mean cowbird abundance between open topography and canyons for points where cowbirds were present.

The affects of vegetation type and host density were difficult to separate. Deciduous riparian areas had the highest host density (Fig. 3; open topography N = 140, df = 2, $\chi^2 = 21$, P < 0.001; canyons N = 50, df = 2, $\chi^2 = 19$, P < 0.001), and whereas cowbird occurrence was not related to vegetation type in canyons (Fig. 4A; N = 50, df = 2, $\chi^2 = 1.1$, P = 0.57), in open topography deciduous areas had higher cowbird occurrence as well (Fig. 4A; N = 140, df = 2, $\chi^2 = 29.8$, P < 0.001). When we considered only locations where cowbirds were detected, the relative abundance of cowbirds was also much higher in deciduous riparian areas than either of the other two vegetation types (Fig. 4B; Mann-Whitney U = 358, N = 95, P = 0.005), but the ratio of cowbirds to hosts did

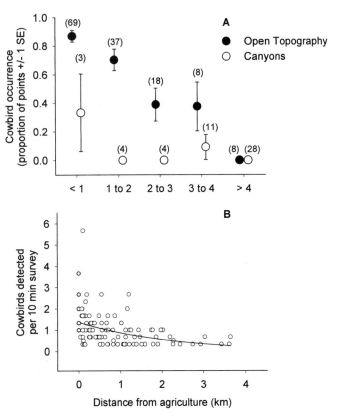

FIGURE 2.   A. Proportion of all census points where cowbirds were detected (mean cowbird occurrence ± 1 SE) in open topography and canyon points as a function of distance from agricultural development. Samples sizes (in parentheses), are the number of point locations surveyed. B. The mean number of cowbirds detected per 10 min survey for points where cowbirds were detected. As cowbirds were only encountered at two canyon points, data presented are for open topography. The regression line follows an exponential fit.

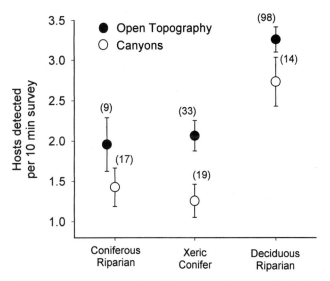

FIGURE 3.   Density of all hosts (mean ± 1 SE) by habitat type and topographic location.

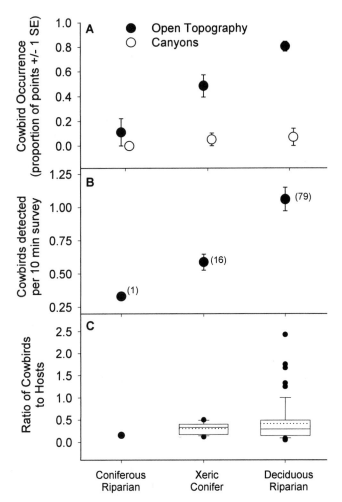

FIGURE 4. A. Cowbird occurrence (mean ± 1 SE) in the three vegetation types (sample sizes are the same as Fig. 3) in both open topography and canyon locations. B. Mean number (± 1 SE) of cowbirds detected per 10 min census for all survey locations where cowbirds were detected. C. Ratio of cowbirds to hosts in the three vegetation types using only points where cowbirds were detected. Shown are the median (solid line), mean (dotted line), 25th and 75th percentiles (boxes), 10th and 95th percentiles (whiskers), and individual points beyond the 10th and 90th percentiles. Cowbirds were detected in only one mesic conifer point (ratio shown as dot in C). Sample sizes for B and C are the same, and are shown in parentheses in B.

not differ between deciduous riparian areas and xeric conifer forest (Fig. 4C; N = 95, P = 0.873).

In logistic regression, host density had a slightly stronger affect on cowbird occurrence than vegetation type, but neither variable appears as important as distance from agriculture and topographic location (Table 2). Stepwise selection failed to enter both variables, further suggesting that they explain much of the same variance in cowbird occurrence (Table 2). The interaction between host density and topographic location included in the stepwise model is due to the very low frequency of cowbird occurrence

in canyons, regardless of host density, coupled with the strong effect of host density on cowbird occurrence in open topography (Fig. 5A; N = 140, df = 5, χ^2 = 14.1, P = 0.015). However, the relative abundance of cowbirds at open topography locations was not strongly affected by host density (Fig. 5B; N = 96, df = 5, χ^2 = 4.6, P = 0.475).

Our a priori logistic regression model correctly predicted the occurrence of brown-headed cowbirds in 84.8% of all cases, better than the full model and slightly better than the model chosen by forward stepwise section (Table 3). All models correctly classified locations with

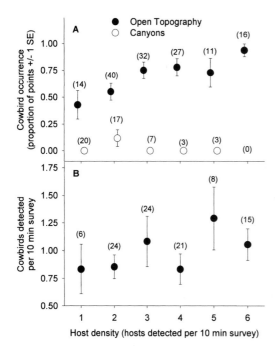

FIGURE 5. A. The relationship between cowbird occurrence (mean ± 1 SE) and the relative density of suitable hosts in open topography and canyons. B. Relative abundance of cowbirds (where present) as a function of relative host density in open topography. See Table 2 for list of all species included in host density calculations.

cowbirds more often than locations where cowbirds were absent.

DISCUSSION

The distribution of cowbirds across potential breeding sites in the Bitterroot Valley appears to be limited by aspects of breeding-site quality and the distance between breeding and feeding areas. Despite our coarse-grain delineation of agricultural areas in the Bitterroot Valley, the distance to the nearest large agricultural area (>2 ha) was the strongest predictor of cowbird occurrence across the landscape. In the Bitterroot Valley, most agricultural areas are used for pasture and row crops, and the strong relationship with agriculture suggests that cowbird distribution in the Bitterroot Valley is limited by the presence and distribution of largely supplemental food sources supplied by human activities. Rothstein et al. (1980), Verner and Ritter (1983), and Wright (*this volume*) reached a similar conclusion in the Sierra Nevada Mountains, where cowbird numbers declined substantially with increasing distance from pack-stations. Young and Hutto (*this volume*) found a similar relationship between cowbird abundance and ag-

TABLE 3. JACKKNIFE RESULTS—EACH MODEL WAS JACKKNIFED 190 TIMES WITH ONE LOCATION LEFT OUT FOR INDEPENDENT CLASSIFICATION

| | Percent of locations classified correctly | | | |
| | Without cow-birds | With cow-birds | Overall | P[a] |
Model				
Primary model	78.9%	90.1%	84.8%	
Forward stepwise model	79.3%	89.8%	84.7%	0.137
Full model	75%	89.8%	82.6%	0.063

[a] Two-tailed McNemar test for difference in predictive power between primary model and other models.

riculture throughout the interior Northwest, and Donovan et al.(in press) and Thompson et al. (in press) found the same relationship in the Midwest.

We found no cowbirds beyond 4 km from agricultural development, and while studies in the Sierra Nevada and the Midwest document cowbirds moving farther than 7 km from feeding areas to breeding areas (Rothstein et al. 1984, Thompson 1994) and greater than 10 km in Texas (Goguen and Mathews *this volume*), the majority of cowbirds studied through radio tracking move less than 2 km (Verner and Ritter 1983, Thompson 1994, Goguen and Mathews *this volume*; Tewksbury and Johnson, unpubl. data). Additionally, where there is an abundance of high-quality breeding habitat close to agricultural areas, such as in the Bitterroot Valley, cowbirds may travel shorter distances from breeding sites to feeding areas. In most of the Bitterroot Valley, the distance from any given feeding area to the nearest riparian area is less than 2 km because of the abundant riparian habitat along the river, and the ratio of breeding habitat to feeding habitat appears high throughout the valley floor. In contrast, Midwestern landscapes are dominated by agriculture and the ratio of breeding habitat to feeding habitat is low; thus, cowbirds may be forced to travel further from breeding to feeding areas (Thompson 1994). In general, cowbirds may travel longer distances in areas where breeding habitat is limited and closer breeding habitats are saturated by cowbirds.

A less intuitive feature influencing cowbird distribution was the landscape topography; cowbirds consistently avoided steep-sided canyons. We currently do not have enough information to characterize the overall influence of topography on cowbird occurrence, or to determine whether cowbirds avoid canyons because of dispersal patterns from feeding areas or because of decisions made when selecting laying territories. Host density was consistently lower in canyons than in open topography (Fig. 3), but this cannot explain the almost complete absence of cowbirds in canyons, as deciduous communities in canyons had higher host density than xeric conifer areas in open topography (Fig. 3), and cowbirds were detected at greater than 40% of these xeric conifer locations. However, canyon points were also on average further from agricultural areas. These effects together make it difficult to judge the generality of topographic effects on the occurrence of cowbirds without further study and testing of the current logistic model on an independent data set.

Outside of canyons, cowbird occurrence in the Bitterroot Valley appears to be influenced not only by distance to agriculture, but also the density of potential hosts (Fig. 5). Host density differed predictably among vegetation types (Fig. 3), making it possible for cowbirds to choose areas of high host density reliably simply by choosing deciduous riparian areas (Fig. 4). Close examination of our results, however, suggests that host density and the ease of finding nests are both primary factors driving cowbird occurrence and relative abundance, and that vegetation type may only be important to the extent that it influences these other factors. Host density was higher in deciduous riparian areas than in xeric conifer, but the ratio of cowbirds to hosts was not different between these habitats, suggesting that cowbird abundance is tracking host density among these habitats. In contrast, host density in coniferous riparian areas was equal to host density in xeric conifer forest, but cowbirds were much less common in coniferous riparian areas (Fig. 4). We suggest that both deciduous riparian and xeric conifer forests are relatively easy habitats for cowbirds to find nests in, but the tall, densely packed trees characteristic of coniferous riparian areas make it difficult for cowbirds to follow hosts to their nests. Additionally, while the diverse host communities characteristic of deciduous riparian and xeric conifer provide suitable nests for cowbirds in all vegetation layers, more than 35% of all hosts detected in coniferous riparian areas were Townsend's Warblers (Table 1), which nest high in conifers (a mean height of 6.7m was reported by Matsuoka et al. [1997]). Cowbirds appear to parasitize lower nests much more frequently than higher nests (Briskie et al. 1990; J. Tewksbury, unpubl. data); thus, Townsend's Warblers may not represent accessible hosts for cowbirds.

Ultimately, if we hold constant the cost of getting to a particular breeding location (e.g., the distance between feeding and breeding areas), the occurrence and abundance of cowbirds should be determined primarily by the density and quality of hosts (Verner and Ritter 1983,

Rothstein et al. 1984, Robinson and Wilcove 1994, Barber and Martin 1996, Tewksbury et al. 1998), modified by any structural differences between habitats that influence the ease with which cowbirds can find host nests (Robinson et al. *this volume*). Our ability to examine the relationship between cowbird abundance and the quality and quantity of available hosts is limited by our understanding of cowbird-host interactions in different vegetation types. Within a vegetation type, cowbirds parasitize some hosts more often than others, and thus may place greater importance on certain hosts (Barber and Martin 1996, Tewksbury et al. 1998). Among vegetation types, the host preference of cowbirds may also change due to differences in the relative abundances of hosts of different quality. Indeed, we may expect cowbirds to switch hosts much like the prey switching of predators (Lawton et al. 1974). A better understanding of host availability and preference in western coniferous forest habitats will allow much greater resolution in predicting the abundance and impact of cowbirds based on attributes of the host community.

MANAGEMENT CONSIDERATIONS

Our results clearly indicate that deciduous riparian areas near agricultural lands have higher cowbird abundance than other habitat types (Fig. 4). These areas also support more species of breeding birds than any other habitat type in the western United States (Johnson et al. 1977, Knopf 1985, Knopf et al. 1988, Dobkin and Wilcox 1986, Saab and Groves 1992, Bock et al. 1993, Knopf and Samson 1994). In many western states, Ohmart (1994) has estimated that as much as 95% of this habitat has been altered or destroyed by human activities. Given the importance and status of deciduous riparian habitats in the West, coupled with the threat of cowbird parasitism in these areas, we feel that research and management efforts should focus on these areas. We found at least 22 species of cowbird hosts in deciduous riparian habitats, and 10 of these species were not found in other habitat types (Table 1). These species fall into two broad management categories with regards to parasitism: species that are heavily parasitized throughout their primary habitats in the region, and species that are parasitized in some areas but escape parasitism in others. The Common Yellowthroat, Red-eyed Vireo, Willow Flycatcher, Yellow Warbler, and Veery all appear to breed only in the large deciduous areas. In the Bitterroot Valley, these areas occur almost exclusively near the Bitterroot River and near agriculture. Detailed studies of the demographic impacts of parasitism should focus on these species, as parasitism pressure on these species may be high throughout their breeding habitat and has the potential to cause regional population declines. In contrast, species such as MacGillivray's Warbler and Warbling Vireo, though heavily parasitized in areas near agriculture, also breed in smaller riparian areas far from agriculture. Though breeding success in these areas has not been sufficiently studied, smaller deciduous riparian areas far from agriculture likely provide escape from cowbird parasitism. For these species, the creation and maintenance of healthy deciduous communities buffered from cowbird feeding areas may be the best way to insure stable populations. Currently, however, deciduous riparian habitat has diminished substantially on the Bitterroot National Forest due to effective fire suppression over the past 50–60 years (McCune 1983). Management action that reintroduces natural disturbance to these forests and promotes deciduous communities within the forest matrix may protect many host species from population declines due to parasitism.

Although we have identified correlates of cowbird abundance in the Bitterroot Valley, before we can safely extrapolate findings based on cowbird occurrence and relative abundance to parasitism rates, we need to examine the strength of the relationship between point-count data and parasitism (Thompson et al. in press). If the abundance or occurrence of cowbirds on a landscape can be used to index parasitism rates accurately, point-counts can be used as an important tool in directing management, but if these relationships are weak, or vary significantly by habitat, census data can only be used as a qualitative guide in directing more detailed research.

Effective management of cowbirds will require a detailed understanding of the relationships between landscapes and cowbird numbers, and between cowbird numbers and parasitism rates. The specifics of these relationships are unlikely to be constant throughout the range of the cowbird, as differences in host populations, habitat types, topographic features and landscape patterns may all change the density and movements of cowbirds and the impact of cowbirds on host populations. Yet cowbirds may react to these changes in predictable ways throughout their range, and our understanding of the nature of these relationships in one location should help guide research and management in others.

ACKNOWLEDGMENTS

For long days and laughter, we would like to thank the nest searchers of the Bitterroot Riparian Bird Project. Additional thanks is due to M. Johnson for radio-telemetry of cowbirds, and T. Musci for establishing plots in 1994. We thank W. Hochachka, S. Robinson and J. Rotenberry for comments on the manuscript. We would also like to thank K. and B. Evans and the many other private landowners who participated in the project. This research was supported in part by The Bitterroot Ecosystem Management Research Project, The Rocky Mountain Research Station, USDA Forest Service, the U.S. Fish and Wildlife Service Non-game Migratory Bird Program, the Montana Cooperative Wildlife Research Unit, the BBIRD (Breeding Biology Research and Monitoring Database) program under the Global Change Research Program of the U.S. Geological Survey, and the Montana Department of Fish, Wildlife, and Parks.

Studies in Avian Biology No. 18:34–40, 1999.

PARASITISM BY BROWN-HEADED COWBIRDS IN THE SHRUBSTEPPE OF EASTERN WASHINGTON

W. Matthew Vander Haegen and Brett Walker

Abstract. Shrubsteppe communities within the Intermountain West have been reduced in area and fragmented by agricultural conversion and land development, yet we know little about the effects of Brown-headed Cowbirds (*Molothrus ater*) on reproductive success of birds that breed in these communities. As part of ongoing research examining landscape effects on avian productivity in eastern Washington, we collected data on parasitism rates and cowbird occurrence. During 1996 and 1997 we surveyed birds using point-counts and searched for nests in big sagebrush (*Artemisia tridentata*) stands in eastern Washington. Cowbirds were common on our study area and were recorded on point-counts at 26 of 29 sites surveyed. Cowbirds arrived on the study area in late April, attaining greatest abundance in May and June. We located and monitored a total of 779 nests of 8 species; only the Brewer's Sparrow (*Spizella breweri*), Sage Sparrow (*Amphispiza belli*), and Vesper Sparrow (*Pooecetes gramineus*) showed evidence of parasitism. Overall parasitism rates were lower than those reported for other bird communities in fragmented landscapes and for other bird communities in shrubsteppe. Low parasitism levels (<10 %) in our study area partly resulted from arrival of cowbirds after initiation of first nests by hosts. Over 40% of Sage Sparrow nests were initiated before cowbirds were observed laying on the study area. Low levels of parasitism also may be related to low availability of elevated observation perches or long distances from study plots to cowbird feeding areas. Determining why parasitism is low in this fragmented landscape may have important implications for managing cowbirds in other areas.

Key Words: *Amphispiza belli*, Brewer's Sparrow, Brown-headed Cowbird, *Molothrus ater*, parasitism, Sage Sparrow, shrubsteppe, *Spizella breweri*, Washington.

Parasitism by Brown-headed Cowbirds (*Molothrus ater*) has been found to depress significantly the reproductive output of some passerines, particularly in fragmented landscapes (Brittingham and Temple 1983, Robinson et al. 1995a). Shrubsteppe communities within the Intermountain West have been reduced in area and fragmented by agricultural conversion and land development (Quigley and Arbelbide 1997), particularly within the Columbia River Basin in eastern Washington (Dobler et al. 1996). Moreover, these communities have a long history of use as rangeland, providing feeding habitat for cowbirds in the form of feedlots, pastures, and lawns. A recent analysis of data from the Breeding Bird Survey for the Columbia River Basin reported significant, declining trends for populations of numerous shrubsteppe-associated species, with more species declining than increasing (Saab and Rich 1997). We know little about the effects of cowbirds on reproductive success of birds that breed in shrubsteppe communities (Rich 1978, Reynolds 1981, Rich and Rothstein 1985, Biermann et al. 1987).

As part of an ongoing research project examining landscape effects on avian productivity in eastern Washington, we collected data on parasitism levels and cowbird occurrence. Here we present a preliminary assessment of cowbird parasitism on the more common nesting passerines in Washington's shrubsteppe.

STUDY AREA AND METHODS

The study took place in the Columbia River Basin of eastern Washington, in vegetation zones classified as shrubsteppe (Daubenmire 1988). The region is primarily semi-arid desert, with cold winters and hot summers. Most of the native vegetation communities in the region have been converted to agriculture, with an estimated 40% of the historical shrubsteppe remaining (Dobler et al. 1996).

Study plots were established in 29 sites in eight different counties. All sites were dominated by big sagebrush (*Artemisia tridentata*) and native bunch grasses (primarily blue-bunch wheatgrass [*Pseudoreginaria spicatum*], *Poa* spp., and *Stipa* spp.) and forbs. Study sites included both large (>10,000 ha) expanses of continuous shrubsteppe and smaller patches (<100 ha) surrounded by agriculture. All but one of the 29 sites were >50 km from the nearest forest community. Study plots ranged in size from 8 to 20 ha and were flagged at 50-m intervals on a quasi-grid defined by a series of adjacent, 100-m diameter point-count circles.

We surveyed birds at each plot in mid-April, mid-May, and mid-June of 1996 and 1997, using 10-min point-counts. Birds were recorded as either within 100 m of the point, or beyond 100 m but within the *Artemisia* stand containing the plot. For the present analysis, cowbirds observed during point-counts within the stand of interest (perched or flying) were counted as present.

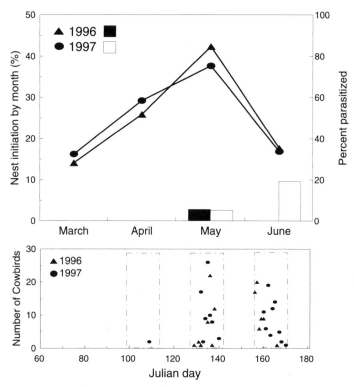

FIGURE 1. Relationship between nesting by Sage Sparrows and parasitism by Brown-headed Cowbirds in eastern Washington. Upper graph shows timing of nest initiation (symbols) by Sage Sparrows in 1996 (N = 85) and 1997 (N = 154), and percent of nests parasitized by cowbirds (bars). Lower graph shows point-count results for cowbirds on study plots in 1996 and 1997. Dotted rectangles show survey period in April, May, and June.

Nests of potential cowbird hosts were located by searching study plots, by following territorial males that were color-banded as part of a productivity study, and by flushing birds from nests while conducting related field work on the plots. Nests were flagged at a distance of > 6m and visited every 2–5 days until fledging or failure. The number of host eggs and young and cowbird eggs and young were recorded at each visit. Nest success was calculated using the Mayfield (1975) method.

RESULTS

Cowbirds were common on the study area, recorded on point-counts at 26 of 29 sites surveyed. Cowbirds arrived on the study area in late April, attaining greatest abundance in May and June (Fig. 1). Most (81%) of the 172 cowbirds of known gender on point-counts were males; the sex of 88 birds was not determined. We located and monitored a total of 779 nests of eight species thought to be potential cowbird hosts (Table 1). Of these eight species, only the Brewer's Sparrow, Sage Sparrow, and Vesper Sparrow showed evidence of parasitism (Table

1). These were the most common species on our study plots and provided the largest sample size of nests. Other shrubsteppe-associated species that occurred on the plots but represented by few nests included Savannah Sparrow (*Passerculus sandwichensis*) and Grasshopper Sparrow (*Ammodramus savannarum*).

The proportion of nesting attempts initiated before cowbird arrival (01 May) varied from >40% for early nesting species such as Sage Sparrows, Horned Larks, and Western Meadowlarks, to ≤5% for late-arriving species such as Brewer's Sparrows and Lark Sparrows (Table 1). Sage Sparrows began nesting in March, reaching a peak of nesting in May of both years (Fig. 1). Parasitism of Sage Sparrow clutches occurred only during May and June, reaching a peak of 20% in June of 1997 (Fig 1). In both years, first nesting attempts for Sage Sparrows were well underway before cowbirds arrived on the study area. Vesper Sparrows initiated > 40% of nests before 01 May in 1996, and < 10% in 1997 (Fig. 2). No Vesper Sparrow clutches showed evidence of parasitism in 1996, whereas in 1997 one clutch each in May and June was

TABLE 1. LEVELS OF NEST PARASITISM BY BROWN-HEADED COWBIRDS FOR POTENTIAL HOSTS IN EASTERN WASHINGTON, 1996–97

Species	Number of nests[a]	Nests initiated before 01 May (%)	Parasitism level (%)
Brewer's Sparrow (*Spizella breweri*)	281	5	5.0
Sage Sparrow (*Amphispiza belli*)	244	43	4.1
Sage Thrasher[b] (*Oreoscoptes montanus*)	95	17	0
Vesper Sparrow (*Pooecetes gramineus*)	77	23	2.6
Western Meadowlark[b] (*Sturnella neglecta*)	36	51	0
Lark Sparrow (*Chondestes grammacus*)	24	0	0
Horned Lark (*Eremophila alpestris*)	12	42	0
Loggerhead Shrike[b] (*Lanius ludovicianus*)	10	20	0

[a] Includes only species with 10 or more nests.
[b] Species known to reject cowbird eggs in some populations.

parasitized. Brewer's Sparrows began nesting in mid- to late April, and nesting reached its peak in May of both years (Fig. 3). Cowbirds were present on the study area for the bulk of the Brewer's Sparrow's nesting period, with parasitism levels reaching their peak in June of both years (Fig. 3).

Brewer's Sparrows successfully fledged their own young from 31% (N = 135 exposure days) of parasitized clutches, compared with 51% (N = 2851 exposure days) for non-parasitized clutches. Sage Sparrows fledged their own young from 20% (N = 115 exposure days) of parasitized clutches, compared with 31% (N = 2320 exposure days) for non-parasitized clutches. Considering only nests where cowbird eggs hatched, host young fledged from 2 of 2 Brewer's Sparrow nests and from 1 of 4 Sage Sparrow nests.

Abandonment rates were greater for parasitized than for non-parasitized clutches. Brewer's Sparrows abandoned 4 of 14 (29%) parasitized clutches, compared with 1.8% (N = 267) of non-parasitized clutches. Sage Sparrows abandoned 1 of 10 (10%) parasitized clutches, compared with 1.2% (N = 234) of non-parasitized clutches. In two instances, cowbirds laid a single egg in the empty, abandoned nest of Sage Sparrows.

Cowbird eggs hatched in 2 of 7 (29%) parasitized Brewer's Sparrow clutches and in 4 of 5 (80%) parasitized Sage Sparrow clutches that successfully hatched any eggs. Cowbirds fledged from 1 of 6 (17%) parasitized Brewer's Sparrow broods and from 2 of 3 (67%) parasitized Sage Sparrow broods that successfully fledged any young. Cowbirds fledged from 2 of 4 Sage Sparrow broods and from both Brewer's Sparrow broods that successfully hatched cowbird eggs.

DISCUSSION

The most definitive result from our analysis was the low level of nest parasitism in this al-

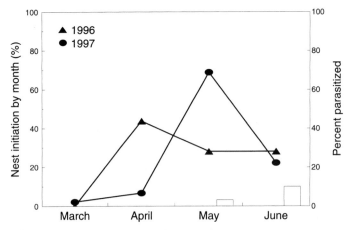

FIGURE 2. Relationship between nesting by Vesper Sparrows and parasitism by Brown-headed Cowbirds in eastern Washington. Symbols show timing of nest initiation by Vesper Sparrows in 1996 (N = 32) and in 1997 (N = 45). Bars show percent of nests parasitized by cowbirds in 1997 (no Vesper Sparrow nests were parasitized in 1996).

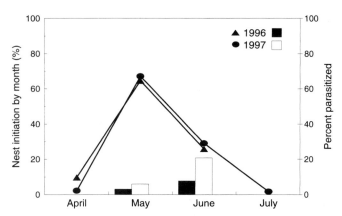

FIGURE 3. Relationship between nesting by Brewer's Sparrows and parasitism by Brown-headed Cowbirds in eastern Washington. Symbols show timing of nest initiation by Brewer's Sparrows in 1996 (N = 93) and in 1997 (N = 179). Bars show percent of nests parasitized by cowbirds in 1996 and 1997.

tered landscape. Although cowbirds were present on almost all of our study sites, overall parasitism rates were substantially lower than those from some other fragmented landscapes (Robinson et al. 1995a) and from other populations in shrubsteppe (20%, N = 20, Rich 1978; 29%, N = 7, Reynolds 1981; 52%, N = 25, Biermann et al.1987). Ellison (*this volume*) also reported a similar, low level of parasitism for Sage Sparrows in southern California. Most previous reports of parasitism rates in shrubsteppe, however, were based on relatively small sample sizes.

Parasitism levels on our sites also were lower than those reported in structurally similar habitats such as continuous coastal scrub, grasslands, and prairies. Parasitism in grassland and open prairie habitats is extremely variable geographically, ranging from 3–85% (Elliott 1978, Buech 1982, Zimmerman 1983, Johnson and Temple 1990, Hill and Sealy 1994, Fondell 1997, Koford et al. in press, Peer et al. *this volume*, Robinson et al. *this volume*). Parasitism in contiguous, open habitats is generally lower than parasitism in many eastern fragmented forests as well as western riparian habitats (Hergenrader 1962, Wiens 1963, Hill 1976, Elliott 1978, Brown 1994, Rothstein and Robinson 1994, several authors in this volume).

Parasitism rates may not be homogeneous across a landscape (Hahn and Hatfield 1995), and cowbirds observed on our surveys in shrubsteppe may focus on hosts in other communities. Several studies have reported lower rates of nest parasitism in grasslands than in adjacent forested habitats (Hahn and Hatfield 1995; Robinson et al. in press, *this volume*). Our study sites were far from the nearest forests, but wooded riparian zones occurred irregularly across the region.

Two studies of Red-winged Blackbird (*Agelaius phoeniceus*) populations within riparian communities in our study area reported parasitism rates of 54% (Orians et al. 1989) and > 30% (Freeman et al. 1990) at the height of cowbird laying activity. Red-winged Blackbirds do not reject cowbird eggs but are aggressive in defending their nests against parasitism (Freeman et al. 1990). Parasitism rates for other potential hosts in these riparian communities have not been examined.

Rates of parasitism reported for our study plots likely underestimate the actual parasitism experienced by host species. Sage Thrashers and Loggerhead Shrikes are know to reject cowbird eggs (Rothstein 1982, Rich and Rothstein 1985) and it is unlikely that we would have observed parasitism in these species. Western Meadowlarks also reject cowbird eggs in some populations (Peer et al. *this volume*), although parasitism rates can be high in others (Davis and Sealy in press). Our parasitism rates for species that abandon (e.g., Sage and Brewer's sparrows) also may be underestimates, as some nests that were parasitized and then abandoned likely went undetected.

TIMING OF ARRIVAL AND
REPRODUCTIVE PHYSIOLOGY

Low parasitism rates in our study area were due, in part, to timing of cowbird arrival relative to initiation of first nests by hosts. Cowbirds arrived in late April and early May, by which time the first nesting attempts of Sage Sparrows, Western Meadowlarks, Horned Larks, and Vesper Sparrows (in 1996) were well underway. This finding corresponds well with information on arrival dates and timing of parasitism at this latitude in the literature. Biermann et al. (1987)

reported that cowbirds did not arrive on sites in Alberta's shrubsteppe until May 10. Even though nesting by Brewer's Sparrows in Alberta did not start until May 26, early Brewer's Sparrow nests were not as heavily parasitized (1 of 5 in May) as later attempts (9 of 12 in June). Near our study sites in eastern Washington, Freeman et al. (1990) documented substantially higher parasitism of Red-winged Blackbirds later in the season compared with earlier broods. Brown (1994) reported similar results for species breeding at a lower latitude. Early nesting species (before May) in the Grand Canyon had parasitism rates below 10% whereas those species whose nesting coincided with peak laying of cowbirds in May and June were parasitized much more heavily. Completion of a significant portion of a potential host's nesting effort prior to laying activity by Brown-headed Cowbirds has been documented in other populations (Ortega and Cruz 1991, Peer and Bollinger 1997).

Female cowbirds present early in the season may not be capable of parasitizing first broods because of physiological limitations or socioecological constraints, such as time involved in initial territory establishment, mate selection, or host selection. The physiological limitation hypothesis is supported by studies of reproductive timing of cowbirds. In Ontario, female cowbirds are physiologically capable of laying in late April/early May and remain active until early July (Scott 1963; Scott and Ankney 1980, 1983). Cowbirds in the central Sierra Nevada mountains of California did not have eggs in their oviducts until the second week of May (Fleischer et al. 1987). Brown (1994) indicated that peak cowbird laying seasons along the Colorado River in the Grand Canyon occurred during the latter half of May and first half of June, despite the early breeding season of hosts at that latitude. Although cowbird populations are known to shift laying dates earlier or later to synchronize with host nesting (Payne 1973, Fleischer et al. 1987, Trail and Baptista 1993), cowbirds may avoid early-nesting hosts because of high rates of nest failure reported in some populations at this time (Freeman et al. 1990). In the present study, success rates of parasitized species were similar for early and mid-season nests, with only Sage Sparrows showing a higher success rate in June (Washington Department of Fish and Wildlife, unpubl. data).

HOST QUALITY

Some species may be unsuitable hosts, resulting in selection against parasitism by cowbirds (Rothstein 1975b). From a diet and nest-accessibility standpoint, the shrubsteppe species considered here would seem to be suitable hosts.

Indeed, both Brewer's and Sage sparrows successfully fledged cowbirds, although high rates of abandonment, particularly for Brewer's Sparrows, depressed the overall success rate. Brewer's Sparrows in Alberta experienced high parasitism and also had high abandonment rates and low cowbird fledging success compared with some other host populations (Biermann et al. 1987). Sage Sparrows also abandon parasitized nests (Rich 1978, Reynolds 1981). Abandonment is clearly a common occurrence among many host species (Rothstein 1976, Graham 1988, Hill and Sealy 1994, Goguen and Mathews 1996) and may become more common in a species after increased exposure to cowbirds (Trail and Baptista 1993). This latter phenomenon may be important from a conservation standpoint, particularly if cowbirds are capable of shifting laying dates to synchronize with early-nesting hosts. It is important to note that we cannot necessarily interpret abandonment of nests as an anti-parasitism adaptation (Rothstein 1975b), as it might instead be caused by a reaction to the presence of an unfamiliar egg, alteration of clutch size, or even violent physical displacement of the host by the cowbird (Rothstein 1975b, Graham 1988, Hill and Sealy 1994, Rothstein and Robinson 1994; J. Tewksbury, pers. comm.). Possibly, certain behaviors of shrubsteppe birds, such as incubating when female cowbirds attempt to lay (Neudorf and Sealy 1994) or remaining on and/or defending the nest against cowbirds, make these species prone to nest desertion.

Increased host defense is suggested to reduce cowbird parasitism among Least Flycatchers (*Empidonax minimus*) and Red-winged Blackbirds (Robertson and Norman 1976, 1977; Briskie et al. 1990; Freeman et al. 1990). Alternatively, host defense also may facilitate nest-finding by Brown-headed Cowbirds (nest-cue hypothesis), although this has recently received mixed support from experiments by Gill et al. (1997) and Banks (1997). In our study, anecdotal observations of Brewer's Sparrows mobbing female cowbirds as they hopped through the sagebrush suggest that cowbirds are recognized as a threat by this species, but it is unknown whether mobbing influences parasitism success.

DISTANCE TO FEEDING AREAS

Our study sites may have been too far from cowbird feeding areas to support sufficient densities of breeding cowbirds. Cowbirds require both host-rich laying areas in the morning for successful reproduction and suitable feeding areas (feedlots, livestock pastures, corrals, bird feeders) during the afternoon (Rothstein et al.

1980, 1984; Dufty 1982a). In fact, cowbirds may be more limited by foraging habitat than by host availability (Hamilton and Orians 1965). Biermann et al. (1987) suggested that the proximity of one of their Alberta study sites to riparian areas, pastures, and feedlots was probably responsible for its high parasitism rates (59%), whereas their study site without any parasitism was >10 km from the nearest feedlot. In Idaho, parasitized Sage and Brewer's sparrow nests were found within 3 km of a neighboring cattle ranch from which cowbirds dispersed in the mornings (Rich 1978).

Distance to feeding areas also may have played a part in the skewed sex ratio of cowbirds recorded on our surveys. The preponderance of male cowbirds on our surveys may indicate that our sites were too far from foraging areas for female cowbirds, suggesting that many of the males on our surveys were unpaired. Point count surveys elsewhere have revealed sex ratios for cowbirds close to 50% (S. K. Robinson, pers. comm.). Identification of cowbird feeding areas on our study area may help to explain the observed patterns of parasitism.

AVAILABILITY OF PERCHES

It may be difficult for cowbirds to find and determine activity levels of host nests in the shrubsteppe due to the low, dense, homogenous vegetation, and the scarcity of elevated observation perches (Norman and Robertson 1975, Gates and Gysel 1978, Gochfeld 1979). These ideas have been suggested by many other researchers, but to our knowledge have not been tested rigorously. Limited correlative data support the perch-limitation hypothesis. In Alberta, sites with parasitized Brewer's Sparrow nests had perches up to 4 m in height located in a nearby riparian strip, whereas sites without parasitism had none (Biermann et al. 1987). In Arizona, parasitism rates for Black-throated Sparrows (*Amphispiza bilineata*) were greater in areas with high (>2 m) perches provided by crucifixion thorn (*Canotia holacantha*) and power lines, compared with sites with only creosote bush (*Larrea divaricata*) (R. Johnson and C. van Riper, unpubl. data). In Minnesota, Johnson and Temple (1990) found that prairie-nesting birds experienced lower parasitism farther from wooded edges.

Cowbirds are known to lay in inactive nests, regardless of the presence or absence of host eggs (Norman and Robertson 1975, Lowther 1979, Freeman et al. 1990), indicating that they cannot always accurately assess the status of nests. On our sites, we identified at least two instances of cowbird eggs laid in recently depredated nests of Sage Sparrows. Presumably, elevated perches make it easier for cowbirds to track the status of active nests and therefore, when perches are absent, they lay eggs more often in inactive nests. Freeman et al. (1990) reported that 21.5% of all cowbird eggs found in their study of Red-winged Blackbirds were in inactive nests and that this occurred more frequently in areas without nearby perches. Moreover, the low hatching rate of cowbird eggs in our study suggests that cowbirds frequently were unable to track nest development and therefore laid in nests that were too advanced for the cowbird eggs to receive sufficient incubation.

WHICH SUBSPECIES?

Mobbing of cowbird females, high abandonment rates of parasitized Brewer's Sparrow nests, and the likely ejection of cowbird eggs by Sage Thrashers suggest that shrubsteppe birds in eastern Washington have been exposed to cowbird parasitism long enough to develop defensive responses. Cowbirds in shrubsteppe habitats of Washington may be of the native subspecies *artemisiae*, rather than the subspecies *obscurus*, the more recent arrival that is presumed to be responsible for recent widespread parasitism in the northwestern states (Rothstein et al.1980, Laymon 1987, Rothstein 1994). Ward and Smith (1998) provided morphological evidence that cowbirds have been present in British Columbia's Okanagan Valley, 100 km north of our study area, long enough to become morphologically differentiated from the *artemisiae* and *obscurus* subspecies. Low observed parasitism of shrubsteppe birds in Washington may result from coevolved defenses on the part of the host species (Mayfield 1965 [but see also Rich 1978 and Robinson et al. *this volume*]).

CONCLUSIONS

Parasitism levels of shrubsteppe species in eastern Washington were low compared with those reported for other bird communities in shrubsteppe and for bird communities in some other fragmented landscapes. Based on analysis of data from the first two years of this study, there appears to be no substantial effect of parasitism on avian reproduction within the big sagebrush communities of Washington's shrubsteppe, at least among the species considered here. Several shrubsteppe-associated species were not represented well in our sample, nor did we sample populations in communities other than big sagebrush. Parasitism levels have been found to vary considerably among years within a host population (Smith and Arcese 1994), so more long-term data will be of considerable value.

Determining why parasitism is low in this

fragmented landscape may have important implications for managing cowbirds in other areas. Further analysis of data from this continuing study in eastern Washington may help to elucidate factors influencing parasitism rates. For now, we suggest that future research on cowbird parasitism in shrubsteppe focus on (1) determining effects of distance, distribution, and size of cowbird feeding areas on rates of nest parasitism, (2) examining how cowbirds find nests in shrubsteppe, focusing on experiments of perch availability, and (3) comparisons of host quality, both through observational studies to determine parasitism, hatching, and fledging rates, and through experiments to further define abandon-ment and ejection rates as well as host ability to raise cowbird young.

ACKNOWLEDGMENTS

Funding for this research was provided by the Washington Department of Fish and Wildlife, the National Fish and Wildlife Foundation, and Battelle-Pacific Northwest Laboratory. Additional support was provided by the Washington Department of Natural Resources. We thank P. Doran, L. Fitzner, D. Freisze, R. Handler, L. Lipinski, L. Marsh, B. Merkle, T. Mohagan, S. Negri, M. Nelson, J. Ogburn, J. Slotterbeck, S. Taylor, and K. Warner for assistance in the field. The paper benefitted from reviews by B. Peer, S. Robinson, J. Rotenberry, G. Vander Haegen, and an anonymous reviewer.

Studies in Avian Biology No. 18:41–51, 1999.

HABITAT AND LANDSCAPE FACTORS AFFECTING COWBIRD DISTRIBUTION IN THE NORTHERN ROCKIES

JOCK S. YOUNG AND RICHARD L. HUTTO

Abstract. We studied the habitat and landscape factors influencing the distribution of Brown-headed Cowbirds (*Molothrus ater*), using data from a region-wide monitoring program conducted in the northern Rockies. Bird, habitat, and landscape data were collected at 7,153 points along 761 transects that were distributed throughout western Montana and northern Idaho. Brown-headed Cowbirds were largely absent from dense, old-growth, and high-elevation forests. They were most abundant in open conifer forest (ponderosa pine [*Pinus ponderosa*] and partially logged sites) as well as grassland, agricultural, and riparian cover types. We found that open lands such as grasslands and agricultural areas were more likely to be used than were clearcuts. In addition, cowbird presence was negatively related to canopy cover when we included data from all cover types, but was not significantly related to this variable within coniferous forest cover types. It appears that the presence of clearcuts does not draw cowbirds to forested regions. The density of potential host species was one of the most important local-scale correlates of cowbird presence. Nonetheless, multivariate models were dominated by landscape variables, and distance to agricultural lands was the strongest predictor of cowbird presence. Cowbirds were so strongly associated with the proximity of agricultural areas that many areas of the forested mountains are probably still safe from parasitism pressure. Our data suggest that cattle grazing and other agricultural practices appear to be directly involved with the expansion of cowbirds in this region (and other parts of the West). Cowbirds may be a textbook example of the importance of landscape context in the distribution of a bird species.

Key Words: habitat, human-induced changes, landscape, *Molothrus ater*, northern Rockies.

The Brown-headed Cowbird (*Molothrus ater*) was historically rare or nonexistent in many parts of the West (Rothstein 1994). The sudden presence of this brood parasite may, therefore, have a serious impact on hosts that are not adapted to its presence. Because the recent spread of cowbirds throughout the West has probably been associated with human land-use activity, we need to better understand exactly which activities or land conditions favor the presence and/or spread of cowbirds. Moreover, because landscape conditions may contribute, in part, to the suitability of a site to cowbirds, there is need for a regional study that incorporates both landscape and local-scale factors into a study of cowbird distribution.

Several years ago, the Northern Region of the U.S. Forest Service (USFS) initiated a Landbird Monitoring Program designed to provide a regional picture of bird-habitat relationships across the region's National Forests and to estimate the overall population trends of a variety of diurnal landbird species. The program involves periodic surveys of birds and habitat conditions surrounding more than 7,000 points that are distributed throughout the region. As far as we know, this is the largest program of its kind in North America, and it provides a unique opportunity to couple information on both local-scale and landscape conditions surrounding points of occurrence for many landbird species, including cowbirds. In this paper, we report on the variables that appear to be most important in pre-dicting the presence of cowbirds within this northern Rocky Mountain region.

METHODS

All 13 National Forests in the USFS Northern Region and the Potlatch Timber Company (a large private landowner in central Idaho) participated in the collection of data on cowbird presence and abundance for our study. The study region covered all of western Montana and northern Idaho (including 19 million acres of non-wilderness Forest Service lands). This entire region is dominated by conifer forest, with deciduous trees largely restricted to riparian areas. Forest composition includes a mixture of conifer species throughout the region, with the most common tree species, in decreasing order of importance, being Douglas-fir (*Pseudotsuga menziesii*), lodgepole pine (*Pinus contorta*), western larch (*Larix occidentalis*) and ponderosa pine (*Pinus ponderosa*). There is a major climate gradient, with the moister, denser cedar/hemlock (*Thuja plicata/Tsuga heterophyla*) and grand fir (*Abies grandis*) forests restricted to the northwestern portion of the region, and drier, sparser forests (mostly Douglas-fir and lodgepole pine) predominating east of the continental divide. Spruce/fir (*Picea engelmannii/Abies lasiocarpa*) forests occur at higher elevations as well as in some riparian situations. Valley bottoms are usually dominated by agriculture (pasture and cropland) and other human disturbance, with grasslands in the foothills, and sagebrush (*Artemisia*

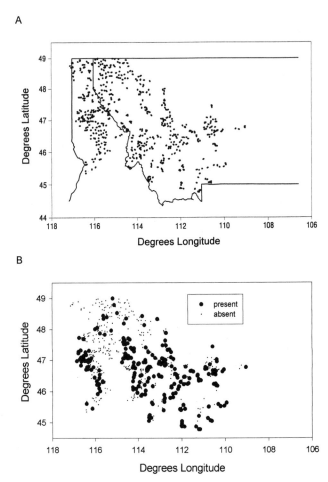

FIGURE 1.   A) Distribution of sampled transects across northern Idaho and western Montana; B) The geographic distribution of Brown-headed Cowbirds across all transects. Each large dot indicates that the species was present on at least one point on that transect, and each small dot represents an entire transect sampled without detecting cowbirds.

spp.) being more extensive in the southeastern section.

We collected bird, habitat, and landscape data at a total of 7,153 points along 761 transects (Fig. 1A). Most of these transects (545), each containing 10 points, were permanently marked as part of a long-term monitoring program. The distribution of these 545 transects was geographically stratified by US Geological Survey 7.5-minute topographic quad maps. Transect start points were located by positioning a random point within each quad quarter-section and then finding the nearest point on an unpaved secondary or tertiary road, or on a trail. The remaining nine points constituting a transect were positioned at 300-m intervals in a single direction along the road or trail. Potential transects were retained only if there was reasonable access.

Used transects were selected from these potential transects as randomly as possible under logistic constraints. There were usually two observers on each National Forest, covering one transect each per day. In addition to these permanently marked points, in 1993 and 1994 we conducted one-time visits to 1,825 additional sampling points (along 216 transects of varying length) that were stratified by cover type to provide greater coverage of some of the rarer vegetation types.

FIELD METHODS

The bird counts followed recommendations discussed by Ralph et al. (1995) and methods described by Hutto et al. (1986). A 10-min point count was conducted at each of the 10 sampling points along a transect. Points were visited once

TABLE 1. DISTRIBUTION OF THE 3,406 NON-EDGE SAMPLE POINTS (IN THE NORTHERN ROCKIES) AMONG 18 MAJOR COVER TYPES, WITH THE PERCENT OCCURRENCES OF BROWN-HEADED COWBIRDS (AS DISPLAYED IN FIG. 2)

Cover type	Number of points	Percent of points	Cowbird occurrence (%)	Median distance to agriculture (km)
Cedar/hemlock	63	1.8	0.0	28.5
Spruce/fir	133	3.9	0.8	16.3
Lodgepole pine	215	6.3	1.9	16.7
Mixed-conifer	1,121	32.9	8.3	11.6
Douglas-fir	289	8.5	6.2	13.3
Ponderosa pine	77	2.3	18.2	3.7
Group selection	112	3.3	12.5	7.1
Shelterwood	75	2.2	21.3	7.7
Seed-tree cut	116	3.4	10.3	9.6
Clearcut	341	10.0	5.0	14.2
Post-fire	58	1.7	8.6	13.5
Sagebrush	88	2.6	13.6	8.2
Grassland	167	4.9	12.6	3.4
Agricultural	56	1.6	19.6	0.0
Marsh, wetland	71	2.1	14.1	10.3
Riparian shrub	294	8.6	18.0	12.3
Cottonwood/aspen	84	2.5	22.6	10.6
Residential	46	1.4	30.4	2.8

each breeding season between mid-May and mid-July. All birds seen or heard within the count period were recorded, noting species, number of individuals, and distance to the bird(s). Field observers began counts at least 15 min after sunrise, and completed transects before 11:30. Counts were not conducted on days with continuous rain or high winds. The order of visits to transects was set by elevation and seasonal access.

We recorded the vegetation cover type in a 100-m radius circle surrounding each point. Cover type was defined according to a scheme based on a combination of the dominant plant species in the tallest vegetation layer and the vertical and horizontal vegetation structure. A series of successional stages for each conifer forest type was included. Our classification of such disturbed forest types was based on the dominant tree species composition and stand structure, without regard to the process that actually caused the structure. We recorded over 200 cover types in the field, but we merged them into 18 general types so that all groups had at least 50 points (Table 1). There were six relatively undisturbed conifer forest types, four relatively disturbed conifer forest types representing different logging regimes, three nonforested cover types, and three riparian vegetation types. The undisturbed conifer types were defined by tree species composition, with >80% of the canopy composed of the named tree species.

To further characterize the surrounding vegetation for use in regression models, we made estimates of the following variables within a 30-m-radius circle centered on each count point: (1)

average height of the tree canopy layer; (2) percent cover of canopy trees (larger than saplings); (3) percent cover of sapling trees (between 5 and 10 cm dbh); (4) percent cover of seedling trees (<5 cm dbh); (5) percent cover of tall shrubs (multi-stemmed woody plants >1 m tall); (6) percent cover of low shrubs (<1 m tall); (7) percent cover of grasses and forbs; and (8) tree species composition, as estimated by the proportionate makeup of each tree species in the overstory canopy.

We used two different sets of species to model host density as a variable that might influence the probability of cowbird presence (Robinson and Wilcove 1994), because it is difficult to decide which species cowbirds may consider as potential hosts in any particular region. Cowbirds have been known to parasitize most open-cup nesting passerines of appropriate size (Friedmann 1963). Therefore, for one species set, we simply chose all open-cup nesting passerine species up to the size of the Brown Thrasher (*Toxostoma rufum*), which is the largest species known to successfully host cowbirds (Friedmann et al. 1977). There were 69 species that fit this criterion, although only 26 of these made up 90 % of the individuals, and seven species made up almost 50% (Dark-eyed Junco [*Junco hyemalis*], Yellow-rumped Warbler [*Dendroica coronata*], Chipping Sparrow [*Spizella passerina*], Swainson's Thrush [*Catharus ustulatus*], American Robin [*Turdus migratorius*], Townsend's Warbler [*Dendroica townsendi*], and Ruby-crowned Kinglet [*Regulus calendula*]). However, it is possible that cowbirds may discriminate among available hosts, or some nests may simply be better hidden. Some species are consistently avoided, and parasitism rates of a single species may vary greatly in different regions (Hoover and Brittingham 1993, Robinson et al. 1995a, Hahn and Hatfield 1995). In the Sierra Nevada of California, tree-nesting species such as Cassin's Vireo (*Vireo cassinii*) and Yellow-rumped Warbler are often parasitized (Rothstein et al. 1980, Verner and Ritter 1983, Airola 1986), even though few records had been recorded for these species previously (Friedmann and Kiff 1985). Cowbird parasitism in western conifer forests has not been sufficiently studied. In an attempt to model a more restricted set of potential hosts that may be more biologically meaningful, we created a second set of likely hosts by excluding species known to reject eggs (Friedman and Kiff 1985), and excluding all species with fewer than 10 records of parasitism in the compilations of Friedman et al. (1977, 1985), unless they were found to be primary hosts (>15 % parasitism) in an ongoing local study (Tewksbury et al. *this volume*). This resulted in 45 species of likely hosts. It is not known if these were actually the most widely used hosts throughout this region, however.

LANDSCAPE VARIABLES

The precise location of both permanent and non-permanent points were marked in the field on the aerial photo associated with each transect, and the aerial photo was subsequently used to position points onto a Geographic Information System (GIS) data layer. The GIS database we used was developed at the University of Montana Wildlife Spatial Analysis Lab, using Landsat TM imagery and ground-truthing in a two-stage classification process (Redmond et al. 1996). Agriculture and riparian areas were added manually to the database from aerial photos, which is a more accurate method than remote sensing.

Within a 1-km radius circle surrounding each point, we calculated several landscape variables from the GIS database. We created variables based on an additional merging of the cover type classification into 15 cover types that correspond as well as possible with our field cover types. These included a conifer series, a riparian series, and an open land series (Table 2). For each of these cover types we calculated the proportion of the 1-km radius circle that was covered by that type, and the distance from the point to the nearest occurrence of each type.

ANALYTICAL METHODS

To determine habitat associations, we used only bird detections that were estimated to be within 100 m of the observer (very few cow-

TABLE 2. DISTRIBUTION OF THE 7,153 SAMPLE POINTS AMONG THE MAJOR GIS COVER TYPES, WITH THE AVERAGE % COVERAGE OF EACH TYPE ACROSS ALL 1-KM RADIUS LANDSCAPE CIRCLES IN THE NORTHERN ROCKIES

Cover type	Number of points	Percent of points	Mean coverage (%)
Mesic conifer	3,633	50.8	55.5
Xeric conifer	510	7.1	7.9
Subalpine conifer	639	8.9	9.9
Mixed conifer/broadleaf	69	1.0	0.9
Broadleaf forest	68	1.0	0.7
Forested riparian	324	4.5	2.3
Non-forested riparian	132	1.8	0.9
Grassland/shrubland	1,530	21.4	17.8
Agricultural land	37	0.5	0.6
Barren land	138	1.9	1.8
Urban/developed	50	0.7	0.8

birds were detected beyond this range), and excluded birds flying over the site. If more than one vegetation cover type occurred within 100 m, the point was designated as being an edge point and was excluded from the local-scale habitat analyses, which cut the sample size nearly in half (3,406). This reduced the chance that birds were detected within a cover type that differed from that associated with a particular census point. We also performed landscape analyses using all points, however.

For a more detailed look at factors affecting the distribution of cowbirds among points, we used logistic regression to predict cowbird presence vs. absence, looking at the continuous habitat variables collected at the point, and combining these with the landscape context of the point taken from the GIS database.

With each point count as a sample unit, almost 98 % of cowbird counts were zero or one (only one cowbird was detected at 77 % of occupied points), so logistic regression is especially appropriate. However, multiple samples of a given cover type within a single transect may not have been statistically independent estimates of bird composition within that cover type. Nevertheless, we used individual points as sample units for all local-scale habitat analyses because (1) transects were inappropriate sample units at this scale, since they crossed multiple cover types, and (2) an average of only four points from each transect were non-edge points that could be used in the analyses.

The landscape variables, however, were based on 1-km radius circles, and points only 300 m apart were clearly pseudoreplicate sample units. Therefore, we redid the landscape analyses using the transect as the sample unit. These analyses did not include local habitat variables because these could not be meaningfully averaged across a transect. The results of these additional landscape analyses were used to corroborate the point-scale analyses.

As a first step in selecting variables for the habitat-relationship model, we fit separate univariate logistic regression equations for each variable (Hosmer and Lemeshow 1989:83). Variables considered for entry into a multivariate model were those for which the univariate test indicated potential significance ($P < 0.15$). Local-scale variables were combined with the landscape variables in a single parsimonious model to explain the distribution of Brown-headed Cowbirds. We used both forward and backward stepwise procedures for building multivariate models. The selection of variables for use in these models was based not only on the statistical significance of each measured variable, but also on our biological knowledge of the species.

We followed the above model-building methods for three different subsets of the data. The first set contained all 7,153 points (including edge points) in all cover types. These models involved comparisons across very different cover types and could only show general patterns of habitat use, as well as landscape effects. It would be valuable to have more detailed information on habitat and landscape effects within a smaller subset of cover types. Specifically, we wanted to predict where cowbirds would occur when they penetrated a typical western coniferous forest landscape (e.g., does opening the forest in various ways affect cowbird distribution, allowing them to penetrate where they otherwise might not?). Therefore, we also conducted analyses using just the subset of 2,250 non-edge points from conifer cover types, ranging from clearcuts to undisturbed forest. This data set still included a wide range of forest types and landscapes, with a multitude of potential reasons for cowbird absences. We used multivariate tests to tease these potential reasons apart. However, in a final attempt to separate local-scale influences from landscape conditions, we analyzed a third subset of the data that included the 517 conifer points within occupied transects only. We assumed that all occupied transects were in at least marginally appropriate landscapes. The discrimination of individual points of use and nonuse by cowbirds within occupied transects (which were less than 3 km in length) would, therefore, likely be due to local factors.

RESULTS

The 3,406 non-edge points were distributed unevenly among the 18 cover types categories (Table 1), with mixed-conifer stands represented

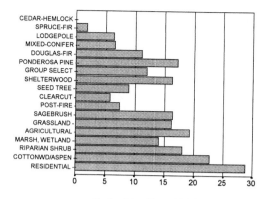

FIGURE 2. The distribution of Brown-headed Cowbirds among 18 major cover types in the northern Rockies. Cowbirds were detected (within 100 m) on 334 of the 3,406 points represented here. Sample sizes for each cover type are given in Table 1. Points with an edge within 100 m were excluded from all non-riparian cover types. The three riparian types (marsh, riparian shrub, and cottonwood bottomland), however, included all points because most of those patches were small or narrow and there was almost always another cover type within 100 m.

by 33 % of the points, and nine cover types having fewer than 100 points.

There were 91 landbird species (54 of which were potential cowbird hosts) that we detected on at least 30 points. We detected Brown-headed Cowbirds on 653 points, or about 9% of the total, but on over one third of the transects (238 of the 638 transects with at least 8 points). Occupied transects were distributed throughout the region, although relatively fewer transects were occupied by cowbirds in the moister forests of northwestern Montana and northern Idaho (Fig. 1B). Cowbirds were relatively common in south-central Montana, with its drier, sparser forests and wider agricultural valleys, and on our extra points in western Montana, which included more agricultural areas, towns, and riparian bottomlands than the permanently marked points.

Cowbirds were uncommon in denser forest cover types and high-elevation forests (Fig. 2), and the only relatively undisturbed forest type in which they were especially common was that dominated by ponderosa pine. All of the relatively undisturbed forest categories (the first six categories in Fig. 2) included a variety of stand ages and even many thinned stands. To further explore these data, we pooled them, and then divided them into different categories based on stand age and disturbance status. We found cowbirds at 1.3 % of 154 points in old growth, 5.1 % of 630 points in mature forest, 5.6 % of 198

TABLE 3. Significance Levels (P-values) of Univariate Logistic Regressions for Each Local-scale and Landscape Variable, and for All Three Subsets of the Data Discussed in the Text (Only Conifer Points Included Within Occupied Transects)

Variable	Sign[a]	All points		Conifer points		Occupied transects
		Statistic[b]	P	Statistic[b]	P	P
Canopy height	+			1	0.35	0.08
Canopy cover	−	64	< 0.01	4	0.06	0.60
Sapling cover	−	22	< 0.01	0	0.88	0.54
Seedling cover	−	12	< 0.01	1	0.44	0.80
Tall shrub cover	−	3	0.07	0	0.99	0.50
Low shrub cover	−	3	0.10	0	0.96	0.86
Ground cover	+	101	< 0.01	36	< 0.01	0.31
Proportion ponderosa pine	+			78	< 0.01	0.02
Proportion Douglas-fir	+			6	0.01	0.45
Proportion western larch				0	0.73	0.41
Proportion lodgepole pine	−			30	< 0.01	0.58
Proportion mesic species	−			5	0.02	0.64
Abundance of all hosts	+	131	< 0.01	83	< 0.01	< 0.01
Richness of all hosts	+	148	< 0.01	108	< 0.01	0.05
Abundance of likely hosts	+	164	< 0.01	110	< 0.01	< 0.01
Richness of likely hosts	+	176	< 0.01	123	< 0.01	0.02
Elevation	−	20	< 0.01	24	< 0.01	0.92
Distance (developed)	−	209	< 0.01	102	< 0.01	0.92
Distance (agriculture)	−	298	< 0.01	112	< 0.01	0.41
Distance (grass/shrubland)	−	52	< 0.01	11	< 0.01	0.58
Distance (riparian)	−	23	< 0.01	14	< 0.01	0.12
Coverage (agriculture)	+	24	< 0.01	0	0.66	0.18
Coverage (grass/shrubland)	+	98	< 0.01	29	< 0.01	0.30
Coverage (subalpine forest)	−	136	< 0.01	88	< 0.01	0.07
Coverage (mesic forest)	−	94	< 0.01	8	< 0.01	0.04
Coverage (xeric forest)	+	68	< 0.01	68	< 0.01	0.02
Coverage (riparian)	+	36	< 0.01	1	0.42	0.62

[a] The sign of the relationship was the same for all data sets.
[b] The chi-square statistic for the likelihood ratio test indicates relative statistical importance.

points in young forest, and 10.0 % of 769 points in selectively cut stands. Cowbirds were also common in more extensively logged forests, but were observed more often in partially logged stands than in clearcuts (Fig. 2). As expected, cowbirds were most commonly detected in open areas, including grassland and agriculture, and riparian vegetation.

Both landscape and local-scale habitat variables were significantly related to cowbird occurrence using logistic regression models that involved all 7,153 points (Table 3). Most landscape variables were significant in the univariate tests, but distance to agricultural lands was the strongest predictor of cowbird presence (Table 3). In fact, about 73 % of points with cowbirds were within 10 km of agricultural areas, and almost 90 % were within 20 km (Fig. 3). Cowbirds were also found closer to developed areas, as well as in landscapes with more open areas and xeric forests, but less subalpine and mesic forests. All of these relationships were strong enough ($P < 0.001$) to remain significant when the data were averaged over each transect, and the 638 transects were then used as sample units.

Most local-scale vegetation variables were also important in the univariate logistic regressions, although some were not examined because they were not relevant to all cover types (height and species composition of canopy were not defined if there was no canopy). Cowbirds were negatively associated with canopy cover, as expected, since they were common in grasslands and agricultural areas, where canopy cover was zero. Ground cover was the strongest predictor of cowbird occurrence among habitat variables. Ground cover tended to be high in areas where cowbirds were common, such as grasslands, ponderosa pine forests, and partially logged forests. All of the measures of host abundance and species richness were strong predictors of cowbird presence (Table 3). The restricted subset of likely hosts appeared to fit the data best. Although species richness was a slightly better predictor than abundance, we thought that abundance was more biologically meaningful.

A

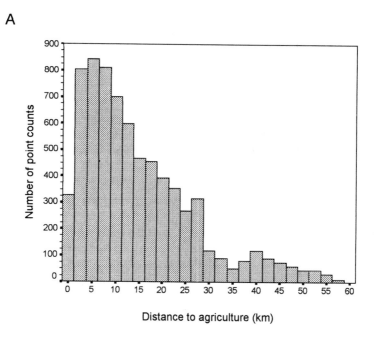

B

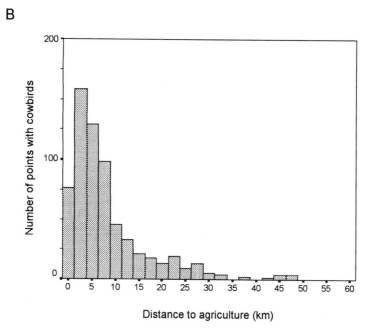

FIGURE 3. Frequency distribution for the distance to the nearest agricultural lands from A) all 7,153 points used in the analyses (median = 11.6 km); B) the 653 points where cowbirds occurred (median = 5.3 km) in northern Idaho and western Montana.

Therefore, we chose the abundance of likely hosts as the variable to test in the multivariate analyses.

When these variables were put together in a multivariate model (Table 4), it was still appar-

ent that cowbirds were closer to agriculture and urban areas, on average. They were not in landscapes with subalpine forests, and they were more common in landscapes with less mesic conifer and more xeric conifer stands, which in-

TABLE 4. SIGNIFICANCE LEVELS (P-VALUES) OF VARIABLES INCLUDED IN MULTIPLE LOGISTIC REGRESSION MODELS FOR ALL THREE SUBSETS OF THE DATA DISCUSSED IN THE TEXT

Variable	Sign[a]	All points	Conifer points	Occupied transects
Canopy height	+	< 0.01		0.02
Canopy cover	−	< 0.01		
Tall shrub cover	−	0.02		
Ground cover	+	0.02		
Proportion ponderosa pine	+		0.05	
Abundance of likely hosts	+	< 0.01	< 0.01	< 0.01
Distance (developed)	−	< 0.01	< 0.01	
Distance (agriculture)	−	< 0.01	< 0.01	
Distance (riparian)	−	< 0.01		
Coverage (subalpine forest)	−	< 0.01	< 0.01	
Coverage (mesic forest)	−	< 0.01		
Coverage (xeric forest)	+	0.04	0.02	0.02
Coverage (riparian)	+	< 0.01		

[a] The sign of the relationship was the same for all data sets.

cluded ponderosa pine, juniper (*Juniperus scopularum*), and limber pine (*Pinus flexilis*). An association with riparian areas was indicated by the inclusion of both the coverage of and distance to these lands. There were also local-scale variables in this multivariate model. Canopy cover and the abundance of likely hosts were the most important. The same model was produced by both forward and backward stepwise variable selection.

To examine the habitat distribution of cowbirds within the conifer cover types only, we conducted additional analyses using the restricted data set of 2,250 non-edge points from conifer habitats. Cowbirds were detected on 172 of these points. Most of the landscape variables were still significant in univariate tests, whereas most of the local vegetation variables were not (Table 3). Although cowbirds tended to occur in sites with less canopy cover (P = 0.06), this relationship was much less apparent when other variables were included in a multivariate model (P = 0.24). The multivariate model was dominated by landscape variables (Table 4), although the abundance of likely hosts was the strongest predictor (P < 0.001). Again, cowbirds were found closer to agricultural areas and were not found in subalpine landscapes. They were more likely to be present in stands with more ponderosa pine in the tree canopy (P = 0.05), which was the only vegetation variable that was even close to significant. The same model was produced by both forward and backward stepwise variable selection. Although the relationships were not significant in the multivariate analyses, cowbirds tended to be in stands closer to riparian areas (P = 0.09), and in landscapes surrounded by more agricultural areas (P = 0.07).

The data set representing only occupied transects contained 517 points, including the same 172 points with cowbirds as above. As expected, landscape variables were of greatly reduced importance when unoccupied transects were removed from the analyses. There was no trend toward a relationship with canopy cover within occupied transects (P = 0.60). Very few variables were significantly related to cowbird presence in this data set (Table 3), and only three were retained in the multivariate model (Table 4). The best predictor was the abundance of potential hosts. There was also a positive association with canopy height. The coverage of xeric forest was the third variable retained in the forward stepwise procedure, and we report it here because it fit the data slightly better than the coverage of mesic forest, which was selected by the backward elimination procedure. These two variables were strongly correlated (r = −0.70). It was not clear whether the local or landscape variable involving xeric pine was the most important, since they were also highly correlated (r = 0.49) and had similar significance levels, both separately (P = 0.02) and together (P = 0.18).

In the above analyses, we used a merged cover type category for non-forested lands other than agriculture and riparian (it included all types of grasslands and upland shrublands). This variable was strongly related to cowbird presence, as expected, with cowbirds occurring closer to these lands, on average. However, it would be interesting to know if different kinds of open lands affect cowbird occurrence differently. To explore this, we separated these lands into components relating to low-elevation grasslands, high-elevation grasslands, upland mesic shrublands, and xeric shrublands. Unfortunately, clearcuts were not well differentiated in the GIS database, since the satellite imagery responded to the reflectance of the ground cover, rather than anything relevant to logging per se. However, clear differences emerged between these categories in their relation to cowbird distribution. Cowbirds were seen more often near low-elevation grasslands. This relationship was nearly as strong as that with the distance to agriculture (although these two variables were correlated, with r = 0.30, they both would enter a regression model together). Cowbirds were less likely to occur nearer high-elevation grasslands, however. Cowbird presence was not correlated with distance to upland shrublands, which was the category that should have included shrubby clearcuts. These relationships held whether we looked at all points or only those in conifer cover types.

Elevation at the sample points ranged from 465 m to 2,620 m. The highest elevation we detected cowbirds was 2,318 m (there were 133 points higher than this without cowbirds). Cowbirds were more abundant at lower elevations (Table 3). However, elevation was correlated with all of the other variables influencing cowbird occurrence in the multivariate models. Therefore, the relationship with elevation was not retained in these models.

Cowbirds were more likely to occur at points where more potential hosts were also observed. The distribution of these potential hosts among cover types (Fig. 4) was generally similar to that of the Brown-headed Cowbird (Fig. 2). Host density was also an important predictor in regression models (Tables 3 and 4). There was not much difference in the predictive abilities of host species richness and the number of potential host individuals. These relationships held within all points and within conifer cover types, and were still highly significant after distance to agriculture and the other variables were included in a multivariate model. We also found that host density was significantly related to cowbird presence on points within occupied transects only. In fact, the abundance of the subset of likely hosts was a better predictor than any other variable in this data set (P = 0.003).

DISCUSSION

The Brown-headed Cowbird can be found in a broad range of cover types in the northern Rockies (Fig. 2), as has been found elsewhere. Rothstein (1994) found that this species was reported on about 60 % of all Breeding Bird Censuses throughout North America during a 5-year period, more than any other species. In a more extensive literature review of studies (including Breeding Bird Censuses) in the northern Rocky Mountain region, Hutto (1995a) found the cowbird to be among the most diverse species in its use of major cover types. In our study, cowbirds occurred in all major cover types except cedar-

hemlock forest. It was not one of the most commonly detected bird species, however, occurring on only 9 % of all points. Nineteen species were seen on more points, and four were detected on over 30 % of the points.

Brown-headed Cowbirds did not use all cover types equally. They were largely absent from dense, old-growth, and high-elevation forests. They were most abundant in open conifer forest (ponderosa pine and partially logged sites) as well as grassland, agricultural, and riparian cover types. A preference for open forests would be biologically understandable, since these habitats would provide numerous perches combined with high visibility for the observation of host species (Norman and Robertson 1975, Gates and Gysel 1978). However, it should be noted that these habitats were also more likely to be closer to agricultural lands (Table 1), so the apparent pattern of habitat use may have been partly a landscape-driven phenomenon.

When detected in conifer forest, cowbirds were much more likely to be near open lands (grassland and agriculture), and when in open lands they were slightly more likely to be near riparian areas (but not conifer forest). Cowbirds are widely known to prefer edges between shrubs or forest and open lands, where breeding and foraging opportunities can be found together (Rothstein et al. 1980, Robinson et al. 1995a). Johnson and Temple (1990) found that rates of cowbird parasitism were higher near forested edges of prairies than in more continuous tallgrass prairie. To use breeding habitat farther from foraging habitat, cowbirds have been known to travel several kilometers (Rothstein et al. 1984).

The arrangement of cover types in the northern Rockies is similar to that of the Sierra Nevada, with extensive open lands and human activity at lower elevations only intermittently penetrating into the conifer forests on the mountain slopes. It is likely that cowbirds exhibit the same type of commuting pattern between breeding and foraging habitats (Rothstein et al. 1980, Verner and Ritter 1983), especially since this behavior is widespread, albeit less strongly expressed, even in regions with better interspersion of cover types (Dufty 1982a, Thompson 1994). Potential feeding sources away from the major agricultural areas were also similar (e.g., pack stations, and small, dispersed meadows with grazing cattle). Many of these microhabitats would not have registered in our GIS database. Our finding that cowbird presence was strongly associated with the proximity of agricultural areas suggests that whatever non-agricultural foraging sites there may be, they have not yet re-

A

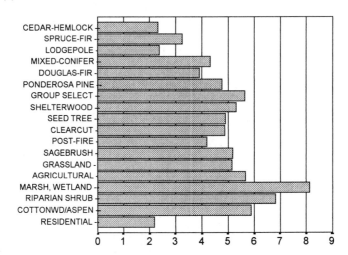

Abundance of likely hosts (individuals/point)

B

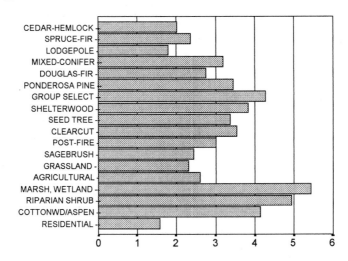

Richness of likely hosts (species/point)

FIGURE 4. Abundance of potential host species across the same major cover types as in Fig. 2: A) total individuals detected per point of likely hosts; B) number of species of likely hosts detected per point in each cover type. Likely hosts were defined as open-cup nesting passerine species of appropriate size, that were not rejectors and had more than 10 published records of parasitism, or were considered primary hosts in a local study (see text).

sulted in widespread penetration of the forested mountains by cowbirds.

We found that open lands such as grasslands and agricultural areas were more commonly used than clearcuts. In addition, canopy cover was not strongly associated with cowbird occurrence within coniferous forest areas. On the landscape scale, the proximity of upland shrub sites, such as clearcuts, was not significantly related to cowbird occurrence. Clearcuts would not be expected to provide good foraging habitat for cowbirds (unless they were grassy and were grazed by cattle, which is sometimes the case), but they may provide good opportunities for nest searching (Robinson et al. 1995a). We found as many potential hosts in clearcuts as in forest cover types (Fig. 4), but perhaps clearcuts did not provide sufficient perches for displaying or observing potential hosts. Hahn and Hatfield (1995) found higher parasitism rates in deciduous forest than in old fields with abundant host populations. Thompson et al. (1992) found that cowbird numbers were similar between extensive forest sites with and without clearcuts. In a review of studies on the effects of logging on bird abundance in the Rocky Mountains, Hejl et al. (1995) found that only three of 19 studies even had cowbirds, and there was no indication that they were more likely to occur in clearcuts than uncut forest. Thus, it appears that the presence of clearcuts does not draw cowbirds into forested regions.

For a species that undergoes such widespread movement patterns, it is not unexpected that we detected cowbirds in a variety of situations. It would, therefore, be useful to know more precisely what our detections represent. Most detections were probably of males. Females are often quiet in breeding habitats (Norman and Robertson 1975, Rothstein et al. 1984), and field observers were less likely to recognize female calls as cowbirds. Like Rothstein et al. (1984), we usually observed cowbirds in forests either socializing and singing from tree perches, or flying overhead emitting characteristic whistle calls (although the latter observations were not included in habitat relationships). Most cowbirds were likely to have been in breeding habitats during the morning hours when we were observing (Rothstein et al. 1984). Although it is the less conspicuous females that parasitize the host species, males also commute to breeding grounds (Rothstein et al. 1984), and often accompany females throughout their breeding ranges (Dufty 1982a). Mate guarding may result in our observations being a reasonable indicator of where female cowbirds searched for host nests, especially since males are often vocal while accompanying females (Darley 1983, Rothstein et al. 1984). It is not known if males accompany females in our region, but it has been shown in several populations of wild (Darley 1983, Dufty 1982a, Rothstein et al. 1984) and captive (Rothstein et al. 1986b) cowbirds.

In terms of major cover types, there appears to be little refuge from cowbirds in the northern Rocky Mountains. Nonetheless, bird species that occupy conifer forests tend to be especially widespread across conifer forest types, and may find refuge from cowbird parasitism in many denser forested areas where cowbirds are uncommon. Remoteness may also provide a refuge for many populations. It is not known whether populations may be negatively affected by cowbirds in forests near agricultural edges. Many of these bird species that occupy conifer forests have few published records of parasitism (Friedman and Kiff 1985), perhaps because they are less-studied western species with hard-to-find nests. The assumption that cowbirds may also have difficulty finding these nests may be incorrect, since the few studies in western forests have found many of them to be parasitized (Verner and Ritter 1983, Airola 1986, Tewksbury et al. *this volume*).

Not all species may be able to find refuge from parasitism, however. Many species are restricted to riparian bottomlands, which are heavily used by cowbirds (Fig. 2) and are often near agricultural areas. These species may be at serious risk from cowbird parasitism. Any other species largely restricted to lowland riparian or open forest habitats may be at risk, as shown for the Lazuli Bunting (*Passerina amoena*; Greene *this volume*). Another possibility may be the Olive-sided Flycatcher (*Contopus cooperi*), which is relatively restricted to open forests such as frequented by the cowbird, and is declining in the West. More needs to be known about this species. In addition, threats to local populations of any species may still be a concern even if the entire species is not at risk.

MANAGEMENT IMPLICATIONS

Our data suggest that cattle grazing and other agricultural practices appear to be directly involved with the expansion of cowbirds in this region. Based on this association, it would certainly be wise to restrict agriculture to areas already dominated by this land use. Because there was such a clear relationship with distance to agricultural areas, it may be supposed that clearcutting, pack stations, and other human activities removed from areas of intense agriculture have not been the primary reasons behind the widespread cowbird invasion in this region. However, we cannot say that such disturbance will continue to be benign. Further penetration of human disturbance to remote areas may still draw more cowbirds into the backcountry.

ACKNOWLEDGMENTS

The Northern Region of the U.S. Forest Service has been the primary source of support and funding for the field work, database maintenance, and data analysis. Other organizations also contributed financial support, access to lands, and field crews, especially Potlatch Timber Company; Montana Fish, Wildlife and Parks; Bureau of Land Management; and Plum Creek Timber Company. We thank W. Williams at the University of Montana Wildlife Spatial Analysis Lab for providing the landscape variables associated with each survey point.

Studies in Avian Biology No. 18:52–61, 1999.

USE OF DIFFERENT HABITATS BY BREEDING BROWN-HEADED COWBIRDS IN FRAGMENTED MIDWESTERN LANDSCAPES

Scott K. Robinson, Jeffrey D. Brawn, Solon F. Morse, and James R. Herkert

Abstract.   We compared levels of brood parasitization and relative abundance of Brown-headed Cowbirds (*Molothrus ater*) in forests, savannas, shrublands, and grasslands in seven regions of Illinois, 1985–1997. Our primary objective was to determine if cowbirds avoid habitats in which rates of nest predation or abundances of unsuitable hosts are high. Bird communities differed significantly among vegetation types in the proportion of species with defenses against cowbirds (rejecter species that abandon or eject cowbird eggs, aggressive nest defense) and in overall nest predation rates. The relative abundance of cowbirds and the community-wide levels of parasitization were lowest in grasslands, which also had significantly higher nest predation rates than the other three vegetation types. Parasitization levels were highest in forests, but community-wide levels of parasitization in forests and savannas did not differ significantly when rejecter species were eliminated from the analysis. The relative abundance of cowbirds was highest in savannas, even though savannas had a significantly higher proportion of species that reject cowbird eggs than forests. Forests and shrublands did not differ significantly in cowbird abundance, in spite of significantly higher proportions of rejecters in shrubland bird communities. We found little evidence that cowbirds avoided habitats with higher nest predation rates within regions; cowbirds avoided grasslands even in regions with low nest predation rates on grasslands birds. These results suggest that cowbird habitat selection is not necessarily fine-tuned to the quality of available hosts in this landscape. Managers can reduce community-wide parasitization in this landscape by restoring grasslands, which are used less by cowbirds, and savannas, which contain a high proportion of species with defenses against parasitization. Future research directions should focus on habitat-specific breeding success of cowbirds, new studies of host defenses, and the behavioral mechanisms underlying habitat and host selection in cowbirds.

Key Words: Brown-headed Cowbird, forest, grasslands, Illinois, *Molothrus ater,* savanna, shrubland, rejecters, use of plant communities.

The Brown-headed Cowbird (*Molothrus ater*) breeds in a wide range of habitats throughout North America (Robinson et al. 1995b). Because cowbirds can breed and forage in different areas, they are much less restricted in their habitat requirements than most birds. This uncoupling of feeding and breeding also gives cowbirds an opportunity to choose habitats based solely on the availability of hosts as long as foraging sites are available nearby (within 7 km; Rothstein et al. 1984, Robinson et al. 1995b). Although cowbirds are extremely generalized in their use of hosts, which may make fine-grained assessment of habitat unlikely, they are also known to revisit nests they have parasitized (Arcese et al. 1996), which gives them an opportunity to assess their own breeding success in an area.

Relatively little is known, however, about cowbird preferences, if any, for particular habitats for breeding (reviewed in Robinson et al. 1995b). Hahn and Hatfield (1995) reported that cowbirds preferred to search for host nests in forest rather than more open, shrubby vegetation types. Similarly, Strausberger and Ashley (1997) and Robinson et al. (in press) reported generally higher levels of parasitization in forest than in shrubland/edge and grasslands in Illinois where all plant communities are within the cowbirds' daily commuting range. None of these studies,

however, compared the relative abundance of cowbirds and suitable hosts (species that do not reject cowbird eggs or abandon parasitized nests) among the different vegetation types. If cowbirds occur in proportion to the availability of suitable hosts, then use of vegetation types may reflect different proportions of suitable hosts. If, on the other hand, cowbirds do not avoid vegetation types with fewer suitable hosts, then differences in community-wide levels of parasitization among vegetation types may simply reflect the proportion of species that reject cowbird eggs and hence have low frequencies of parasitization (Strausberger and Ashley 1997). To distinguish among these possibilities, we need data on the ratio of cowbird abundance to host abundance in different vegetation types.

The issue of habitat use by cowbirds has important management implications. Restoring plant communities that cowbirds avoid may be a high conservation priority in chronically fragmented landscapes in which nearly all areas are accessible to cowbirds. Restoration of plant communities that contain high proportions of unsuitable hosts may also be effective. If cowbirds do not avoid vegetation types with high proportions of rejecters or in which nest predation rates are high, then such vegetation types may act as population sinks (Pulliam 1988) and

TABLE 1.   STUDY AREAS BROKEN DOWN BY REGION IN ILLINOIS

Region (years of study)	Location	Plant communities included (number of sites)
Driftless Area (1992–1994, 1997)	Extreme northwestern Illinois in Jo Daviess and Carroll counties	Grassland (1), shrubland (3), forest (6)
Prairie Parklands (1995–1997) (Joliet Arsenal/Midewin National Tall-grass Prairie)	Northeastern Illinois in Will County	Grassland (3), shrubland (2)
Rock River Valley (1994–1997)	Northcentral Illinois in Lee and Ogle counties	Grassland (1), shrubland (2), forest (3)
Illinois River Valley (1994–1996)	Central Illinois in Tazewell, Peoria, and Mason counties	Savannah (3), forest (3)
Illinois Ozarks (1989–1997)	Southern Illinois in Union, Alexander, and Jackson counties	Shrubland (2), forest (4)
Cache River (1993–1997)	Southern Illinois in Johnson and Pulaski counties	Grassland (1), shrubland (3), forest (8)
East-central Illinois (1985–1997)	Champaign, Piatt, Vermillion, Moultrie, and Shelby counties	Shrubland (2), forest (4)

ecological traps (Gates and Gysel 1978) for cowbirds, as argued by Donovan et al. (in press).

In this paper, we explored habitat use by Brown-headed Cowbirds in a landscape where all possible study areas were equally accessible to cowbirds (i.e., all were within 7 km of extensive cowbird feeding habitat; Thompson 1994, Thompson et al. in press). We documented composition of host communities in each vegetation type, relative abundance of cowbirds, and levels of parasitization for forests, savannas (including open woodlands), shrublands, and grasslands. We used these data to test the following hypotheses for differences among vegetation types in parasitization levels (Strausberger and Ashley 1997, Robinson et al. in press). (1) Cowbirds prefer forests (Hahn, and Hatfield 1995). If true, we predicted that both community-wide parasitization levels and the ratio of cowbird abundance to host abundance should be significantly lower in more open vegetation types (e.g., shrublands, savannas, and grasslands) than in forests. (2) Cowbirds avoid some habitats because they have a higher proportion of rejecters (i.e., species that eject cowbird eggs or abandon parasitized nests). If cowbirds behave adaptively, then we predicted that cowbirds would avoid vegetation types with more rejecters or that cowbird:host ratios would reflect the availability of suitable hosts rather than all potential hosts (including rejecters). Alternatively, if cowbirds do not avoid these habitats, then lower parasitization levels in some vegetation types may simply reflect high proportions of rejecters. To test this hypothesis, we also compared parasitization levels of species that do not reject cowbird eggs. (3) Cowbirds avoid habitats that have a higher proportion of species that mob cowbirds, which

prevents cowbirds from parasitizing other species in the community as well (Robertson and Norman 1976, Clark and Robertson 1979, Neudorf and Sealy 1992). We predicted that vegetation types with lower parasitization levels would also have a significantly higher proportion of mobbers. (4) Cowbirds avoid habitats with chronically higher levels of nest predation. If cowbirds do not avoid habitats with high predation rates, then they may be susceptible to ecological traps (i.e., they may prefer population sinks). (5) Differences in vegetation structure among vegetation types may account for varying parasitization levels. We cannot test this hypothesis directly because it is not clear which habitats should be easiest for cowbirds to search for nests. For this reason, we discuss this hypothesis, but did not make or test any predictions derived from it.

STUDY AREAS AND METHODS

Study areas were located throughout Illinois (Table 1); we only included sites in an agricultural landscape matrix in which all sites were surrounded by row crops where cowbirds feed in Illinois (Thompson 1994), and we excluded sites in urban areas such as Chicago. We divided our sites into seven regions (Table 1), each of which contained at least two vegetation types for which we have data. Grasslands included a diverse array of management types, including native and non-native vegetation, burned and unburned sites, and grazed and ungrazed sites. Shrublands included regenerating clearcuts, old fields at varying stages of succession, areas in which shrubs had invaded grassland plant communities (e.g., unburned areas and willow thickets in wet areas), and shrubby borders of forest tracts and forest streams. Savannas included oak (*Quercus*)-dominated forests on dry, sandy soils and on ridgetops. All savanna sites had been burned to retain canopy openness. Forests included both upland and floodplain sites and were all dominated by various species of oaks and hickories (*Carya*). We excluded forests dominated by non-native trees such as pines (*Pinus*) and black locusts (*Robinia pseudoacacia*). Landscapes within a 10-km radius around study sites (Robinson et al. 1995a) varied among regions from mostly (>70%) row crops (Prairie Parklands, Illinois River Valley, Rock River, Cache River, East-central Illinois) to roughly 50% forested (Illinois Ozarks).

Within each study site, we censused birds and searched for and monitored the progress of nests following protocols used previously in the Midwest (Robinson 1992, Robinson et al. 1995a, Brawn and Robinson 1996). Censuses were conducted from 15 May to 5 July (southernmost sites), 25 May to 5 July (central sites), and 1 June to 10 July (northernmost sites). Censuses were conducted only by experienced observers carefully trained in point count methods (Hutto et al. 1986) from 05:40–11:00 CST on days with little wind and no rain. Censuses usually ended by 10:00 except for occasional days when singing activity (number of detections per point) did not drop until later in the morning. Depending upon the plot, census points were either arranged in a grid at 150–300 m intervals (small plots), or along transects (large study areas) at 150–300 m intervals. Observers stopped at each census point and began counting birds immediately. For each bird heard or seen, we estimated its distance from the census point, noted whether it was heard or observed, and noted its compass direction. Birds heard or seen flying overhead were not recorded. Censuses lasted 5 minutes. Any birds flushed from near the census point as the observer approached were counted as having been recorded during the census under the assumption that they would likely have remained at the point had they not been scared away by the observer. Special care was taken to avoid double-counting birds either at the same point or at consecutive points by carefully noting compass directions to verify countersinging (two or more individuals singing at the same time) and possible movements. For species in which both sexes vocalize (e.g., Northern Cardinal *Cardinalis cardinalis*, Acadian Flycatcher *Empidonax virescens*, Eastern Wood-Pewee *Contopus virens*), we recorded songs versus calls separately (Acadian Flycatcher) and tried to distinguish between pairs by not double-registering birds that were singing close to each other. This method is somewhat subjective, but was often facilitated in

cardinals by extensive interactions between the sexes (calling, alarm behavior, feeding fledglings) that often made it possible to see both sexes of a pair.

For forests, shrublands, and savannas, we used all birds within a 70-m radius (Robinson et al. in press). We only used data from sites at which at least 15 point counts were conducted (either 15 separate points or replicates of a smaller number of points for smaller tracts). For grasslands, we used a 100-m radius to accommodate the much greater visibility and reduced obstruction to sounds in this very open environment. Special care was made in grasslands to record singing males separately to reduce overestimates of species in which females often perched conspicuously (e.g., meadowlarks *Sturnella* spp., Red-winged Blackbird *Agelaius phoeniceus*).

To compare relative abundance of cowbirds and hosts, we used the cowbird:host ratio of Robinson et al. (in press). To calculate this ratio, we summed up all cowbird registrations per point within a 70-m radius using only cowbirds giving the distinctive "rattle" vocalization, which is given mainly by females (over 99% of the time; S.K. Robinson, unpubl. data). We used only female registrations because many vocalizing males appeared not to be mated and therefore posed no threat to hosts. We then summarized all records of potential host species recorded within 70 m of census points. The ratio of female cowbirds:hosts within 70 m of census points was then calculated and used as an index of the relative abundance of cowbirds. For forests, the cowbird:host ratio appears to be a good predictor of parasitization levels (Robinson et al. in press). This ratio, however, has never been used in more open vegetation types in which many potential hosts have effective defenses against parasitization. For this reason, we calculated two ratios, one for all potential hosts (open-cup nesters, mass less than 70g to exclude large species that are rarely parasitized, such as Blue Jay *Cyanocitta cristata*, Common Grackle *Quiscalus quiscula*, and Mourning Dove *Zenaida macroura*; Strausberger and Ashley 1997) and another for hosts that lack strong defenses against parasitization. For this latter ratio, which we refer to as the cowbird:suitable host ratio, we excluded unsuitable hosts, which include species that eject cowbird eggs (Eastern Kingbird *Tyrannus tyrannus*, Gray Catbird *Dumetella carolinensis*, Brown Thrasher *Toxostoma rufum*, American Robin *Turdus migratorius*, Warbling Vireo *Vireo gilvus*, Western Meadowlark *Sturnella magna* [B.D. Peer, unpubl. data], and Baltimore Oriole *Icterus galbula*), species that often abandon parasitized nests (Bell's Vireo *Vireo bellii,* Yellow Warbler *Dendroica petechia,* Prairie Warbler *D. bicolor,* Chipping Sparrow *Spizella passerina,* and Field Sparrow *S. pusilla*), and species that aggressively mob cowbirds (Eastern Wood-Pewee, Eastern Kingbird, Willow Flycatcher *Empidonax traillii,* and Redwinged Blackbird). All of these species are at least occasionally parasitized in Illinois (e.g., Strausberger and Ashley 1997). But, if cowbirds generally avoid these unsuitable hosts, then the cowbird:suitable host ratio may be a better index of relative abundance of cowbirds. If, on the other hand, cowbirds do not discriminate among suitable and unsuitable hosts, then the index derived from all potential cowbird hosts (suitable and unsuitable hosts that build open-cup nests) may be a better index of habitat suitability. Information on host defenses was obtained from multiple sources, including Friedmann (1929, 1963), Berger (1951), Mumford (1952), Barlow (1962), Rothstein (1975 a,b), Slack (1976), Friedmann et al. (1977), Robertson and Norman (1977), Scott (1977), Nolan (1978), Friedmann and Kiff (1985), Graham (1988), Freeman et al. (1990), Hill and Sealy (1994), Neudorf and Sealy (1992), Sealy (1996), and Burhans (in press).

All sites in Table 1 were subjected to at least one field season of intensive nest searching and monitoring. Nest searching began in late April and continued until late July-early September. In this paper, we only used nests that were built from 20 April to15 July, the main period of cowbird egg laying in Illinois (S.K. Robinson, unpubl. data). Nest contents were checked every 3 days until young fledged, eggs or young were depredated, or the nest abandoned. We used the Mayfield (1975) index to estimate daily predation rates for the incubation and nestling periods combined. For each species, we used all nests over all years from a region to obtain composite nest parasitization levels (percentage of nests parasitized only) and daily predation rates (percentage of nest contents eaten by predators per day).

Our methods may overestimate predation rates if we are attracting predators to some nests and may underestimate nest predation events that occur late in the nestling phase. We tried to reduce these biases by placing flagging tape at least 5 m from nests and checking nests from as far away as possible, especially in plant communities with dense ground-level vegetation (e.g., unburned and ungrazed grasslands, shrubby old fields). It seems inevitable, however, that our activities made some nests more conspicuous to some predators and that this potential bias is different among vegetation types (e.g., visually hunting predators may have an easier time watching nest monitoring crews in open plant communities). For this reason, inter-habitat comparisons of nest predation rates must be interpreted with caution. To reduce possible underestimates of predation rates late in the nest cycle, we made a concerted effort to find families or look for nearby renesting attempts in the area around nests that were found empty late in the nestling phase.

STATISTICAL ANALYSIS

For each species, we derived a region-specific nest predation rate and frequency of parasitization for each habitat for up to seven regions. We arbitrarily included only species for which we had at least 10 nests within a region to reduce potential artifacts of small sample sizes. To compare state-wide levels of nest predation and cowbird parasitization, we combined data from all seven regions to generate frequency distributions of parasitization levels and daily nest predation rates for each vegetation type. Therefore, the combined nests of a species in a given region was the unit of replication for this analysis. We chose this method because we think it better represents state-wide parasitization levels because widespread species present in a habitat throughout the state are weighed more heavily than rare, or geographically restricted species that may not represent a significant potential resource to cowbirds. We also compared and explored habitat-specific nest predation rates and levels of parasitization among vegetation types within each region. We compared the frequency distributions of predation and parasitization rates among plant communities (overall or within regions) with exact Kruskal-Wallis tests (Mehta and Patel 1995). Exact tests (based on permutation procedures) are free from assumptions about the asymptotic properties of test statistics that may be violated with small samples. We compared vegetation types on a pairwise basis and adjusted our judgement of significance based on the Bonferroni inequality and a 0.05 nominal alpha level.

To compare relative abundance of cowbirds among vegetation types, we calculated site-specific cowbird:host ratios. Sites that were less than 5 km apart were combined. Sites that were greater than 5 km apart were treated as separate samples to increase sample sizes of vegetation types that are only present in a few regions (Table 1). We log transformed the cowbird:host ratios and performed one-way analyses of variance (ANOVA) to compare vegetation types. Homogeneity of variances were evaluated with Levene's test; in case where heteroscedasticity was detected, we derived Welch F-statistics where degrees of freedom are approximated. Post-hoc differences were carried out with pairwise t-tests using Bonferonni-adjusted signifi-

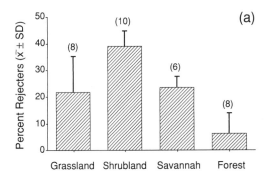

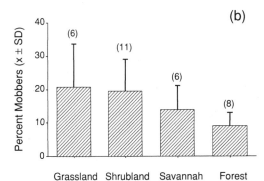

FIGURE 1. Percentage of rejecters (a) and species that mob cowbirds (b) in different vegetation types detected in census samples from sites located at least 50 km apart in Illinois. (N) = number of sites censused.

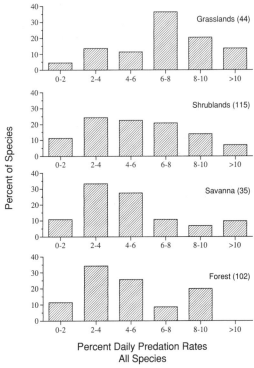

FIGURE 2. Distribution of daily nest predation rates in different vegetation types calculated using the Mayfield (1975) index. Data from all seven regions in Table 1 are pooled for this analysis.

cance levels. Other habitat traits such as percentage composition were compared with one-way ANOVA on arcsine-transformed data. We used the same census data to calculate proportions of the total number of potential hosts detected within 70 m of census points that reject cowbird eggs or mob nest predators.

RESULTS

HOST COMMUNITY COMPOSITION

Proportion of rejecters

The proportion of known rejecter species (those that abandon parasitized nests or eject cowbird eggs) varied significantly ($F_{3, 14} = 38.02$, $P < 0.001$) among vegetation types (Fig. 1a). In shrublands, an average of 40% of the hosts detected during point counts were rejecters compared with 23–26% in grasslands ($P < 0.01$) and savannas ($P < 0.05$) and 6% in forests ($P < 0.01$). In forests, only the American Robin was a rejecter, and it only nested in 3 of the 8 forest sites. We know relatively little, however, about egg rejection by such grassland cowbird

hosts as the Bobolink (*Dolichonyx oryzivorus*), which is rarely parasitized, and the Eastern Meadowlark (*Sturnella neglecta*), which at least occasionally ejects cowbird eggs (B.D. Peer, unpubl. data).

Proportion of mobbers

Plant communities varied significantly in the proportion of mobbers ($F_{3, 27} = 2.97$, $P = 0.044$). Forests generally had a lower proportion of individuals that mob cowbirds, but we detected no specific pairwise among plant communities differences (Fig. 1b); the Eastern Wood-Pewee is the only forest species that attacks cowbirds regularly (S.K. Robinson, pers. obs.). Grassland and shrublands have the highest proportion of mobbers, mainly as a result of high populations of Red-winged Blackbirds. Red-wings, however, were absent or very rare in three of the six grasslands censused.

Comparative nest predation rates

Community-wide levels of nest predation generally varied significantly between vegetation types (Fig. 2). Nest predation rates were

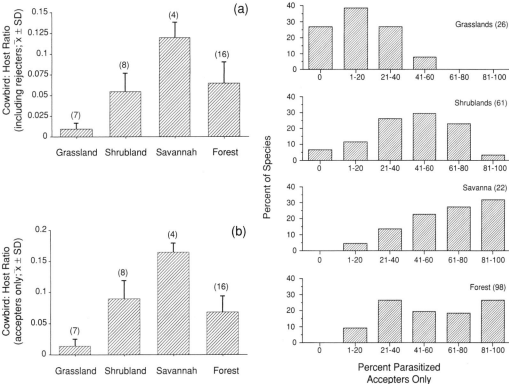

FIGURE 3. Ratio of female cowbirds to hosts (a) including hosts that eject cowbird eggs and abandon parasitized nests and (b) including hosts that usually accept cowbird eggs detected within 70-m radii of census points in sites separated by at least 50 km.

FIGURE 4. Distribution of parasitization levels of all cowbird hosts that accept cowbird eggs. Data from all seven regions in Table 1 are pooled for this analysis.

higher in grasslands than in shrublands (K = 8.35, P = 0.004), savannas (K = 13.35, P < 0.001), and forests (K = 14.67, P < 0.001). None of the other vegetation types differed significantly (shrub vs. savanna K = 1.253, P = 0.263; shrub vs. forest: K = 2.01, P = 0.151; savanna vs. forest: K = 0.025, P = 0.878).

COWBIRD USE OF DIFFERENT HABITATS

Cowbird:host ratios differed significantly among vegetation types whether all hosts were included (Fig. 3a; $F_{3, 31}$ = 20.53, P < 0.001; all pairwise comparisons differed at P < 0.01 except for shrublands and forests) or only suitable hosts were included (Fig. 4; $F_{3, 31}$ = 29.53, P < 0.001; all pairwise comparisons different at P < 0.01 except for shrublands and forests). Grasslands consistently had the lowest relative abundances of cowbirds and savannas had the highest abundances. Shrublands and forests did not differ significantly in the relative abundance of cowbirds.

LEVELS OF PARASITIZATION IN EACH VEGETATION TYPE

Levels of cowbird parasitization were lower in grasslands than in all other vegetation types regardless of whether rejecters were included (Fig. 5; Kruskal Wallis tests, grassland vs. shrublands, K = 3.46, P = 0.06; grasslands vs. forests, K = 68.78, P < 0.01,; grassland vs. savannas K = 11.97, P < 0.001) or excluded (Fig. 4; Kruskal Wallis tests, grasslands vs. shrublands, K = 22.4, P < 0.001, grasslands vs. savannas, K = 27.8, P < 0.001; grasslands vs. forests, K = 38.14, P < 0.001). Community-wide levels of parasitization were significantly higher in shrubland and savannas than in forests (Fig. 5; shrubland vs. forest, K = 59.33, P < 0.001; savannas vs. forests, K = 5.046, P = 0.022; savanna vs. shrubland, K = 6.955, P = 0.006). Savannas and forests, however, did not differ significantly from forests when rejecters were excluded from the analysis (Fig. 4, K = 1.714, P = 0.193). Shrublands had relatively fewer heavily parasitized species (80–100% par-

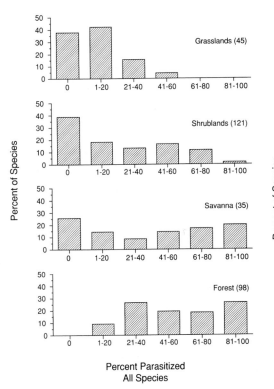

FIGURE 5. Distribution of parasitization levels experienced by all potential host species nesting in different vegetation types in Illinois. Data from all seven regions in Table 1 are pooled for this analysis.

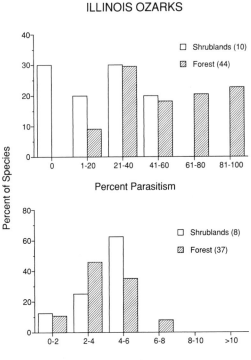

FIGURE 6. Habitat-specific distribution of levels of cowbird parasitization and daily nest predation rates within the Illinois Ozark region of extreme southwestern Illinois.

asitization levels) than forests (K = 7.44, P = 0.006) and savannas (K = 10.45, P < 0.001).

PARASITIZATION VS. NEST PREDATION

To determine if cowbirds were less abundant in areas with high nest predation rates, we compared levels of parasitization and nest predation within regions where we had data from more than one habitat (Figs. 6–9). In the Cache River (Fig. 6), levels of nest predation were significantly higher in shrublands (K = 6.47, P < 0.001) in which parasitization levels were low, although not significantly lower than forest (K = 3.61, P = 0.062). In the Illinois Ozarks, however, parasitization levels were significantly lower in shrublands (Fig. 7; K = 10.54, P < 0.001), but levels of nest predation did not differ between forests and shrublands (K = 0.28, P = 0.597). In the Rock River area (Fig. 8), parasitization levels were significantly lower in grasslands than in forest (K = 8.656, P = 0.002) and were lower in shrublands than in forest (K = 5.618, P = 0.166), but levels of nest predation did not differ significantly among plant communities. Similarly, in the Driftless Area (Fig.

9), parasitization levels were significantly lower in grasslands than in forest (K = 14.31, P < 0.001) and lower in shrubland than in forest (K = 10.49, P < 0.001), but nest predation rates did not differ significantly among any of the vegetation types.

DISCUSSION

We found pronounced differences among different vegetation types in parasitization levels, but there was little to suggest that these differences represented adaptive habitat selection by cowbirds. Cowbirds consistently were less abundant in grasslands (see also Strausberger and Ashley 1997, Robinson et al. in press), even in one area in which nest predation rates were lower in grasslands than in adjacent forests. Cowbirds were not less abundant in savannas and shrublands even though these vegetation types typically contained high proportions of rejecters and mobbers and even though nest predation rates were often higher in shrublands than in forests. The differences in community-wide levels of parasitization in shrublands, savannas, and

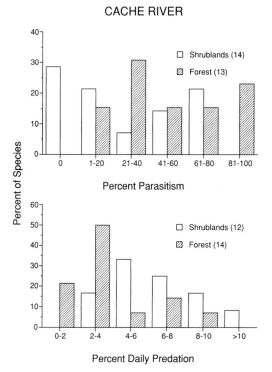

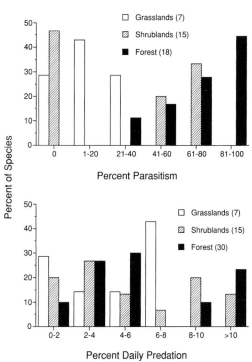

FIGURE 7. Habitat-specific distribution of levels of cowbird parasitization and daily nest predation rates within the Cache River region of extreme southcentral Illinois.

FIGURE 8. Habitat-specific distribution of levels of cowbird parasitization and daily nest predation rates in the Driftless region of far northwestern Illinois.

grasslands (Fig. 5) were much less apparent when rejecters were excluded from the analysis (Fig. 4). Prime cowbird hosts gain little or no protection from parasitization by nesting in communities with a high proportion of rejecters. Cowbirds were most abundant in savannas even though the proportion of suitable hosts was generally lower than in closed-canopy forests.

We did not find strong support for any of the predictions we tested. Based on cowbird:host ratios, cowbirds were not disproportionately abundant in forests (hypothesis 1) in this landscape, as found by Hahn and Hatfield (1995). The relative abundance of cowbirds was highest in savannas, intermediate in shrublands and forests, and consistently lowest in grasslands. The apparent avoidance of grasslands is interesting given that this is the habitat in which cowbirds historically were most abundant (Mayfield 1965). Although a detailed analysis of landscape composition around each site is beyond the scope of this paper, we have no evidence that cattle pastures were more prevalent near savannas. Several of our grassland sites were being actively grazed during our study.

We also found no evidence that cowbirds

were less abundant in vegetation types with high proportions of rejecters (hypothesis 2) and mobbing species (hypothesis 3). Cowbirds were most abundant in savannas, which had intermediate abundances of rejecters and mobbers; similarly, they were just as abundant in shrublands as they were in forests even though shrublands had much higher proportions of mobbers and rejecters. We know relatively little about the defensive behavior of many grassland hosts. Recent experiments in the Driftless Area showed that Western Meadowlarks usually eject cowbird eggs and Eastern Meadowlarks eject about half of the eggs from experimentally parasitized nests (B. D. Peer, unpubl. data). If comparable defenses are also found in such rarely parasitized species as the Bobolink, then we may be underestimating the extent to which grassland birds have evolved resistance to parasitization. The mobbing activities of Red-winged Blackbirds may deter cowbirds from some grasslands, but many grasslands with no red-wings were also avoided by cowbirds (J. L. Herkert, unpubl. data).

Evidence that cowbirds avoided vegetation

ROCK RIVER SITES

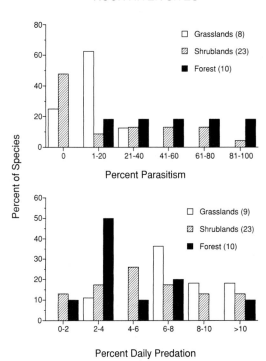

FIGURE 9. Habitat-specific distribution of levels of cowbird parasitization and daily nest predation rates in the Rock River region of northcentral Illinois.

types with higher nest predation rates (hypothesis 4) was mixed. Data from one of the four sites for which we have enough data to compare nest predation rates among vegetation types (Figs. 6–9) showed reduced parasitization levels in a habitat with higher nest predation rates (Fig. 8). Data from the other regions, however, showed strong differences in parasitization levels, but not predation rates (Figs. 7–9). In another site in a suburban landscape of northeastern Illinois, Strausberger and Ashley (1997) found high levels of cowbird parasitization in a shrubby area in which nest predation rates were generally over 85%. They concluded that nest predation rates may be too unpredictable to provide reliable cues to habitat selection or host selection within vegetation types.

Although we did not test the hypothesis that vegetation structure affects habitat selection (hypothesis 5), there are some indications that vegetation structure is important. Grasslands may be extremely difficult for cowbirds to search because of a lack of perches, the difficulty of detecting nests in dense grass, and the cryptic behavior of hosts near their nests (Zimmerman 1983). Parasitization levels tend to be higher

near woody vegetation in grasslands, but even near such potential cowbird perches, parasitization levels were still less than 20% for nearly all species (J.L. Herkert and S.K. Robinson, unpubl. data). The other three plant communities generally have many potential perches and no vegetative layer as dense as grass in unburned tallgrass prairie. The marked preference for savannas may reflect a preference for this vegetation type, which usually occurs at the transition of grasslands and forests. Historically, savannas and shrubby streamside vegetation may have often been the closest source of both host nests and suitable perches for searching.

CONSERVATION IMPLICATIONS

The apparent avoidance of grasslands by cowbirds and the comparatively high proportion of species with effective defenses against cowbirds in more open vegetation types suggest that the best approach to reducing cowbird parasitization in chronically fragmented landscapes may be to maintain and restore grasslands, shrublands, and savannas. Cowbirds appear not to be a significant problem for most grassland birds and many of the cowbird's most frequent hosts are much less abundant in savannas than in forests (J. D. Brawn, unpubl. data). Similarly, shrublands contain few prime cowbird hosts and many species with effective defenses, or long breeding seasons that extend well beyond the period of cowbird breeding activity (S. K. Robinson and J. D. Brawn, unpubl. data). Regional landscape composition may influence the effectiveness of favoring one habitat over another. Tallgrass prairie bird communities in Kansas, for example, have extremely high levels of parasitization (Elliott 1978), as do shrubland bird communities in at least one suburban area in Illinois (Strausberger and Ashley 1997). For this reason, restoring more open plant communities may not always reduce parasitization. In the less-fragmented sections of Illinois, parasitization levels can be reduced for some species by increasing the proportion of forest interior (Morse and Robinson, in press). In most of the agricultural Midwest, however, it is unlikely that forest tracts will ever be large enough to provide a complete refuge from cowbirds.

Restoring more open plant communities may also negatively affect cowbird populations if heavily used habitats such as savannas and shrublands are population sinks for cowbirds, whereas forests are not. In this scenario, shrublands and savannas may be ecological traps because they attract cowbirds, but fail to provide conditions for successful nesting. Before we can assess this possibility, however, we need additional studies of habitat-specific breeding productivity of cowbirds and to determine whether or not cowbirds avoid unsuitable hosts and plant communities in which nest predation rates are high. The cowbird's well-documented habit of revisiting parasitized nests (Arcese et al. 1996) may enable them to assess host-specific nesting success and modify subsequent choice of hosts and even breeding habitat. We found no evidence for such fine-grained assessment of habitat quality by cowbirds, but perhaps this reflects the saturation of all vegetation types and hosts within communities in Illinois (see below).

FUTURE RESEARCH QUESTIONS

1. Are cowbirds more selective of habitats in regions where they are less abundant? In the agricultural Midwest cowbirds are very common and, it is possible that habitats are saturated. In regions where cowbirds are less abundant, preference for forests may be more evident because cowbirds seek those plant communities first. In the scenario, we might expect forests to fill up initially and other, less productive plant communities to be used secondarily. A reduction in cowbird populations might lead to disproportionate reduction in intensity of parasitization in savannas and shrublands. The reduced abundance of cowbirds in the northeastern U.S. compared with the Midwest (Hoover and Brittingham 1993) might explain why cowbirds avoided shrublands in Hahn and Hatfield's (1995) study area. In addition, we might expect cowbirds to be more selective of hosts within plant communities, although Weatherhead (1989) and Strausberger and Ashley (1997) found little evidence of adaptive avoidance of poor hosts in shrubland plant communities.

2. To what extent do cowbirds contribute to nest predation rates? Scott and McKinney (1994) and Arcese et al. (1996) found evidence that cowbirds may depredate unparasitized nests to increase future availability of nests to parasitize. We have little evidence of higher nest predation rates in vegetation types with high abundance of cowbirds. Savannas, for example, had similar nest predation rates to forests even though cowbirds were most abundant in savannas. Evaluating this hypothesis would require cowbird removal experiments.

3. Do cowbirds avoid unsuitable hosts or are

low parasitization levels in nests of rejecters simply caused by hosts removing eggs before they are counted by observers? The Gray Catbird, an ejector species, is parasitized in some plant communities in northeastern Illinois (Strausberger and Ashley 1997; J. D. Brawn, unpubl. data), indicating that cowbirds may not always avoid this species (see also Scott 1977, Slack 1996).

4. Are there additional species with previously undescribed defenses against parasitization and are these species more likely to be found in more open vegetation types? Low parasitization levels of species such as Bobolinks (Strausberger and Ashley 1997), Northern Cardinals (Scott and Lemon 1996) and Yellow-breasted Chats (*Icteria virens*) (Thompson and Nolan 1973), may result from partial defenses against cowbirds. Recent experimental manipulations of grassland birds in Illinois revealed surprisingly high frequencies of egg ejection in two species of meadowlark (B. D. Peer, unpubl. data). Additional experiments will help identify the true proportion of suitable hosts in different vegetation types and will also shed light on Mayfield's still uncorroborated hypothesis (Robertson and Norman 1976, 1977, Rothstein and Robinson 1994) that birds of open plant communities, which presumably have a longer coevolutionary history with cowbirds, are more resistant to cowbirds. Similarly, multi-species defensive aggregations (Clark and Robertson 1979) might be more prevalent than suspected.

ACKNOWLEDGMENTS

This paper would not have been possible without the efforts of more than 100 dedicated and tireless field assistants, and students who found and monitored the 15,000 plus nests used in this analysis. In particular, we thank S. Bailey, S. Daniels, R. Jack, K. Bruner, D. Meisenheimer, B. Peer, J. Nesbitt, S. Fernandez, J. Hoover, D. Robinson, K. McKay, M. Ward, P. Enstrom, J. Nelson, B. Penar, S. Buck, B. Lane, C. Morse, R. Olendorf, J. Knapstein, B. Condon, G. Fizzell, B. Peak, and L. Chapa. We also thank our many sources of funding, including the Illinois Department of Natural Resources (Wildlife Preservation Fund), Federal Aid in Habitat Restoration (W-115-R.), National Fish and Wildlife Foundation, U.S.F.W.S., Illinois Chapter of the Nature Conservancy, Audubon Council of Illinois. U.S. Army Construction Engineering Research Laboratory, North Central Experiment Station (U.S. Forest Service).

Studies in Avian Biology No. 18:62–67, 1999.

THE DENSITY AND DISTRIBUTION OF BROWN-HEADED COWBIRDS: THE CENTRAL COASTAL CALIFORNIA ENIGMA

CHRIS FARMER

Abstract. I examined the density and distribution of Brown-headed Cowbirds (*Molothrus ater*) in Central Coastal California. I focused on Vandenberg Air Force Base, which contains some of the most extensive riparian vegetation along the 550 km Central Coast. Cowbirds were found only in riparian vegetation during morning point count surveys. All detected parasitization events occurred in riparian vegetation. The mean density of cowbirds on Vandenberg was 0.14 cowbird/point count in 1996 (N = 83 point counts) and 0.12 cowbird/point count in 1997 (N = 84), extremely low values compared to other regions. Breeding Bird Survey data also showed a low density of cowbirds in the vicinity of Vandenberg ($\bar{x}$ = 0.47 cowbird/route), and within the entire Central Coast ($\bar{x}$ = 1.79 cowbirds/route) when compared to other areas of California. While the causes for the low density of cowbirds along the Central Coast are unclear, this pattern shows that not all riparian zones are heavily used by cowbirds, with the subsequent parasitization risk for hosts.

Key Words: Breeding Bird Survey, Brown-headed Cowbird, *Molothrus ater,* riparian vegetation.

The need to understand the factors underlying the distribution of the Brown-headed Cowbird (*Molothrus ater*) is particularly acute due to its impact on endangered and sensitive species. Cowbird parasitization has been implicated as a cause in the decline of many passerine species (Gaines 1974, Mayfield 1977, Walkinshaw 1983, Brittingham and Temple 1983, Laymon 1987, Robinson and Wilcove 1994, Robinson et al. 1995a, Averill et al. *this volume,* Halterman and Laymon *this volume*). The impact of cowbirds on the Southwestern Willow Flycatcher (*Empidonax traillii extimus*) (Unitt 1987, Whitfield 1990) and the Least Bell's Vireo (*Vireo bellii pusillus*) (Franzreb 1989a) in California has been of particular concern. Because of impacts on these Federally Endangered species there have been many management plans and control efforts targeting cowbirds, aimed at protecting these vulnerable hosts. These programs frequently view cowbirds as a threat that needs to be eliminated as quickly as possible. Understanding the causes of the distribution of cowbirds could lead to the implementation of more effective host conservation efforts. There is also the possibility that understanding the factors behind the distribution of cowbirds could generate landscape-based management alternatives to cowbird trapping.

Brown-headed Cowbirds favor riparian vegetation for breeding in the western United States, presumably due to the high density of potential hosts in this vegetation type (Grinnell and Miller 1944, Rothstein et al. 1980, Verner and Ritter 1983, Lowther 1993). However, research presented in these proceedings makes the important point that cowbirds are not limited to using riparian vegetation in the West (Ellison *this volume,* Vander Haegen and Walker *this volume*).

My study investigated two basic questions concerning cowbird ecology. The first was, do cowbirds show a preference for riparian vegetation in Central Coastal California? I compared the density of cowbirds on point counts in riparian versus non-riparian vegetation on Vandenberg Air Force Base. The second question was, what is the density of cowbirds within this region, and how does it compare to other areas of California? I examined this question on a local scale by comparing point counts from Vandenberg with other counts I conducted along the Central Coast. I also used Breeding Bird Survey data to compare the densities of this region to other areas of California.

METHODS

STUDY SITE

Vandenberg Air Force Base (VAFB) covers 39,838 ha, and extends along more than 56 km of coastline in northern Santa Barbara County, California, from 34°30′–34°56′N at 120°35′W. There are five perennial watersheds on VAFB: Honda Creek, Bear Creek, the Santa Ynez River, San Antonio Creek, and Shuman Creek. The first two are on South Vandenberg Air Force Base (SVAFB), while the other three are on North Vandenberg Air Force Base (NVAFB). Because cowbirds have only been found breeding on NVAFB (Farmer 1998, unpubl. report to Vandenberg Air Force Base), the halves of VAFB are treated separately in the examination of the distribution and abundance of cowbirds. VAFB supports large, contiguous areas of native vegetation that were once much more common in this region, with approximately 80% of the Base retained in an essentially wild state (Ferren and Collins 1997, unpubl. report to Vandenberg Air Force Base).

The three dominant plant communities found on VAFB are grasslands (native or exotic grasses), coastal sage chaparral (*Baccharis* spp. or *Artemisia* spp.), and Burton Mesa chaparral (*Arctostaphylos* spp.). Riparian vegetation comprises approximately 7% of VAFB's area (Farmer 1998, unpubl. report to Vandenberg Air Force Base). The dominant riparian vegetation on-Base is arroyo willow (*Salix lasiolepis*) with an understory of blackberry (*Rubus ursinus*), poison oak (*Toxicodendron diversilobum*), stinging nettles (*Urtica dioica*), and bulrushes (*Scirpus* spp.) (Farmer 1998, unpubl. report to Vandenberg Air Force Base).

FIELD SURVEYS

The number and identity of each avian species was recorded during a 5 min, unlimited distance point count at a site (Ralph et al. 1994). Point counts were conducted from 0400–0900 PST, between 1 May–30 June, 1996–1997. Because cowbirds are known to be highly mobile in the mornings (Rothstein et al. 1984), all counts were separated by 400 m to avoid recounting the same individual birds. The majority of riparian and palustrine regions on-Base were surveyed, but some sites could not be reached before 0900. The survey route followed the watercourse or shoreline. There were 83 riparian point counts conducted in 1996 and 84 riparian counts in 1997, of which 76 counts were replicated between years. Because the replicated counts were done at the same location each year, they are not independent. Therefore, the data were not pooled across years to avoid inflating any confound from landscape factors associated with a site (e.g., distance to feeding stations).

Additional point counts were conducted at two geographical scales to investigate cowbird density across the landscape. The first was a series of local surveys conducted in the riparian vegetation adjacent to VAFB outside the Base's boundary, upstream of the five major drainages. These counts were within 1 km of VAFB's boundary, except for those conducted along the Santa Ynez River. The riparian corridor is eliminated by agricultural lands within 1 km for all the drainages except the Santa Ynez River, where the riparian vegetation continues far beyond VAFB. The river was surveyed from VAFB to the town of Buelton (34°37′N, 120°12′W), a distance of 34 km. The majority of these local surveys were within the town of Lompoc, and these counts are referred to as LOMP hereafter. There were 24 counts in 1996 and 22 counts in 1997, with 20 counts replicated between years. The second series of comparative surveys was conducted on a regional scale and was composed of sections to the north and

southeast of VAFB. The southeastern riparian vegetation (SRIP) section extended from Gaviota (34°28′N, 120°14′W) to Santa Barbara (34°25′N, 119°40′W) (8–80 km southeast of VAFB, with the same eight counts performed in 1996 and 1997. The northern riparian vegetation (NRIP) section extended from Orcutt (34°52′N, 120°27′W) to Cayucus (35°28′N, 120°55′W) (2.5–88 km north of VAFB). There were 22 counts conducted in 1996 and 34 counts in 1997, with 19 of these counts replicated between years. Across both the local and regional scale, there were 137 total point counts done in 1996 and 148 total counts done in 1997.

All point counts were on the west or south of the coastal mountain ranges, and below 500 m elevation to minimize differences in vegetation. All publicly accessible rivers, streams, lakes, and ponds between Santa Barbara and Cayucus meeting these criteria were examined, and those locations with the most extensive riparian vegetation censused. I used this selection criteria to make the comparative points more similar to those on VAFB. However, compared to the on-Base vegetation, the off-Base riparian corridor appeared much narrower with less understory and associated breeding habitat for hosts (Gates and Gysel 1978, Chasko and Gates 1982). To measure this quantitatively, aerial photos of the entire study region were examined and the width of the riparian corridor at each count was compared. The photos were from the 1994 National Aerial Photography Program (1: 40,000).

A separate series of 41 point counts was done in non-riparian vegetation on VAFB in 1997. The survey protocol for these counts was the same for the riparian counts. They were conducted in the three predominant vegetation types found on VAFB. There were 10 counts in grasslands, 12 in coastal sage chaparral, and 19 in Burton Mesa chaparral. The non-riparian surveys were all done on NVAFB, and were compared with the NVAFB subset of the 1997 riparian counts (N = 61). Because past cowbird research showed a preference for riparian vegetation, I used a one-tailed Mann Whitney U test to examine habitat use.

Transects of the riparian vegetation were used to independently compare the distributional pattern of cowbirds with that determined from the point count data. Each drainage or lake shore was partitioned into 500-m sections and censused between 14 April and 18 July, 1996. A transect consisted of the surveyor walking 500 m along the waterway, and noting the species and abundance of all birds detected. Only those transects completed within 15–60 min and initiated between 0400–0900 PST were used for my analysis. There were 108 transects which met these standards, and this dataset is denoted STREAM hereafter. Because this survey effort was not as rigorously controlled as the point counts, statistical analysis is problematic. However, the stream transects covered the entire length of the five major drainages on VAFB, and extended to areas that were not covered by the point count surveys. The stream transects also included data from off-Base locations for comparative purposes.

The field notes from another extensive avifaunal study that occurred on VAFB between 1995–1997 were examined for any opportunistic detections of cowbirds (Holmgren and Collins 1998, unpubl. report to Vandenberg Air Force Base). This study was concentrated in grasslands, Burton Mesa chaparral, and coastal sage chaparral. These data were not rigorous, but were used to confirm the distributional patterns of cowbirds. Only observations in non-feeding habitat were considered. Feeding sites were defined as areas with horses or cattle, or short grass lawns, where numerous Red-winged Blackbirds (*Agelaius phoeniceus*), Brewer's Blackbirds (*Euphagus cyanocephalus*), Tricolored Blackbirds (*Agelaius tricolor*), and European Starlings (*Sturnus vulgaris*) tended to feed communally (Friedmann 1929, Rothstein et al. 1987, Lowther 1993, Thompson 1994). When cowbirds were detected at such sites, they were not searching for nests, and were observed actively foraging (Farmer 1998, unpubl. report to Vandenberg Air Force Base).

BREEDING BIRD SURVEYS

The Breeding Bird Survey (BBS) provides data for examining cowbird populations at large geographical scales. I used data from the BBS World Wide Web site to compare cowbird densities between routes from selected areas (Sauer et al. 1997). The BBS has partitioned North America into 99 strata, based on vegetative and physiographic characteristics. VAFB is in the California Foothills stratum, which is immense and contains a large array of vegetation types. It ranges from Mexico to Redding, California (34°52′N, 122°00′W), a distance of 1007 km, and encircles the Central Valley, going from the Pacific Ocean to the Sierra Nevada. Because of this, an analysis between a subset of individual routes from this stratum seemed more appropriate than the normal comparison between strata. Each route is 39.7 km long with 3 min point counts done every 0.81 km, and is conducted along secondary roads (Sauer et al. 1997). I only used routes that had been run three or more times over the most recent ten years of the BBS data. Each route's data point for my analysis was the mean of all performances of that route from 1987–1996. While some routes were conducted by the same observer over these ten years, the majority had multiple observers. Inter-observer variability, combined with the range of environmental conditions over the ten years, could introduce some variability in the results (Verner 1985).

I compared four areas using the BBS data. The Central California Coast region contained eight BBS routes, and ranged from Ventura (34°20′N, 119°15′W) to 47 km north of Highway 46 (35°50′N, 121°05′W). These are all the routes within 50 km of my entire study region. The Northern California Coast contained 17 BBS routes, and ranged from San Francisco (37°40′N, 122°30′W) to Oregon (42°00′N, 124°15′W). The Southern California Coast contained five BBS routes, and ranged from Los Angeles (34°10′N, 118°15′W) to Mexico (32°33′N, 117°00′W). The routes in each coastal region were within 70 km of the Pacific Ocean. The fourth region was California's Central Valley, which adjoins the Central Coast to the northeast and contained 16 BBS routes and ranged from Bakersfield (35°15′N, 119°00′W) to Stockton (38°00′N, 121°19′W). All routes in this region were between the coastal mountain ranges and the Sierra Nevada, and lower than 500 m elevation.

Additional insight concerning the local density of cowbirds in the vicinity of VAFB can be gained through comparing the BBS routes nearest VAFB with the adjacent regions described above. There are three BBS routes within 50 km of VAFB, and these local measures of the cowbird density near my intensive surveys serve as an index relating my work to the BBS routes. Due to the scant number of routes, the statistical power is limited and only qualitative patterns are presented.

NEST SEARCHES

There are 34 cowbird hosts known to breed on VAFB (Farmer 1998, unpubl. report to Vandenberg Air Force Base). Intensive nest searching for all possible hosts was conducted from 15 April–31 July, 1995–1997 in the riparian vegetation on-Base. Searches were conducted by attempting to find the nests of birds exhibiting nest building or other nesting behaviors. In the latter part of the breeding season surveyors attempted to discover family groups, and received additional training to detect the loud, distinctive begging call of juvenile cowbirds. Concurrent projects studying the breeding biology of all avifauna on VAFB covered the major plant communities in 1995–1997, and most likely would have discovered any cowbird breeding if it was occurring in these areas (Holmgren and Collins

TABLE 1. MEAN (± SD) AND MEDIAN COWBIRD NUMBERS DETECTED DURING RIPARIAN SURVEYS CONDUCTED EACH YEAR FOR THE VARIOUS STUDY REGIONS IN CENTRAL COASTAL CALIFORNIA

Region	N	$\bar{x}$ ± SD	Median
Point counts, 1996 (n = 137)			
SVAFB	22	0.00 ± 0.00	0.00
NVAFB	61	0.20 ± 0.51	0.00
NRIP	22	0.36 ± 0.85	0.00
LOMP	24	0.58 ± 0.82	0.00
SRIP	8	0.63 ± 0.74	0.50
Point counts, 1997 (n = 148)			
SVAFB	23	0.00 ± 0.00	0.00
NVAFB	61	0.16 ± 0.49	0.00
SRIP	8	0.25 ± 0.46	0.00
NRIP	34	0.35 ± 0.73	0.00
LOMP	22	0.41 ± 0.59	0.00
Stream transects, 1996 (n = 108)			
SVAFB	23	0.00 ± 0.00	0.00
NVAFB	58	1.09 ± 1.37	1.00
LOMP	27	1.48 ± 2.62	0.00

1998, unpubl. report to Vandenberg Air Force Base; Holmgren and Gallo 1998, unpubl. report to Vandenberg Air Force Base).

RESULTS

HABITAT USE

The comparison of the 41 non-riparian point counts with the 61 riparian counts, all 102 of which were conducted on North VAFB in 1997, showed a strong preferential use of riparian vegetation by cowbirds. Cowbirds were detected on 8 of 61 (13.1%) riparian counts and 0 of 41 non-riparian counts (Mann Whitney U = 1086.5, P = 0.008). Further support for a differential use of riparian vegetation came from the opportunistic detections of cowbirds over the three years of the study, with 189 of 207 (91.3%) non-feeding site detections before 0900 PST occurring in riparian vegetation. Nesting and fledgling records showed that all 34 parasitization events detected from the VAFB region from 1995–1997 were in riparian vegetation.

COWBIRD DENSITY

The median number of cowbirds per point count in the riparian vegetation of VAFB was significantly less than that found in the riparian vegetation adjacent to the Base (LOMP), or in the NRIP and SRIP regions, in both 1996 and 1997 (1996: Kruskal Wallis H = 17.32, P = 0.002; 1997: Kruskal Wallis H = 12.16, P = 0.016) (Table 1). Even though cowbirds were never found on SVAFB, because of the extremely low density of cowbirds on NVAFB the difference between NVAFB and SVAFB was not quite significant in either year (Mann Whitney U test, 1996: P = 0.058, 1997: P = 0.069). Cowbirds were not concentrated at certain sites; only one cowbird was present at the majority of sites where cowbirds were detected (Fig. 1). The distributional pattern was corroborated by the STREAM dataset (Kruskal Wallis H = 19.94, P < 0.001) (Table 1). However, even with points selected to minimize differences in vegetation, the riparian zone on VAFB was wider than off-Base sites. Based on aerial photos, the mean width of the riparian vegetation at VAFB sites was 240 m with a median of 120 m, whereas

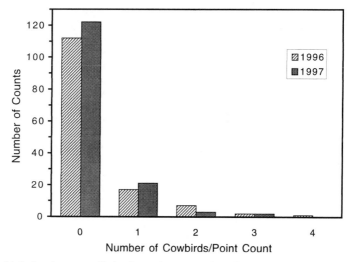

FIGURE 1. Cowbird abundance on all riparian point counts done from Santa Barbara to Cayucus, CA, 1996–1997.

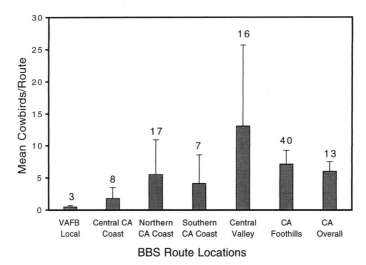

FIGURE 2.   Cowbird abundance on California Breeding Bird Survey routes, mean ± sᴅ (1987–1996). The number of routes in each region is shown above the bars.

the off-Base sites had a mean width of 78 m and a median of 60 m (Mann Whitney U = 1379.5, P < 0.001).

BREEDING BIRD SURVEYS

The BBS data showed a similar pattern of low cowbird density in the local Vandenberg area. The mean for the three routes closest to VAFB was 0.47 cowbird/route (Fig. 2). The cowbird density on these three local routes was an order of magnitude lower than both California overall and the California Foothills stratum, with values of 6.01 and 7.13 cowbirds/route, respectively. The more statistically rigorous analysis of the four regions defined above showed a mixed pattern. The density of cowbirds in the Central California Coast BBS routes, with a mean of 1.79 cowbirds/route and a median of 0.98 cowbird/route, was significantly lower than the routes in the Northern California Coast, which had a mean of 5.52 cowbirds/route and a median of 3.86 cowbirds/route (Mann Whitney U = 31, P = 0.031) (Fig. 2). The difference between the Central Coast and the South Coast, which had a mean of 4.13 cowbirds/route and a median of 2.67 cowbirds/route, was not significant (Mann Whitney U = 14.0, P = 0.38) (Fig. 2). BBS results from the Central Coast were significantly lower than the Central Valley, which had a mean of 13.9 cowbirds/route and a median of 11.44 (Mann Whitney U = 19.0, P = 0.006) (Fig. 2).

DISCUSSION

Brown-headed Cowbirds displayed a strongly disproportionate use of the riparian vegetation on Vandenberg Air Force Base for breeding. This followed the pattern of other studies in the West (Rothstein et al. 1980, Verner and Ritter 1983, Lowther 1993), and contrasted with studies from Maryland (Evans and Gates 1997) and Missouri (Thompson 1994), both of which found no strong preference for riparian areas.

The differences in the habitat edges of eastern and western landscapes is a possible explanation for this variation. The riparian corridors in the West tend to have sharply defined edges, with the entire corridor composed of edge habitat. The adjacent vegetation on VAFB tends to be xeric communities such as coastal sage chaparral or grasslands. The surrounding vegetation in eastern landscapes tends to be more mesic, with a less abrupt ecotone. The evidence concerning the influence of edges on cowbird distribution has been mixed, but most work has been done in the Midwest and East. Some studies have shown that cowbirds use forest edge habitats more than the interior portions of the forest (Gates and Gysel 1978, Chasko and Gates 1982, Brittingham and Temple 1983, Gates and Griffin 1991, Thompson et al. in press), whereas other studies have found no edge effect in cowbird distribution or parasitization rates (Robinson and Wilcove 1994, Hahn and Hatfield 1995). However, no study has explicitly examined how edges influence cowbird distribution in the West.

The density of cowbirds on both North and South Vandenberg Air Force Base was lower than both the local (LOMP) and regional (NRIP, SRIP) areas. Cowbirds were most abundant where the riparian vegetation was narrower with less understory vegetation, and presumably fewer available breeding opportunities for their hosts (Gates and Gysel 1978, Chasko and Gates 1982). The narrow riparian corridors in the LOMP, NRIP, and SRIP regions had proportionally more edge habitat than either portion of VAFB. This relationship seemed to imply that cowbirds not only favor riparian vegetation in the West, but in the Central Coast of California preferred edge habitat, with its concomitant sparse understory, as opposed to the more extensive riparian vegetation available on VAFB.

The Breeding Bird Survey results supported my intensive point count results. Whereas the density of cowbirds on the Central Coast routes was significantly lower than the Central Valley or North Coast routes, it was no different from the South Coast routes. Although adjacent to the Central Coast, the Central Valley has the highest density of cowbirds in California (Sauer et al. 1997, Peterjohn et al. in press), so this contrast was unsurprising. Although not a significant difference, the comparison between the South Coast ($\bar{x}$ = 4.13 cowbirds/route) and the Central Coast ($\bar{x}$ = 1.79 cowbirds/route), strongly suggested that the Central Coast actually does have a lower density of cowbirds than the South Coast. Not only did the Central Coast have a low density of cowbirds compared to the other regions, but within this region the three counts nearest to VAFB had a much lower density than the five remaining routes from this region ($\bar{x}$ = 0.47 and $\bar{x}$ = 2.59, respectively). These results confirmed that VAFB has a low density of cowbirds within the Central Coast, and that the Central Coast has a low density of cowbirds within the surrounding regions. The BBS results suggested that the low density of cowbirds I detected with my riparian point counts was a true distributional pattern.

These results have two important ramifications for cowbird management and endangered species protection. The first is that not all riparian vegetation in the West has high cowbird abundance, and subsequent high levels of cowbird parasitization. Whenever riparian vegetation is disturbed or destroyed, cowbird control programs are often implemented without documenting the cowbird population density or parasitization risks of the local avifauna. But if cowbirds are already at a low density, such control programs can do nothing to help the target species. The second consideration my results suggest is that when cowbird management is necessary, habitat restoration could be a highly effective means of reducing the level of cowbird parasitization in an area. Through increasing the width and extent of riparian vegetation to more resemble the VAFB landscape, habitat restoration could potentially be more effective over the long term than cowbird trapping.

ACKNOWLEDGMENTS

This study was funded by the Department of Defense Legacy Program (Air Force Grant #95–218). I thank N. Read of the VAFB Environmental Resources Department for her assistance with logistical arrangements and all other aspects of this study. I also thank D. Guttilla, A. Miller, D. Mitchell, R. Owens, and S. Werner for their assistance with nest searching. I am indebted to K. Kudrak, J. Greaves, M. Holmgren, and Y. Thomson for sharing their riparian transect and point count data. I appreciate the above biologists as well as P. Collins, K. Fahy, J. Gallo, K. Knight, J. Storrer, and K. Whitney for sharing their data on the avifaunal distribution and breeding activity of VAFB. I also thank K. Burnell, S. Rothstein and J. Uyehara, for editorial suggestions and advice on all phases of this study.

Studies in Avian Biology No. 18:68–72, 1999.

LANDSCAPE EFFECTS ON COWBIRD OCCURRENCES IN MICHIGAN: IMPLICATIONS TO RESEARCH NEEDS IN FORESTS OF THE INLAND WEST

JOHN M. STRIBLEY AND JONATHAN B. HAUFLER

Abstract. We evaluated cowbird distributions relative to landscape-level conditions in northern Michigan. We located 113 study sites in mature, northern hardwood forests with varying stand conditions and land-uses in the surrounding landscape, characterized out to a radius of 3 km. The probability that a cowbird would occur at any given site was 3–3.5 times greater when agricultural lands were present within 3 km of a study site. Intra-stand structural diversity and surrounding habitat heterogeneity were important predictors of cowbirds when agriculture was present within 3 km. Without the presence of agriculture, cowbird occurrence was low, regardless of surrounding habitat heterogeneity. The distribution of cowbirds in forested landscapes of the inland forests of the western U.S. is poorly understood. Studies similar to that described for Michigan need to be conducted to determine landscape and stand factors influencing cowbird occurrences, and their potential negative effects on breeding success of passerines. Complicating this possible experimental design is the open ranges of this region, and the widespread distribution of cattle. Until data on breeding success of passerines and landscape influences on this success are available, questions concerning fragmentation of western forests will remain.

Key Words: agriculture, brood parasitism, cowbirds, forest management, habitat fragmentation, habitat analysis, landscape effects, *Molothrus ater.*

Studies have implicated parasitism by Brown-headed Cowbirds (*Molothrus ater*) as a significant negative influence on the breeding success of bird populations (Mayfield 1965, Payne 1977, Airola 1986, Robinson et al. 1995b). Fragmentation of forested landscapes has been documented to increase cowbird parasitism rates (Robinson et al. 1995b). Brittingham and Temple (1983) found that cowbird parasitism in Wisconsin decreased from 65% to 18% for nests located 100 m and 300 m from an opening, respectively. This led to the generalized recommendation that creation of forest edges should be avoided (Alverson et al. 1994) in order to provide for forest interior species.

We investigated the influences of landscape characteristics, including the proximity of edges, on the probability of occurrence of cowbirds in northern hardwood stands in northern Michigan. We evaluated our results in relation to concerns about forest fragmentation. Finally, we evaluated the implications of our findings in Michigan to research needs in forested landscapes in the western United States.

STUDY AREAS

Research was conducted in the Huron National Forest (Alcona County) of northeastern lower Michigan, Pigeon River Country State Forest (PRCSF) (Cheboygan, Otsego, and Montmorency Counties) of north-central lower Michigan, Hiawatha National Forest (Delta County) in the central upper peninsula of Michigan, and the Huron Mountain Club (HMC) (Marquette County) in the northwestern upper peninsula of Michigan. Multiple landuse activities including timber harvesting, farming, prescribed burning, and recreational activities occurred at varying levels throughout these regions (Lantz 1976, Beyer 1987). Climatic conditions within each of these regions are moderated by the Great Lakes with mean annual temperatures of 5.8 C and total annual precipitation ranging from 71–81 cm (Michigan Weather Service 1974, U.S. Department of Commerce 1979, Simpson et al. 1990).

Agricultural lands and urban-suburban development were interspersed with forested lands throughout the Huron National Forest study sites. The PRCSF was a relatively contiguous state forest (33,590 ha) with agricultural lands and urban-suburban development adjoining its boundaries. The Hiawatha National Forest has a limited number of agricultural lands within its boundaries, and a small amount of urban-suburban areas. Agricultural lands were present on the southern portions of the Hiawatha National Forest, but not in the northern portions. The HMC is a privately owned reservation. Since its inception in 1889, the HMC has grown to include over 7200 ha of contiguous, mature-old growth forest. With the exception of a 20% selective cut for white pines (*Pinus strobus*) in the 1890's and some peripheral clearcuts of hemlock (*Tsuga canadensis*), sugar maple (*Acer saccharum*), and yellow birch (*Betula alleghaniensis*) from 1939–1950's, HMC has received little silvicultural treatment (Simpson et al. 1990).

METHODS

Research was conducted at a total of 113 study sites during spring, 1992 and 1993, with 57 sites surveyed for both years. Study sites were located in mature northern hardwood forest stands, no less than 4 ha in size, at least 50 years old, and surrounded by a variety of forest stand conditions and land use activities. Maximum stand size occurred in the HMC, where approximately 85% of this 7200 ha area was northern hardwoods with inclusions of other cover types. No stands containing mean tree sizes < 8 cm diameter at breast height (dbh), streams > 3 m in width, clearings (> 1.0 ha in area and having < 50% canopy cover), human dwellings, or similar disturbances within 100 m of a sampling point were selected. Study sites were selected based on current geographic information system (GIS) coverage, U.S. Forest Service vegetation maps, and ground truthing.

The avifauna at each study site was censused using 20-min, unlimited-radius point counts according to Indice Ponctuel d'Abondance (IPA) protocol (Blondel et al. 1981). The approximate center of each forest stand (study site) served as the IPA census station. In the HMC area, 20 point counts were distributed throughout the 7200 ha area, without attempting to locate individual stands or stand centers, but were placed > 100 m from an edge. Characteristics of each point, the stand it occurred in, and the surrounding landscape were measured, and treated as independent samples in the analysis. Presence of any cowbirds was recorded during its breeding season (early May–mid July). Each study site was censused three times during the breeding season, once in mid-May, once in early–mid June, and once in late June–early July.

The vegetation structure and composition of each forest stand was sampled in the immediate vicinity of the census station. Sapling density (woody stems < 8 cm dbh and > 1.5 m tall) was measured in two, 2-m × 40-m perpendicular belt transects centered upon each census point and oriented to the four cardinal directions. The line intercept method (Gysel and Lyon 1980) was used to determine the percent vertical cover within each of three height strata (0–1 m, 1–7 m, and > 7 m) along a 20-m transect that extended 270 degrees (randomly selected) from each census station. Horizontal cover was measured in four height intervals (0–0.3 m, 0.3–1 m, 1–2 m, and 2–3 m) using a profile board. Mean forest canopy height and mean basal area were measured using a Haga altimeter and tubular gauge at the center and end points of the sapling belt transect array. The point-centered quarter method (Cox 1990) was used to estimate

the tree species composition and density within each surveyed stand at five points positioned every 50 m along a 200-m transect, oriented east-west and centered on the census station.

Landscape patterns were quantified using an acetate dot-grid overlay in tandem with collages of U.S. Forest Service vegetation maps and recent aerial photos. A percent measure of the area occurring as agricultural, grassland, and mixed opening (upland and lowland brush, seedling-sapling stage forests, and/or selectively cut forests with < 50% canopy coverage) vegetation types was calculated within 0.5-km, 1.0-km, 2.0-km, and 3.0-km radii of each study site. Distances from each census station to the nearest edge and opening were measured (in meters) from the collage base maps using a metric ruler. Edges were defined as areas in early successional stages, at least 12 m wide, with no trees > 8 cm dbh (e.g., primary and secondary roads, transmission line corridors, shorelines, openings). Openings were defined as areas > 0.4 ha with > 50% open canopy (e.g., grasslands, agricultural fields, and mixed openings).

Logistic regression using the variable selection method (Hosmer and Lemeshow 1989) was used to assess which habitat variables (covariates) were important predictors of cowbird occurrence at census stations. For sites that were sampled in both 1992 and 1993, only one year's sampling was used in the analysis, the year being chosen randomly. Exceptions were any sites that underwent silvicultural treatment between years, which were then assumed to be independent observations. We did not analyze each year individually as we wished to focus our analysis on the overall landscape characteristics affecting cowbird distribution and occurrence rather than short term temporal dynamics of cowbird populations.

The chi-square test of independence (Ott 1988:249–258) ($\alpha < 0.1$) was used to analyze the occurrence of cowbirds at sites possessing specific a priori defined conditions: (1) census stations in mature (> 50 years old) hardwood forest stands with > 90% canopy coverage > 400 m from an edge, as defined above; (2) census stations in forested regions (4 sections [2.59 km²/section] in size) where > 80% of the area was comprised of forest stands having > 50% canopy cover of trees > 8 cm dbh; and (3) census stations in selectively harvested forest stands having a mean basal area > 16 m²/ha.

Two-sample t-tests and F-tests were performed on all variables measured in sites having cowbirds versus those lacking cowbirds. A variable was considered for inclusion in the logistic regression model if its t-test P-value was < 0.25. This liberal P-value served to include potentially important interaction terms. The F-tests were used in selecting the appropriate t-test for equal or unequal variances. Correlation analysis of the variables provided insight as to which variables met the independence assumption in logistic regression. Those variables that correlated significantly ($\alpha = 0.05$) with relative cowbird abundance and were independent or potentially biologically significant, and had a significant t-test result, were used in the saturated logistic regression model. An examination of the Wald statistic as well as each variable's estimated coefficient within the saturated model and the model with only that variable were compared. Those variables exhibiting significance ($P < 0.10$) were noted and remained in the model.

Quantile analyses on variables remaining in the model were implemented to ascertain the correct scaling for the covariates (Hosmer and Lemeshow 1989). Estimated quantile coefficients (β) exhibiting a quadratic or U-shaped pattern required an appropriate design variable to be used in the model given that these functions tend to exhibit a non-significant zero slope. Upon completion of this analysis, any variable having a non-significant Wald statistic was removed except for potential biologically relevant parameters (based on prior investigations from the literature and a priori selected land use variables). These remaining covariates represented the main effects model.

RESULTS

Cowbirds occurred in all of the four general locations examined except for the HMC. Mean relative cowbird abundance was 5.6% (number of cowbirds as a percentage of total birds observed) for Huron National Forest sites, 0.7% for both PRCSF and Hiawatha National Forests sites, and 0.0% for HMC sites. The proportion of study sites with cowbirds present was 0.701 for Huron National Forest sites, 0.487 for PRCSF sites, 0.207 for Hiawatha National Forest sites, and 0.0 for HMC sites.

The logistic regression analysis indicated that cowbird occurrence in northern Michigan hardwood forest stands could be predicted (91.6% concordance) based on five habitat variables: occurrence of agriculture within 3.0 km of a census station, total percent of non-agricultural openings within 0.5 km of the census station, percent vertical cover in the 1–7 m stratum, percent vertical cover in the 0–1 m stratum, and mean canopy height in meters (Table 1). The most influential variable in the logistic regression model in terms of cowbird predictions was the presence or absence of agriculture within 3 km of a study site (Stribley 1993). Further analysis indicated that cowbirds were 3–3.5 times

TABLE 1. LOGISTIC REGRESSION MODEL (CONCORDANT = 91.6%, TIED = 0%, DISCORDANT = 8.4%) FOR PREDICTING COWBIRD OCCURRENCE IN NORTHERN MICHIGAN HARDWOOD FOREST STANDS, 1992–1993

Variable	β[a]	SE[b]	Wald χ^2	Prob $> \chi^2$
Intercept	4.182	2.435	2.950	0.0859
Height[c]	−0.4009	0.1226	10.70	0.0011
Ver Cover1[d]	5.654	1.583	12.76	0.0004
Ver Cover2[e]	2.591	1.159	4.997	0.0254
Ag Pres[f]	1.564	2.360	2.880	0.0172
Openings[g]	4.005	0.657	5.671	0.0897

[a] Estimated coefficient.
[b] Standard error of estimated coefficient.
[c] Mean canopy height (m).
[d] Percent vertical cover in the 0–1 m stratum.
[e] Percent vertical cover in the 1–7 m stratum.
[f] Occurrence of agriculture within 3.0 km of a study site.
[g] Total percent of non-agricultural openings (primary and secondary roads, ≤ 20 year-old clearcuts, selective cut areas with < 50% canopy closure, grassland areas, upland and lowland brush) within 0.5 km of a study site.

more likely to occur in a forest stand when agriculture was present in the surrounding landscape (3 km). However, the probability of finding cowbirds at a study site dropped appreciably when the nearest agricultural lands were no closer than 2 km.

The chi-square test for independence indicated that cowbirds were significantly less likely to occur in forest stands that were > 300 m from an edge and had > 70% canopy cover. A comparison of the distance to the nearest edge with the distance to the nearest grassland or agricultural opening for those stands meeting the > 400 m and > 90% canopy closure requirements indicated the distance to the nearest opening was not significant, whereas the distance to the nearest edge was. Study sites with mean tree basal areas < 16 m²/ha were significantly more likely to have cowbirds present than absent. Correlation analysis indicated, however, that mean tree basal area did not correlate significantly with relative cowbird abundance. Covariates that did correlate significantly with relative cowbird abundance included mean tree canopy height, percent vertical cover in the 0–1 m stratum, percent vertical cover in the 1–7 m stratum, percent agriculture within 3 km of a study site, and percent mixed openings within 0.5 km of a study site.

Results of the chi-square test of independence indicated that as much as 20% of a 4-section sized forested area can occur in open vegetation types while maintaining a significantly lower probability of cowbird occurrence than similar areas with > 20% in open vegetation types.

DISCUSSION

The distribution of Brown-headed Cowbirds in northern Michigan is clearly influenced by landscape characteristics. Logistic regression identified five variables that influenced the occurrence of cowbirds in northern hardwood stands. The variable with the greatest influence was the presence of agricultural lands in within a 3-km radius of a northern hardwood stand. These findings are consistent with other studies that have identified the proximity of cowbird feeding sites as a major influence on the occurrence or abundance of cowbirds (Ankney and Scott 1980, Rothstein et al. 1984). The implication of this to northern Michigan landscapes is significant, with the HMC as a good example. Agricultural lands do not occur within 3 km of these study sites, and no cowbirds were detected. Christy (1925) reported the occurrence of cowbirds in the HMC at a time when the club maintained a horse stable and pasture area.

This relationship is further demonstrated in Delta County. Four study sites in the southern part of this county were interspersed with agriculture and urban-suburban areas, and all had cowbirds present. The remaining 21 sites were located further north and did not have agricultural lands within 3 km, and had (with one exception) no recorded cowbirds present, regardless of silvicultural activities or other landscape characteristics.

In landscapes with agriculture present, other factors then influenced the likelihood of cowbirds occurring in a northern hardwoods stand. The proximity of edges was found to increase the likelihood of occurrence in these landscapes. Census stations that were more than 300 m from an edge, as defined for this study, for stands having >70% canopy coverage had significantly lower occurrence of cowbirds. Similarly, if 80% of a 4-section sized area was maintained in closed canopy stands, the occurrence of cowbirds was significantly less.

Certain stand characteristics were also found to influence the occurrence of cowbirds once agricultural lands were in the surrounding area. Percent cover in the 0–1 m stratum was the most significant predictor of cowbird occurrence after the presence of agricultural lands. Cowbird probability of occurrence was also found to increase as the percent mid-story cover (1–7 m) increased. These relationships may have been caused by the increased availability of nesting sites for host bird species in stands with higher structural diversity, attracting cowbirds to these stands.

Our results differ from those of Robinson (1990), who reported that cowbirds were pervasive throughout the Shawnee National Forest of southern Illinois regardless of distance (> 400 m) from edges or agricultural lands. Robinson et al. (1993) proposed that cowbirds in this area

of Illinois were so prevalent that the forests were simply saturated with cowbirds. The Illinois landscape differs from that of northern Michigan, the former being more of a mosaic of forest patches within an agricultural landscape while the latter is agricultural patches within a forested landscape. Coker and Capen (1995) conducted a similar study to ours that investigated cowbird occurrences in Vermont landscapes. They also found the presence of agriculture (livestock areas) significantly influenced cowbird occurrence.

We conclude that the occurrence of cowbirds in northern hardwood forests of northern Michigan is most limited by the presence of agricultural lands, which provide feeding areas for cowbirds (Rothstein et al. 1984, Thompson 1994). Those forest stands occurring within 3 km of an agricultural field had the highest probability of cowbird occurrence. In the presence of agricultural influences and, we assume, other potential feeding areas (e.g., bird feeders, horse corrals), habitat heterogeneity and intra-stand structural diversity become important factors in determining where cowbirds will occur.

MANAGEMENT IMPLICATIONS IN MICHIGAN

Direct effects of cowbird parasitism on reproductive success of bird populations in northern hardwood stands in northern Michigan have not been extensively researched. Studies conducted in other parts of the Midwest (Brittingham and Temple 1983, Robinson 1990) have found that cowbirds can have significant influences on populations of breeding birds. These findings have raised concerns about fragmentation as a contributor to cowbird parasitism rates throughout the Midwest. Our results indicate that more specific factors than a general description of fragmentation are important in understanding potential cowbird influences on bird populations in northern Michigan. When agricultural lands (or other major cowbird feeding areas) are not present in the surrounding landscape, the heterogeneity of stand types or structures, and the presence of edges or openings, will not have a major influence on cowbird occurrence. We think that only when agricultural lands or other major feeding areas are within 2–3 km of a site does the influence of fragmentation by forest edges have significance for cowbird occurrence, and thus parasitism. In northern Michigan, through further analysis of landscape conditions, it may be found that the limited extent of agricultural lands leave sufficient areas that are not close to agriculture so that overall concerns with cowbirds may be negligible.

Our results also indicate that if cowbird parasitism continues to be a concern in northern

Michigan, then two different strategies may be used to address these concerns. In areas with limited numbers or amounts of agricultural lands, one strategy might be to remove these lands from agriculture through land purchases or conservation easements. While this is contrary to many government programs designed to maintain agricultural activities, the implications to native species of maintaining limited amounts of agricultural practices in marginal agricultural areas may need reevaluation. In areas lacking agricultural lands, other potential foraging areas (e.g., certain bird feeders, campgrounds, horse paddocks) may need to be identified and managed to minimize cowbird utilization if cowbirds are to be kept from occurring. Where agricultural activities will continue to be a major activity in a landscape, the second strategy would strive to maintain stand and landscape characteristics to reduce cowbird occurrences in specified locations.

IMPLICATIONS FOR INLAND FORESTS OF THE WESTERN UNITED STATES

Based on findings from studies conducted in other regions of the country, concerns about habitat fragmentation have been raised about forestlands in the inland area of the western United States (DellaSala et al. 1995). Increased densities of cowbirds in National Forests in the Pacific Northwest have been identified as a concern (Sharp 1995). However, no data have been reported on the effects of cowbirds on breeding populations of birds in this region (Sharp 1995). Sharp (1995) did report, based on work by Rothstein et al. (1980), Verner and Ritter (1983), and Airola (1986), that cowbirds were congregating near cattle in the Sierra Nevada. Sharp (1995) also reported that in the Umatilla National Forest cowbirds were associated with riparian zones where cattle occurred, and found low cowbird numbers in "fragmented" conifer forests.

These studies reveal that little empirical information exists about cowbird distributions or effects on breeding bird populations in the inland forests of the West, but that relationships seem to exist with cattle. This points to the need to conduct further landscape level research to determine the influence of parameters, such as the proximity of agricultural lands, on the distribution of species such as the cowbird. As our work in northern Michigan demonstrates, general assumptions about effects of habitat fragmentation or other factors may not apply to all landscapes. Haufler (1998) discussed a strategy for bird research to address information needs for bird conservation in forested ecosystems of the western United States.

A complicating factor for landscape level studies on cowbirds in the western United States is the open range laws of many states. Cattle occur throughout most areas of both private and public lands as free-ranging animals. The implication of this to the distribution of cowbirds has not been investigated, and designing replicated research projects is difficult. Effective studies may require collaborative efforts of agencies, ranchers, and other private landowners. Only through such well-designed studies that generate empirical data on land management questions will controversies be minimized and supportable conservation strategies identified.

ACKNOWLEDGMENTS

Funding for the Michigan research was provided by a grant from McIntire-Stennis and support from the Michigan Agricultural Experiment Station at Michigan State University. Special thanks are extended to the Huron Mountain Wildlife Foundation for providing access to the research facilities of the Huron Mountain Club. We thank S. Winterstein, D. Beaver, T. Gibson, G. Roloff, J. Jarecki, P. Anderson, D. Riegle, and D. Gosling for their assistance.

Studies in Avian Biology No. 18:73–79, 1999.

BROWN-HEADED COWBIRDS IN PONDEROSA PINE/DOUGLAS-FIR-DOMINATED LANDSCAPES IN THE NORTHERN ROCKY MOUNTAINS

SALLIE J. HEJL AND JOCK S. YOUNG

Abstract. Little is known about the habitat and landscape associations of Brown-headed Cowbirds (*Molothrus ater*) within conifer-dominated landscapes in the northern Rocky Mountains. We counted Brown-headed Cowbirds in 16 mature second-growth and 16 old-growth ponderosa pine (*Pinus ponderosa*)/Douglas-fir (*Pseudotsuga menziesii*) forests in western Montana and eastern Idaho during the breeding seasons of 1989, 1990, and 1991. We used aerial photo interpretation and ground-truthing to establish the landscape conditions surrounding each stand, and examined cowbird-habitat relations at two spatial scales: stand (mean = 143 ha) and landscape (518 ha).

Both second-growth and old-growth stands were located in landscapes composed primarily of forest. Second-growth stands were closer to more agricultural land. The amount of forest land, open land, grassland, recent logging, riparian habitat, and residences did not differ between landscapes surrounding both stand types.

Brown-headed Cowbirds were more abundant in mature second-growth stands and in landscapes with more mature forest (naturally occurring and second growth), open land (agricultural land and grassland), and deciduous riparian habitat, and less old-growth forest. Neither forest cover (including all ages of conifer forest), logged openings, residences, nor elevation were important predictors of cowbird numbers.

Our results suggest that landscape context was more important in determining cowbird numbers than stand attributes in pine-fir forests at the scale we examined. The strong negative relationship between cowbirds and landscapes with more old-growth implies that pristine landscapes had fewer cowbirds. We believe that amount of and distance from feeding sources are prime determinants of cowbird numbers in these landscapes, and that landscape features such as agricultural land and grassland sometimes represent feeding sources. In addition, cowbird numbers may be greater in pine-fir forests near riparian areas as a "spillover effect": cowbirds are attracted to riparian areas since they are dense with potential hosts and venture into nearby conifer forests secondarily. These hypotheses need to be tested in future studies.

Key Words: Brown-headed Cowbird, Douglas-fir, landscapes, mature second growth, *Molothrus ater,* old growth, ponderosa pine.

Little is known about the habitat and landscape associations that influence Brown-headed Cowbird (*Molothrus ater*) abundance within conifer-dominated landscapes in the northern Rocky Mountains (Robinson et al. 1995a; but see Tewksbury et al. *this volume,* Young and Hutto *this volume*). We studied lower elevation ponderosa pine (*Pinus ponderosa*)/Douglas-fir (*Pseudotsuga menziesii*)-dominated landscapes in western Montana and eastern Idaho. Two different types of human-induced changes in landscape patterns surrounding these forests have occurred in the years since European settlement: (1) habitat conversion of some forests and grasslands to human settlements (including housing, horse pastures, and agricultural land), and (2) habitat modification of many forests in terms of age, structure, and plant species composition by many different types of logging treatments and by fire suppression (Hejl 1992, 1994; Hann et al. 1997).

Old-growth ponderosa pine dominated the lower elevation conifer landscapes during pre-settlement times (estimates of approximately 60% old-growth ponderosa pine for western Montana; Losensky 1993). Continuous logging since settlement (around 1900; Losensky 1993) has transformed this old growth to a patchwork of clearcuts, immature, and mature forest with little of the original old growth remaining (estimates of 1–7% on the Lolo National Forest; J. M. Hillis, pers. comm.). To identify some of the impacts of this logging on bird communities, we initiated a study to compare the distribution of birds in old-growth ponderosa-pine/Douglas-fir forests with those in mature second-growth forests. We examined the effects of local habitat change and landscape patterns on bird distributions (for preliminary stand-level results, see Hejl and Woods 1991). Herein, we present our results on Brown-headed Cowbird abundances in relation to these habitat and landscape level patterns.

We examined cowbird-habitat relations at two spatial scales: stand and landscape. Our objectives were (1) to compare the abundance of cowbirds between mature second-growth and old-growth ponderosa pine/Douglas-fir stands, and

(2) to determine if components in the surrounding landscape affect the abundance of cowbirds within these forest stands.

METHODS

STUDY SITES

We selected 16 old-growth and 16 mature second-growth ponderosa pine/Douglas-fir-dominated sites in western Montana and eastern Idaho that met criteria for usable stands. The criteria for old-growth stands (determined by on-site inspection) were: (1) each study site was homogeneous in vegetative structure and composition, (2) each area was at least 8 ha in size and at least 200 m wide, (3) the dominant species on each site were Douglas-fir and ponderosa pine, (4) sites ranged from near 100% Douglas-fir to near 100% ponderosa pine for the large dominant trees, (5) the dominant trees were near-maximal age for the species in this geographic area (based on size of trees; often one to two trees were cored on a site to help with determinations) and had old-age characteristics, (6) no obvious large-scale disturbance by people had occurred on any site (except for the exclusion of fire in this region for roughly the past 50 years), and (7) stands were at least 0.8 km (0.5 mile) apart. The criteria for mature second-growth stands were the same as for the old-growth sites except that the dominant trees were younger and obvious large-scale human disturbance (logging 70 or more years ago, and sometimes thinning and prescribed fire) had occurred on the site. Old-growth stands were greater than 170 years old and mature second-growth stands were approximately 70 to 120 years old. Elevation ranged from 1,024 to 1,841 m.

We call our second-growth stands "mature second growth" throughout, because mature stands can result from logging (which we call second growth) or natural regeneration after a natural disturbance process such as fire (naturally occurring mature stands), and, for our stand analyses, we want to distinguish between human-induced and naturally created stands. We were unable to make this distinction for our landscape analyses, where natural and human-induced mature stands are pooled together.

BIRD OBSERVATIONS

Four observers conducted 10-min point counts during each breeding season (13 May to 9 July) in 1989, 1990, and 1991 (as suggested by Verner 1985, 1988). Five points were located at 200-m intervals in each stand (with the exception of two stands, one with four points and the other with two; total = 156 points). Each site was visited four times. One to two sites (from two to ten points) were visited by an observer during a day. To remove observer bias from treatment effects, each observer visited each site once during a breeding season. Some observers differed between years (SJH was an observer all 3 years and JSY and another observer sampled in 1990 and 1991). Visits to a site occurred at 1- to 2-week intervals. Bird counts were conducted between one-half hour after dawn and 1100, and were confined to days with good weather. To sample points at different times in the morning, the transects were traveled in opposite directions on alternate visits. A two-week training session was conducted each year to minimize observer differences.

All observations of adult birds considered to be using the stand (i.e., at unlimited distances) were included in the analyses. Birds flushed as the observer traveled to the point were counted. Only the first detection of an individual bird was included in the abundance estimates. Repeat detections of the same individual from later point counts on the same stand were ignored.

LANDSCAPE MEASUREMENTS

We defined our landscapes as 518-ha circular areas centered at the mid-point of each bird transect (radius = 1.3 km). We chose this size based on inspection of topographic maps for western Montana and eastern Idaho and determined that many third-order drainages approximated this size. Because we began with a community-based study, we selected a size that would likely be relevant for habitat selection for the majority of birds breeding on that site, not necessarily for Brown-headed Cowbirds. In a separate study designed to determine the appropriate scale for predicting cowbird distribution in deciduous riparian habitats in western Montana, Tewksbury et al. (1998) determined that the scale of 1 km correlated with cowbird numbers in riparian habitats better than other local scales.

Three of us (SJH, JSY, and S. Colt) independently interpreted aerial photographs of each site and the surrounding landscape. Each of us had spent one or more seasons in the field on each of these sites before we interpreted the photos. After each of us created overlays on orthophotoquads based on the aerial photographs, we then decided by consensus a single interpretation of each landscape. We ignored discontinuities less than 2 ha. In summer 1991, we ground-truthed a majority of cover types in each consensus landscape, emphasizing borderline cases, and made any necessary changes. One difficult distinction was between different ages of forest. For borderline cases, we cored one or two dominant trees in a stand to index tree age. Based on tree-aging data from our mature and old-growth stands, the mature category for the landscape analyses was arbitrarily chosen to be 70 to 169 years old (which included natural and second-growth stands) and old growth was greater than 170 years old.

We entered our landscapes into a GIS using a digitizing table and summarized the coverage of 14 vegetation categories. The categories we used were: old conifer forest, mature conifer forest, young conifer forest, shrub/scrub, grassland, agriculture, deciduous riparian, clearcut, logged (with leave trees), rock/scree, upland deciduous trees, water, road, and residences. Five of these categories were rare. For the landscape analyses, we used those categories that were prevalent and that, based on our biological intuition, we thought were potentially meaningful for cowbird occupancy: old conifer forest, mature conifer forest, total conifer forest, grassland, agriculture, open land (combination of grassland and agricultural land), deciduous riparian, logged (including clearcut with and without leave trees), and residences. In addition, because others (Verner and Ritter 1983) have had trouble isolating the importance of elevation from other variables, we also obtained the elevation of each site at the mid-point of each transect and analyzed this separately.

DATA ANALYSIS

Because Brown-headed Cowbird numbers were count data, we created Poisson regressions (McCullagh and Nelder 1983) between cowbird numbers and the stand and landscape variables.

To examine stand association, we created Poisson regressions between cowbird numbers (average number of adult cowbirds/point/visit to a site) and stand type (mature second-growth versus old-growth stands).

For landscape descriptions, we used Mann-Whitney U-tests to compare the acreage of each landscape variable between the two stand types and Kendall's Tau-b correlations to investigate relationships among landscape variables.

For landscape associations, we used the average number of adult cowbirds per point per visit to a site as the response variable. First, we created univariate Poisson regressions to examine the relationships between cowbird abundances and coverage of each of the landscape components and with elevation. Second, we created multivariate Poisson regressions with all appropriate landscape variables, considering that two or more landscape variables might work in concert to determine cowbird abundances. We examined scatterplots of the significant correlations at each stage. If needed, we examined the effects of outliers on our analyses. We chose an α of 0.05 for all analyses.

For the multivariate Poisson regression analysis, we started with the full model (including stand type as an indicator variable and all relevant two-way interactions among the landscape variables) and then removed variables one at a time whose parameter estimates were not significant at the 0.05 level, starting with the least significant term first. We included stand type as an indicator variable to examine whether stand or landscape associations were more important in determining cowbird numbers in these habitats. We used an r^2-like measure (model deviance/total deviance, hereafter called "r^2") to describe the goodness-of-fit of the model (D. Turner, pers. comm.).

RESULTS

COWBIRD ASSOCIATIONS AT THE STAND LEVEL

Brown-headed Cowbirds were more abundant in mature second-growth than in old-growth stands ($P < 0.01$). Cowbirds were present on all 16 mature second-growth stands, with an average of 0.52 birds/point/visit (range: 0.10–1.47). Cowbirds were present only on 6 old-growth stands and averaged 0.05 birds/point/visit (range: 0.00–0.27).

LANDSCAPE DESCRIPTIONS

Both mature second-growth and old-growth sites were located in landscapes composed primarily of forests, averaging 79% and 86%, respectively (Table 1). The mature second-growth stands were found in landscapes consisting mainly of mature forests, with little old growth nearby. Old-growth stands were located in landscapes composed of both mature and old-growth forests. Second-growth stands, on average, were closer to more agricultural land. The amount of forested land, open land, grassland, recent logging, riparian habitat, and residences did not differ between landscapes surrounding both stand types.

The amount of mature forest in these landscapes was negatively correlated with only one landscape variable, the amount of old growth in the landscape (Table 2). The amount of old growth in these landscapes was negatively correlated with the amount of open land, agricultural land, and residences.

COWBIRD ASSOCIATIONS AT THE LANDSCAPE LEVEL

Univariately, the number of cowbirds was positively associated with the amount of mature forest and open land (agriculture and grassland) in these landscapes and was negatively associated with the amount of old growth (Table 3). The number of cowbirds was not associated with the amount of forest cover, grassland, logged

TABLE 1. AVERAGE (AND SE) COVERAGES (IN HA) FOR SELECTED VEGETATION CATEGORIES IN THE LANDSCAPES SURROUNDING AND INCLUDING THE 16 MATURE SECOND-GROWTH AND 16 OLD-GROWTH PINE-FIR STUDY SITES, AND STAND ELEVATION

Landscape variable	Mature second-growth	SE	Old growth	SE	P[a]
Elevation (m)	1,258	36.8	1,366	49.7	0.09
Total conifer forest	410	17.4	446	13.0	0.13
Mature	377	18.9	183	19.3	<0.01
Old growth	9	3.6	196	28.7	<0.01
Open land	60	15.3	23	6.3	0.10
Grassland	35	12.7	21	6.2	0.71
Logged	25	8.9	18	8.5	0.62
Agriculture	25	8.2	2	1.1	0.01
Deciduous riparian	14	3.7	9	1.5	0.57
Residence	11	4.4	1	0.8	0.10

[a] Result of Mann Whitney U-test comparing between stand types.

openings, agricultural land, riparian habitat, or residences. In addition, elevation was not a predictor of cowbird numbers.

When examined multivariately, Brown-headed Cowbirds were negatively associated with the amount of old-growth forest in the landscape (P < 0.01; "r^2" = 0.61). When we examined scatterplots of the multivariate relationship, we found that we had one strong outlier. The number of cowbirds on one of these sites was much greater than on the other 31 sites. The outlier site had 1.47 cowbirds/point/visit; the other 21 sites with cowbirds averaged 0.36 (SD = 0.29; range = 0.02–1.02) cowbirds/point/visit. Because the outlier site was located near (< 8 km) another one of our sites (which had the third highest cowbird numbers) and far (> 30 km) from the other sites, we removed both sites, and re-ran the analyses. With the two sites removed, cowbirds were positively associated with mature forest (P < 0.01), open land (P < 0.01), and deciduous riparian habitat (P < 0.01) in the multivariate Poisson regression and had a good fit of "r^2" = 0.81.

After we discovered the importance of an outlier, we re-did our univariate tests with the outlier site and its neighbor removed (Table 3). The positive relationships of cowbird numbers with mature forest and open land and negative relationship with old growth remained, but a negative relationship to total forest and positive relationships to grassland, agricultural land, and residences appeared, suggesting that most landscapes with cowbirds shared these features.

DISCUSSION

COWBIRD ASSOCIATIONS AT THE STAND LEVEL

Brown-headed Cowbirds were more abundant in 16 mature second-growth ponderosa pine/Douglas-fir stands than in 16 old-growth ones in western Montana and eastern Idaho. Most of our sites would be classified as mixed conifer by Young and Hutto (*this volume*). In their regionwide survey of bird distribution, Young and Hutto found that cowbirds were more abundant in ponderosa pine forests than any other conifer type, of intermediate abundance in Douglas-fir

TABLE 2. KENDALL'S TAU-B CORRELATIONS BETWEEN ACREAGES OF MATURE AND OLD-GROWTH CATEGORIES WITH ELEVATION AND WITH ALL OF THE OTHER SELECTED VEGETATION CATEGORIES IN THE LANDSCAPES

Landscape variable	Mature		Old growth	
	Correlation	P	Correlation	P
Elevation	−0.17	0.16	0.25	0.05
Total forested	−0.05	0.67	0.25	0.05
Mature	1.00	<0.01	−0.67	<0.01
Old growth	−0.67	<0.01	1.00	<0.01
Open land	0.08	0.52	−0.29	0.03
Grassland	−0.04	0.76	−0.15	0.26
Logged	0.04	0.75	−0.13	0.36
Agriculture	0.21	0.13	−0.33	0.02
Deciduous riparian	0.01	0.94	0.02	0.88
Residences	0.16	0.23	−0.34	0.02

TABLE 3. POISSON REGRESSIONS (SIGN OF THE COEFFICIENT, CHI-SQUARE AND ASSOCIATED P-VALUES) BETWEEN BROWN-HEADED COWBIRD NUMBERS AND LANDSCAPE CATEGORIES IN THE 518-HA CIRCLES SURROUNDING AND IN-CLUDING THE 16 MATURE SECOND-GROWTH AND 16 OLD-GROWTH PINE-FIR STUDY SITES

Landscape variable	All study sites			Without outlier and neighbor		
	Sign	Chi-square	P	Sign	Chi-square	P
Elevation	−	1.99	0.16	−	3.22	0.07
Total forested	−	2.66	0.10	−	10.63	<0.01
Mature	+	13.65	<0.01	+	7.12	0.01
Old growth	−	19.08	<0.01	−	19.20	<0.01
Open land	+	6.02	0.01	+	27.80	<0.01
Grassland	+	3.04	0.08	+	11.64	<0.01
Logged	+	0.10	0.75	−	0.39	0.53
Agriculture	+	3.59	0.06	+	11.34	<0.01
Deciduous riparian	−	0.00	0.98	+	1.87	0.17
Residences	+	2.61	0.11	+	7.24	0.01

and mixed-conifer forests, and rare in other co-nifer types. We found that within mixed-conifer stands, cowbirds are much more abundant in mature second-growth than in old-growth stands. Therefore, our intensive study, focusing on two types of stands primarily within Young and Hutto's mixed conifer forests, complements their extensive surveys within the northern Rocky Mountains.

COWBIRD ASSOCIATIONS AT THE LANDSCAPE LEVEL

We found Brown-headed Cowbirds to be more abundant in landscapes with more mature forest, open land, deciduous riparian habitat, and with less old growth. Young and Hutto (*this volume*) found them to be most abundant near agriculture and developed areas, with riparian being important in some cases.

RELATIVE IMPORTANCE OF STAND VS. LANDSCAPE ASSOCIATIONS

Our results suggest that landscape context is more important than stand conditions in pine-fir forests. Because stand type was not in either of the multivariate Poisson regressions, it is unlike-ly that the association with mature forests was simply a reflection of most cowbirds being in mature second-growth stands. The negative as-sociation of cowbirds with landscapes with more old growth implies that more pristine land-scapes, those landscapes with less open land, ag-ricultural land, and residences, had fewer cow-birds. Old-growth stands in this study were pri-marily located in the less accessible, and in some cases unlogged, portions of these moun-tains. Most of the old-growth stands were locat-ed far from human concentrations, although some were near individual houses, many of which had horses. Our results suggest that old-growth stands in similar landscape situations to

those surrounding mature second-growth stands would have a similar number of cowbirds. Cur-rently, most old-growth stands are in different situations.

In addition to the amount of mature and old-growth forests, proximity to open land (agricul-tural land and grassland combined) was a con-sistent predictor of cowbird distribution and abundance. Because cows and horses rarely oc-curred on these sites, we think that cowbirds probably uncoupled their breeding and foraging behavior in our study landscapes, similarly to cowbirds in the eastern Sierra Nevada (Rothstein et al. 1984) and to some in the western Sierra Nevada (Verner and Ritter 1983). We suggest that our category of open land weakly represents cowbird feeding areas. We often saw cows and horses on many of the lands that we called ag-ricultural land and grassland. Cowbirds were present and foraging in many of these locations when cows or horses were present (especially agricultural lands), but not all agricultural lands or grasslands in the area of our study had graz-ing cows or horses, and the presence of grazing animals within any particular place likely changed during the course of our study. The fact that open land was a better predictor than either agricultural land or grassland alone provides fur-ther support for this hypothesis. Furthermore, if the proximity to feeding areas is a prime deter-minant of cowbird presence and abundance in ponderosa pine/Douglas-fir forests, we believe we would have found stronger relationships if we had the ability to determine the timing and extent of grazing or locations of bird-feeders on the landscapes we studied (Tewksbury et al. 1998). Cowbird feeding areas elsewhere in the West include meadows with free-ranging cattle, livestock corrals, feedlots, and bird-feeders (Ver-ner and Ritter 1983, Rothstein et al. 1984, Airola 1986).

The two sites with high cowbird numbers that we removed in our final analysis may have been located in a unique area compared to the other 14 mature second-growth forests. When we removed both sites, cowbird relationships to landscape variables changed both univariately and multivariately. These two sites were located on forested hills in the middle of a bowl-shaped valley; the valleys on two sides of these forests have many agriculture lands, but no agricultural land was located within the landscape associated with either site. Most of the other 14 mature forests had nearby agricultural lands in only one direction. Therefore, not just the amount of nearby agricultural land, but the location of it in relation to the stand of interest, may be important in determining cowbird numbers in a particular conifer stand.

Proximity to potential feeding areas seems to be more important than proximity to openings per se near these mature second-growth and old-growth pine-fir forests. Cowbird presence did not correlate with the amount of logged openings (clearcuts and seed-tree cuts) in the landscape. Cows or horses were rarely found in the logged openings near our study sites. Regionwide, however, cowbirds were abundant in logged areas, but the proximity to agricultural lands was a greater determinant of cowbird presence than logging type (Young and Hutto *this volume*). In northern Idaho, no cowbirds or cowbird parasitism was found in an area punctuated with clearcuts or in extensive forest, although cowbirds were seen 11 km away (Hejl and Paige 1994; S. Hejl, unpubl. data). It is unclear from studies done elsewhere (Rosenberg and Raphael 1986, Thompson et al. 1992, Schmiegelow et al. 1997) if landscape effects via feeding sources are a more important determinant of cowbird abundance than openings per se across regions, or if the effects of silvicultural treatments on cowbirds vary by region.

The relative importance of distance from nearest known feeding source has been difficult to tease apart from elevation in other cowbird studies in the West (e.g., Verner and Ritter 1983). In our case, elevation was not an important predictor of cowbird abundance in pine-fir forests. Based on data from just a few locations, Verner and Ritter (1983) also suggested that elevation was not a driver of cowbird numbers in forests in the Sierra Nevada, but cowbird feeding sites in general co-varied with elevation, so they could not clearly isolate the effect of elevation.

The potential importance of the proximity of deciduous riparian areas to cowbird distribution in these conifer forests was only noted when the outlier and neighboring site were removed. In at least some conditions in the northern Rockies, therefore, cowbirds are more abundant in mixed-conifer forests that are located near riparian areas. Riparian areas in this part of the northern Rockies have greater densities of cowbirds and potential hosts than do pine-fir forests (Tewksbury et al. *this volume*, Young and Hutto *this volume*). We suggest that cowbird numbers are sometimes greater in the pine-fir forests near riparian areas as a "spillover effect": cowbirds are attracted to riparian areas because they are dense with potential hosts and venture into nearby conifer forests secondarily. This same effect could explain the higher density of cowbirds near riparian areas regionwide (Young and Hutto *this volume*). In eastern forests, Gates and Giffen (1991) found numbers of cowbirds and brood parasitism rates higher along a natural corridor created by a stream running through forest habitat and decreasing with distance from the stream. They similarly suggested that cowbirds are attracted to the higher density of nests along riparian corridors.

The trend of fewer cowbirds in more forested pine-fir landscapes parallels brood parasitism results by Tewksbury et al. (1998) obtained from deciduous riparian systems in agricultural and forested landscapes near some of our sites. Brood parasitism decreased in deciduous habitats in which the forested portion of the landscapes increased, but this result was attributed to decreased human habitation in more forested landscapes. We also suggest that forest cover is a surrogate variable. In pine-fir forests in western Montana and eastern Idaho, conifer forest cover is negatively associated with agricultural lands and grasslands, primary areas used by cowbirds for feeding. Indeed, the relationship between cowbird abundance and forest cover was weaker than relationships between cowbird abundance and four other significant landscape variables (all but residences and mature forest).

We are uncertain what landscape scale would be best for future studies in pine-fir forests. Our interpretations are limited to the landscape size that we selected (1.3 km). We believe that cowbirds on our outlier site and its neighboring site would have had similar landscape relations to the other sites, if we had chosen a larger landscape size. We suggest that future investigators of this topic select a larger scale and look at various scales nested within the largest size. Radiotelemetry results from the Sierra Nevada indicate that cowbirds commute 2–7 km between breeding and feeding habitats (Rothstein et al. 1984). Young and Hutto's (*this volume*) point count data from across the northern Rockies suggest 7–10 km as an upper limit for distance from agriculture. Tewksbury et al.'s (*this vol-*

ume) point count data for conifer and riparian systems in western Montana suggest 1–2 km from feeding sources, while radio-telemetry indicates that cowbirds travel from 0.5–3 km from feeding sources to riparian systems. Tewksbury et al.'s (1998) ideal scale for western Montana riparian systems was 1 km. The optimum scale for conifer systems may be different from riparian systems and may depend on habitat type, landscape variable of interest, and local cowbird feeding sources.

Because the association between cowbirds and deciduous riparian areas only appeared in the final analyses, we suggest future investigators test the hypothesis that cowbirds are sometimes more abundant in mixed-conifer forests that are located near riparian areas in the northern Rockies. Other interesting questions include the need to examine the importance of stand characteristics (e.g., forest composition and structure) to cowbird abundance, host density, cowbird-host relationships, and diurnal cowbird use patterns to understand more completely cowbird abundance in pine-fir stands, at a diversity of spatial scales (see Hochachka et al. *this volume*). In addition, we would like to know if landscape effects via feeding sources are a more important determinant of cowbird abundance than openings per se across regions, or if the effects of silvicultural treatments on cowbirds vary by region.

MANAGEMENT RECOMMENDATIONS

The presence, amount of, and distance to cowbird feeding sources (e.g., grazing animals in agricultural land, grasslands, or in logged openings; proximity to pack stations and bird feeders) are important factors to consider for cowbird management in western Montana and eastern Idaho. Cowbird feeding sources may in fact be the primary determinant of cowbird numbers in pine-fir forests in the northern Rockies. Cowbird numbers were greater in mature second-growth than in old-growth pine-fir stands in the northern Rocky Mountains, but this relationship was influenced by landscape factors that probably reflect cowbird feeding locations. In addition, the number of cowbirds on these sites (i.e., the greater abundance in mature second-growth versus old-growth stands) could change depending upon future cowbird feeding locations. If meadows with free-ranging cattle, livestock corrals or pastures, feedlots, bird-feeders or other cowbird feeding sources were located near old-growth stands, those stands could have

as many or more cowbirds using them than did the second-growth stands during our study. Proximity to deciduous riparian areas may be a secondary factor determining which conifer stands are searched by cowbirds.

We do not know if any host species is threatened as a result of these relationships, although a number of potential hosts were more abundant in second-growth stands (Dusky Flycatcher [*Empidonax oberholseri*] and Cassin's Vireo [*Vireo cassinii*], two high priority species in this physiographic region according to Partners in Flight [C. Beardmore, pers. comm.], and Chipping Sparrow [*Spizella passerina*]; Hejl and Woods 1991). Olive-sided Flycatcher (*Contopus cooperi*), Hammond's Flycatcher (*Empidonax hammondii*), Warbling Vireo (*Vireo gilvus*), Nashville Warbler (*Vermivora ruficapilla*), Yellow-rumped Warbler (*Dendroica coronata*), Townsend's Warbler (*Dendroica townsendi*), and MacGillivray's Warbler (*Oporornis tolmiei*) are other potential hosts that breed in these stands and are high priority species in this area according to Partners in Flight. Hammond's Flycatcher, Townsend's Warbler, and MacGillivray's Warbler were more abundant in old-growth stands (Hejl and Woods 1991); it would be ideal to maintain current forest-dominated landscapes without cowbird feeding sources around these areas. Because each of the above-mentioned potential host species is found in both pine-fir stand types and in other habitats across the northern Rocky Mountains (R. Hutto, unpubl. data), it is unlikely that any species is threatened based solely on relationships in these habitats. With our current state of knowledge, we do not know if management activities such as silvicultural or fire treatments in these conifer stands would affect cowbird numbers in these landscapes.

ACKNOWLEDGMENTS

S. Colt helped us create all of our landscape descriptions. R. Woods Sparks and L. Rutledge helped set out the transects. D. Anderson, E. Beringer, J. Holmes, P. Hunt, L. Seguela, and A. Wildman assisted in collecting the cowbird data. R. Campbell, S. Colt, T. Ferraro, T. Platt, L. Watson, and R. Woods Sparks collected vegetation data and helped ground-truth the aerial photo interpretation. T. Thompson helped run the statistical analyses. Lolo National Forest (especially J. M. Hillis), Bitterroot National Forest, and Lubrecht Experimental Forest provided logistical support for this study. C. B. Goguen, R. L. Hutto, M. L. Morrison, T. D. Rich, J. J. Tewksbury, and an anonymous reviewer reviewed earlier drafts of the manuscript. We appreciate all of the help we received.

Studies in Avian Biology No. 18:80–88, 1999.

SCALE DEPENDENCE IN THE EFFECTS OF FOREST COVERAGE ON PARASITIZATION BY BROWN-HEADED COWBIRDS

W. M. Hochachka*, T. E. Martin*, V. Artman, C. R. Smith, S. J. Hejl, D. E. Andersen, D. Curson, L. Petit, N. Mathews, T. Donovan, E. E. Klaas, P. B. Wood, J. C. Manolis, K. P. McFarland, J.V. Nichols, J. C. Bednarz, D. M. Evans, J. P. Duguay, S. Garner, J. Tewksbury, K. L. Purcell, J. Faaborg, C. B. Goguen, C. Rimmer, R. Dettmers, M. Knutson, J. A. Collazo, L. Garner, D. Whitehead, and G. Geupel

Abstract.   Previous work has shown that the rate at which Brown-headed Cowbirds (*Molothrus ater*) parasitize forest nesting birds is affected by the proportion of a local landscape that is forested. However, much of the previous work has been restricted to a relatively small part of the cowbird's range, and has looked at forest coverage in very restricted areas around study plots. We used data from a wider geographical area, the entire width of the United States, and examined forest coverage in relatively large areas (10-km and 50-km radii) around study plots to determine if forest coverage is a generally useful statistic for predicting rates of brood parasitization. As was found in previous studies, we showed that increased amounts of forest coverage within 10 km of an area resulted in lower rates of parasitization by cowbirds. This pattern held not only among widely separated sites, but also within local clusters of study plots. However, we found that increased amounts of forest within 50 km of a study site resulted in slightly increased rates of parasitization in sites west of the Great Plains, contrary to previous research findings. Forest structure, as indicated by the relationship between forest coverage and other measures of forest distribution and abundance, differed across the United States. However, differences in forest structure were not obviously related to differences in the manner that parasitization and forest coverage covaried from east to west across the continent. Even given the variable patterns found, management for higher proportions of forest within 10-km radius areas should result in decreased rates of parasitization of host species; however, the impact of such a management strategy will vary across the continent.

Key Words: Brown-headed Cowbird, forest coverage, geographical variation, landscape structure, *Molothrus ater,* parasitization rate, scale.

Areas containing a greater proportion of forest have a lower abundance of Brown-headed Cowbirds (*Molothrus ater*) (Donovan et al. 1997, Donovan et al. in press, Tewksbury et al. 1998), and show a lower rate of parasitization of the nests of host species (Robinson et al. 1995b, Thompson et al. in press). The conclusion of this previous research is that larger proportions of forest, relative to all terrestrial habitats (the landscape), will result in a lower impact of Brown-headed Cowbirds on their hosts.

However, the majority of work relating forest coverage to rates of parasitization is from the eastern edge of the Great Plains (e.g., Robinson et al. 1995b, Donovan et al. 1997, Donovan et al. in press, Thompson et al. in press; but see Coker and Capen 1995, Tewksbury et al. 1998 for exceptions). We might expect the relationship between forest coverage and parasitization to differ away from the Midwest for a number of reasons. Variation in cowbird abundance may not only affect absolute rates of parasitization (Thompson et al. in press), but also the pattern

of variation in parasitization rate with varying forest coverage. Cowbirds in different parts of the continent encounter communities of hosts with different lengths of exposure (e.g., Mayfield 1965) and responses (e.g., Briskie et al. 1992) to parasitization, and host species with longer exposure to cowbirds may be resistant to parasitization regardless of the proportion of forest in a landscape.

Geographical variation in the relationship between forest coverage and parasitization rate also may result because of geographical differences in the pattern of forest in a landscape. Cowbirds may respond to the amount of edge (Gates and Gysel 1978, Brittingham and Temple 1983, Thompson et al. in press), distance from foraging sites (Donovan et al. in press), or other features correlated with forest coverage. Within a region, the proportion of forest in a landscape may correlate well with measures such as the amount of edge (Robinson et al. 1995b). However, land-use practices and topography vary across the continent, such that the relationship between forest coverage and features such as edge may vary across the continent.

The relationship between cowbird parasitiza-

---

* Ordering of names of authors subsequent to T. E. Martin determined using a random number generator.

tion and forest coverage may vary as a function of the local area over which forests were measured, in addition to varying among widely separate regions of the continent. Research relating forest coverage to rates of cowbird parasitization initially examined effects of variation in the size of individual forest patches and distance from forest edges (e.g., Paton 1994), and only recently has looked at local landscapes around individual forest patches (e.g. Robinson et al, 1995b, Donovan et al. in press, Tewksbury et al. 1998). Within these local areas, forest coverage varied in its power to predict parasitization, depending on the size of the area over which forest coverage was measured (Donovan et al. in press, Tewksbury et al. 1998). However, it is still not clear whether the range of areas measured (up to 10-km radius) encompass those that give the best predictions of the rate of parasitization. Local variation in forest coverage may only affect the movements of individual cowbirds (functional responses). Better predictions of the rate of cowbird parasitization may be provided by measuring forest coverage over larger areas than previously considered, if forest coverage over larger regions predict the abundance of cowbirds (a numeric response) and rates of parasitization are better predicted by cowbird abundance than the behavior of individual cowbirds. Knowledge of the most appropriate scale on which to manage forest coverage is essential for informed decisions about land management.

Differences in forest coverage may not predict the same change in the rate of parasitization depending on whether the sites being compared are widely separated. To date, studies have looked at variation in cowbird abundance or parasitization in relation to either local (e.g., Tewksbury et al. 1998) or regional (e.g., Robinson et al. 1995b, Thompson et al. in press) variation in forest coverage, but not both simultaneously. It is still unclear whether parasitization rates vary with local differences in forest coverage in the same manner as they respond to differences in forest coverage among more widely spaced sites, because the proportion of forest in a local landscape may be highly correlated with the proportion of forest within a far wider region.

This paper examines four questions: (1) does the relationship between forest coverage and other measures of landscape structure (e.g., amount of edge, size of forest patches) vary across the continent? (2) do changes in forest coverage over small distances predict the same variation in parasitization rates as changes in forest coverage among sites more widely separated? (3) does the relationship between forest coverage and cowbird parasitization vary with the size of the region over which forest coverage

is measured? and (4) does the relationship between forest coverage and parasitization differ among the eastern, central, and western United States? In conducting our analyses, we had no prior expectations of the patterns that would emerge. Our goal was to document patterns that could affect the way land managers use the previously described pattern of lower cowbird parasitization in areas containing a higher proportion of forested land.

METHODS

The data on parasitization rates of forest birds come from the Breeding Biology Research and Monitoring Database (BBIRD), with data from 23,448 individual nests being represented in our analyses. BBIRD is a collaborative project in which researchers across the United States have monitored nests and recorded data following a standardized protocol (Martin et al. 1997). There were 26 study sites (Fig. 1) on which the nesting success of forest-nesting birds was monitored. Data from five sites were previously used in the analyses of Robinson et al. (1995b). Each study site included 2 to 31 separate study plots (median = 9), with a total of 366 study plots in the data set. The spatial arrangement of study plots into local groups (termed "study sites") allowed us to contrast the effects of local (within tens of kilometers), and large-scale (across hundreds of kilometers) variation in forest coverage. This comparison was made by examining the relationship between forest coverage and the rate of parasitization both within study sites and among study sites.

The data obtained from each study plot were the proportion of nests containing cowbird eggs or young; potential hosts were only included when at least one nest of a species was recorded as having been parasitized in our database. Proportions were calculated across all species of hosts combined. Roughly 75% of all variance in the rate of parasitization occurred among plots within individual study sites (calculated following Sokal and Rohlf [1981:216]; we excluded data from sites on which cowbirds were not present). Given the high proportion of variance in parasitization rate that occurred within individual sites, we treated each of the study plots as an independent data point; i.e., we treated the data from each study plot as independent estimates of the rate of parasitization within the area that encompassed the separate study plots that compose a site.

The data on landscape structure came from an ARC/INFO GIS layer that was produced for the USDA Forest Service's Forest and Rangeland Renewable Resources Planning Act (RPA) 1993 Assessment Update (Anonymous no date). Data

FIGURE 1.   Locations of study sites. Diamond-shaped points indicate sites designated as "eastern", triangles as "Midwestern", and squares as "western". Each site plotted on this map is composed of several independent study plots.

were derived from NOAA satellite images (AVHRR data), with the Forest Service project being completed at the end of 1992. The finest resolution of the GIS layer is a 1 km square that is classified as either water, non-forest, or forest; within forested areas the type of forest was specified as one of 22 types (e.g., oak-hickory, pinyon-juniper). The relatively coarse resolution of the GIS layer placed constraints on our use and interpretation of the data on forest coverage. Each one of the 1-km squares could easily represent multiple patches of forest, detail that would be lost from our analyses. Additionally, our circles were approximate, with edge pixels from the GIS layer being included within a "circle" if >50% of that pixel was included within the circle. Because of the coarse resolution of the GIS layer, we used circles of 10-km radius (over 300 km^2) as the minimum area in which forest coverage was measured. We made this decision in order to average measurement errors caused by individual pixels in the GIS layer containing fractions of both forested and non-forested land. However, in interpreting our results, we do not know what fraction of the unexplained variance in parasitization rates was caused by variation in the spatial arrangement of forest at a resolution finer than was provided by our GIS layer.

Statistics describing landscape structure were obtained using FRAGSTATS (McGarigal and Marks 1995). The areas in which landscape structure was described were circles of 10-km and 50-km radius surrounding each study plot. The 10-km radius, chosen to allow comparison with Robinson et al. (1995b), was based on observations of distances that female cowbirds fly between feeding and nesting areas in the Midwest (Thompson 1994). Although female cowbirds have also been found flying distances of under 10 km in California (Rothstein et al. 1984), work in New Mexico (C. B. Goguen and D. R. Curson, unpubl. data) has found female cowbirds flying in excess of 10 km between foraging and nesting sites. Thus landscape structure further than 10 km from study plots can potentially affect cowbirds' presence and abundance. Fifty km was arbitrarily chosen to represent larger spatial scales. The circles of 50-km radius contain 25 times the surface area as the 10-km circles and roughly 9 times greater area than was used in any previous study examining effects of forest coverage on cowbird abundance (Donovan et al. 1997). We did not use data from 50-km circles in comparisons of the rate of parasitization within study sites, because within individual study sites the study plots were often so closely spaced that 50-km forest coverage were essentially identical among the plots within a single study site. In analyses examining presence and absence of parasitization among study sites, forest coverage for each site was calculated as the weighted average forest coverage around each study plot. Forest coverages were weighted by the proportion of a site's potential hosts that were found on each plot.

The proportion of a landscape in forest was used as the primary measure of landscape structure in this paper following the conventions of previous studies (e.g., Robinson et al. 1995b). However, other metrics generated by FRAGSTATS were also collated for each study plot: size of largest patch (as a proportion of the landscape), number of forest patches, mean size of forest patches, standard deviation in patch size, edge density (m/ha of edge), and the number of types of forest. Some of these metrics require further explanation because our FRAGSTATS calculations were done separately for each of the types of forest recognized in the original data set. As a result, we calculated edge density as the amount of non-forest edge, assuming that most non-forest edges were with forest. Additionally, the largest patch of forest in a landscape may be contiguous with other areas of forest of a different type, and the number of patches may not represent the actual number of discrete units of forest because patches of one type of forest may be nested within another type of forest. Still, these metrics represent some aspects of the spatial complexity of a landscape. Mean and standard deviation of patch size were calculated by decomposing the mean and SD for each forest type into sums and sums of squares and then calculating an overall mean and SD by combining this information across forest types.

Analyses relating parasitization rates to forest coverage were of two types: those examining whether variation in forest coverage affected whether any nests were parasitized, and those examining variation in the rate of parasitization given that at least some nests were parasitized. The former analyses concerned the presence or absence of parasitization, and we tested for patterns using logistic regression. For the latter analyses we used generalized linear models, and excluded sites on which no parasitization was found. Plots varied in the number of nests monitored, and thus the accuracy of our estimates of parasitization rates also varied. This varying accuracy was taken into account in our analyses by weighting each data point by 1/SE of the estimated rate of parasitization, which resulted in greater importance being placed on those data that were estimated with the greatest accuracy. In all analyses, continent-wide geographical variation in patterns were examined by dividing

study sites into three regions (Fig. 1): west of the Great Plains, Midwest (eastern edge of the Great Plains), and east. Data were also divided into two categories, east or west of the Great Plains, to test if better predictions were made when two or three regions were used in analyses.

Data from all sites were used simultaneously in analyses that tested for variation in parasitization rate within individual sites. To use data from all sites in a single analysis, we standardized forest coverages and rates of parasitization to have a mean value of zero within each group of study plots. This standardizing eliminated overall differences in forest coverage and rate of parasitization among these sites, and thus analyses of within-site variation exclusively examine variation relative to the average parasitization rate and forest coverage for a site. Forest coverages used in this analysis were within a 10-km radius of each study.

All statistical analyses were conducted using SPSS 7 (SPSS 1996). We refer to results from statistical tests as being "statistically significant" when $P \leq 0.05$. However, because statistical significance is not necessarily an indication of biological reality or importance (e.g., Thomas 1997), we have also noted instances in which the results of statistical tests approached but did not meet the arbitrary criterion of $P = 0.05$. In these instances, we have presented confidence limits (e.g., Greenland 1988, Steidl et al 1997, Thomas 1997) around parameters estimated in the analyses as a more refined indication of the potential biological significance of results.

RESULTS

Our results are divided into three sections. First, we examined landscape structure to show that landscape structure differed across the continent. These differences could provide a biological explanation for differences in the relationship between forest coverage and rates of cowbird parasitization across the continent. The second set of analyses examined whether variation in forest coverage was associated with the presence or absence of cowbird parasitization in a study area. Finally, where cowbirds were present, we show how the rate at which nests were parasitized was associated with forest coverage. These last two sets of analyses tested for geographical variation in parasitization rates, as well as for differences in the predicted effects of forest coverage that resulted from varying the area over which forest coverage was measured.

We examined the relationship between forest coverage and parasitization rates, both within local clusters of study plots and among widely separated study areas. The within-site analyses

TABLE 1. VARIATION IN LANDSCAPE STRUCTURE ALONG A GRADIENT OF FOREST COVER (10 KM SCALE). RESULTS ARE FROM GENERALIZED LINEAR MODELS

Forest metric	% Forest (10 km) β	SE	P	Region β	SE	P	Interaction[c] β	SE	P	R^2
% Forest (50 km)	0.630	0.046	<0.001	6.736[a]	5.860	<0.001	-0.096[a]	0.075	<0.001	0.74
				-17.068[b]	4.358		0.217[b]	0.059		
# Forest Types	0.028	0.004	<0.001	-1.703[a]	0.451	<0.001	0.00915[a]	0.006	<0.001	0.35
				1.185[b]	0.335		-0.0230[b]	0.005		
# Forest Patches	0.196	0.038	<0.001	-4.775[a]	4.732	<0.001	-0.00219[a]	0.061	<0.001	0.18
				19.971[b]	3.513		-0.262[b]	0.048		
Mean Patch Size (ha)	12.131	13.713	0.001	-36.895[a]	1687.8	0.899	31.379[a]	21.795	0.354	0.12
				-521.68[b]	1253.1		11.016[b]	17.212		
SD Patch Size (ha)	30.978	7.721	<0.001	640.56[a]	950.3	0.014	8.117[a]	12.272	0.005	0.38
				-1547.6[b]	705.6		30.363[b]	9.691		
Edge Density (m/ha)	0.121	0.012	<0.001	4.496[a]	0.447	<0.001	-0.0467[a]	0.006	<0.001	0.73
	-0.001[d]	0.000	<0.001	3.588[b]	0.335		-0.0473[b]	0.005		
Max. Patch Size (%)	0.450	0.055	<0.001	-8.296[a]	6.553	0.003	0.330[a]	0.085	<0.001	0.71
				-16.447[b]	4.866		0.328[b]	0.067		

[a] Regression coefficients for eastern sites (see Fig. 1).
[b] Regression coefficients for sites from the Midwest. Coefficients for western sites were set to zero in the analysis.
[c] Statistical interaction between % Forest and Region.
[d] Coefficient for quadratic term of the regression.

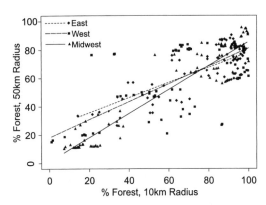

FIGURE 2. Relationship of forest coverage measured on different scales for the same study plots. Regression coefficients are given in Table 1. Regions noted in the legend correspond to those shown in Fig. 1.

were used to determine whether parasitization varied with local variation in landscape structure, whereas the among-site analyses show whether parasitization rates varied with differences in average forest coverage among widely separated regions.

RELATIONSHIPS AMONG FOREST METRICS

Measuring forest coverage at one scale predicts forest coverage at other scales, but the statistical relationships differed among geographical regions across the continent (Table 1). Low forest coverages, measured within 10-km radii of study plots, indicated even lower proportions of forest within 50 km in the Midwest than in either eastern or western landscapes (Fig. 2).

The relationship between forest coverage and most of the other measures of landscape structure that we compiled also differed across the United States. The only exception was mean size of forest patches; as the proportion of forest in the landscape increased, the mean size of forest patches increased consistently across the United States. Edge density was always highest at intermediate levels of forest coverage, and for a given amount of forest cover the amount of edge was highest in eastern forests and lowest in western forests (Fig. 3).

All other forest metrics varied linearly with increasing forest coverage, and the patterns were typically that landscapes with greater forest coverage also contained a larger number of forest types, larger size for the biggest forest patch, greater variation in patch size, and greater number of forest patches (Table 1). The one exception was for numbers of forest patches; in eastern and western sites greater forest coverage meant a larger number of patches, but in the Midwest greater forest coverage meant fewer

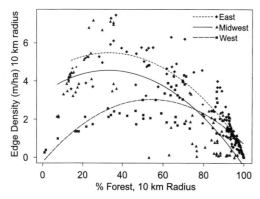

FIGURE 3. Relationship between forest coverage and edge density in different regions. Regions noted in the legend correspond to those shown in Fig. 1.

patches. This relationship at least partially resulted from different types of forest being treated as separate patches, in combination with the number of forest types remaining relatively unchanged with increased forest coverage in the Midwest (Table 1).

Forest Coverage and Presence of Cowbird Parasitization

We found no indication that local variation in forest coverage affected the presence or absence of cowbird parasitization on a given study plot. Twelve of 26 sites had plots both with and without detected cowbird parasitization. For each of these 12 sites, we determined whether increased forest coverage (measured within a 10-km radius of each study plot) resulted in a change in the probability of finding cowbird eggs or nestlings. No single regression was statistically significant (range $P = 0.11$ to $P = 0.99$), which may reflect the low statistical power resulting from the small number ($N = 5–31$) of data points in each analysis.

Further, we also found no indication of an effect even when results from individual analyses were combined in a meta-analysis. The meta-analysis used the regression coefficients from the individual logistic regressions as data points. Each regression coefficient was weighted by 1/

SE of the coefficient, meaning that the coefficients that were estimated more precisely were given greater importance in the analysis. These weighted regression coefficients were used in a 1-sample t-test to determine if on average greater forest coverage lead to a greater or lower probability of detection of parasitization on study plots. The results of the meta-analysis were not significant ($P = 0.64$, df = 11, weighted mean regression coefficient = -0.0121 ± 0.025 SE), again indicating that when cowbirds were present in a region (i.e., at least one nest was parasitized on a study plot within a site) they did not avoid parasitizing nests on specific study plots in relation to local variation in forest coverage.

Sites with greater forest coverage tended to have a lower chance of cowbird parasitization, although the pattern only approached statistical significance (Table 2). For this analysis each of the separate study sites was treated as a single data point. The probability of detecting cowbird parasitization was not significantly affected by forest coverage on either scale of measurement (10-km or 50-km radii; Table 2). However, confidence limits around the regression coefficients showed a 95.3% probability that increased forest coverage within 10 km of study plots resulted in a decreased likelihood of cowbird parasitization at that site. Confidence limits also indicated a 92.7% probability that sites east of the Great Plains were less likely to have any cowbird parasitization.

Forest Coverage and the Rate of Parasitization

Although we found some evidence that forest coverage affected the presence or absence of cowbird parasitization (above), we found more consistent evidence that the proportion of nests that were parasitized was related to forest coverage. Hosts were parasitized at lower rates when there was greater forest coverage, in comparisons both among study plots within the same study site and among widely separate study sites.

We examined the effects of local variation in forest coverage on the rate of brood parasitiza-

TABLE 2. Variation in Forest Coverage, and Presence or Absence of Cowbird Parasitization. Results Are From Logistic Regressions

Scale, forest coverage	% Forest			Region[a]		
	β	SE	P	β	SE	P
10-km radius	−0.055	0.033	0.09	1.55	1.07	0.15
50-km radius	−0.0088	0.019	0.64	1.33	0.93	0.64

[a] Denotes whether sites were east or west of the Great Plains; results were similarly non-significant when data were divided into east, Midwest, and west. Regression coefficient is for data east of Great Plains; regression coefficient for west of Great Plains is zero.

TABLE 3. VARIATION IN FOREST COVERAGE AND THE PROPORTION OF NESTS PARASITIZED. RESULTS ARE FROM GENERALIZED LINEAR MODELS

Test	% Forest			Region			Interaction[c]			R²
	β	SE	P	β	SE	P	β	SE	P	
Within Site (10 km)	−0.00099	0.0003	<0.001	−0.011[a] −0.004[b]	0.013 0.010	0.71				0.08
Among Site (10 km)	−0.00054	0.0003	0.001	0.235[a] −0.004[b]	0.070 0.038	0.003	−0.0020[a] 0.0004[b]	0.001 0.001	0.031	0.13
Among Site (50 km)	0.0014	0.0005	0.082	0.317[a] 0.103[b]	0.079 0.036	<0.001	−0.0046[a] −0.0019[b]	0.001 0.0007	<0.001	0.16

[a] Regression coefficients for eastern sites (see Fig. 1).
[b] Regression coefficients for sites from the Midwest. Coefficients for western sites were set to zero in the analysis.
[c] Statistical interaction between % Forest and Region.

tion by comparing forest coverage and the rate of parasitization among study plots within the same study site. A 10% increase in forest coverage was predicted to result in a roughly 1% decrease in the proportion of nests that were parasitized (Table 3). This effect did not vary across the continent, either when sites were divided as east or west of the Great Plains, or east, Midwest, and west. We added forest coverage as a quadratic term to the statistical model to test for non-linear relationships between forest coverage and parasitization rate. No quadratic effect approached statistical significance, and we conclude that non-linearity in the relationship was minimal.

Both forest coverage and geographical location affected the rate of parasitization in comparisons among widely separate regions; additionally, the effect of forest coverage varied with the scale at which forest coverage was measured (Table 3). The typical pattern was as expected: the rate of parasitization was lower with increased forest coverage. However, an increase in parasitization with increased forest coverage was found from sites west of the Great Plains, but only when forest coverages were measured within 50-km radii of study plots (Table 3, Fig. 4). Confidence intervals around this regression coefficient indicate that there was only a 0.4% chance that the true pattern was for parasitization to be lower in areas of higher forest coverage. Regression models better fit the data when study sites were divided into 3 regions than when only categorized as being either east or west of the Great Plains. When forest coverage was added as a quadratic term to the models, the goodness of fit of regressions was identical or improved over the relationships given in Table 3. However, the qualitative patterns shown in Fig. 4 remained unchanged.

The magnitude of the effect of forest coverage on parasitization rate (i.e., slope of the regression) was greater when differences in forest coverage were measured among widely separated sites; however, this result was not robust. Within a given geographical region, the slopes of the within- and among-site regressions were within 2 SE (a roughly 95% confidence interval) of each other, with confidence intervals calculated assuming that the main and interaction effects in the among-site analyses were independent. To further test for differences within and among sites, we calculated separate regressions for each geographic region, both within and among sites; in this case, regression coefficients within a re-

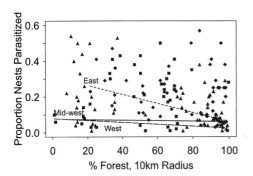

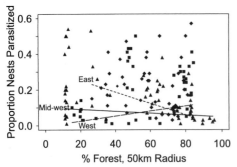

FIGURE 4. Variation in the rate of parasitization of nests as a function of forest coverage. Different point and line styles correspond to the legends in Figs. 2, 3.

gion all overlapped in confidence limits of 1 SE (roughly 68% confidence limits).

DISCUSSION

Generally, we found that rates of parasitization were lower in areas of greater forest coverage (Fig. 4), as previously described (Robinson et al. 1995b, Donovan et al. in press, Tewksbury et al. 1998). This pattern was perhaps minimally due to increased forest coverage tending to result in a lower probability of any cowbird parasitization (Table 2). However, the clearer effect was a statistically significant decrease in the proportion of nests parasitized with increasing forest coverage (Table 3, Fig. 4). The relationship between greater forest coverage and lower rates of parasitization held regardless of whether we examined variation in forest coverage among plots within a local area or among widely separated study sites (Table 3). The presence of a relationship between forest coverage and parasitization rate, even within single study sites, suggests that behavioral decisions of individual cowbirds were at least partially responsible for the larger-scale variation in parasitization rate previously found (e.g., Robinson et al. 1995b).

However, the generalization that lower rates of parasitization are associated with a greater proportion of forest is not universal; greater rates of parasitization were found in areas of greater forest coverage in sites west of the Great Plains (Fig. 4, bottom panel) when forest coverage was measured within a 50-km radius of study plots. We suspect that traits other than landscape structure, such as human land-use practices (e.g., Tewksbury et al. 1998) may be responsible for our findings (Fig. 4, bottom panel). This result was not an artifact of a narrower range of forest coverages from the western sites (Fig. 4), nor did data from a single site create the pattern. Although landscape structure varied with changes in forest coverage across the continent (Table 1; Figs. 2, 3), we found no traits for which western forests differed qualitatively from both eastern and mid-western forests. Hence, we do not think that our results (Fig. 4) were due to differences in landscape structure east and west of the Great Plains. Neither are we aware of any substantial differences in the behavior and habitat requirements among the races of Brown-headed Cowbird (Lowther 1993). We also do not think that our results (Fig. 4) were an artifact of combining data from all host species into a single measure of parasitization, because an artifact of differing species composition would be manifested at both scales of measurement of forest coverage (top and bottom panels of Fig. 4). Finally, although cowbird abundance declined westward, away from the center of the cowbird's range (Thompson et al. in press), the lower abundance of cowbirds in the west should simply lower the rate of parasitization but not cause a completely opposite response of parasitization rate to variation in forest coverage.

Our results indicate that the predicted rate of parasitization can be affected by the area over which forest coverage is measured (Table 3; Fig. 4, compare top and bottom panels). Previous work (Donovan et al. in press, Tewksbury et al. 1998) has shown that some scales of measuring forest coverage provide better predictions of the rate of parasitization than other scales. Our results indicate that not only the goodness of fit (measured as a correlation), but the actual predicted rates of parasitization (regression intercept and slope) were dependent on the scale at which forest coverage was measured (Table 3). However, we were not able to estimate the effects of variation in forest coverage on parasitization with great accuracy. The 95% confidence limits around the effect of forest coverage (10-km radius) in the eastern U.S. (Table 3) showed that the estimated effect could be somewhere within a 35-fold range of values! If this variation is due to insufficient sampling, the variation is probably sufficiently large to make the current estimates unsuitable for attempts to model (i.e., Hilborn and Mangel 1997, Starfield 1997) the demographic consequences to host species of modifying forest coverage. If the variation is biologically real, then our results indicate that relying on measurement of forest coverage to accurately predict rates of parasitization is probably not a fruitful endeavor.

The low accuracy of estimates is an indication that forest coverage explains only a small fraction of variation in the rate of parasitization (Table 3). As noted above, roughly 75% of all variance in the rate of parasitization was within local clusters of study plots, even though less than 23% of all variance in forest coverage was found among study plots within these same local clusters. While some of the within-site variance in the rate of parasitization was due to sampling error, variation in species composition of hosts among plots, and other random effects, we feel that the importance of non-forest landscape features (e.g., Tewksbury et al. 1998) should not be underestimated. One known reason is the need by female cowbirds to have both feeding sites and breeding areas in close proximity (Rothstein et al 1984, Thompson 1994, Donovan et al. in press), and feeding sites are often human-related features of landscapes (Verner and Ritter 1983, Airola 1986).

The one consistent finding of this study was that lower rates of parasitization of host species occurred with greater forest coverage within 10 km of a location, a result that held in spite of the different communities of hosts and their histories of exposure to cowbirds (Mayfield 1965) from east to west across the continent. This consistent result suggests that management for greater forest coverage even over relatively small spatial extents can decrease rates of brood parasitization. However, managers should realize that variation in forest coverage may show qualitatively different relationships with the rate of parasitization across the continent (Table 3, Fig. 4). The most extreme case was the sites from west of the Great Plains (Fig. 4), but we feel that data from additional sites are needed to substantiate the relationship between larger scale (50-km radius) forest coverage and rates of parasitization that we have found.

Nevertheless, it is clear that patterns found in one part of the continent should not be blindly extrapolated to other regions. Managers should also be aware that non-forest features such as feeding sites can play an important role in determining the rate of parasitization by cowbirds in a region (e.g., Airola 1986, Tewksbury et al. 1998, Thompson et al. in press). The effects of non-forest features should be carefully examined if demographic modeling is to be a useful part of a research and management strategy (e.g., Starfield 1997), because the effects of forest coverage alone on rates of parasitization are variable enough that accurate predictions of parasitization rate were not possible, even with a data set as large as was available for this study.

ACKNOWLEDGMENTS

The long list of authors reflects the highly collaborative effort among principal investigators associated with the BBIRD project; each has contributed significantly to the preparation of this manuscript, including the provision of previously unpublished data. The results presented here are the product of the labor of well in excess of 100 field workers; thank-you all, anonymous though you must remain. The data on landscape structure were calculated by M. Thornton and W. Williams of the Wildlife Spatial Analysis Lab, at the University of Montana. Comments by D. Reinking, P. Vickery, T. Rich, members of the Montana Cooperative Wildlife Research Unit, and one anonymous reviewer improved this manuscript. Funding and logistical support for this work was provided by at least 27 federal, state, local, and private sources, with primary funding sources being: Biological Resources Division of the US Geological Survey, USDA Forest Service, US National Fish and Wildlife Foundation, US Fish & Wildlife Service, and the US National Science Foundation.

Studies in Avian Biology No. 18:89–93, 1999.

PAST AND PRESENT DISTRIBUTION OF THE BROWN-HEADED COWBIRD IN THE ROCKY MOUNTAIN REGION

Jameson F. Chace and Alexander Cruz

Abstract. The Brown-headed Cowbird (*Molothrus ater*) historically occupied a range similar to that of the American bison (*Bison bison*). The range of the cowbird and bison on the Great Plains has been well documented. In the Rocky Mountains the bison range included both the eastern grasslands and higher-elevation ridges and mountain parks up to an elevation of 3900 m in Colorado. Based on the commensal relationship of the brood parasitic Brown-headed Cowbird with bison, we suggest that the cowbird had a larger elevational range in the Rocky Mountains than previously known, and subsequently has had a long-term host-parasite relationship with high-elevation breeding songbirds. The change from free-ranging bison herds of the past to the restricted movements of fenced cattle herds today has probably increased the duration and intensity of parasite pressure on cowbird hosts in localized areas.

Key Words: American bison, *Bison bison*, cowbirds, *Molothrus ater*, Rocky Mountains.

The Brown-headed Cowbird (*Molothrus ater*) is a well-studied obligate brood parasite (Rothstein 1975a, Friedmann et al. 1977, Rothstein 1990, Robinson et al. 1995a, Smith et al. in press) that historically occupied a range similar to that of the American bison (*Bison bison*) (Friedmann 1929). Cowbirds ranged over the Great Plains in commensal association with bison. "Buffalo birds" are thought to have foraged among the grazed grasslands for insects stirred up by herd movements (Friedmann 1929, Mayfield 1965, Thomas Say in Evans 1997:171). Cowbirds expanded their range with the clearing of forests and introduction of domestic livestock (Mayfield 1965, Rothstein 1994). In the Rocky Mountains, Brown-headed Cowbirds have undergone a recent elevational range expansion possibly due to habitat alteration and cattle grazing in the high country (Hanka 1985), as have cowbirds in the Sierra Nevada Range and the Far West (Rothstein et al. 1980, Rothstein 1994).

The historical range of bison on the Great Plains is well documented (Allen 1877, Roe 1970, McDonald 1981). In addition, mountain bison (*Bison bison athabascae*) ranged far west of the Great Plains (Christman 1971). While the subspecies separation of Great Plains bison (*B. b. bison*) from *athabascae* is not entirely clear (Meagher 1986), we use "mountain bison" to refer to those bison that ranged west of the Great Plains, in lowland shrub-steppe of the Great Basin and high-elevation coniferous forests, subalpine meadows, and alpine tundra. Mountain bison in the Rocky Mountains ranged above timberline in Colorado, Idaho, Montana, and Wyoming (Henderson 1870; Fryxell 1926, 1928; Warren 1927, Bergtold 1929, Davis 1935, Beidleman 1955, Pattie and Verbeek 1967, Armstrong 1972, Meaney and Van Vuren 1993). We suggest that, based on their commensal relation-

ship with bison, Brown-headed Cowbirds have had a longer high-elevation range distribution in the Rocky Mountains than previously described, and that the recent elevational range expansion (Hanka 1985) is actually a re-expansion back to their former range.

Our purpose is to demonstrate that (a) bison occurred at high elevations in the mountains west of the Great Plains, (b) the first observations of cowbirds in the western states occurred during the period between extirpation of bison from and movement of cattle into the higher elevations, and (c) the number of high-elevation records of cowbirds has increased historically with increasing cattle numbers in the West in general, but also specifically at high-elevations. We argue that many hosts have had a long-term association with the cowbird in the West.

METHODS

We reviewed records of bison distribution (Christman 1971, McDonald 1981) and cowbird parasitism (Freidmann 1929, 1963; Freidmann et al. 1977, Chace and Cruz 1996) in the West. We reviewed agriculture statistics for Colorado, Idaho, Montana, Utah, and Wyoming (yearbook of the U.S. Department of Agriculture) to obtain the number of cattle in each state per year from 1896 to 1996 to determine the timing and abundance of cattle introductions to the Rocky Mountain states. Colorado counties east and west of the Front Range were analyzed separately, with Front Range counties containing >40% grassland habitat designated as eastern (see Chace and Cruz 1998 for delineation of counties). Cattle numbers were summed per year by eastern and western designation. This designation also has important bison implications. Eastern counties contained Great Plains bison, and a few along the eastern edge of the Front

Range may have also contained mountain bison; western counties had only mountain bison if they had any bison at all. Although cattle are not the only livestock that attract cowbirds (Rothstein et al. 1980), they are by far the most numerous and probably are a good index of livestock numbers in general.

RESULTS

The maximum range expansion of the bison was achieved approximately 2000 years before present (BP), although mountain bison remains have been found as early as 10,000 years BP (Lyman and Livingston 1983). Mountain bison ranged far west of the Great Plains and throughout the Rocky Mountain region and occurred at all elevations (Christman 1971, Meagher 1986). Archeological findings include mountain bison kill sites in Waterton Valley in southwestern Alberta as old as 7500 years BP (Reeves 1978), and 7000 years BP in southwestern Idaho (Agenbroad 1978). Other archeological localities with, presumably, mountain bison stretch west beyond the Great Plains to eastern Washington and Oregon, to the Sierra Nevada of California, south to Arizona and New Mexico, and north, at least to southwestern Alberta (Christman 1971, Butler 1978, Reeves 1978, Lyman and Livingston 1983, Van Vuren and Bray 1985). Nearly half the specimens of mountain bison between 1500 to 600 years BP in Colorado, Arizona, and New Mexico were associated with low-elevation ponderosa pine and pinyon-juniper forests (Christman 1971).

Mountain bison were found not only west of the Great Plains but also at high elevations. Bergtold (1929) speculated that bison were widely distributed across the high country of Colorado at least during the last 300 years, which was verified by Meaney and Van Vuren (1993). Meaney and Van Vuren (1993) recorded all known bison specimens in Colorado west of the Great Plains, from which we calculated that 56.9% of 116 bison specimens were collected above 2500 m. In Montana, Fryxell (1928) found a "fairly complete and perfect skeleton of a very large bull buffalo on top of Pryor Mountains [2750 m] in south central Montana," which confirmed Grinnell's earlier comment to Fryxell (1928) that "I have frequently seen bison living at and above timberline . . . in Montana . . . ." Indeed, Pattie and Verbeek (1967) found skeletal evidence of bull, cow, and calf bison in the Beartooth Mountains. Bison also ranged at high elevations in Wyoming. Henderson (1870) commented that in June ". . . thousands of buffalo [were] quietly grazing" on Buffalo Plateau, Yellowstone National Park. Additionally, bison remains have been found in the Medicine Bow

Mountains (2850–3600 m) and slopes of the Gros Ventre Mountains above Jackson Hole, Wyoming (Fryxell 1928). We found no records that suggest a similar use of high-elevation areas in Utah or Idaho, even though bison were found in high numbers at lower elevations (Ross in Davis 1935, Roe 1970).

Current free-ranging mountain bison herds have seasonal elevational movements through open ponderosa pine (*Pinus ponderosa*), pinyon-juniper woodlands (*P. monophylla* and *Juniperus scopulorum*), and across subalpine forest-parkland habitat (Fuller 1962, Van Vuren 1983, Van Vuren and Bray 1986, Shaw and Carter 1990). Furthermore, based on specimens taken (Figgins 1933), some herds of mountain bison wintered in the high-elevation montane grasslands (parks) and migrated into alpine zones through forested communities during the summer (Meaney and Van Vuren 1993). Some mountain bison may have wintered on the windswept alpine tundra, like the 5% to 10% of the Rocky Mountain National Park elk herd today (Stevens 1980). Mountain bison achieved maximum abundance west of the Rocky Mountains approximately 3000 to 1500 years BP (Butler 1978) but never reached the population densities found on the plains east of the Rockies (Schroedl 1973). Extant reintroduced free-ranging bison in forested montane habitats of the Henry Mountains of Utah have smaller group sizes and larger home ranges than bison of the Great Plains, and this was probably true of former high-elevation mountain bison herds in the Rocky Mountains (Van Vuren 1983, Van Vuren and Bray 1986, Meaney and Van Vuren 1993).

Bison are not well adapted for deep snow (Telfer and Kelsall 1984). In Colorado, Benedict (1993, and pers. comm.) speculates that bison were extirpated from the Estes Park area by 1859 in part because of deep snow during the spring of 1844. The heavy snowfall during the winter of 1837–1838 had a similar effect on bison herds in Idaho and Utah (Stansbury 1852, Roe 1970), and deep snow accumulation continues to exact a heavy toll on the Yellowstone bison population (Meagher 1976). Increased hunting pressure with the arrival of Europeans probably restricted the seasonal movements of mountain bison as they did Great Plains bison. Higher numbers of mountain bison were probably forced to stay at higher elevations in large open parks and meadows during the winter where the effects of deep snow and less forage would have reduced numbers. The harsh winters of 1837–1838 and 1843–1844 in combination with market hunting may have been the cause of the bison decline in the Rocky Mountains in general. Most wild bison in western states were extirpat-

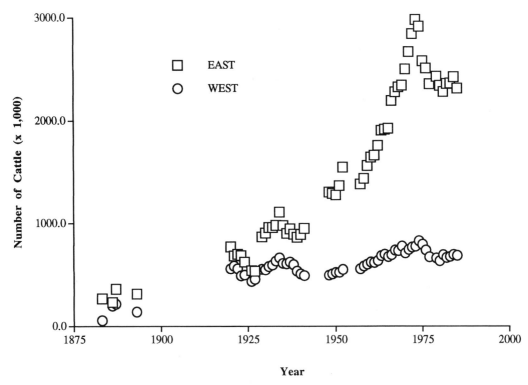

FIGURE 1.　Number of cattle in Colorado, east and west of the Continential Divide (1883–1985).

ed by the 1880s, although a few may have survived until 1904 (Warren 1906).

Although the first livestock were introduced to the West in 1598 in New Mexico (Scurlock and Finch 1997), it was not for another 250 years that cattle reached substantial numbers. Bison abundance was very low by the late 1800s when cattle were becoming fairly abundant in the Rocky Mountains. In Colorado, nearly equal numbers of cattle occurred in eastern (plains) counties and western (higher elevation) counties through the 1920s (Fig. 1). Western counties reached their present levels of cattle by 1959 with a peak in 1974. Since 1941, the number of cattle in eastern counties consistently doubled the number of cattle west of the plains, with a peak in 1973 (~ 3 million head). We feel that the trend of high-elevation cattle numbers lagging behind numbers in low-elevation grasslands in Colorado is consistent with other western states. Although the total abundance of cattle differs among states, the increase of cattle from 1940 to 1975 is consistent across states (Fig. 2). Overall, cattle number patterns are similar among Colorado and Montana, and Wyoming and Idaho (Fig. 2). Utah shows only a slow, steady increase in cattle numbers (Fig. 2). For the first 50 years of recorded cattle abundance

in Colorado, Idaho, Montana, Utah, and Wyoming, the total number ranged between 3.5 and 6 million head. Following 1940 the number of cattle increased to a peak of nearly 12 million in the mid-1970s. Cowbirds began to be recorded at high elevations in the west during this period of peak cattle abundance.

Early records of cowbird parasitism or cowbird presence rarely mentioned exact elevation. Naturalists in Colorado recorded cowbirds as occurring in the grasslands and lower foothills (Drew 1885, Gale 1893 unpublished field notes, Cooke 1897, Sclater 1912, Saunders 1921, Hayward 1941, 1945). Since 1966 cowbirds have been recorded at higher elevations (3300 m) in Colorado (Hanka 1985, Spencer 1985), Montana (Pattie and Verbeek 1966), and (2500 m) Utah (Hayward et al. 1976, Behle et al. 1985). Recent evidence in California and Colorado suggests that cowbirds expanded their elevational range in response to montane livestock (Rothstein et al. 1980, Hanka 1985), and cowbirds subsequently have parasitized species at those elevations (Table 1).

DISCUSSION

Over the past 5000 years in the Rocky Mountain states cowbirds probably had a historical,

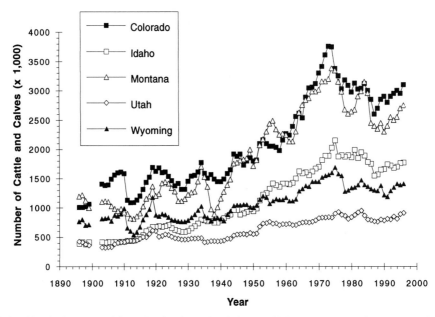

FIGURE 2. Hundred-year trend in cattle abundance for Colorado, Idaho, Montana, Utah, and Wyoming (1896–1996).

geographical, temporal, and elevational distribution similar to that of the bison, with an upper elevational limit at ca. 3800 m. Even though they occurred at lower densities than Great Plains bison, mountain bison probably were numerous enough to support commensal flocks of cowbirds during the avian breeding season. While deep snows may have been present into the early summer and prevented bison, and consequently cowbirds, from reaching the habitats of forest breeding birds until after incubation, we cannot rule out the possibility that mountain bison wintered above treeline and thus provided cowbirds with a foraging location next to subalpine forest breeding birds. As bison approached extirpation in the mid-1800s, herds were small and scattered and cowbirds probably were mostly restricted to lower elevations where

cattle were just beginning to occur in appreciable numbers in the mountain West (Fig. 2). During the late 1800s and early 1900s cowbirds probably became associated with the growing low-elevation cattle herds. By the turn of the century, naturalists had covered many high elevation areas in the region and reported cowbirds as birds of the grasslands and foothills. Even though higher elevations were surveyed (Drew 1885, Sclater 1912), cowbirds were primarily found from the grasslands up to the foothills and mountain parks < 2500 m (Gale 1893 unpublished field notes, Cooke 1897), although Friedmann (1929) reported one observation of a female cowbird in association with horses at 2895 m in Colorado. Cowbirds began to be recorded at high elevations during the peak of cattle abundance in the Rocky Mountian states from the

TABLE 1. PASSERINE SPECIES PARASITIZED AT HIGH ELEVATIONS IN COLORADO

Species	Number	Year	Elevation	Reference
Poecile gambeli	1	1984	2280 m	Brockner 1984
Regulus calendula	3	1985	>2400 m	Chace and Cruz 1996
Wilsonia pusilla	1	1985	3180 m	Spencer 1985
Wilsonia pusilla	7	1990, 1992	>2800 m	Chace and Cruz 1996
Catharus guttatus	2	1990, 1994	2400 m	Chace and Cruz 1996
Dendroica petechia	1	1990	2800 m	Chace and Cruz 1996
Spizella passerina	1	1985	>2400 m	Spencer 1985
Melospiza lincolnii	3	1990, 1992	>2800 m	Chace and Cruz 1996
Euphagus cyanocephalus	18	1985	2895 m	Hanka 1985

mid-1960s to the present (Keeler-Wolf et al. 1972, Hanka 1985). The association of cowbirds with herding ungulates is strong, and their historical elevational distribution may be as great as the former range of the bison, and now cattle. We suggest that Brown-headed Cowbirds occurred at high elevations in the Rocky Mountains until the extirpation of bison and have recently regained their former range with introduction of domestic livestock.

Cowbird distribution is not wholly dependent on the presence of bison, cattle, or other large ungulates. Rothstein (1994) suggested that despite the presence of preferred habitat, elk herds, and potential hosts, cowbirds were absent from the Central Valley of California until 1922. Cowbirds entered this region in 1922 following anthropogenic changes (irrigation and agriculture) that improved feeding and breeding conditions for the cowbird (Rothstein 1994). We feel that along the Rocky Mountains the long-term presence of mountain bison probably enabled cowbirds to move easily between high-elevation bison herds and those of the Great Plains. High-elevation herds provided foraging opportunities and allowed cowbirds to parasitize the nests of many high-elevation songbirds.

As in the Sierra Nevada of California (Verner and Ritter 1983, Rothstein 1994), present-day populations of cowbirds in the Rocky Mountains often forage among large grazing animals. Feeding sites are anthropogenic, e.g., horse corrals, pastures with livestock, bird feeders, or campgrounds. From 1986–1989, 164 Brown-headed Cowbirds were trapped and banded at a feeding station on Mount Evans, Colorado (elev. 3260 m). Cowbirds were trapped from April to August, with highest numbers in May (mean captures per month = 29.0); males outnumbered females 2.35:1 (L. E. Reiner, unpubl. data).

The center of cowbird abundance today (Robinson et al. 1995a) overlaps the former center of bison abundance among the grasslands of the Great Plains (McDonald 1981, Meagher 1986). Although mountain bison have been recorded in the high-elevation areas in the Rocky Mountains, little is known about the distribution of cowbirds in the Great Basin prior to the extirpation of the bison. They were probably located along major tributaries, such as the Colorado River (Rothstein 1994), and were associated with far western mountain bison herds. Following cattle introductions in the Great Basin, western populations of cowbirds may also have re-expanded their elevational distribution; however, a distributional change along the west slope of the Rocky Mountains has not been as well documented as along the east slope.

Prior to the extirpation of bison in the late 1800s, Brown-headed Cowbirds probably parasitized the nests of many songbird species in the high-elevation regions. Cowbird numbers at higher elevations likely declined as bison were extirpated, then resurged following the introduction of cattle. When cowbirds followed the nomadic bison herds, their parasitic efforts and eggs were dispersed over the range of the seasonal movements of the bison herds, whereas now cowbird breeding populations are as stationary as the herds of livestock around which they forage. While free-ranging herds occur at lower densities and may disperse cowbird activity over a larger area, many cattle containment areas are at high densities and largely stationary through the early part of the breeding season. The implications of this changing pattern on songbird communities are likely very important. Where once songbird communities may have encountered brood parasitism for only a portion of their breeding season, now the pressure of parasitism is pronounced throughout their reproductive season. In addition, because of the strong site fidelity of many songbirds (Greenwood and Harvey 1982, Holmes and Sherry 1992) and annual timing of cattle movement among pastures, the pressure of parasitism may exist throughout the lifetime reproductive effort of many individual birds.

ACKNOWLEDGMENTS

Initial concepts for this paper came through thoughtful discussions with Jim Benedict. This paper benefited from comments made by S. K. Robinson, J. Verner, S. Hejl, C. P. Ortega, A. D. Benedict, J. B. Benedict, D. M. Armstrong, H. Kingery, and C. A. Meaney.

Studies in Avian Biology No. 18:94–96, 1999.

DISTRIBUTION AND ABUNDANCE OF BROWN-HEADED COWBIRDS IN THE WILDERNESS OF CENTRAL IDAHO

ANTHONY L. WRIGHT

Abstract. The value of wilderness as an ecological control area where anthropogenic factors are minimal and as a demographic source area for neotropical migrant birds is diminished by exotic species such as the Brown-headed Cowbird (*Molothrus ater*). I observed Brown-headed Cowbirds at 9 of 10 small, developed sites within the Selway-Bitterroot and Frank Church-River of No Return wildernesses of Idaho during 1993–1997. None were detected during 290 5-minute point counts at undeveloped sites in the Selway-Bitterroot Wilderness. During daily counts at a small ranch on the Selway River, where 6 or fewer horses or mules were kept year-round, the minimum number of adult cowbirds present was highest in mid-May and mid-July and low in June and after late July. Because Brown-headed Cowbirds are restricted spatially and are not numerous in the wilderness of central Idaho, current impacts are probably minor and effective control may be possible in local problem spots.

Key Words: abundance, Brown-headed Cowbird, distribution, Idaho, *Molothrus ater*, wilderness.

Brown-headed Cowbirds (*Molothrus ater*) are obligate brood parasites that may cause reductions in populations of vulnerable host species (Mayfield 1965, Brittingham and Temple 1983). Originally associated with American bison (*Bison bison*), they were probably absent from the wilderness of central Idaho before homesteading occurred in the early twentieth century (Laymon 1987). The earliest known historical reference, a crude bird list made for District 5 of the Nez Perce National Forest in 1922, suggests they arrived in the area between 1905 and 1922. In the northern Rockies region cowbirds are known to be common in agricultural/forest mosaics and fringes (Hejl and Young *this volume*, Tewksbury et al. *this volume*) and on urban fringes (Greene *this volume*), but their status in extensive wilderness is poorly known. In this paper I compare the numbers of cowbirds observed at developed and undeveloped sites within wilderness and document seasonal changes in abundance at one developed site over five years.

METHODS

The central Idaho wilderness consists of 1.5 million ha of contiguous, federally-designated wilderness comprising the Selway-Bitterroot, Frank Church-River of No Return, and Gospel Hump wildernesses. The vegetation is a mosaic of conifer stands of various types and open areas including brush fields, wet meadows, and steep slopes of grasses and forbs. Elevations range from 670 to 3000 m. Developed areas, both public and private, are generally under 60 ha and are located along rivers or large creeks.

The focal point of this study was Running Creek Ranch on the Selway River, a 12-ha research station with irrigated lawns and hayfields, where horses and mules have been kept since the early 1900s. About five head were kept there

year-round during the study. These animals concentrated their activities near the ranch, wandering up to 1 km away into the grazing allotment 1 June–15 August but returning to the corral daily. Two similar ranches are located 2.5 and 13 km down river. A trailhead, U.S. Forest Service guard station, and an outfitter's camp, all located 13 km up river, received heavy stock use.

From 1993–1997 when I, or observers I had trained, visited developed sites in the Idaho backcountry, we recorded the numbers of adult male, adult female, and juvenile cowbirds present. Feeding habitat and associated grazing animals were noted. Five sites were visited on more than 10 different days, two sites on five different days, one site on three different days, and two sites only once.

I counted and classified by age and sex cowbirds seen during the course of nearly every day's activities at Running Creek Ranch. I considered the highest count achieved each day to be the minimum number present for an age/sex category. Because the chances of seeing cowbirds varied greatly from day to day depending on the day's activities, minimum numbers present were subsequently converted from a daily to a weekly figure. Also, I watched and listened for cowbirds during 290 5-minute point counts (Ralph et al. 1995) conducted from June 1 to July 10 in four vegetation types that dominate the study area: lower canyon (N = 120), mixed conifer (N = 60), lodgepole transition (N = 60), and whitebark pine-spruce/fir (N = 50). Points were located 200 m apart in patches at least 1900 m wide. Of these points, 72 were located ≤ 1 km from developed sites, 167 from 1 to 10 km from developed sites, and 51 ≥ 10 km from developed sites. I watched and listened for cowbirds during 222 hr of travel on foot to and from point counts. During June and July of 1994–

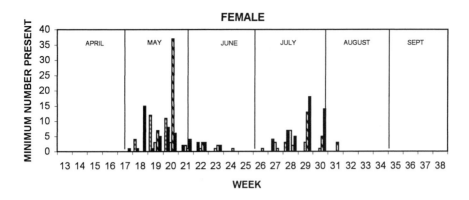

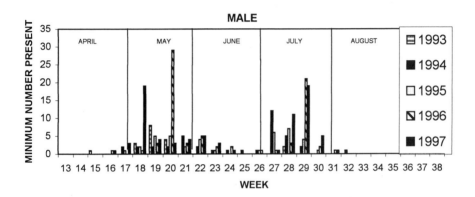

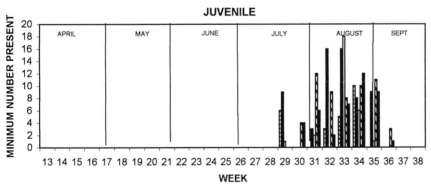

FIGURE 1. Minimum number of adult female, adult male, and independent juvenile Brown-headed Cowbirds present each week 1993–1997 at Running Creek Ranch in the Selway-Bitterroot Wilderness, Idaho.

1997, I also searched for cowbirds during repeated visits to three sites ≤1 km and four sites between 1 km and 10 km from developed areas as a volunteer contribution to a nation-wide research project (Rosenberg et al. 1996).

RESULTS

Cowbirds were seen at 9 of 10 backcountry, developed sites including the highest site (1900 m). They were observed feeding in short or sparse vegetation of lawns, airstrips, or corrals at all sites. Cowbirds associated with horses at six sites and wild cervids, primarily moose (*Alces alces*) using a salt block, at one site. The single developed site where no cowbirds were detected was visited on only two different days.

At Running Creek Ranch the minimum number of adult cowbirds present followed a bimodal temporal pattern for both sexes in all years (Fig. 1). A first peak occurred 6–22 May, followed by a period of very low numbers from about 7 June–7 July, a second peak 10–20 July, and very low numbers again by the final days of July. Juvenile cowbirds first appeared 23–26 July, reached a peak 18–24 August, and disappeared by 6 September (Fig. 1).

No cowbirds were detected during point counts in the wilderness surrounding Running Creek Ranch. On five occasions I saw cowbirds with the horse herd in undeveloped areas less than 0.5 km from the ranch. These were the only cowbirds I detected during travel or other activities in undeveloped areas.

DISCUSSION

Although Brown-headed Cowbirds were widespread in the Idaho backcountry, they were only detected in the vicinity of widely scattered developed sites. The types of areas used for feeding were similar to those reported by Rothstein et al. (1980) and Verner and Ritter (1983) in the Sierra Nevada. Most developed sites in the Idaho backcountry are located in riparian zones where potential host species nest; thus, food and host resources are in close proximity.

Both adults and independent juveniles used Running Creek Ranch for brief time periods, about 10 and 8 weeks per year, respectively. The peaks in adult numbers that occurred each year in May probably included migrants. In some years peak counts were made when cowbirds traveled in transient, mixed flocks with other blackbird species. During the last 3 weeks of June and the first few days of July, cowbirds either left the ranch or became secretive and abandoned their usual feeding areas. Data from my study were not sufficient to explain patterns of cowbird abundance during the summer, but I did note a number of consistent environmental patterns that could have been related. The early summer period with few cowbird detections probably coincided with incubation and rearing of the first brood by common host species. Large numbers of female horseflies (*Tabanus* spp.) were present on horses and mules each year from mid-July through mid-August and cowbirds were often observed feeding on them. Adult cowbirds disappeared from the Ranch at about the time flocks of independent juveniles began to congregate at the corral.

The restricted spatial and temporal use of the Idaho backcountry by Brown-headed Cowbirds may indicate a host-rich/food-poor environment. Because Brown-headed Cowbirds are fairly restricted both temporally and spatially in the wilderness of central Idaho, current impacts are probably minor and effective control may be possible in local problem spots.

ACKNOWLEDGMENTS

T. Holubetz and B. Leth of the Idaho Department of Fish and Game assisted with data collection. The Hornocker Wildlife Institute and the Richard King Mellon Foundation provided funding.

Studies in Avian Biology No. 18:97–103, 1999.

ABUNDANCE AND RATES OF BROOD PARASITISM BY BROWN-HEADED COWBIRDS OVER AN ELEVATIONAL GRADIENT IN THE SOUTHERN SIERRA NEVADA

Kathryn L. Purcell and Jared Verner

Abstract. We studied Brown-headed Cowbird (*Molothrus ater*) parasitism rates in four forest types (ponderosa pine, mixed conifer, true fir, and lodgepole pine) over an elevational gradient in the southern Sierra Nevada. Cowbirds were most abundant and parasitism rates were highest at the lowest sites. All but one of 17 parasitized nests were found in the ponderosa pine type and cowbirds were detected only in ponderosa pine and mixed-conifer forest types. A hypothesis that cowbird breeding and egg-laying are limited by late release of livestock at higher elevations was not rejected. Data also supported a second hypothesis—that host abundance and richness influence cowbird abundance and parasitism rates. Bird species richness was a better predictor of cowbird abundance than abundance (total count per plot per year, pooled across species), and models including all passerines were better predictors than models with only host species. Brood parasitism rates were low overall, although rates for Warbling Vireos (*Vireo gilvus*), Cassin's Vireos (*Vireo cassinii*), and Black-throated Gray Warblers (*Dendroica nigrescens*) were high enough to warrant some concern. We recommend continued monitoring of cowbird parasitism rates for these three species in the Sierra Nevada.

Key Words: Black-throated Gray Warbler, brood parasitism, Brown-headed Cowbird, bird species richness, Cassin's Vireo, *Dendroica nigrescens*, elevation, *Molothrus ater*, ponderosa pine, Sierra Nevada, *Vireo cassinii*.

The Brown-headed Cowbird (*Molothrus ater*) is a fairly recent addition to the avifauna of the west slope of the Sierra Nevada, having invaded the region only within the last 60 to 70 years (Rothstein et al. 1980). This raises a concern about potential impacts on endemic populations of host species that have only recently been exposed to cowbird parasitism. Twenty-seven species have been confirmed as hosts of Brown-headed Cowbirds in the Sierra Nevada (Table 1), and populations of these species may be particularly vulnerable to the loss of productivity associated with brood parasitism.

As part of an ongoing study of productivity of forest birds in four forest types, we accumulated data on relative abundance of cowbirds and rates of brood parasitism over an elevational gradient in the Sierra National Forest. Our objectives were to examine patterns of abundance of cowbirds, patterns and rates of brood parasitism, and their potential effects on host species.

Although Verner and Ritter (1983) found cowbirds at all elevations when pack stations and other anthropogenic food sources were nearby, we observed in the present study that cowbird abundance and parasitism rates decreased with increasing elevation. To investigate the observed pattern of higher parasitism rates at lower elevations, we examined two hypotheses. First, because cowbirds in the Sierra seem to depend on supplemental food sources related to various sorts of human activity, especially those connected to livestock, breeding and egg-laying by cowbirds may depend on the timing of livestock release ("cattle on-dates") into the mountains. This hypothesis predicts that cattle on-dates at the higher elevations were later in relation to the arrival and laying dates of the host species. Second, because host abundance and richness tend to be greater at lower elevations, one or both of these variables could influence cowbird abundance.

METHODS

From 1995–1997, we censused birds and monitored nests of all bird species in four forest types over an elevational gradient on the Kings River Ranger District of the Sierra National Forest on the western slope of the southern Sierra Nevada—ponderosa pine (*Pinus ponderosa*; four sites, 1024–1372 m), mixed-conifer (six sites, 1707–2012 m), true fir (four sites, 2170–2347 m), and lodgepole pine (*Pinus contorta*; four sites, 2469–2774 m). All sites consisted of at least 60 ha of mature forest with relatively high canopy cover. Within the 60-ha sites, 40-ha gridded plots were established to allow censusing and facilitate mapping and relocation of nests. The sites tended to be heterogeneous—most included small meadows, creeks, and open, rocky areas. Only the mixed-conifer sites were close to large campgrounds and pack stations. We are not aware that bird feeders play a role in cowbird abundance in any of our study areas. In addition, the ponderosa pine sites were relatively remote and inaccessible, particularly early in the nesting season. All sites were protected from major disturbances, including timber harvest, road construction, and major fuel breaks.

TABLE 1. PERCENTAGE OF BROODS OF PASSERINE SPECIES PARASITIZED BY BROWN-HEADED COWBIRDS (TOTAL NUMBER OF NESTS FOUND[a]) IN FOUR FOREST TYPES, 1995–1997, AND REFERENCES FOR CONFIRMED HOSTS (*) IN THE SIERRA NEVADA

Species	Ponderosa pine	Mixed conifer	True fir	Lodgepole pine	References[b]
Olive-sided Flycatcher (*Contopus cooperi*)*	0 (1)				D
Western Wood-Pewee (*Contopus sordidulus*)*	0 (17)	0 (4)	0 (1)		D, J
Black Phoebe (*Sayornis nigricans*)	0 (1)				
Hammond's Flycatcher (*Empidonax hammondii*)*	0 (4)	0 (15)	0 (2)		D
Dusky Flycatcher (*Empidonax oberholseri*)*		0 (65)	0 (25)	0 (21)	D, J
Pacific-slope Flycatcher (*Empidonax difficilis*)	0 (12)	0 (2)			
Cassin's Vireo (*Vireo cassinii*)*	25 (20)	10 (10)	0 (1)		D, E, I, J, L, N
Hutton's Vireo (*Vireo huttoni*)*	9 (23)				N
Warbling Vireo (*Vireo gilvus*)*	67 (3)	0 (24)	0 (3)	0 (1)	H, I, J, M, N
Steller's Jay (*Cyanocitta stelleri*)	0 (8)	0 (5)	0 (1)		
Mountain Chickadee (*Poecile gambeli*)	0 (1)	0 (19)	0 (39)	0 (19)	
Bushtit (*Psaltriparus minimus*)	0 (6)				
Red-breasted Nuthatch (*Sitta canadensis*)	0 (6)	0 (10)	0 (4)		
Brown Creeper (*Certhia americana*)	0 (10)	0 (10)	0 (5)	0 (14)	
House Wren (*Troglodytes aedon*)		0 (1)			
Winter Wren (*Troglodytes troglodytes*)		0 (1)			
Golden-crowned Kinglet (*Regulus satrapa*)*		0 (1)	0 (1)		J
Ruby-crowned Kinglet (*Regulus calendula*)*					D, E
Blue-gray Gnatcatcher (*Polioptila caerulea*)	0 (4)				
Townsend's Solitaire (*Myadestes townsendi*)		0 (2)	0 (5)		
Hermit Thrush (*Catharus guttatus*)*		0 (6)	0 (5)	0 (10)	D
American Robin (*Turdus migratorius*)	0 (25)	0 (14)	0 (15)	0 (10)	
Wrentit (*Chamaea fasciata*)	0 (3)				
Nashville Warbler (*Vermivora ruficapilla*)*	17 (6)	0 (2)			N
Yellow Warbler (*Dendroica petechia*)*		0 (2)			H, I, J, L
Yellow-rumped Warbler (*Dendroica coronata*)*	0 (1)	0 (9)	0 (2)	0 (12)	D, J, L
Black-throated Gray Warbler (*Dendroica nigrescens*)*	29 (14)				E, I, M, N
Hermit Warbler (*Dendroica occidentalis*)*	0 (2)	0 (2)			A, E, J, M
MacGillivray's Warbler (*Oporornis tolmiei*)*		0 (12)	0 (1)		D, I, J, L, M
Wilson's Warbler (*Wilsonia pusilla*)*					D, E, F
Western Tanager (*Piranga ludoviciana*)*	9 (11)	0 (14)	0 (4)		D, L, N
Black-headed Grosbeak (*Pheucticus melanocephalus*)	0 (41)				
Green-tailed Towhee (*Pipilo chlorurus*)*		0 (4)			D, H, K
Spotted Towhee (*Pipilo maculatus*)	0 (48)	0 (4)			
California Towhee (*Pipilo crissalis*)*					D, M
Chipping Sparrow (*Spizella passerina*)*	0 (10)	0 (2)			L
Fox Sparrow (*Passerella iliaca*)*		0 (8)	0 (4)		D, L
Song Sparrow (*Melospiza melodia*)*					D, H, I, M
Lincoln's Sparrow (*Melospiza lincolnii*)*		0 (1)	0 (1)		D, G, M
White-crowned Sparrow (*Zonotrichia leucophrys*)*					M
Dark-eyed Junco (*Junco hyemalis*)*	4 (51)	0 (76)	0 (55)	0 (46)	B, C, D, E, H, J, L, N
Pine Grosbeak (*Pinicola enucleator*)				0 (2)	
Gray-crowned Rosy-finch (*Leucosticte tephrocotis*)*					M
Purple Finch (*Carpodacus purpureus*)	0 (12)	0 (1)			
Cassin's Finch (*Carpodacus cassinii*)		0 (1)	0 (2)	0 (3)	
Pine Siskin (*Carduelis pinus*)				0 (1)	
Lesser Goldfinch (*Carduelis psaltria*)	0 (1)				
Evening Grosbeak (*Coccothraustes vespertinus*)			0 (1)		

[a] Number of nests we could look into to confirm parasitism.
[b] References (chronologically): A—Friedmann 1963, B—Orr and Moffitt 1971, C—White 1973, D—Friedmann et al. 1977, E—Gaines 1977, F—Stewart et al. 1977, G—Rothstein 1978, H—Rothstein et al. 1980, I—Gaines (in Rothstein et al. 1980), J—Verner and Ritter 1983, K—Friedmann and Kiff 1985, L—Airola 1986, M—Gaines 1988, N—this study.

We censused 8 (1995) or 16 (1996–97) plots each year, using a timed transect method. Transects were 1000 m in length and observers walked at a rate of 50 m per 3 minutes. We recorded birds <50 and >50 m from the transect line. Observers received training in bird vocalizations at the beginning of the season and before moving up to a new elevational band. Each transect was counted six times during the breeding season, with two visits by each of three observers. All censuses were completed by 0930 PDT.

We searched for nests of all bird species and monitored nests every 3 to 4 days. Open nests were checked directly where possible, or with a mirror on a pole. Cavity nests were checked with a fiberscope (Purcell 1997). When nests were too high to reach from the ground, and nest substrates were sturdy, we climbed to nests using a variety of climbing techniques. Laying dates were determined by backdating, assuming one egg laid per day.

Personnel from the Kings River Ranger District provided data on dates when cattle were released onto grazing allotments each year. All livestock permitted for a given allotment were released annually on the date each was open to grazing and generally the cattle had dispersed over the full allotment within a couple of days. Most allotments in a particular forest type had the same on-date. Livestock release preceded the presence of horses at pack stations, and the study sites were not in locations where we would expect cowbirds to occur because of pack stations. Radio-tagged cowbirds on the eastern slope of the Sierra Nevada traveled up to 7 km between feeding and breeding sites (Rothstein et al. 1984). We assume here that cowbirds could have traveled up to 7 km from feeding sites (cattle allotments) to breeding sites (our study sites), although they traveled a maximum of only 4.5 km in an earlier radio-tracking study in the same watersheds as the present study (J. Verner, unpubl. data).

Host abundance and richness were analyzed for correlations with cowbird abundance. Our measure of abundance was the total number of individuals detected per plot per year. Richness was the total number of species detected per plot per year. Two groups of species were used in analyses of host abundance and richness: (1) the 14 species identified as cowbird hosts in the combined results of this study and Verner and Ritter (1983), also done in the Sierra National Forest; and (2) all confirmed Sierran host species (Table 1). Common Ravens (scientific names listed in Table 1) were omitted from analyses. We used Poisson regression to model cowbird abundance because the errors in count data generally are non-normally distributed. The regression parameters were estimated using SAS (SAS Institute 1997). Because count data are typically overdispersed (the variance is greater than the mean), we used a scaled deviance formula to accommodate the assumption of a Poisson distribution (Littell et al. 1996). Plots of deviance residuals showed homogeneity of variance, indicating that this was an appropriate approach. We included a year term in all models to control for year effects.

RESULTS

We monitored 300 nests of 31 passerine species in 1995 for which we were able to confirm the presence or lack of parasitism, 323 nests of 35 species in 1996, and 360 nests of 36 species in 1997. During the three years, all but one of the 17 parasitized nests were found in ponderosa pine habitat (Table 1). Brown-headed Cowbirds were most abundant and parasitism rates were highest in the ponderosa pine forest type, i.e., sites at the lowest elevations. Cowbirds were never detected in our true fir or lodgepole pine sites (Table 2, Fig. 1), nor was brood parasitism. This study added two new species to the list of confirmed hosts in the Sierra Nevada: Hutton's Vireo and Nashville Warbler. Overall rates of cowbird parasitism were low—1.4% of all passerine nests and 3.8% of all passerine nests in ponderosa pine sites. Considering only nests in the ponderosa pine sites, parasitism rates of some individual species were high (Table 1), although sample sizes were small for many species.

Our first hypothesis, that timing of livestock release may influence the timing of cowbird breeding and egg laying, was not rejected. Grazing allotments on the lodgepole pine sites were rested or vacant during the study, except for 10 cow/calf pairs released on 1 July (Julian date = 182) in 1997 within 7 km of 2 plots, and cowbirds were not detected in these sites. In the ponderosa pine sites, cattle were released prior to the first egg dates of nearly all nests, whereas cattle did not arrive in the mixed-conifer and true fir sites until about the middle of the laying period (Fig. 2). Cowbirds arrived only after livestock release in the ponderosa pine sites, and did not begin laying until about two weeks later (Fig. 2a). In the mixed conifer sites, cowbirds arrived just prior to livestock release, and the only parasitized brood was coincident with livestock release (Fig. 2b.). While there does not appear to be a close connection between cattle on-date and cowbird laying date, cowbirds are rare and do not regularly breed in areas where food sources (associated with cattle) are not available until late in the breeding season.

The second hypothesis, that host abundance

TABLE 2.   BROWN-HEADED COWBIRD ABUNDANCE, HOST SPECIES RICHNESS, AND HOST ABUNDANCE (SE) IN FOUR FOREST TYPES

	Ponderosa pine	Mixed conifer	True fir	Lodgepole pine
Cowbird abundance	7.3 (0.8)	0.9 (0.3)	0	0
Species richness				
14 Sierran hosts	10.1 (0.5)	11.0 (0.2)	7.8 (0.2)	4.9 (0.4)
All Sierran hosts	12.1 (0.9)	13.6 (0.3)	9.9 (0.3)	6.2 (0.5)
All passerines	28.6 (1.4)	26.6 (1.1)	22.0 (0.9)	17.2 (0.6)
Host Abundance[a]				
14 Sierran hosts	212.7 (16.5)	261.0 (16.1)	211.8 (11.5)	151.7 (13.1)
All Sierran hosts	220.5 (17.6)	292.0 (20.0)	227.2 (14.3)	159.7 (14.0)
All passerines	396.9 (26.8)	387.8 (27.5)	327.6 (23.8)	263.8 (20.9)

Notes: The 14 Sierran hosts include species parasitized by cowbirds in this study and the study by Verner and Ritter (1983). "All Sierran hosts" included all confirmed Sierran host species (Table 1). Common Ravens were excluded from the passerine group.
[a] Mean total count per site per year, N = 12 (3 years × 4 sites).

and richness influenced cowbird abundance, was also supported by the data. Host abundances and richness across the four forest types are given in Table 2. Species richness was a better predictor of cowbird abundance than summed species abundance (Table 3), and adding abundance did not significantly improve the model. Models including all passerine species were better predictors of cowbird abundance than models including only known host species (Table 3). The best model, in terms of goodness of fit and significance, included richness of all passerine species and year (Table 3; Fig. 3). Outliers from that model reveal that richness of all passerines tended to underestimate cowbird abundance at lower elevations and to overestimate it at higher elevations (Fig 3), providing further evidence for an elevation effect. (Estimated equations available from K. Purcell)

DISCUSSION

Cowbird abundance was related to both the timing of livestock release and the number of passerine species. These hypotheses are not mutually exclusive and both may be important influences on the observed patterns of higher abundance of cowbirds and higher rates of brood parasitism at lower elevations. Of course, even a highly significant statistical model cannot imply cause and effect, and we do not rule out the possibility that other factors may contribute to the observed patterns.

Other studies have found that cowbird abundance or parasitism rates were related to host densities (Barber and Martin 1997, Evans and Gates 1997, Tewksbury et al. *this volume*). Donovan et al. (1997) found that cowbird abundance was positively associated with host abundance

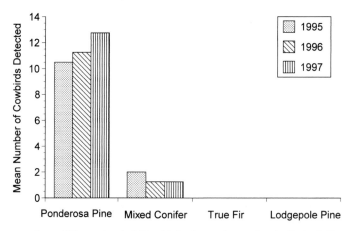

FIGURE 1.   Mean number of Brown-headed Cowbirds detected per plot (unlimited distance) in four forest types from 1995–1997. N = 8 plots in 1995 and 16 in 1996 and 1997.

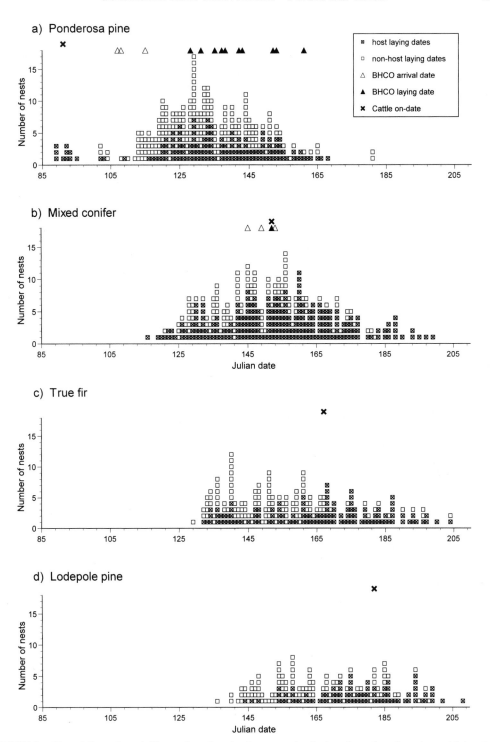

FIGURE 2. Host (all confirmed Sierran hosts) and other passerine laying dates (non hosts), cowbird arrival and laying dates, and cattle on-dates for the four forest types from 1995–1997. Laying dates for hosts, other passerines, and cowbirds represent specific nests and represent all attempts. Cowbird arrival dates are the earliest date cowbirds were recorded in a forest type each year. Cattle on-dates are the date that cows are released onto grazing allotments annually. The cattle on-date for the lodgepole pine sites represents 10 cow/calf pairs released on 1 July (Julian date = 182) within 7 km of two of the four plots only in 1997.

TABLE 3.   POISSON REGRESSION ANALYSIS OF BIRD SPECIES RICHNESS AND ABUNDANCE ON BROWN-HEADED COW-
BIRD ABUNDANCE

		dev/df[a]	Chi-square	P
Species richness				
14 Sierran hosts	richness	3.96	12.19	0.001
	year		7.15	0.067
All Sierran hosts	richness	4.39	7.59	0.006
	year		4.17	0.244
All passerines	richness	2.24	49.54	0.000
	year		39.34	0.000
Abundance[b]				
14 Sierran hosts	abundance	5.22	0.60	0.438
	year		0.82	0.845
All Sierran hosts	abundance	5.30	0.07	0.798
	year		0.93	0.818
All passerines	abundance	3.23	23.18	0.000
	year		19.30	0.000

[a] Deviance/df ratio is the dispersion parameter. This value indicates the goodness of fit of the model and should be close to 1.
[b] Total count per plot per year.

in core habitats but negatively associated with host abundance in edge habitats. S. Rothstein (pers. comm.) argues that parasitism rates should be more closely related to richness because individual species have a distinct breeding "pulse," resulting in more pulses and a longer period of high availability of host nests for cowbirds when many potential species are present. In eastern Sierran sites, S. Rothstein (pers. comm.) also found that richness of passerine species predicted cowbird abundance better than the number of individuals.

Elevation, per se, is not an impediment to cowbirds if they have supplemental food sources. Rothstein et al. (1980) reported that cowbirds were ubiquitous over most or all of the Sierra Nevada, but most of their study sites were close to human influences such as roads, towns, campgrounds, and pack stations. Verner and Ritter (1983) found that cowbird abundance in the

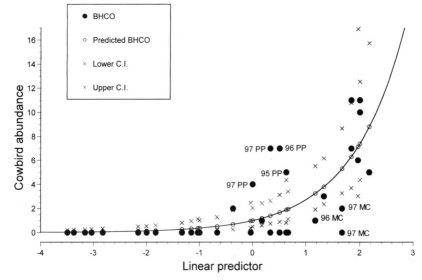

FIGURE 3.   Plot of cowbird abundance (BHCO), predicted cowbird abundance (predicted BHCO), and upper and lower confidence limits on the linear predictor for the Poisson regression of cowbird abundance on richness of all passerine species. Outliers are labeled by forest type (PP = ponderosa pine, MC = mixed conifer) and year of census.

Sierra National Forest was positively related to proximity to human disturbance and negatively related to elevation. Sampling mountain meadows, they found that remote meadows without cattle did not have cowbirds, whereas meadows close to supplemental food sources did. Because most of their high-elevation sites were also far from pack stations and other livestock, they concluded that the negative correlation with elevation was spurious. Our high-elevation study sites were not in locations where we expected cowbirds to occur because no pack stations or livestock were nearby. Livestock at high elevations, if they occurred at all, were brought in too late for the cowbirds to use them as a focal point for foraging to promote reproduction. It thus appears that distance to food sources, timing of food sources, host species richness, and elevation are all influences on cowbird abundance in the Sierra Nevada.

Does this level of parasitism impact population viability for any species studied? Warbling Vireos, Cassin's Vireos, and Black-throated Gray Warblers had parasitism rates of 25% or greater (Table 1). Compared to parasitism rates in fragmented landscapes in the Midwest (Robinson et al. 1995b; S. Robinson, pers. comm.), the levels of cowbird parasitism we observed are not high, suggesting that parasitism is probably not a problem for these species, especially if they are double-brooded. Rothstein et al. (1980), Verner and Ritter (1983), and Verner and Rothstein (1988) suggested that Warbling Vireos might be significantly impacted by brood parasitism in certain localities. Warbling Vireos in this study had the highest parasitism rates in ponderosa pine sites, although the sample size was small (Table 1). Because they are most abundant in mixed-conifer stands, where brood parasitism rates were low, productivity of populations there is probably adequate to sustain their numbers in the Sierra Nevada, especially in areas ≥7 km from feeding sources. Cassin's Vireos are abundant in both ponderosa pine and mixed conifer forests. Parasitism rates were low in mixed-conifer forests (Table 1), suggesting that viable populations may exist in this forest type in areas free or nearly free of cowbirds. Black-throated Gray Warblers breed in ponderosa pine forests and lower-elevation oak types, but they occur only rarely above 1830 m (Verner and Boss 1980). Most populations are probably exposed to cowbird parasitism. Black-throated Gray Warblers deserve further monitoring to determine if they are significantly impacted by cowbird parasitism in the Sierra Nevada.

Although we found that cowbird parasitism rates for most species nesting in this portion of the Sierra Nevada are not high, cowbirds are still a relatively new addition to the avifauna there, and they bear continued watching as cowbird numbers have not stabilized. Based on point-count data from both the western and eastern slopes of the Sierra Nevada, cowbird numbers decreased between the late 1970s and the early 1990s (S. Rothstein, pers. comm.). The decline could have occurred at any time during that period, and may or may not be continuing. The elevational pattern for cowbird abundance and rates of parasitism that we found has not been previously reported. The proximate cues for cowbird settling appear to be related to both the timing of livestock release and species richness, although the latter could also be an ultimate factor if cowbirds are evolutionarily tied to their hosts. This does not seem to be the case, as richness of all passerine species was a better indicator of cowbird abundance than was host richness. Further research to identify the relative importance of each of these variables will need to involve the manipulation of cattle on-dates in relation to cowbird arrival and laying dates, and the laying dates of host species.

ACKNOWLEDGMENTS

We would like to thank the large flock of field assistants who helped collect data for this study: K. E. Bagne, K. K. Bush, D. J. Cubanski, S. W. Deal, D. A. Drynan, B. A. Gibson, J. R. Jacobson, J. P. Lindsey, K. M. Mazzocco, R. B. Miller, L. T. Nason, N. A Sherman, B. M. Nielsen, R. A. Steffensen, S. K. Sutton-Mazzocco, R. L. Swanberg, E. M. Talamantez, K. A. Thumlert, J. G. Turner, K. C. Weeks, M. E. Westehuebe, R. J. Young. The manuscript benefited from reviews by C. B. Goguen, S. Mori, S. I. Rothstein, and an anonymous reviewer.

Studies in Avian Biology No. 18:104–108, 1999.

SECTION II: THE BASIS FOR COWBIRD MANAGEMENT: HOST SELECTION, IMPACTS ON HOSTS, AND CRITERIA FOR TAKING MANAGEMENT ACTION

James N. M. Smith

THE PROBLEM

The Brown-headed Cowbird (*Molothrus ater*) uses many different hosts over its large range (Friedmann and Kiff 1985, Lowther 1993). Because of this fact, countless host populations are exposed to potential reproductive costs from cowbirds. The papers in this section deal with two key questions: (1) What are the magnitudes of these costs to specific host populations? (2) When is intervention necessary to protect vulnerable populations of hosts, and are there general rules of thumb to help managers decide that intervention is timely?

Before discussing these issues in more detail, I note that the costs imposed by cowbirds on hosts, and the occasional need to intervene to reduce these costs, are emotionally charged matters. To some managers of sensitive species (e.g., papers in Section III *this volume*), and to many members of the amateur birding community (Holmes 1993), cowbirds seem an obvious threat to populations of small songbirds, and one that can be readily ameliorated by trapping. However, four points in opposition to this view should be considered: first, the Brown-headed Cowbird is a native North American species (even though it has expanded its range greatly in the past) with certain intrinsic rights; second, the abundance of Brown-headed Cowbirds is low in areas of extensive forest; third, Brown-headed Cowbird numbers have recently declined over much of their range (Robinson et al. 1995a, Peterjohn et al. 1999, Wiedenfeld 1999); fourth, even where interactions with host individuals are strong, cowbirds may have little effect on host population dynamics (see below). Even people inclining to the view that cowbird impacts on host are often small (e.g., Rothstein and Robinson 1994), however, acknowledge that there are situations that justify strong management intervention.

ESTIMATING IMPACTS OF COWBIRD PARASITISM

THE RANGE OF COSTS IMPOSED BY COWBIRDS

Cowbirds impose a variety of costs on individual hosts (reviewed in Lorenzana and Sealy, this section): (1) egg removal (Sealy 1992) and (2) egg puncture (Peer and Sealy, this section), both of which can lead to desertion of clutches; (3) occasional nestling removal (Tate 1967); (4) destruction of entire clutches or broods of hosts (Scott and McKinney 1994; Averill-Murray et al., this section); (5) reduced hatching success of host eggs (Peer and Bollinger 1999; Peer and Sealy, this section); (6) reduced survival of host young (Payne 1977, May and Robinson 1985, Payne and Payne 1998; Sedgwick and Iko, Chace and Cruz, this section); (7) increased energetic expenditure while rearing broods of nestlings and fledglings containing cowbirds (Smith and Merkt 1980, Woodward 1983) and perhaps consequent delays in renesting; (8) reduced post-fledging survival (Whitfield and Sogge, Sedgwick and Iko, this section); (9) reduced adult survival (Sedgwick and Iko, this section) and (10) reduced future fecundity (Lorenzana and Sealy, this section).

Brood parasitism always imposes costs on host individuals that get parasitized, but parasitism does not necessarily have any effect on the dynamics of host populations. Failure to appreciate this fact explains much of the lack of understanding between advocates and opponents of killing cowbirds in control programs. Costs due to parasitism, however, are likely to have consequences for populations if average reproductive success per host is already near the threshold level required to replace adult mortality in the absence of parasitism. If, on the other hand, hosts are reproducing at well above the level needed to replace adults that die, and host numbers are regulated by site-dependent mechanisms such as limited breeding habitat (Rodenhouse et al. 1997), parasitism merely removes host individuals that would otherwise emigrate or die before reproducing. Finally, host populations experiencing poor reproductive success because of frequent parasitism may remain stable because they are rescued by immigration from healthy populations elsewhere (Smith et al. 1996, Rogers et al. 1997). Only isolated populations cut off from immigrants are denied the possibility of rescue.

Three factors affect the cost of parasitism to a host population, and should therefore be considered when estimating this cost. First, the selection of hosts by cowbirds determines the degree to which particular hosts in a community are affected. Host selection by cowbirds is highly variable, with the same host species often experiencing different levels of use in different places (Robinson et al. 1995a). Second, costs to individual hosts are generally low where female cowbirds are scarce relative to hosts (<1% of a host community). Finally, some taxa are intrinsically more vulnerable to cowbird parasitism than others. Larger hosts such as Red-winged Blackbirds (*Agelaius phoeniceus*; Røskaft et al. 1990) and Wood Thrushes (*Hylocichla mustelina*; Hoover and Brittingham 1993) are resistant to parasitism and show little cost unless a nest receives two or more cowbird eggs (Røskaft et al. 1990, Trine in press). Other hosts, such as vireos, generally suffer severely even when parasitized with one cowbird egg (Grzybowski et al. 1986; papers by Averill-Murray et al., Kus, and Chace and Cruz, this section). I now consider the papers in this volume.

HOST SELECTION BY BROWN-HEADED AND BRONZED COWBIRDS

Knowledge of local host selection is critical to estimating costs due to parasitism, as only hosts that are parasitized frequently are likely to show any population cost. The extensive survey of Halterman et al. found that, on average only 23% of host species were ever parasitized in eight western National Parks. Among the parasitized species, many were parasitized only once. In host species where over 20 nests were found, parasitism barely exceeded 10% for the four most commonly parasitized species: Bell's Vireo (*Vireo bellii*), Warbling Vireo (*V. gilvus*), Wilson's Warbler (*Wilsonia pusilla*), and Song Sparrow (*Melospiza melodia*). These data suggest that cowbirds living at low to moderate densities in extensive natural areas like large parks mainly use a few favored and suitable host species. In support of this pattern, Ellison found minimal parasitism of four species of sparrows in southern coastal California, while the California Gnatcatcher (*Polioptila californica*) was parasitized frequently at the same site (Braden et al. 1997b). Peer and Sealy also found very little use of almost all suitable hosts by Brown-headed and Bronzed (*Molothrus aeneus*) cowbirds at a site in Texas where the two species are sympatric, and community-wide levels of parasitism were low. The Northern Cardinal (*Cardinalis cardinalis*) was preferentially parasitized (88% of all cases of parasitism) by both species of cowbird. Spautz found that the frequency of parasitism of Common Yellowthroats (*Geothlypis trichas*) varied strongly across habitats within a local area.

In contrast to these cases of strong host selection, Hahn et al. described seemingly unselective use of hosts in an area with dense cowbird populations and frequent multiple parasitism of several hosts (see Strausberger and Ashley 1997 for a similar pattern). They marked female cowbirds individually and radio-tracked some of these. Their paper also reports the first DNA-based analysis of host selection by cowbirds, and is pioneering because host selection is related to the use of space by individual cowbirds. As in a previous molecular study by Fleischer (1985), Hahn et al. found that individual cowbirds at Millbrook, NY, behaved as host generalists. In summary, host selection is still a poorly understood aspect of cowbird biology, but selectivity may vary inversely with the female cowbird: host ratio within a landscape.

COSTS OF PARASITISM TO HOST INDIVIDUALS

Several papers in this section found that cowbirds imposed high costs on host individuals. Chace and Cruz and Averill-Murray et al. report large costs for the Plumbeous Vireo (*Vireo plumbeus*) and Arizona Bell's Vireos (*V. bellii arizonae*), respectively. In contrast, other papers report lower costs to individuals. Halterman et al. found that none of the many host species that they studied in eight western National Parks were parasitized frequently enough to reach their threshold (30% of nests parasitized) of concern about the population effects of parasitism. Whitfield and Sogge and Greene found generally high but spatially variable frequencies of parasitism across several study sites for Willow Flycatchers (*Empidonax traillii*) and Lazuli Buntings (*Passerina amoena*), respectively. At some sites and years, all the bunting nests that Greene found were parasitized. These small hosts seldom rear any of their own young when a cowbird egg hatches in their nests.

Most estimates of individual costs, including many of those found here, are based on comparisons of fledgling production in parasitized and unparasitized nests, and this estimate is subject to biases (Lorenzana and Sealy). Only the paper by Sedgwick and Iko here measured the effect of parasitism on seasonal reproductive success, and made the useful comparison of production from parasitized nests, unparasitized nests, and all nests. Finally, Sedgwick and Iko calculated the first estimate of the lifetime cost of cowbird parasitism to individual hosts. Parasitized females raised 45% fewer young than unparasitized females over their life spans.

The meta-analysis by Lorenzana and Sealy is a welcome application of this technique to studies of brood parasitism. They summarized several of the most detailed studies of parasitism and calculated effect size for the numbers of host fledglings lost through parasitism. Losses varied in a coherent pattern with host size, with smaller hosts losing more fledglings per attempt than larger hosts.

COSTS OF PARASITISM TO HOST POPULATIONS

It is much more difficult to estimate the effects of parasitism on host populations than effects on host individuals. To estimate costs to populations requires a demographic analysis of the effects of parasitism on host population growth. The paper by Sedgwick and Iko in this section is one of the most detailed demographic analyses of the consequences of parasitism conducted to date. They found that an average frequency of parasitism of 23% was insufficient to have a detectable influence on Willow Flycatcher population growth in eastern Oregon. Their paper is also a benchmark for predicting the effects of higher levels of parasitism on endangered populations of Southwestern Willow Flycatchers (*Empidonax traillii extimus;* see Whitfield and Sogge, this section).

Most estimates of the population-level costs of parasitism have employed formal demographic modeling. The pioneering study by May and Robinson (1985) used difference equations to model population costs. Their results suggested that costs to populations could be severe, especially in short-lived hosts.

Current approaches usually employ matrix models (e.g., Greene, and Citta and Mills, this section), which are readily available in software packages for analyzing population viability. These models make simplifying assumptions (such as stable age distributions and density-independent vital rates) that may make field biologists uncomfortable, but they generate useful insights. Greene's stochastic and deterministic models both predict that isolated local populations of buntings are vulnerable to extinction when parasitized. In a second study of this host species, Greene et al. (this section) used landscape models to estimate the amount of habitat where the Lazuli Bunting may be exposed to frequent cowbird parasitism. They found that virtually the entire range of the bunting in the state of Montana consists of good cowbird habitat, and concluded that the buntings are regionally at risk of extinction. However, temporal and spatial variation in parasitism levels were both high (Greene, this section), and nearby source populations may reduce the risk of extinction below that suggested by the models, which did not incorporate dispersal.

In a novel use of matrix models, Citta and Mills explore how cowbird control options affect population growth in cowbirds. They found several interesting results. First, cowbird population growth is very sensitive to the survival rate of cowbird eggs in host nests. Second, kill-

ing adult cowbirds in the breeding season does little to reduce cowbird numbers in the future, an empirical result found by most cowbird removal programs. Modeling suggests that removals outside the breeding season would be more effective at reducing cowbird population growth, but Citta and Mills consider winter removals to be impractical because of the high dispersal capability of the cowbird (see also Rothstein and Cook in press). Finally, the costly management practice of removing cowbird eggs from host nests (see Kus, this section) may do little to reduce cowbird population growth. Citta and Mills also note that habitat alteration may be a more effective way of managing cowbirds than removal programs (see also papers in section III, *this volume*).

The models in this section reveal that we still lack reliable estimates of some key demographic parameters needed to model the impacts of parasitism reliably. The most difficult parameter to estimate is juvenile survival after fledging. Even the careful work of Sedgwick and Iko found that local juvenile survival was far too low (0.11) to fill local territorial vacancies, presumably because open Willow Flycatcher populations in Oregon exchange dispersers frequently. Higher estimates of juvenile survival are available for island populations where water barriers frustrate dispersal. The mean proportion of juvenile Song Sparrows surviving from 30 days to breeding age on Mandarte Island, BC, was 0.37 (N = 15 years, Arcese et al. 1992). Such estimates, however, may not apply well to open populations on the mainland. Until we have the methods to measure juvenile dispersal and survival accurately in the field, all population models of the effects of parasitism will have considerable uncertainty associated with their predictions.

A final way to estimate population and community-level costs is by manipulative experiment. De Groot et al. showed that trapping female cowbirds markedly reduced the frequency of local nest failure in the Song Sparrow, but trapping did not increase numbers of breeding sparrows the next year (M. J. Taitt and J. N. M. Smith, unpubl. data). Costs to a host population may be higher than those calculated from differential production of fledglings from parasitized and unparasitized nests, if cowbirds commonly induce total nest failure in a species, as they seem to in the Song Sparrow (De Groot et al.; Arcese and Smith, in press). There are additional reasons to think that cowbirds contribute to source-sink dynamics in this species in the Pacific Northwest (Smith et al. 1996, Rogers et al. 1997). Data are needed to test if cowbirds markedly increase rates of total nest failure in species other than the Song Sparrow. Until it is confirmed that cowbirds frequently depredate nests in a range of host species, De Groot et al.'s result should not be used to justify broad-scale cowbird removal programs. Appropriate data can be obtained from pilot removal programs or by comparing sites with variable abundance of cowbirds (Arcese and Smith in press).

De Groot et al. also report the first systematic attempt to measure community-wide impacts of cowbirds. They used a long-running cowbird removal program to test the idea that cowbirds alter quantitative patterns of host abundance in communities. Such effects are apparently present, but relatively weak, in pine forests of the Lower Peninsula of Michigan.

Two types of management decisions should flow from accurate assessments of population costs that are due to cowbirds. First, new habitat restoration or cowbird removal programs should be initiated to reduce newly recognized and severe population costs. Second, if cowbird pressure on a host population is low, or has decreased below a threshold of concern (see below), any management action already in progress should be scaled down so that scarce funds are matched to current conservation priorities. The Southwestern Willow Flycatcher population on the South Fork of the Kern River (Whitfield and Sogge, this section; Whitfield et al., section III; Whitfield in press, Rothstein and Cook in press) may be a case of the latter type. Despite several years of cowbird trapping, and consequent large reductions in the local frequency of parasitism, there has been little recovery of flycatcher numbers. Despite the lack of a population response at the South Fork Kern River, cowbird control efforts to protect this subspecies elsewhere are being expanded (Rothstein and Cook in press).

De Groot et al.'s study is also of interest in this context. Costs of parasitism to individual Kirtland's Warblers (*Dendroica kirtlandii*) were high before 1972 (Walkinshaw 1983), and led to the initiation of a 26-year cowbird removal program to protect the warbler population (De-Capita in press). De Groot found that trapping was remarkably effective and removed virtually all cowbirds locally. However, she found only 0.016 female cowbirds per suitable host (De Groot, unpubl. point count data) in jack pine (*Pinus banksiana*) habitat in Michigan > 10 km distant from trapping areas. This value is low enough to suggest that cowbirds are no longer abundant enough regionally to pose a serious threat to the warbler population. Cowbird numbers have declined in the region since 1960 (Peterjohn et al. in press) and it may be time to cease killing cowbirds in part of the Kirtland's Warbler's breeding habitat. Such an action

would test whether current cowbird removal programs to protect the warbler are still needed and would be timely, given recent suggestions that winter habitat, not reproductive output, limits warbler numbers (Haney et al. 1998).

RULES OF THUMB FOR MAKING MANAGEMENT DECISIONS

One rule of thumb used in this section is that parasitism is of concern (and a host population may need protective management) when the frequency of parasitism exceeds 30% (Halterman et al.). This rule originates from a paper by Mayfield (1977), who also noted in the same paper that Ovenbirds (*Seiurus aurocapillus*) reproduced well despite 50% parasitism. It is of interest that only two of the papers in this section (Averill-Murray et al. and Chace and Cruz) reported average frequencies of parasitism of over 50% across a region. Recent simulations by Grzybowski and Pease (in press) have revealed that the relationship between percent parasitism and seasonal reproductive success (seasonal fecundity) of hosts is complex, and that 30% of nests parasitized is probably much too low to be a threshold of concern in most populations.

I therefore close with a suggested rule of thumb for managers to consider when contemplating action to reduce the costs of cowbird parasitism. I choose what might seem to be a high threshold for four reasons. First, there are few good examples of severe costs of parasitism to host populations (as opposed to high costs to host individuals, which are frequent). Second, some recent cases where moderate to high costs to individuals have been studied in detail in the field, they have had little or no effect on host populations (Smith and Arcese 1994, Rogers et al. 1997; Sedgwick and Iko, this section). Third, simulations by Grzybowski and Pease (in press) suggest that passerines can often tolerate frequencies of parasitism exceeding 50%. Finally, two studies where parasitism lowered mean host productivity so markedly that local populations were sinks (Robinson et al. 1995b, Rogers et al. 1997) reported frequencies of parasitism of 65–95%. My suggested rule of thumb is:

Managers should consider initiating cowbird management programs when the frequency of parasitism in a sample of 30 or more nests gathered in a locality in each of two or more years, consistently exceeds 60%.

Only one study in this section (Averill-Murray et al.) meets this criterion. It may be no coincidence that the Arizona Bell's Vireo that they studied is a race of the only cowbird host that has shown consistent and large increases in local numbers after effective cowbird removal (Kus, this section; Griffith and Griffith in press; but see Rothstein and Cook in press).

My suggested rule, however, should be modified if one or more of the following additional factors applies. If one or more of factors 1–5 below apply, a lower threshold of concern, perhaps > 50%, is appropriate.

1. The habitat of the host is so poor, or so restricted in extent, that even unparasitized females are reproducing poorly.

2. The host species belongs to a particularly vulnerable taxon (e.g., vireos).

3. The population of concern is spatially isolated and appropriately listed as threatened or endangered (Kus, and Whitfield and Sogge, this section).

4. The host's local or regional population has been in a prolonged state of decline (e.g., Whitfield and Sogge, this section).

5. There is frequent multiple parasitism (e.g., Hahn et al. this section).

If, however, factors 6–8 below apply, they would raise the threshold of concern.

6. There is a period early in the year when the host can reproduce in the absence of cowbirds, as often seen in birds of the U.S. southwest (e.g., Finch 1983; Braden et al. 1997b; Ellison, this section).

7. The host has a widespread distribution and generally healthy populations in much of its range, so that local populations performing poorly are likely to be rescued by immigration (Robinson et al. 1995b, Brawn and Robinson 1996, Rogers et al. 1997).

8. Host numbers are increasing locally in the absence of management action.

A final and fairly common situation is that both brood parasitism and nest depredation are frequent locally (e.g., Brawn and Robinson 1996, Rogers et al. 1997). Since cowbirds can behave like nest predators (see above), there is a possibility that cowbird management may solve both problems simultaneously. In other cases, predator management, not cowbird control, may be the appropriate management action.

In conclusion, the papers in this section offer many insights into host selection by cowbirds and the costs of parasitism. I encourage readers to distinguish costs severe enough to lower numbers of adult hosts in the future, which are of considerable management significance, from those that merely reduce the breeding success of individual hosts without changing host numbers the following year. Managers will generally need detailed local data on host populations and parasitism levels to make wise decisions. Even with such data, careful judgement will still be needed in deciding when to initiate or terminate cowbird management programs.

AKNOWLEDGMENTS

I thank K. De. Groot, A. Lindholm, M. Morrison, J. Rotenberry, and J. Shapiro for helpful comments on a draft, and C. Ortega for useful discussions.

Studies in Avian Biology No. 18:109–120, 1999.

COWBIRD PARASITISM OF ARIZONA BELL'S VIREOS (*VIREO BELLII ARIZONAE*) IN A DESERT RIPARIAN LANDSCAPE: IMPLICATIONS FOR COWBIRD MANAGEMENT AND RIPARIAN RESTORATION

ANNALAURA AVERILL-MURRAY, SUELLEN LYNN, AND MICHAEL L. MORRISON

Abstract. We determined microhabitat characteristics associated with both nest-site selection by the Arizona Bell's Vireo (*Vireo bellii arizonae*) and discovery of vireo nests by Brown-headed Cowbirds (*Molothrus ater*) on the Bill Williams River National Wildlife Refuge, Arizona, during the 1994 and 1995 breeding seasons. Nest sites had greater foliage cover than random sites, particularly in the low canopy layer (0.7–4.5 m high). This may have concealed nests and/or parental activity from predators and brood parasites. The probability of nest discovery by cowbirds was a function of distance to a mature cottonwood or willow tree. Nests that were 5–12 m from a mature cottonwood or willow tree were 4.5 times more likely to be discovered by cowbirds than nests with a mature cottonwood or willow tree within 5 m. However, nests that were 12–30 m and >30 m from a mature cottonwood or willow tree were 1.3 and 3.2 times less likely to be discovered by cowbirds, respectively, than nests with a mature cottonwood or willow tree within 5 m. We also conducted point counts and monitored parasitization rates and nesting success in 1994, 1995, and 1997. The proportion of Bell's Vireo nests parasitized ranged from 88% to 93% from late April to early July 1994 and 1995. Parasitization rates in 1997 were 38% for the entire breeding season and 58% for nests initiated after 29 April. The lower parasitization rate in 1997 may be related to several factors, including the initiation of cowbird control on the refuge in 1996 and decreased forage availability for Brown-headed Cowbirds with the temporary cessation of ranching operations upriver. The leading cause of nest failure was nest abandonment in 1994 and 1995, and predation in 1997.

Key Words: Arizona Bell's Vireo, parasitization rates, riparian restoration, vegetation management, *Vireo bellii arizonae*.

Habitat loss and high parasitization rates by Brown-headed Cowbirds (*Molothrus ater*) are often related factors in the decline of songbird populations (e.g., Terborgh 1989, Rosenberg et al. 1991, Rothstein 1994). While cowbird parasitism has been implicated in the near extirpation of several species, including Least Bell's Vireo (*Vireo bellii pusillus*; Franzreb 1990) and Kirtland's Warbler (*Dendroica kirtlandii*; Walkinshaw 1972), habitat loss is the ultimate cause behind these population declines. Cowbird control via live-decoy trapping has been used successfully to manage small populations of neotropical migratory songbirds with narrow geographic ranges (Robinson et al. 1993). However, habitat restoration on the breeding grounds through vegetation management may be a better option for permanently reducing parasitization rates and increasing nest success (Laymon 1987, Robinson et al. 1993, Larison et al. 1998, Staab and Morrison *this volume*).

The relationship between vegetation features, Brown-headed Cowbird abundance, and brood parasitization rates is well documented. However, past studies have primarily focused on landscape-level effects, such as total forest area, distance to edge, and level of habitat fragmentation (e.g., Robinson 1992, Paton 1994). Few studies have addressed the relationship between

microhabitat features at nest sites and brood parasitization rates (Robinson et al. 1995a), and few have considered the potential this information has as a management tool.

Our study focused on identifying microhabitat characteristics associated with (1) nest-site selection by Arizona Bell's Vireos (*Vireo bellii arizonae*) and (2) discovery of vireo nests by Brown-headed Cowbirds in the lower Colorado River Valley, Arizona. Many riparian-obligate songbirds have experienced population declines in this region since the turn of the century (Rosenberg et al. 1991). The Arizona Bell's Vireo (hereafter, Bell's Vireo) has declined dramatically since the 1950s and is currently listed as endangered at the state level by the California Department of Fish and Game (Rosenberg et al. 1991).

Bell's Vireos have been heavily parasitized in the lower Colorado River Valley since the early 1900s (Brown 1903, Grinnell 1914) without experiencing population declines until recently (Rosenberg et al. 1991). The destruction of gallery cottonwood (*Populus fremontii*)-willow (*Salix gooddingii*) forests in the valley since the turn of the century has likely increased the vulnerability of the Bell's Vireo to cowbird parasitism (Rosenberg et al. 1991). With the exception of the cottonwood-willow and mesquite

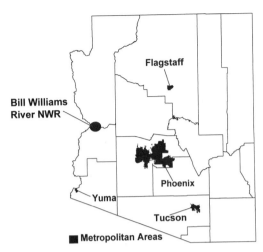

FIGURE 1. Bill Williams River National Wildlife Refuge, Mohave and La Paz Counties, Arizona.

(*Prosopis* spp.) woodlands of the Bill Williams River drainage, the Bell's Vireo is no longer a common summer resident in the lower Colorado River Valley. To restore native vegetation (i.e., cottonwood, willow, and mesquite), revegetation efforts were initiated along the lower Colorado River in the 1970s (Rosenberg et al. 1991). As of 1997, few bird species nested in these revegetation sites, and those that did experienced high parasitization and predation rates (A. Averill-Murray and S. Lynn, unpubl. data). Therefore, identification of vegetation features in cottonwood-willow forest associated with nests discovered by cowbirds may be useful in designing and managing revegetation sites.

STUDY AREA

Our study was conducted on the Bill Williams River National Wildlife Refuge (BWRNWR) located in the Sonoran Desert, La Paz and Mohave counties, Arizona (Fig. 1). The Bill Williams River is one of the principal tributaries of the lower Colorado River and is the site of the largest remaining stand of cottonwood-willow forest in the lower Colorado River Valley. However, the cottonwood-willow community has been altered by extended flooding, fire, and the introduction of saltcedar (*Tamarix ramosissima*; Rosenberg et al. 1991). Though natural regeneration of cottonwoods and willows occurs along the Bill Williams River drainage, few old trees remain.

Common understory species of the cottonwood-willow forest included saltcedar, mesquite (*Prosopis glandulosa*), arrowweed (*Pluchea sericea*), *Baccharis veminosa*, and cattail (*Typha latifolia*). Surrounding vegetation was typical of the lower Colorado River biome; desert uplands were characterized by creosote bush (*Larrea tridentata*), cholla cacti (*Opuntia* spp.), and saguaro (*Carnegiea gigantea*), and desert arroyos were characterized by ironwood (*Olneya tesota*), catclaw acacia (*Acacia greggii*), paloverde (*Cercidium* spp.), mesquite, and quail bush (*Atriplex lentiformis*). Several non-functional ranches bordered the riparian forest of the Bill Williams River, including one that temporarily ceased operations in 1994. These areas were typified by fallow fields bordered by a narrow band of mesquite trees.

METHODS

AVIAN COMMUNITY SURVEYS

We conducted 5-min point counts at 200-m intervals along transects established in the riparian zone of the Bill Williams River. We surveyed 83 point-count stations in 1994 and 1995 and 45 point-count stations in 1997. Data presented here are for point-count stations that were surveyed in all three years. We used the variable circular plot method (Reynolds et al. 1980) to estimate the abundance of Brown-headed Cowbirds, Bell's Vireos, and other cowbird host species. We truncated data at 60 m to increase the chance of detecting most birds while decreasing the chance of double counting birds at neighboring point-count stations. We conducted three surveys between late April and late June in 1994, 1995, and 1997. We calculated the ratio of Brown-headed Cowbirds to suitable hosts, defined as species that accept cowbird eggs and feed their young insect diets (Rogers et al. 1997).

RATES OF BROOD PARASITIZATION AND NEST SUCCESS

We searched for Bell's Vireo nests from late April to early July 1994 and 1995 and early April through June 1997. In 1994 and 1995, we searched for nests within 50 m of point-count transects, concentrating on areas where Bell's Vireos were heard singing during early-morning surveys. Additional nest-searching transects were established in areas characterized primarily by mesquite. In 1997, we established nine 5-ha nest-searching plots along point-count transects. We located nests by systematically searching vegetation and observing adult behavior (Martin and Guepel 1993). We monitored nests approximately every five days to determine brood parasitization rates and nest failure.

We calculated brood parasitization rates as the percent of all nesting attempts that were discovered by cowbirds. We considered a nest "discovered" if we found one or more cowbird eggs or nestlings in the nest or cowbird eggs on the ground below the nest. We defined successful brood parasitism as those instances in which the cowbird egg was deposited early in a vireo's nesting attempt (i.e., egg-laying or early incubation) and unsuccessful brood parasitism as those instances in which the cowbird egg was deposited in the nest during late incubation or subsequent to hatching. We considered a brood unparasitized if the nesting attempt did not fail prior to incubation and there were no cowbirds in the nest. This assumption is probably valid because (1) host species with small bills, such as Bell's Vireos, probably do not eject cowbird eggs due to the large cost associated with this behavior (Rohwer and Spaw 1988), and (2) nests found during the brooding stage often contained three or four vireo nestlings (a full clutch size). We calculated the intensity of brood parasitization as the average number of cowbird eggs per discovered nest.

We calculated nest success as the proportion of nests that successfully fledged at least one host young. We assumed that a nest was successful if fledglings were seen near the nest, if the nest had a flattened rim and fecal matter on the edge, or if the nest had large nestlings close to fledging age at the time of the last nest check and there was no subsequent evidence of depredation. We assumed that the number of fledglings was equivalent to the number of nestlings present in the nest at the last visit, as long as these nestlings were within a few days of fledging. We attributed nest failure to complete predation (loss of entire clutch or brood), parasitization (raising only cowbird young), abandonment following partial predation (in nests with or without cowbird eggs), abandonment of nests containing only cowbird eggs (no evidence of partial predation), abandonment during nest building, and unknown factors (Rogers et al. 1997).

We calculated parasitization and nest success rates in 1997 for (1) all nests and (2) nests found after 29 April to allow comparison with 1994 and 1995 data. Cowbird control was initiated on BWRNWR in 1996. In 1997, we trapped cowbirds on two-thirds of the nest-searching plots, and we addled cowbird eggs on half of these plots. Ongoing research will examine the relationship between parasitism, nest success, and varying levels of cowbird control.

VEGETATION SAMPLING AT NEST AND
RANDOM SITES

We measured vegetation characteristics associated with nest sites at the end of the 1994 and 1995 breeding seasons to quantify differences between nests that were and were not discovered by cowbirds. The location of each nest was broadly classified as being in either the cottonwood-willow riparian zone or the mesquite woodland-desert wash zone. We measured specific vegetation features at the nest and within a 5-m radius circular plot centered on the ground below the nest (Appendix; Martin and Roper 1988). We also measured vegetation characteristics within randomly placed 5-m radius circular plots to determine which vegetation features were associated with nest-site selection for Bell's Vireos. We examined nest-site selection within the general vegetation types associated with Bell's Vireo nests by stratifying random plots among the nest-searching transects, one random plot per nest plot (Martin and Roper 1988). We established a random plot for each nest found on a transect, including nests of other bird species, resulting in a larger number of random plots than Bell's Vireo nest plots. We located plots by generating two random numbers, the first of which determined the distance along the transect and the second of which determined the distance away from the transect (0–50 m) at which to place each plot. We spun a compass to determine which side of the transect the plot would be located. On random plots we measured a subset of the variables measured at nest plots: distance to nearest shrub, distance to nearest mature tree, canopy cover, ground cover, and vertical height diversity within a 5-m radius circle (Appendix).

We calculated shrub and tree dispersion, plant species composition by height class, percent canopy and ground cover, and average nest concealment for use in vegetation analyses (Appendix). We used logistic regression to build two models, a model that would discriminate between nest and random sites (hereafter, nest-site selection model) and a model that would discriminate between nests discovered and undiscovered by cowbirds (hereafter, parasitism model). For the purpose of the model, we limited "discovered" nests to those containing successfully parasitized broods; "undiscovered" nests included those nests in which no cowbird eggs or nestlings were found and those containing unsuccessfully parasitized broods. We decided on this grouping because nests discovered by cowbirds late in a vireo's nesting attempt had a success rate closer to undiscovered nests than nests discovered by cowbirds early in a vireo's nesting attempt (Averill 1996). This grouping also lessened the disparity between sample sizes of discovered and undiscovered nests. Nests initiated before the onset of cowbird breeding were considered unavailable for brood parasitism and were not included in the parasitism model.

We screened vegetation variables with univariate analyses prior to logistic regression mod-

TABLE 1. PARASITIZATION RATES AND NESTING SUCCESS FOR THE BELL'S VIREO, BILL WILLIAMS RIVER NATIONAL WILDLIFE REFUGE, 1994–1995 AND 1997

Variable description	1994	1995	1997[a]
Number of nests studied	49	86	43 (26)
Proportion of nests discovered by cowbirds	0.88	0.93	0.38 (0.58)
Proportion of broods successfully parasitized	0.81	0.81	0.33 (0.54)
Cowbird eggs per discovered nest[b]	1.66 ± 0.83	1.94 ± 0.97	1.40 ± 0.63
Cowbird eggs per successfully parasitized brood[b]	1.75 ± 0.84	2.07 ± 0.98	1.46 ± 0.66
Size of unparasitized clutches[b]	3.50 ± 0.58	3.20 ± 0.45	3.62 ± 0.50
Size of parasitized clutches[b]	2.71 ± 0.92	2.25 ± 0.95	2.77 ± 0.93
Proportion of nests succeeding	0.11	0.11	0.66 (0.48)
Proportion of nests failing due to:			
Complete predation	0.31	0.22	0.16 (0.24)
Abandonment after partial predation in nests containing cowbird eggs	0.29	0.29	0.08 (0.14)
Abandonment with cowbird eggs in nest, no evidence of partial predation	0.13	0.15	0.03 (0.05)
Abandonment with only host eggs in nest, no evidence of partial predation	0.00	0.00	0.03 (0.00)
Abandonment during nest building	0.04	0.11	0.00
Raised only cowbird young	0.09	0.07	0.05 (0.10)
Unknown causes	0.03	0.05	0.00
Vireos fledged per nest[b]	0.31 ± 0.97	0.24 ± 0.78	1.41 ± 1.37 (1.00 ± 1.35)
Vireos fledged per successful nest[b]	2.80 ± 1.30	2.50 ± 0.93	2.29 ± 1.00 (2.44 ± 0.88)

[a] In 1997, nest-searching efforts began three weeks earlier than 1994–1995. The first number includes all nests found in 1997. The number in parentheses includes only nests found after 29 April, which is directly comparable to efforts in 1994–1995.
[b] Means ± SD.

eling (Hosmer and Lemeshow 1989). We tested for significant differences between (1) nest and random sites, and (2) discovered and undiscovered nests with the Chi-square test for categorical variables and the Mann-Whitney U test (corrected for ties) for continuous variables. The significance level for entry into logistic regression was set at 0.25 (Hosmer and Lemeshow 1989). Independent variables were also screened for high intercorrelation. Only one of each pair of variables with a Pearson's correlation coefficient $\geq |0.80|$ was selected for entry into the model. We used forward stepwise variable selection with variables entered into the model if the score statistic was <0.10 and removed from the model if the likelihood ratio was >0.11. There was a large disparity between sample sizes of discovered and undiscovered nests in the parasitism model. Therefore, we ran 50 logistic regression analyses by subsampling from the larger outcome category (i.e., discovered nests).

RESULTS

AVIAN COMMUNITY SURVEYS

In 1994–1995, the predominant songbird species in rank order of decreasing abundance were Brown-headed Cowbird, Yellow-breasted Chat (*Icteria virens*), Song Sparrow (*Melospiza melodia*), Abert's Towhee (*Pipilo aberti*), and Bell's Vireo. The ratio of Brown-headed Cow-

birds to suitable host species was 0.28. In 1997, the predominant songbird species in rank order of decreasing abundance were Yellow-breasted Chat, Bell's Vireo, Blue Grosbeak (*Guiraca caerulea*), Common Yellowthroat (*Geothlypis trichas*), and Verdin (*Auriparus flaviceps*). The ratio of Brown-headed Cowbirds to suitable host species was 0.07. Potential nest predators that were detected on point counts included Bewick's Wren (*Thryomanes bewickii*), Marsh Wren (*Cistothorus palustris*), Cactus Wren (*Campylorhynchus brunneicapillus*), Great-tailed Grackle (*Quiscalus mexicanus*), Greater Roadrunner (*Geococcyx californianus*), and Common Raven (*Corvus corax*).

RATES OF BROOD PARASITIZATION AND NEST SUCCESS

The proportion of Bell's Vireo nests discovered by cowbirds in 1994–1995 ranged from 88% to 93% (Table 1). The proportion of successfully parasitized broods was slightly lower (81%). However, this sample consisted mainly of nests initiated after April, with the earliest recorded parasitism event occurring on 2 May. In 1997, discovery rates were lower: 38% for all nests (including those initiated in early April) and 58% for nests found after 29 April. We found no cowbird eggs prior to 8 May in 1997. Fifty percent of discovered nests received more than one cowbird egg in 1994, and 61% received

TABLE 2.   RESULTS OF UNIVARIATE AND FORWARD STEPWISE LOGISTIC REGRESSION ANALYSES FOR BELL'S VIREO NEST-SITE SELECTION AND PARASITISM MODELS[a]

Variable	Mann-Whitney U		Logistic regression		
	U Statistic	P-value	Coeff. (B) ± SE	Wald statistic	P-value
Nest site selection model[b]					
Foliage cover, 0.7–4.5 m high	5377.5	<0.01	0.021 ± 0.005	16.28	<0.01
Total mesquite foliage cover	8122.5	<0.01	0.019 ± 0.005	14.36	<0.01
Saltcedar cover, 4.6–7.5 m high	7716.0	<0.01	0.022 ± 0.009	5.91	0.02
Mean distance to tree >8 cm dbh	7210.5	<0.01	−0.042 ± 0.022	3.66	0.06
Total saltcedar foliage cover	7689.5	<0.01	0.009 ± 0.005	3.11	0.08
Parasitism model[c]					
Distance to cottonwood or willow tree >8 cm dbh	514.0	0.02	−0.015 ± 0.006	5.47	0.02

[a] Variables that were included in forward stepwise logistic regression models.
[b] Model χ^2 = 76.01, P < 0.01.
[c] Model χ^2 = 6.09, P = 0.01.

multiple cowbird eggs in 1995, with an average of 1.66 and 1.94 cowbird eggs per nest in 1994 and 1995, respectively. In 1997, the percent of nests with multiple cowbird eggs was lower (33%).

Clutch size (i.e., the number of vireo eggs per clutch) was significantly lower in discovered than undiscovered nests in all but one year (1994: U = 16.0, P = 0.07; 1995: U = 40.5, P = 0.02; 1997: U = 46.0, P = 0.01; Table 1). Success rates were also significantly lower for parasitized broods in all but one year, despite the fact that we addled cowbird eggs in 40% of the parasitized broods in 1997 (Fisher's Exact Test; 1994: P = 0.08; 1995: P < 0.01; 1997: P < 0.01). All of the parasitized broods that successfully fledged vireo young in 1997 were located in nest-searching plots in which cowbird eggs were addled. The proportion of nests that fledged vireo young was very low in 1994 and 1995 compared to 1997, even if only nests initiated after 29 April are considered. The leading cause of nest failure in 1994 and 1995 was nest abandonment (approximately half of all nests were abandoned, either during nest building, egg laying, or incubation). The majority of abandoned nests appeared to be discovered and partially depredated by cowbirds prior to desertion. Complete predation was the leading cause of nest failure in 1997, accounting for 16% of nest loss (24% for nests found after 29 April). In 1994 and 1995, 31% and 22% of nests, respectively, failed due to complete predation.

NEST-SITE SELECTION MODEL

We measured vegetation at 129 Bell's Vireo nests and 154 random sites. Sixty-seven percent of nests were located in the cottonwood-willow riparian zone, and 33% were located in the mesquite-desert wash zone. Seven plant species were used as nest substrates: 52% of nests were

in saltcedar, 28% were in mesquite, 10% were in arrowweed, 6% were in cottonwood or willow trees, and the remaining 4% were in either *Baccharis* sp. or quail bush. Vegetation structure at nest and random plots was significantly different (P < 0.25) for 16 variables, all of which were used in the forward stepwise logistic regression procedure. These variables included distance to the closest shrub and mature tree; canopy and ground cover within 5 m; foliage cover in all height categories except >7.5 m; and cottonwood-willow, saltcedar, mesquite, arrowweed, and total shrub foliage cover within 5 m.

Five variables were significant predictors of nest-site selection (Table 2). These variables are listed in Table 2 in rank order of their relative contribution to the model. Nest sites had greater foliage cover in the low tree canopy layer (0.7–4.5 m high) than random sites. Nest sites were also characterized by greater mesquite and saltcedar foliage cover and a shorter average distance to a tree >8 cm dbh (Fig. 2).

PARASITISM MODEL

Vegetation structure at discovered and undiscovered nests was significantly different (P < 0.25) for ten variables, all of which were used in the forward stepwise logistic regression procedure (Table 3). Only one variable, distance to cottonwood or willow tree >8 cm dbh, met the criteria for entry into the model when all cases were considered. Nests discovered by cowbirds were generally closer to a mature cottonwood or willow tree than undiscovered nests (Fig. 3). When we transformed this continuous variable into a categorical variable based on quartile ranges (Hosmer and Lemeshow 1989), a specific pattern emerged. Nests that were 5–12 m from a mature cottonwood or willow tree were 4.5 times more likely to be discovered by cowbirds than nests with a mature cottonwood or willow

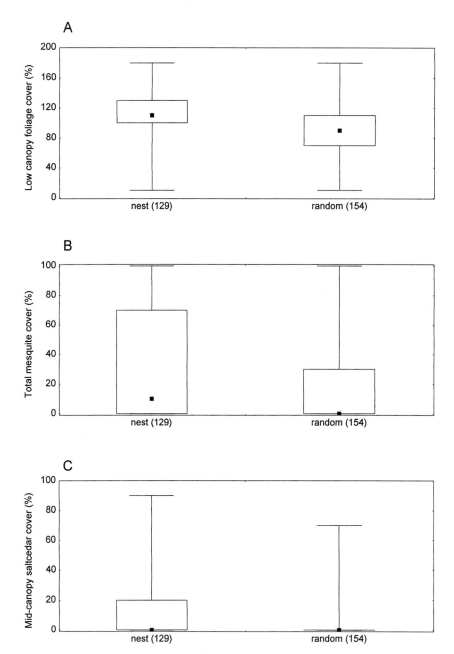

FIGURE 2.   Box and whisker plots for variables included in the nest-site selection model: (A) Percent foliage cover, 0.7–4.5 m high, within 5 m of nest; (B) Total mesquite foliage cover within 5 m of nest; (C) Saltcedar foliage cover, 4.6–7.5 m high, within 5 m of nest; (D) Mean distance to the closest tree >8 cm dbh; (E) and Total saltcedar foliage cover within 5 m of nest. Box and whiskers represent 25th and 75th percentile values and minimum and maximum values, respectively. Dark square represents median value. Figure continued next page.

tree within 5 m. However, nests that were 12–30 m and >30 m from a mature cottonwood or willow tree were 1.3 and 3.2 times less likely to be discovered, respectively, than nests with a mature cottonwood or willow tree within 5 m.

No nests that were placed within a cottonwood or willow tree were discovered by cowbirds, whereas 83% of nests in saltcedar, 88% of nests in mesquite, and 67% of nests in shrubs (arrow-weed, quail bush, and *Baccharis* sp.) were dis-

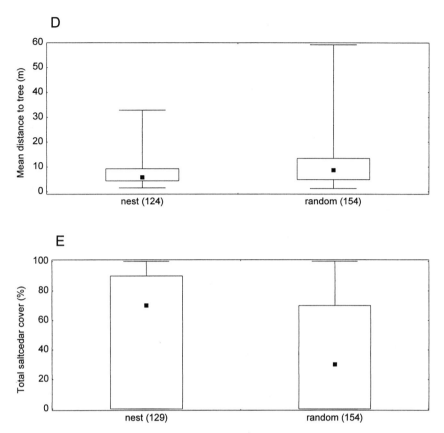

FIGURE 2.   Continued.

covered by cowbirds (χ^2 = 3.80, P = 0.28). Additionally, there was not a significant difference (Fisher's exact test, P = 0.41) in the proportion of nests discovered by cowbirds in the cottonwood-willow riparian zone (92%) and the mesquite-desert wash zone (89%).

When regression models were built by subsampling from the discovered nest category, all ten

TABLE 3.   VEGETATION VARIABLES USED IN LOGISTIC REGRESSION ANALYSES FOR BELL'S VIREO PARASITISM MODEL, BILL WILLIAMS RIVER NATIONAL WILDLIFE REFUGE, 1994–1995

Variable[a]	U statistic	P-value	Percent of LR models in which variable was included[b]
Distance to cottonwood or willow tree >8 cm dbh	514.0	0.02	36
Nest height	576.5	0.05	24
Average lateral concealment at nest	525.5	0.09	24
Total cottonwood and willow foliage cover	646.5	0.11	14
Total shrub foliage cover	639.0	0.12	10
Canopy cover within nest patch	632.5	0.14	18
Foliage cover, 0.0–0.6 m high	646.0	0.15	8
Mean distance to shrub	612.5	0.19	12
Cottonwood and willow cover, 4.6–7.5 m high	688.0	0.22	6
Cottonwood and willow cover, 0.7–4.5 m high	690.0	0.23	4

[a] Variables used in forward stepwise logistic regression modeling based on univariate screening at P < 0.25.
[b] Percent of forward stepwise logistic regression models in which variable was included when 50 analyses were run by subsampling from larger outcome group (successfully parasitized broods).

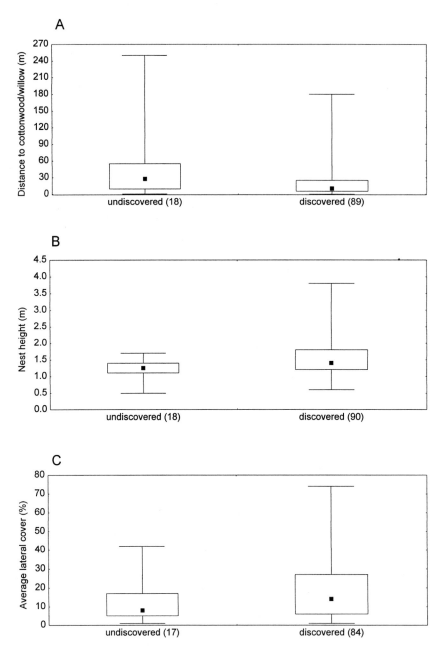

FIGURE 3. Box and whisker plots for variables included in >20% of the parasitism models built by subsampling: (A) Distance to the closest cottonwood or willow tree >8 cm dbh; (B) Nest height; and (C) Average lateral cover at the nest. For purposes of this model, "discovered" refers to nests that were found by cowbirds early in a vireo's nesting attempt (egg-laying or early incubation); "undiscovered" refers to nests that were never found by cowbirds or were found late in a vireo's nesting attempt (mid-incubation or later). See Fig. 2 legend for details on box and whisker plots.

vegetation structure variables were included in at least two models (Table 3). However, only three variables—distance to cottonwood or willow tree, nest height, and average lateral concealment at the nest—were included in more than 20% of the subsampled models. Nests discovered by cowbirds were placed higher and had greater lateral concealment than undiscovered nests (Fig. 3).

DISCUSSION

PARASITIZATION RATES AND NESTING SUCCESS

Years of high cowbird abundance: 1994–1995

The Brown-headed Cowbird was the most abundant passerine species on BWRNWR between late April and late June, 1994 and 1995. There were 11 suitable host species breeding on the refuge, and the ratio of cowbirds to suitable hosts was 0.28. Ratios above 0.10 have been associated with high levels of brood parasitism in other regions (Donovan et al. in press, Thompson et al. in press, cited in Rogers et al. 1997). On BWRNWR, 88–93% of Bell's Vireo nests found between late April and early July 1994 and 1995 had at least one cowbird egg or nestling, and over half of these had more.

Bell's Vireos typically arrive in the lower Colorado River Valley in mid-March and begin breeding in late March to early April (Rosenberg et al. 1991, A. Averill-Murray, pers. obs.). Therefore, parasitization and nest success rates in 1994 and 1995 are not representative of the entire breeding season (i.e., early-season nests and first brood attempts are under-represented). In 1997, the parasitization rate for late-season broods was 20% higher than the parasitization rate for the entire breeding season. This suggests that parasitization rates may also have been lower in April 1994 and 1995, before we started nest searching.

Parasitization rates along the Bill Williams River were high relative to other locales along the Colorado River. Brown (1994) reported parasitization rates of 7% for the Bell's Vireo (N = 57) in Grand Canyon National Park. On the other hand, parasitization rates $\geq$ 50% have also been documented for the Kirtland's Warbler (Walkinshaw 1983), Black-capped Vireo (*Vireo atricapillus*; Gryzbowski, unpubl. data, Tazik and Cornelius, unpubl. data, cited in Robinson et al. 1995a), and Least Bell's Vireo (Goldwasser et al. 1980, Franzreb 1989a) prior to cowbird control. These species breed in a wide range of habitats, ranging from jack pine (*Pinus banksiana*) forest to scrub vegetation to riparian woodland. However, all require or prefer early successional stages for breeding (Robinson et al. 1995a).

Bell's Vireos experienced low nesting success on BWRNWR between late April and early July, 1994 and 1995. Cowbird parasitism directly or indirectly accounted for the failure of approximately 50% of nests in 1994 and 1995. Barlow (1962) also reported that brood parasitism by Brown-headed Cowbirds was the primary cause of low nest success for Bell's Vireos. Approximately 43% of vireo nests along the Bill Williams River were abandoned shortly after they were discovered by cowbirds. Nest desertion is a common rejection behavior in small host species (Friedmann 1963, Graham 1988). Though nest abandonment may lower total reproductive success by limiting the number of broods a female successfully rears, this strategy may be preferable for small host species that incur a higher fitness by raising one unparasitized brood rather than two parasitized broods (Petit 1991). Bell's Vireos rarely fledge their own young from parasitized broods (Mumford 1952, A. Averill-Murray, pers. obs.). This may partly explain the high desertion rate of parasitized broods observed in this species.

Twenty-two to 31% of nests failed due to complete predation in 1994 and 1995. The majority of depredated nests were undisturbed (i.e., the nest was not missing or torn and the nest lining was not pulled up; A. Averill-Murray, unpubl. data) suggesting that snakes may be a common nest predator in this region. In fact, common kingsnakes (*Lampropeltis getula*) were seen near nests on more than one occasion.

Year of low cowbird abundance: 1997

In 1997, the ratio of Brown-headed Cowbirds to suitable host species was lower than 0.10, and this was correlated with lower parasitism rates on Bell's Vireos (38% of nests discovered by cowbirds, 58% of nests found after late April). The incidence of multiple parasitism was also substantially lower. Several factors may have contributed to the lower number of cowbirds on BWRNWR in 1997: (1) cowbird trapping efforts removed a total of 264 female cowbirds in 1996–1997; (2) temporary cessation of ranching operations upriver in 1994 may be limiting forage availability for cowbirds; and (3) unknown factors on the wintering grounds and during migration may be contributing to a decline in cowbird numbers. The shift in rank relative abundance of other avian species on the BWRNWR may be attributable, in part, to random variation and interobserver variability. In addition, the actual change in abundance of any particular host species relative to other host species between study years was small. For example, Bell's Vireos comprised 12% of the detections of suitable cowbird host species in 1994–1995 (0.50 vireos/point) and 15% of the detections in 1997 (0.53 vireos/point).

Nest success was high in 1997, 66% overall and 48% for nests found after 29 April. This is also high compared to values reported for passerine species in other studies. Martin (1992) reviewed published reports of nesting success for 32 species from 35 different studies or locations and found an average nest success of 44% based on fraction estimates (the number of successful nests divided by the total number of nests studied). Complete predation was the primary nest mortality agent for Bell's Vireos along the Bill Williams River in 1997, as is typical for many species in other locales (Martin 1992). Nest abandonment dropped dramatically, from 55% in 1995 to 14% in 1997.

On BWRNWR, there were several occasions where cowbird eggs were found on the ground below a nest, pierced on a branch near a nest, or broken inside a nest. This frequently coincided with the appearance of another cowbird egg, suggesting that female cowbirds with overlapping laying areas may remove the eggs of competing cowbirds. In addition, the partial brood reduction of a Yellow-breasted Chat nest in 1997 coincided with the appearance of a cowbird egg. A bloody chat nestling was discovered dangling from the nest. Nestling removal by cowbirds has also been documented by other researchers (Scott and McKinney 1994, Sheppard 1996).

Bell's Vireo populations in the lower Colorado River Valley have been heavily parasitized since the turn of the century (Brown 1903, Grinnell 1914); however, this species is still found in isolated pockets, including the Bill Williams River delta (Rosenberg et al. 1991). Rothstein (1994) suggested that parasitization rates reported by early researchers may apply only to the nests most easily located (i.e., those on the edge of dense riparian forest). The landscape of the lower Colorado River Valley has changed dramatically since 1900: the riparian corridor is narrow and fragmented with little interior forest remaining (Robinson et al. 1993). Along the Bill Williams River, Bell's Vireos were not typically found in dense, interior cottonwood-willow stands but were common in forest edges, early successional stands of cottonwood and willow, and shrubby mesquite groves. Bell's Vireos may be persisting along the Bill Williams River because some birds arrive early enough to produce first broods before the cowbird breeding season fully commences. There is evidence that first broods in 1994 and 1995 experienced low parasitization rates; we found no cowbird eggs in April, and there were sightings of vireo fledgling groups during May, 1994 and 1995.

Bell's Vireos may still be in danger of regional extirpation if brood parasitization remains at the current level. Parasitization rates >25% (Robinson et al. 1993) or >30% (Laymon 1987) could threaten the persistence of local populations of host species. Though cowbird control may lower parasitization rates in the lower Colorado River Valley (A. Averill-Murray and M. L. Morrison, unpubl. data), it is not a permanent solution and may not be effective over large, fragmented landscapes with agricultural areas that provide cowbirds with numerous feeding grounds. Habitat restoration through revegetation of native plant species may be the key to maintaining many local breeding bird populations. Determining vegetation features associated with nest-site selection by sensitive songbird species and nest discovery by cowbirds will aid in the planning of revegetation sites along the lower Colorado River.

VEGETATION FEATURES ASSOCIATED WITH NEST-SITE SELECTION AND PARASITISM

In the lower Colorado River Valley, Bell's Vireos were most abundant in cottonwood-willow forest (A. Averill-Murray and S. Lynn, unpubl. data). Within this general vegetation type, percent cottonwood-willow foliage cover did not differ (P > 0.15) between nest and random plots. However, Bell's Vireos selected nest sites with greater saltcedar foliage cover than random sites, especially in the middle canopy layer (4.6–7.5 m high). The majority of nests (52%) were in saltcedar while only 6% of nests were in cottonwood or willow trees. Therefore, saltcedar may be an important understory component for shrub-nesting species along the Bill Williams River. On the other hand, monotypic stands of saltcedar do not attract and support many birds in the lower Colorado River Valley, although this tree species is heavily used in other areas of the southwest (Hunter et al. 1988). This regional difference is attributed to saltcedar's lack of structural complexity and inability to provide shelter from the extreme summer heat typical of the lower Colorado River Valley. However, saltcedar may provide suitable nesting sites when an overstory of cottonwood or willow provides shelter from the extreme summer heat.

The nest-site model further indicated that Bell's Vireos may be selecting mesquite. Twenty-eight percent of Bell's Vireo nests were placed in mesquite trees; 33% of nests were located in areas typified by mesquite and other desert wash vegetation. Of 12 general vegetation types found in the lower Colorado River Valley, Bell's Vireos were abundant in mesquite vegetation, second only to the cottonwood-willow association (A. Averill-Murray and S. Lynn, unpubl. data).

Bell's Vireo nests were associated with vegetation features that potentially affect nest concealment. For example, nest plots had higher percent foliage cover in the low canopy layer (0.7–4.5 m high) than random plots. This corresponds to the height at which most Bell's Vireo nests were placed (0.5–3.8 m). High foliage cover in the low canopy layer may have concealed nests or parental activity from predators and brood parasites and may be indicative of a high number of potential nest sites nearby. This could lower predator or parasite search efficiency by increasing the number of sites that must be searched (Martin 1988). Likewise, Staab (1995) and Staab and Morrison (*this volume*) found that greater vegetation volume near the nest significantly reduced the likelihood of parasitization for several host species breeding in a riparian area of central Arizona.

Tall cottonwood or willow trees near vireo nests may have aided nest discovery by cowbirds. Cowbirds use tall trees as perches from which to survey the surrounding area for nests to parasitize (Norman and Robertson 1975), and parasitization rates have been shown to increase with proximity of tall trees (Alvarez 1993) and snags (Anderson and Storer 1976). Tall trees with adjacent open areas may allow cowbirds to observe the movements and behaviors of potential hosts more easily than when host activities are confined to more interior, dense patches of vegetation. Brittingham and Temple (1996) found that parasitized broods occurred in nests characterized by a more open subcanopy (3–10 m) and canopy (>10m) than nests with unparasitized broods. This may have enabled cowbirds to find elevated perches with unobstructed views of host activity in the understory vegetation.

Bell's Vireo nests discovered by cowbirds had greater lateral concealment than undiscovered nests. However, vireo nests were typically placed within a small clearing in the shrubby undergrowth and were rarely well concealed from close range. Brittingham and Temple (1996) suggested that host species that nest in shrubs within small openings may be particularly vulnerable to parasitism, especially when potential cowbird perches are nearby. In addition, Bell's Vireos are not secretive around their nest but rather sing and scold aggressively. Therefore, host behavior may have further aided cowbird nest-searching efforts.

In conclusion, we have identified vegetation characteristics associated with cowbird nest discovery in cottonwood-willow forest that could be useful in designing and managing revegetation sites. High vegetation volume in the low canopy layer may be an important component of breeding habitat for many shrub-nesting species by concealing nests from predators and brood parasites. Saltcedar is the predominant woody species providing foliage cover at nests along the Bill Williams River. Therefore, removal of saltcedar *per se* is not a preferred management technique unless dense, native vegetation (e.g., willow, mesquite) is reestablished. Additionally, revegetation efforts that focus on planting rows of cottonwoods without providing for a dense understory could actually enhance the ability of cowbirds to locate nests by providing elevated survey perches with unobstructed views.

ACKNOWLEDGMENTS

This work fulfilled part of the requirement for a Masters of Science degree from the Wildlife and Fisheries Science Program, School of Renewable Natural Resources, University of Arizona. Funding for our work was provided by the US Fish and Wildlife Service, Southwest Regional Office; Bill Williams River National Wildlife Refuge; and the US Bureau of Reclamation, lower Colorado Regional Office. N. Gilbertson, B. Raulston, K. Milne, W. Howe, M. Walker, and J. Swett assisted with establishment of the study. For field assistance we thank D. Drumtra, M. Duttenhoffer, P. Hurley, J. Jollivette, A. Kuenzi, J. Martin, T. McNicholas, W. Romonchuk, and T. Weninger. For assisting with logistics on related aspects of this study, we thank the School of Renewable Natural Resources, University of Arizona; R. Hill, Planet Ranch; and personnel of Havasu (C. Smith, G. Wolf, J. Good), Imperial (C. Kennedy, S. Hill, and A. Loranger), and Cibola (A. Montoya, E. Johnson, and T. Green) National Wildlife Refuges. We also appreciate the assistance of W. Martin throughout our studies. R. Averill-Murray helped with the figures and S. Stolenson and A. Kuenzi provided helpful comments that improved this manuscript.

APPENDIX 1. VEGETATION VARIABLES MEASURED AT NEST AND RANDOM PLOTS AND CALCULATED VARIABLES USED IN LOGISTIC REGRESSION ANALYSES

Variable	Description
Measured variables	
Nest substrate type	Plant species in which nest was located.
Height of nest	Measured with a pole calibrated to decimeters or a tape measure.
Height of nest substrate	Measured with a pole calibrated to decimeters. If the plant substrate was >6.5 m, substrate height was visually estimated using the pole as a reference.
Nest concealment	Vegetation cover below, above, and lateral to nest. Lateral nest concealment was measured one meter from the nest in each of the four cardinal directions. A 25-cm diameter circle was projected onto the nest and the percent of the circle obscured by vegetation was estimated (Martin and Roper 1988, Ralph et al. 1993). Concealment above and below the nest was the percent obscurement of a 25-cm diameter circle centered on the nest and projected to the ground and through the canopy.
Distance to closest shrub and mature tree[a]	Distance to the closest shrub/sapling (woody plant >0.6 m tall and <2.5 cm dbh) and tree (>8 cm dbh) in each of four quadrants formed by extending perpendicular lines in the cardinal directions from a point directly below the nest or random site. Measured with a tape measure or estimated by pacing.
Distance to closest mature cottonwood or willow tree	Distance from nest to closest cottonwood or willow tree >8 cm dbh. Measured with a tape measure or estimated by pacing.
Cottonwood and willow tree density	Estimated as the number of cottonwood or willow trees >8 cm dbh within 30 m of the nest.
Vertical height diversity within 5 m[a]	Estimated using the point-intercept method (Bonham 1989). Two 5-m radii were established, centered on the nest/random site and oriented in the east-west direction. At meter intervals, we recorded the plant species whose foliage intercepted an imaginary vertical line that was divided into four height categories following Anderson and Ohmart (1986): 0.0–0.6 m, 0.7–4.5 m, 4.6–7.5 m, and >7.5 m. Estimates were aided by the use of an ocular tube (James and Shugart 1970).
Canopy and ground cover within 5 m[a]	Estimated by sighting up and down through an ocular tube and recording presence or absence of vegetation cover where the crossthreads intersect. Measurements taken at meter intervals along east-west radii.
Calculated variables	
Average lateral concealment at nest	Average percent lateral concealment from the four cardinal directions.
Total nest concealment	Sum of lateral, above, and below nest concealment.
Minimum and mean distance to closest shrub and mature tree	1) Distance to the closest shrub and tree >8 cm dbh and 2) average distance to the closest shrub and mature tree in four quadrants formed by extending perpendicular lines in the cardinal directions from a point directly below the nest or random site.
Dispersion index for shrubs and mature trees	Coefficient of Variation {(standard deviation/mean) × 100} for distance to closest shrub and mature tree
Percent live foliage cover by height class within 5 m	The number of times foliage was recorded in a particular height interval divided by the total number of sample points.
Percent plant species composition within 5 m	The percent of sample points within 5 m of nest/random site at which each plant species was recorded. Percent cover by plant species was also calculated for each of the four height categories.
Percent ground and canopy cover within 5 m	Percent of sample points at which ground or canopy cover was recorded.

[a] Vegetation characteristics measured at random sites.

Studies in Avian Biology No. 18:121–134, 1999.

WHAT DO DEMOGRAPHIC SENSITIVITY ANALYSES TELL US ABOUT CONTROLLING BROWN-HEADED COWBIRDS?

JOHN J. CITTA AND L. SCOTT MILLS

Abstract. While Brown-headed Cowbird (*Molothrus ater*) control efforts are fairly common, the effects of control programs on cowbird populations are unknown. We apply analytical-based and simulation-based demographic sensitivity analysis to the problem of cowbird management. Collectively, the analyses indicate that natural variation of egg survival likely determines population growth when mean values of egg survival are low (yet plausible) or when high variation exists around mean rates. When the natural range of egg survival does not encompass low rates, yearling survival increases in importance. Due to uncertainty in vital rates, it is currently impossible to ascertain the true sensitivity of these two vital rates. Management actions that decrease only adult survival on breeding ranges are not expected to regulate population growth. In contrast, trapping on wintering ranges is expected to be more effective as this technique reduces both adult and yearling survival. However, the impacts of winter trapping may be swamped by high egg survival. When this analysis is combined with life history and logistical realities, we believe that widespread trapping efforts will be largely ineffectual for controlling cowbird populations on either breeding or wintering ranges. We suggest that cowbird vital rates be specifically examined with respect to host communities, vegetation type, and land use in order to rank management priorities.

Key Words: Brown-headed Cowbird, cowbird management, demographic analysis, *Molothrus ater,* population control, sensitivity analysis.

Land managers have long realized that Brown-headed Cowbirds (*Molothrus ater*) may decrease nesting success of passerine hosts (e.g., Hofslund 1957, McGeen 1972, Mayfield 1977, Elliott 1978, Brittingham and Temple 1983, Weatherhead 1989). Due to the negative effect cowbirds have on some host species, land managers have attempted to control cowbird populations since the early 1970s. For example, control programs in Michigan typically remove 3,000 or more female cowbirds and cowbird eggs yearly (Kelly and DeCapita 1982; M. DeCapita, pers. comm.) and trapping efforts on the Ft. Hood military reservation in Texas remove upwards of 3,000 to 5,000 female cowbirds per year (J. D. Cornelius, pers. comm.). These control programs usually target cowbirds to protect federally listed endangered species and commonly involve the removal of adults from feeding areas (Rothstein et al. 1987), the removal of adults and yearlings from communal wintering areas (J. D. Cornelius, pers. comm.), and to a much lesser extent, the removal of eggs from host nests. While cowbird control efforts are fairly common and such efforts are capable of decreasing parasitism rates, the effect of such efforts on cowbird population growth remains unknown.

Better knowledge of cowbird population dynamics is necessary to assess the efficacy of current management strategies and to aid the design of more efficient management strategies. Here we apply traditional techniques and new matrix-based techniques of sensitivity analysis to investigate how different management options may influence cowbird population dynamics. Specifically, we use sensitivity analysis to determine how we can most effectively decrease the growth rate of cowbird populations. Our objectives are three-fold: (1) to determine the relative importance of various demographic components to Brown-headed Cowbird annual population growth rates (λ); (2) to determine the robustness of model predictions when vital rate estimates vary due to measurement error and/or environmental variation; and (3) to discuss the implications of this analysis for management and research.

METHODS

We examine the sensitivity of annual population growth rate (λ) to perturbations in specific Brown-headed Cowbird vital rates with traditional analytical-based and new simulation-based techniques.

ANALYTICAL-BASED TECHNIQUES

Traditional sensitivity analysis (Caswell 1989) is an analytical technique used to evaluate expected response of population growth rates to perturbations in single vital rates (i.e., birth or death rates) one-at-a-time and by equal amounts. Sensitivity, as defined by Caswell (1989), is the absolute infinitesimal change in population growth rate given an absolute infinitesimal change in a vital rate, while all other vital rates are held constant. If a is a matrix of transition probabilities, v and w are the vectors of reproductive values and stable age distributions (SAD) associated with matrix a, respectively, and $\langle vw \rangle$ is the scalar product of the two vectors, the sensitivity of matrix element a_{ij} (row i, column j) is equal to:

$$\text{Sensitivity } (s_{ij}) \text{ of } \quad a_{ij} = \left(\frac{v_i w_j}{\langle vw \rangle}\right). \quad (1)$$

Elasticities are similar, but are calculated on a proportional scale, where λ is the geometric population growth rate at SAD:

$$\text{Elasticity } (e_{ij}) \text{ of } \quad a_{ij} = \left(\frac{v_i w_j}{\langle vw \rangle}\right)\left(\frac{a_{ij}}{\lambda}\right). \quad (2)$$

Intuitively, elasticity is the sensitivity of a_{ij} weighted by its proportional change with λ. The change in vital rates and λ is assumed to be infinitesimal and linear.

When matrix elements are composed of more than one vital rate, component sensitivities and elasticities can be calculated for each vital rate that appears in one or more matrix elements. Chain rule differentiation is required for each a_{ij} that contains a particular vital rate x. For n elements that contain vital rate x, the sensitivity and elasticity of x are:

Component sensitivity of vital rate x

$$= \sum^n [(s_{ij})(\text{product of non-}x \text{ components})]$$
$$(3)$$

Component elasticity of vital rate x

$$= (\text{Component sensitivity of vital rate } x)\left(\frac{x}{\lambda}\right). \quad (4)$$

What do analytical techniques of sensitivity analysis imply biologically? Because sensitivity and elasticity are partial derivatives, they represent the slope of the relationship between a small change in a vital rate to the corresponding change in λ. Traditionally, researchers and managers have assumed that vital rates with high sensitivities or elasticities should be the focus of management actions, as perturbation of these vital rates produce the greatest change in λ. This assumption is not always correct (Mills et al., in press).

SIMULATION-BASED TECHNIQUES

Traditional sensitivities and elasticities may mislead managers because inevitable variation imposed by nature, by management action, or by measurement error will not be infinitesimal or equal across all vital rates (Gaillard et al. 1998; Mills et al., in press). To account for vital rate variation on scales that are neither absolutely or proportionally equal across vital rates, we also

use the sensitivity technique used by Wisdom and Mills (1997). Upper and lower limits of vital rates, determined from literature review, are incorporated into high and low matrices and a computer program constructs 1,000 matrices with each vital rate of each matrix randomly chosen from a distribution bounded by the high and low values. A population growth rate (λ) is then calculated for each matrix. The relative importance of a stage specific vital rate is assessed by regressing λ for each replicate against the value of that rate for all replicates to derive coefficients of determination (R^2). In terms of traditional definitions of sensitivity, R^2 for any component vital rate is analogous to the squared sensitivity weighted by the relative variance of a vital rate (H. Caswell, pers. comm.).

The regression method is appealing, because it allows variation in particular vital rates to alter according to the scale perceived to occur in the field. With the regression technique, variation in vital rates can be incorporated to represent natural amounts of variation, levels of variation imposed by management, or measurement error. Furthermore, vital rates can be selected from distributions that mimic natural distributions. For the selection of vital rates, we favored a uniform distribution over other distributions. Without knowing how likely different vital rates are, all vital rates should have equal likelihood of selection and this distribution evaluates the scenario where extreme changes in rates under management have the same likelihood as small changes from the current mean.

Because all possible λs are plotted, the regression technique also has the advantage of being able to detect non-linearities that traditional methods may not. This is similar to the covariance technique used by Brault and Caswell (1993), but is computationally and intuitively easier to manage. If non-linearities do not exist in the data, then varying vital rates on absolute and proportional scales should produce similar results as traditional sensitivities and elasticities (Mills et al., in press).

MODEL STRUCTURE AND INPUT FOR COWBIRD ANALYSIS

We use two-stage Leftkovitch matrices (see Appendix 1) to model cowbird populations. Stage specific demographic data form the matrix and the model projection interval is 1 year. Eigenanalysis of the matrix, or projection of the matrix over time, provides annual population growth rates (λ). Consequently, all techniques of sensitivity analysis assume populations are at stable age distribution (SAD). It is an all female model, a reasonable approach given the excess of adult males in natural populations (Darley

1971, Arnold 1983). Fecundities are divided in half to account for female eggs only and are multiplied by annual cohort survival to account for a post-breeding census.

We derive inputs to the matrix model, in terms of estimated stage-specific ranges of vital rates, from the literature (Table 1). The top row of the matrix (F_{11} and F_{12} ; see Appendix 1) contains reproductive information based on both survival of females to breed and number of eggs laid (fecundity). Historically, cowbird fecundity has been difficult to determine and estimates of the number of eggs laid per female varied widely. Much of this variation is removed when daily laying rates are considered. When multiplied by the length of the breeding season, daily laying rates are likely to be the most accurate estimator of annual female fecundity (Rothstein et al. 1986b). Consequently, we only consider daily laying rates and, to avoid non-constant laying rates over the breeding season, assume a 40-d breeding period within which laying rates are constant (Table 1). To determine the possible importance of low fecundity, we include Holford and Roby's (1993) fecundity estimates for calcium deprived individuals in captivity. From these data we estimate the suppressed daily egg laying rate to be approximately 0.37. While this figure is significantly lower than the lowest estimate of daily egg laying rate measured under natural conditions (0.51 eggs per day), inclusion in the model illustrates the consequences of extremely low fecundity on λ. Finally, we assume adults and yearlings have the same maximum and minimum daily laying rates. Although Jackson and Roby (1992) indicate that yearlings have lower fecundity than adults, the lowest measured daily laying rate for yearlings is greater than the rate for calcium deprived individuals. This implies that the lower daily laying rate used in the model (that for calcium deprived individuals) represents a worst case scenario for both adults and yearlings.

Matrix element G_{21} (Appendix 1) is the mean survival from stage 1 to stage 2, and represents a composite of egg, nestling, and yearling survival. Egg survival is defined as the probability that an egg survives to hatch. This life stage is assumed to be 15 d. While the average incubation period is approximately 10–13 d (Briskie and Sealy 1990), these estimates do not include time before incubation is initiated. In other words, because eggs are likely to remain within the nest some number of days before incubation is initiated (see Nice 1954), a 15 d pre-hatching period is realistic. Nestling survival is defined as the probability that a nestling survives to fledge, given that it hatched. This period is assumed to be 10 d (Norris 1947, Hann 1937). Yearling sur-

TABLE 1.   VITAL RATES FOR THE COWBIRD TRANSITION MATRIX (SEE APPENDIX 1)

Vital rate	Average (N)	High	Low	Citations
Adult Fecundity[a]	0.69 (4)	0.8	0.51 (lab) 0.37 (calcium limited)	Scott and Ankney 1979 (California), 1980 (Ontario); Rothstein et al. 1986 (California); Holford and Roby 1993 (captive population)
Yearling Fecundity[a]	0.56 (1)	N/A	N/A	Jackson and Roby 1992
Egg survival	0.38 (pooled across 9 studies; N = 1346 eggs)	0.68 (single species study)	0.08 (host community study)	Hann 1937, Norris 1947, Berger 1951, Hofslund 1957, McGeen 1972, Elliot 1978, Weatherhead 1989, Marvil and Cruz 1989, Smith and Arcese 1994
Nestling survival	0.64 (pooled across 6 studies; N = 224 nestlings)	0.76	0.46	Hann 1937, Norris 1947, Berger 1951, Hofslund 1957, Marvel and Cruz 1989, Weatherhead 1989
Yearling survival	0.24	0.32	0.15	Dhondt 1979 for Great Tits, Woodward and Woodward 1979
Adult survival[b]	0.47 (4)	0.63	0.31	Darley 1971, Fankhauser 1971, Arnold 1983 (provides 2 estimates)

[a] Daily laying rate; we assume this constant over a 40 day laying interval (see Appendix 1).
[b] Female only rate.

vival is defined as the probability that a juvenile survives to breed, given that it fledges. This period is assumed to be the remaining 340 d of a cowbird's first year. Estimating yearling survival rates are problematic, because only one study (Woodward and Woodward 1979) quantified cowbird fledgling survival rates (only until independence at approximately 30 d). For an upper bound, we assume yearlings attain adult survival rates immediately after independence and we combine the Woodward and Woodward (1979) yearling rate for the first month after fledging (0.48) with the highest estimate of adult survival for the remaining 310 d before breeding. This yields an upper bound for yearling survival of 0.32. The lower bound for yearling survival (0.15) is assumed equal to known lower bounds for Great Tits (*Parus major*) (Dhondt 1979). While using data from other species is not ideal, Great Tits are one of the only passerine species with known yearling survival rates, thereby providing insight into a lower bound of cowbird survival.

Matrix element P_{22} is the mean survival to remain within stage 2. This is simply an adult female survival rate between annual birth events, and is estimated via return rates or recoveries (Table 1).

RESULTS

If variation is artificially constrained to be small and equal around all vital rates, we would expect the simulation-based technique to rank the importance of all vital rates similarly to the traditional analytical-based sensitivity analysis (L. S. Mills et al., unpubl. data). Although traditional sensitivities and R^2 sensitivities are not directly comparable, because they are different statistics, we do in fact find that with small and equal absolute change of ± 0.10 for each rate, the rankings of vital rate effects on λ are identical for both approaches (Fig. 1a). Likewise, incorporating proportional changes in the regression technique (± 10 %) produces similar rankings as traditional elasticities (Fig. 1b). The small deviations between the sensitivities or elasticities and the simulation-based measure are likely due to the effect of non-linearities on sensitivities or elasticities (Mills et al., in press). The vital rates with the highest sensitivities on an absolute scale of variation are yearling survival and nestling survival. The vital rates with the highest sensitivities on a proportional scale are egg, nestling, and yearling survival.

Of course, neither of these vital rate ranges, determined by fixed and equal absolute or proportional change, are likely biologically realistic. Therefore, we used the regression technique to determine R^2 sensitivities for the entire range of

cowbird variation, letting different rates vary by different amounts according to the upper and lower bounds presented in Table 1; we refer to this as the empirical range of variation (Figs. 2 and 3). Egg survival alone appears to account for over 60% of the variation in population growth rates. The vital rate accounting for the next largest amount of variation in λ is yearling survival ($R^2 = 0.14$).

While the regression technique is likely to be more realistic than traditional methods because it selects vital rates from biologically realistic upper and lower bounds, it is possible that vital rate ranges that are too large or too small may artificially increase or decrease the R^2 value of a vital rate (Wisdom and Mills 1997). Unfortunately, the sparse data available for most species makes determination of vital rate ranges difficult. This is especially true for threatened or endangered species that we model the most, but is also true for common species such as cowbirds. A critical question is thus: what are the consequences of under- or over-estimating our range of variation in demographic parameters? If altering the range of an uncertain vital rate has little effect upon R^2, then accurate range estimation is unimportant. However, if R^2 is sensitive to small changes in the range of vital rates, then correct range estimation is critical. To assess this with our data, we altered the range of each vital rate one-at-a-time while holding the other vital rates at the empirical range width (Table 1). Vital rate ranges were decreased by 25 and 50% and increased by 25% (50% increases were not possible because some survival rates would exceed 1).

Generally, we find that increasing or decreasing range widths results in a monotonic increase or decrease in R^2 values (Fig. 4), as expected from the fact that R^2 for any component vital rate is weighted by the variance in that rate. Although in this case we do find the statistically expected change in absolute R^2 values with changes in vital rate ranges, the biologically important result is that the relative rankings do not change for the vital rates that account for most of the variation in λ.

Because egg survival was identified as the vital rate most affecting population growth when vital rates vary between empirically determined bounds, and because decreasing the range of egg survival can decrease the R^2 value of egg survival, it is relevant to ask how much of a decrease in the range of egg survival is necessary before another rate replaces egg survival as the rate most affecting λ. In the most extreme case of a 50% decline in range width, we find that most of the change in R^2 (40%) was partitioned as increased R^2 for yearling survival and that the

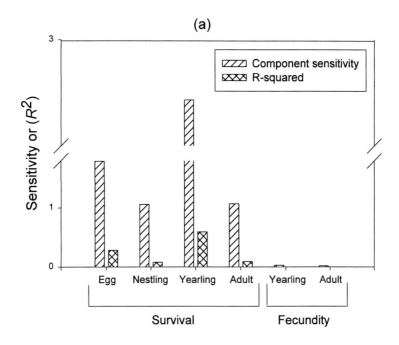

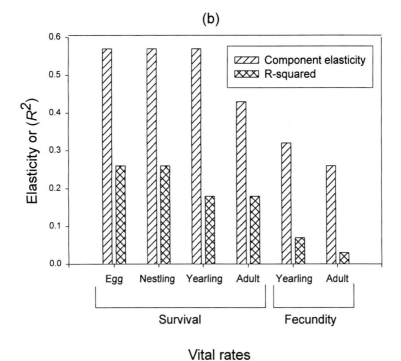

FIGURE 1.   Comparison of component sensitivities and R^2 values for Brown-headed Cowbird vital rates with (a) range standardized on an absolute scale (plus or minus 0.10) and (b) range standardized on a proportional scale (plus or minus 10%). Only rankings are directly comparable between component sensitivities and R^2 values.

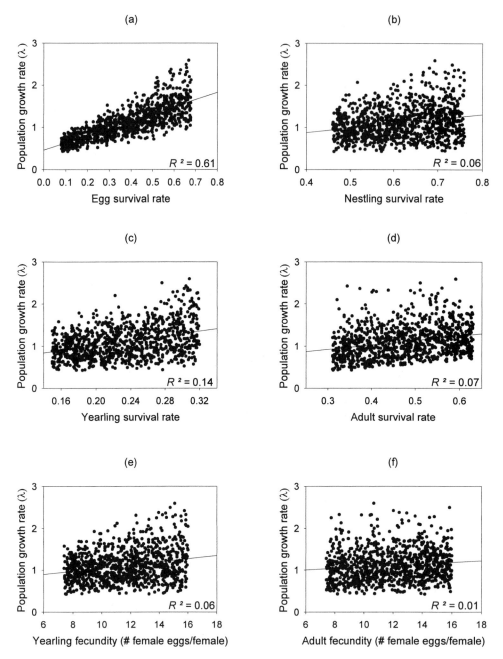

FIGURE 2.   Amount of variation in Brown-headed Cowbird population growth rate (R^2) as accounted for by (a) egg survival rate, (b) nestling survival rate, (c) yearling survival rate, (d) adult survival rate, (e) yearling fecundity rate, and (f) adult fecundity rate in 1000 matrices with randomly selected vital rates. Coefficient of determination (R^2) and linear regression line presented.

total R^2 for yearling survival approached that of egg survival (compare Fig. 5 to Fig. 3).

In addition to range width, mean vital rates must also play a role in determining the effect of a change in any rate on λ. The variance

around the regression line for egg survival is non-constant (Fig. 2a), indicating that R^2 values will change as the mean values of vital rates change. To investigate this further, we determined how sensitivities were affected by alter-

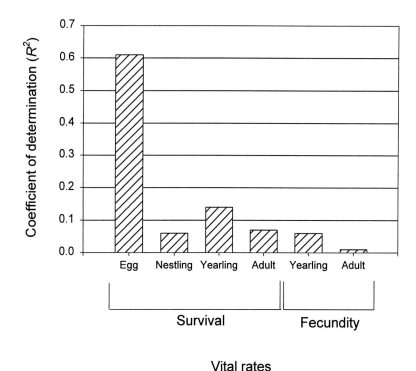

FIGURE 3.   Sensitivities of Brown-headed Cowbird vital rates as indexed by the coefficient of determination (R^2) in 1000 matrices with randomly selected vital rates regressed against corresponding population growth rates.

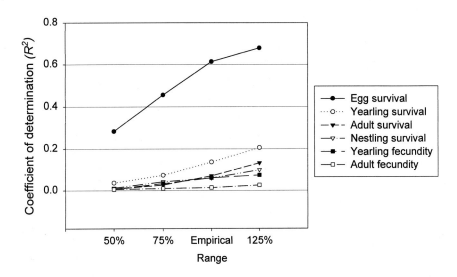

FIGURE 4.   Changes in R^2 for Brown-headed Cowbird life stages when vital rate ranges are altered. Each point equals R^2 for a vital rate range which is 50%, 75%, 100%, or 125% of the original empirical range, while all other vital rate ranges are held at the empirical range.

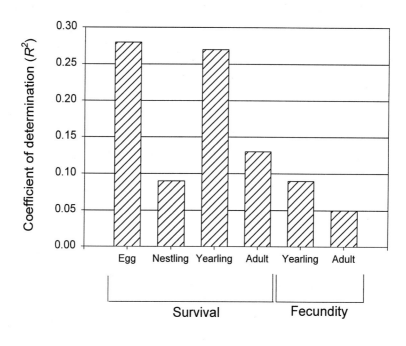

FIGURE 5.   Sensitivities of Brown-headed Cowbird vital rates as indexed by the coefficient of determination (R^2) in 1000 matrices with randomly selected vital rates regressed against corresponding population growth rates when the range of egg survival is 50% of the empirical range. Compare to Fig. 3.

ing the mean egg survival rate, while holding the range of variation constant. To keep the total range of variation within the biologically plausible range of variation, we again restricted the range of egg survival (50% of the empirical range), and then increased and decreased the mean vital rate by 25%. We find that even with a small range of egg survival, if the mean egg survival rate is low, then the egg stage has the highest R^2 (Fig. 6a). Alternatively, if the mean egg survival rate is high, yearling survival has the highest R^2 (Fig. 6b).

DISCUSSION

How Vital Rates Affect Population Growth

The egg survival stage is likely to be the vital rate that most affects population growth rate whenever the range of variation in egg survival is high or in situations where the mean egg survival rate is low. The only studies that examine cowbird egg survival across the entire community of hosts within an area yield mean rates of 0.08 (Elliot 1978) and 0.43 (Norris 1947), indicating that the sensitivities in any of our simulations are plausible. Unfortunately, we do not know how often low rates of egg survival occur

and, more importantly, how much egg survival varies within and between sites over time. In situations with high mean egg survival rates and low levels of variation around those mean rates, the yearling stage may play the biggest role in impacting λ.

An obvious question is: with what degree of certainty have we estimated our vital rate ranges? This question is most critical with regard to egg survival. Range estimation for egg survival is problematic, because most studies observe only one host. Furthermore, cowbird researchers tend to study highly parasitized hosts, hosts that accept cowbird eggs and are parasitized enough to be analyzed statistically. Unfortunately, cowbirds do not exclusively parasitize one species, but typically parasitize a number of hosts within the breeding area. Host communities likely yield rates of egg survival that differ from the rates observed in any single species. Furthermore, egg survival rates are sure to be systematically overestimated, because egg ejections or eggs laid in inactive nests are unlikely to be detected. The extent of this bias is unknown and likely dependent upon the host community and vegetation type. While many host species are known ejec-

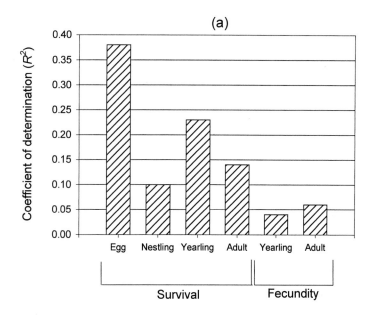

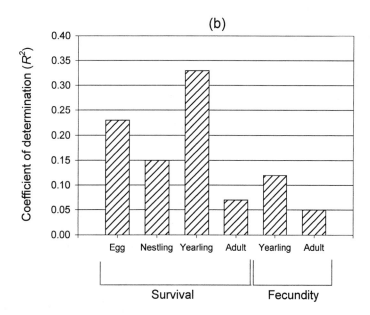

FIGURE 6. R^2 for Brown-headed Cowbird vital rates when the range of egg survival is 50% of the empirical range and the mean rate is (a) decreased 25% from the empirical mean (new mean = 0.29) and (b) increased 25% from the empirical mean (new mean = 0.48). All other vital rates have the empirical means and ranges.

tors, very little is know about how often these species are parasitized as eggs may be almost immediately ejected (Rothstein 1975b, Friedman et al. 1977). Although not well quantified, the rate at which cowbirds lay eggs in abandoned nests appears to highly variable. Berger (1951) reported a rate of 1.35% for Song Sparrows (*Melospiza melodia*) and Freeman et al. (1990) reported a rate of 21.5% for Red-winged Blackbirds (*Agelaius phoeniceus*). The high rates of inappropriate egg laying noted by Freeman et al. (1990) appear to be a function of not having perch sites; they hypothesized that without perches, the cowbirds were not able to assess correctly whether a nest was abandoned.

In summary, traditional analytical techniques indicate that egg, yearling, and nestling survival are the most sensitive vital rates. Regression-based techniques indicate that egg and yearling stages are the most sensitive. Regression-based techniques also indicate that the relative importance of egg versus yearling stages depends upon the range of variation and the mean rate of egg survival. Whenever egg survival rates are low or if the range of egg survival encompasses low rates then egg survival will most affect population growth. Adult survival, adult fecundity, and yearling fecundity were not important factors in any of the modeled scenarios.

LIMITATIONS OF MODELING TECHNIQUES

Although sensitivity analysis is capable of revealing non-intuitive relationships, several limitations must be kept in mind. First, neither the analytical- nor simulation-based technique accounts for density dependent relationships. While positive or negative correlations between vital rates could be included within either the analytical-based technique (van Tienderen 1995) or within the simulation-based technique (M. J. Wisdom et al., unpubl. data), these data are not available. Furthermore, density dependent correlations between vital rates may change as management perturbations are intensified and these changes may not be predictable under current conditions.

Second, and related to density dependence, the techniques do not account for compensatory effects. One possible compensatory effect is the replacement of breeding females and may occur as present non-breeding "floaters" occupy empty egg laying areas. If removed females are replaced, then adult survival is not functionally decreased as modeled and the predicted sensitivity is biased high. We predict that the sensitivity (traditional and regression-based) of adult survival is maximized when non-breeding floaters are not present. Conversely, if many floaters are present, adult removals will not be effective un-

til the number of adult females drops below the amount necessary to parasitize all available nests. In short, if cowbirds exhibited extremely high replacement rates, then it is unlikely that trapping of adults near sensitive host species would be effective. Trapping records from the effort to protect the Kirtland's Warbler show that most female cowbirds are captured within the first few weeks of the breeding season (Kelly and DeCapita 1982), indicating that trapping efforts are capable of removing all females within a short time period and that floaters are not a concern to this analysis.

Third, neither technique accounts for spatial considerations. As modeled, Brown-headed Cowbirds are treated as one large population and we assume perturbations are population-wide. Management actions must consider the ratio of the size of the target population to the size of the total population, because managing only a subset of individuals dilutes population-wide effects. In other words, if we manage only a part of a cowbird population, we may have little effect on the population as a whole. Identifying exactly what effect any given management action will have on cowbird populations will require delineation of population boundaries and knowledge of movement rates between populations within and between breeding seasons. Trapping records from the effort to protect the Kirtland's Warbler (Kelly and DeCapita 1982) and the Black-capped Vireo (Barber and Martin 1997) show that trapping does not reduce the number of cowbirds in subsequent years; this indicates that there is either a large level of movement between populations or that the target population is much smaller than the total population. Unfortunately, there are little or no data identifying the spatial structure and dynamics of cowbird populations.

Finally, matrix-based calculations of λ also assume populations are at Stable Age Distribution (SAD). SAD is the proportion of individuals in any age or stage class over time, given a constant matrix. It is unlikely that populations in fluctuating environments exist at SAD for long periods of time. Currently, it is unknown how deviations from SAD in a fluctuating environment affect either traditional or the regression-based techniques.

IMPLICATIONS FOR COWBIRD MANAGEMENT

Although egg survival is likely the vital rate which most affects population growth rate in many situations, it is nearly impossible to manage with current techniques and logistical constraints. We identify four problems with egg removal programs. First, host nests are difficult and expensive to find (Martin and Geupel 1993).

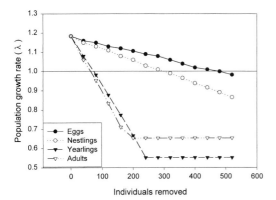

FIGURE 7. Number of individual eggs, nestlings, yearlings, and adults removed and the resulting population growth rates for a hypothetical population of 5,000 cowbirds. Removals are assumed to impose additive mortality. See Appendix 2 for details.

Second, removing cowbird eggs may increase nest predation rates or result in nest abandonment (Major 1990, Gotmark 1992), although correct protocols can reduce disturbance (Martin and Geupel 1993). Third, to be effective, egg removals must target a large proportion of the total cowbird population. Egg removals will likely have to exist at scales much larger than study sites, management areas, and wildlife refuges. The exact scale of management will depend upon the size of the cowbird population and movement rates between populations, which remain unknown. Fourth, eggs are expected to be numerous. At the time of breeding, over 90% of the population is in the egg stage at stable age distribution; consequently, management actions may remove many eggs, yet have little impact upon total egg survival rates.

To illustrate how a management imposed change in a vital rate is affected by the number in that age class, we provide an example. Using the mean matrix (Appendix 1) and assuming a population size of 5,000 cowbirds, there are over 4,600 eggs resulting from approximately 400 adults at the time of breeding (Appendix 2). Suppose that from this population we remove equal numbers of eggs, nestlings, fledglings, and adults, assuming that this mortality was additive. We find that by removing large numbers of eggs, we impact total population growth very little compared to other stages (Fig. 7). For example, on an individual basis, removing approximately 100 adults or fledglings will have the same impact as removing over 475 eggs, because there are fewer adults or fledglings in the population. In short, there are so many cowbird eggs that even large egg removals may have little impact

upon total egg survival rates. While environmental variation and the consequences of having different host communities determine the population-wide survival rate of eggs, and therefore affect population growth, the effects of management on egg survival and the resulting changes in population growth are likely minuscule. When the problems of finding nests, human induced impacts upon hosts, large management scales, and the preponderance of eggs are considered jointly, we conclude that egg removal is not a viable management option.

Because reducing egg survival is not a wide-scale management option, we must consider what vital rates can be managed. Currently, the most common management options are trapping on the breeding grounds and trapping on the wintering grounds. Trapping on the breeding grounds typically involves the trapping of adults, while trapping on the wintering grounds involves the removal of adults and yearlings. We shall consider each of these options in turn.

Cowbird population growth rates are generally less affected by fluctuations in adult survival than other vital rates and the effects of adult removals may be masked by variation in egg and/or yearling survival. During the breeding season, the replacement of breeding females (via floaters and immigrants) exacerbates this problem and makes population growth rates even less sensitive to adult removals. To illustrate the significance of this problem, consider that cowbird trapping programs in Michigan typically remove 3,000 cowbirds per year with no noticeable decline in cowbird populations between years, despite the fact that virtually all individuals are removed during the breeding season (Kelly and DeCapita 1982; M. DeCapita, pers. comm.). The lack of any effect of trapping on cowbird populations may be due to either targeting only a small proportion of the total cowbird population or high rates of immigration. Either alternative leads to the same conclusion: adult removal programs on breeding grounds are not likely to regulate populations unless they are conducted on a much larger scale. However, this does not invalidate trapping programs during the breeding season, as such programs are usually intended to protect sensitive host species at a local scale and can successfully do so (Kelly and DeCapita 1982, Barber and Martin 1997; M. DeCapita, pers. comm.; J. Cornelius, pers. comm.).

Trapping adult and yearling cowbirds on the wintering ranges is expected to be much more effective in controlling cowbird population growth. While population growth is not sensitive to perturbations in adult survival, adults are only a small proportion of the total population.

Hence, adult survival may be greatly altered by removing only a small absolute number of adults (Appendix 2). In contrast to adult survival, population growth is likely sensitive to perturbations in yearling survival; there are also relatively few yearlings in any given population. Therefore, our sensitivity analysis and our age distributions suggest that winter trapping programs are more likely to decrease cowbird population growth rates than by removing eggs or trapping on breeding grounds. In addition to these life history considerations, winter trapping has many logistical advantages because cowbirds concentrate on large communal wintering grounds.

Unfortunately, there are also serious limitations with using winter trapping to control cowbird populations. Removing cowbirds from all wintering areas may be logistically impossible, because wintering ranges extend from Texas into Mexico (Bray et al. 1974, Arnold 1983). Also, even massive control in a limited number of wintering areas may produce extremely diffuse effects on the breeding ranges (Rothstein and Robinson 1994), because individuals in one wintering range may breed throughout North America (Bray et al. 1974, Dolbeer 1982). Finally, the large effect of egg survival on population growth rate may make trap efforts on other age classes ineffectual. For example, note that for the lowest rates of yearling and adult survival, many of the matrices have positive growth rates (Fig. 2c). So, while winter removals of adults and yearlings are expected to be more effective than removing eggs or adults on the breeding ranges, they do not have a high likelihood of regulating population growth rates unless most or all wintering areas are targeted for management. Furthermore, the effects of winter removals may be swamped by natural variation in egg survival rates.

Given the formidable logistical difficulties in lowering the vital rates that most affect cowbird population growth, we believe that the most effective method of cowbird control is likely to be the management of land uses to disfavor cowbirds. Cowbird presence is often significantly correlated with the presence of livestock (Schulz and Leininger 1991, Knopf et. al. 1988, Mosconi and Hutto 1982; but also see Kantrud 1981), agriculture (Rothstein et al. 1984, Rothstein et al. 1987, Tewksbury et. al. 1998), and forest fragmentation (Chasko and Gates 1982, Coker and Capen 1995, Tewksbury et al. 1998). By managing grazing patterns, availability of agricultural waste grain (often an important food source), and forest fragmentation, we may be able to indirectly eliminate or at least control the presence of cowbirds before they parasitize host species.

IMPLICATIONS FOR COWBIRD RESEARCH

Much research has focused upon the effects of limiting cowbird fecundity or determining what limits cowbird fecundity. We feel that this is a valid research topic for life history information, but is of little management interest unless fecundity can be decreased to rates near zero. We varied fecundity to rates lower than anything ever measured in nature (the calcium deprived rates) and then decreased that rate to assess the effect of larger variation in vital rate ranges. In all simulations but one (Fig. 6b) fecundity had the least effect on λ of any vital rate.

To date, most cowbird research has focused upon parasitism of specific host species, not upon parasitism of host communities within habitats or by land use practice. Because parasitism rates, predation rates, host communities, and the ability of hosts to fledge cowbirds vary across the landscape, it is unlikely that all vegetation types and host communities are equally productive for cowbirds. Furthermore, the presence of cowbirds may not reflect cowbird habitat quality. As long as adequate foraging habitat (feeding grounds) exist within flight range, cowbirds may parasitize host nests in habitats which barely provide positive growth rates or provide negative growth rates. By focusing research efforts upon cowbird vital rates in different vegetation types and host communities, researchers may be able to identify habitats and land use practices which are most important for (or possibly are responsible for) cowbird population growth. If the goal of management is to regulate populations of cowbirds, we suggest focusing management plans on regulating land uses which favor cowbirds in areas with positive cowbird growth rates. For example, livestock grazing in areas that have vegetation types and host communities that lead to negative cowbird population growth rates should be a lower management priority (assuming no endangered species are present) than livestock grazing in areas which lead to positive cowbird population growth rates. Currently there is no knowledge of how cowbird population growth rates may vary across combinations of vegetation types and host communities.

Last, we stress that more data are needed to understand cowbird population structure. Our model assumes that cowbirds exist in one large population, because there are no data for constructing spatially-explicit models. Without more knowledge of population boundaries and how adult and juvenile cowbirds move between populations over time, managers will not be able to predict the true efficacy of management alternatives and may choose inappropriate scales for management.

ACKNOWLEDGMENTS

We thank T. E. Martin, E. Greene, M. Morrison, J. Rotenberry, T. L. George, and H. Salwasser for reviewing this manuscript. We also thank M. Wisdom and S. Hoekman for providing helpful discussion. Our project was supported by the Boone and Crockett Wildlife Conservation Program, the U.S. Forest Service Pacific Northwest Research Station, LaGrande, and the Wildlife Biology Program at the University of Montana, Missoula.

APPENDIX 1. BROWN-HEADED COWBIRD STAGE-BASED MODEL

COWBIRD LIFE CYCLE DIAGRAM AND MATRIX

The biologically relevant projection interval for cowbirds is 1 year, so elements within the matrix represent annual rates (Fig. A1). However, in the first year of life, there are three relevant stages: egg, nestling, and yearling; thus we let the first year of life have egg, nestling, and yearling components. We only include one adult stage (as opposed to annual age classes) because age specific adult survival rates are not available and management techniques target all adults concurrently.

Transition matrix:

$$\begin{bmatrix} F_{11} & F_{12} \\ G_{21} & P_{22} \end{bmatrix}$$

DEFINITIONS OF MATRIX ELEMENTS AND VALUES FOR THE MEAN MATRIX:

Mean survival from stage 1 to stage 2 $[G(2,1)]$ = mean egg survival (0.38) × mean nestling survival (0.64) × mean yearling survival (0.24) = 0.06

Mean survival from stage 2 to stage 2 $[P(2,2)]$ = mean annual adult survival = 0.47

Mean yearling fertility $[F(1,1)]$ = mean daily laying rate (0.56) × laying period (40 d) × proportion of female eggs (0.5) × mean first year survival (0.06) = 0.65

Mean adult fertility $[F(1,2)]$ = mean daily laying rate (0.69) × laying period (40 d) × proportion of female eggs (0.5) × mean adult survival (0.47) = 6.49

These transition probabilities are incorporated into a mean matrix and have the resulting stable stage distribution and deterministic population growth rate (λ):

$$\begin{bmatrix} 0.65 & 6.49 \\ 0.06 & 0.47 \end{bmatrix}\begin{bmatrix} 0.9244 \\ 0.0756 \end{bmatrix} \quad \lambda = 1.184$$

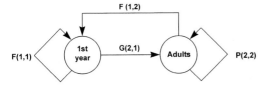

FIGURE A1.   Life cycle diagram used for the Brown-headed Cowbird analysis.

STAGE SPECIFIC TIME INTERVALS

The projection interval is one year (365 d):
  1st year:
    egg survival stage: 15 d
    nestling survival stage: 10 d
    yearling survival stage: 340 d
  2nd year + (Adults):   1 yr

APPENDIX 2. ANALYSIS OF A HOW A GIVEN REMOVAL MAY AFFECT BROWN-HEADED COWBIRD SURVIVAL AND POPULATION GROWTH RATE

This analysis is included to clarify how the sensitivity analysis must be interpreted. Specifically, we were concerned that our analysis would lead to time, effort, and money being prematurely applied towards egg removal programs. When we include environmental variance in the analysis, egg survival has the largest impact upon population growth rate. However, it is not clear how removing cowbird eggs actually alters egg survival rates. We investigate this link with the following crude analysis, where we decrement cowbird vital rates one-at-a-time by removing a specified number of individual eggs, nestlings, yearlings, or adults.

We start with the following assumptions:

1. There is a population of 5,000 cowbirds at the beginning of a breeding season.

2. This population has the vital rates of the mean matrix in Appendix 1.

3. All mortality is additive (no compensatory effects) and immigration is nonexistent.

4. Populations are at stable age (stage) distribution.

To calculate the number of individuals in particular life stages within a population of 5,000, at time t, we must first determine the number of individuals at time $t-1$:

$$N_{t-1} \times \lambda = 5,000$$

$$N_{t-1} = 4222.97.$$

By multiplying N_{t-1} by the stage distribution vector (Appendix 1), we determine the total number of eggs and adults at time $t-1$:

$$4222.97 \times \begin{bmatrix} 0.9244 \\ 0.0756 \end{bmatrix} = \begin{bmatrix} 3903.72 \text{ eggs} \\ 319.26 \text{ adults} \end{bmatrix}$$

We then multiply the matrix by the stage distribution vector at time $t-1$ to determine the initial number of individuals in each stage at time t:

Initial number of eggs:

$$(F_{11} \times V_1) + (F_{12} \times V_2) = 4621.81$$

Initial number of adults:

$$(G_{21} \times V_1) + (P_{22} \times V_2) = 377.90.$$

Immediately after breeding, we have a population size of 377.90 adults and 4621.81 eggs. This is our total population of 5,000. To calculate the number of individuals in intermediate stages, the total number of eggs is decrement by egg, nestling, and yearling survival rates successively:

Initial number of nestlings:

Initial number of eggs × egg survival rate

= 1756.29

Initial number of yearlings:

Initial number of nestlings × yearling survival rate

= 1124.03.

We simulate individual removals by decreasing the number of individuals in a life stage by increments of 40. This mortality is assumed to occur after the initial probabilistic mortality of that stage class (i.e., it is assumed to be additive). For example, if management removes 200 eggs, then the adjusted egg survival rate is calculated as follows:

[(Initial number of eggs × original egg survival rate)

− 200 eggs]/Initial number of eggs

= New egg survival rate

$$\frac{(4621.81 \times 0.38) - 200 \text{ eggs}}{4621.81} = 0.34$$

In this example, removing 200 eggs reduced egg survival rates by only 11%. The altered survival rates are then incorporated into the mean matrix to calculate the resulting population growth rate (Fig. 7).

Studies in Avian Biology No. 18:135–143, 1999.

LAZULI BUNTINGS AND BROWN-HEADED COWBIRDS IN MONTANA: A STATE-WIDE LANDSCAPE ANALYSIS OF POTENTIAL SOURCES AND SINKS

ERICK GREENE, JENNIFER JOLIVETTE, AND ROLAND REDMOND

Abstract. Although Lazuli Buntings (*Passerina amoena*) are currently widely distributed in the western United States and southwestern Canada, parasitization by Brown-headed Cowbirds (*Molothrus ater*) is high in many populations. Demographic models suggest that isolated Lazuli Bunting populations with greater than about 20% parasitization are not self-sustaining. To examine the spatial structure of potential source and sink populations, we developed landscape models of Lazuli Bunting and Brown-headed Cowbird distributions for Montana. These models were derived from a comprehensive GIS database that contains information on vegetation types, topographic relief, and hydrography for all 38,081,490 ha in Montana, with a resolution of land cover types of 90 m^2. These models suggest that Lazuli Buntings may be more vulnerable to Brown-headed Cowbirds than is currently appreciated: of the 8,070,163 ha identified as potential Lazuli Bunting breeding habitat, 98.5% fell in areas with a high and medium risk of Brown-headed Cowbird presence; only 1.5% of potential Lazuli Bunting breeding habitat was in areas in which Brown-headed Cowbirds are not predicted to occur. Furthermore, Lazuli Buntings breed in vegetation patches that occur in spatial configurations that make them especially vulnerable to Brown-headed Cowbirds; patches tend to be small (more than 90% of patches are less than 10 ha in size) with high edge to interior ratios, and are generally surrounded by locations that could support livestock.

Key Words: brood parasite, Brown-headed Cowbird, demography, GIS models, landscape ecology, Lazuli Bunting, metapopulation, *Molothrus ater,* parasitization, *Passerina amoena,* source-sink populations.

Many natural areas are becoming degraded and fragmented by human activities, with many organisms living in increasingly remote or isolated patches (Askins 1995). Concern over such threats has lead to monitoring programs for populations of many species, which rely on estimates of the distribution and abundance of the species of interest. Although these data are important, they do not in themselves provide information on the reproductive performance of a population, and they may be misleading about its underlying dynamics (Donovan et al. 1995a, Brawn and Robinson 1996). For example, a species may be a common resident in an area, thus suggesting that the local population is reproducing well enough to be self-sustaining, but persists because of immigration and recolonization by individuals from other source populations. Although some species of neotropical migrant birds still occur in many small woodlots during the spring and summer in mid-western and eastern North America, their reproductive success can be well below that required for replacement. These ecological sinks are being replenished by frequent immigration of individuals from source areas (Robinson et al. 1995a, Villard et al. 1989).

Thus, the number, sizes, spatial relationships of breeding sub-populations, correlation of ecological conditions among patches, reproductive performance and survivorship in patches across a landscape, and the patterns of dispersal of individuals between patches are important in determining the dynamics of a species on a large spatial scale (Harrison and Quinn 1989, Gutzwiller and Anderson 1992, Donovan et al. 1995a, b, Brawn and Robinson 1996). These characteristics are difficult to measure and are generally poorly known for most species, but have been the impetus for such population monitoring programs as Breeding Biology Research and Monitoring Database (BBIRD) and Monitoring Avian Productivity and Survivorship (MAPS). The emerging fields of metapopulation dynamics and landscape ecology seek to provide insights to such critical questions.

Lazuli Buntings (*Passerina amoena*) occur commonly during the breeding season in a variety of vegetation types throughout western United States and southwestern Canada (Greene et al. 1996). In many areas with high shrub cover in western Montana they are the among the most abundant species during the breeding season. Based solely on their distribution and abundance, this species appears to be doing well. Indeed, Partners in Flight's monitoring scheme suggests that Lazuli Buntings are not at risk; an analysis of Breeding Bird Survey data suggests that most populations are stable, or perhaps even increasing (Butcher et al. 1992).

However, the apparent abundance and wide geographic distribution of Lazuli Buntings may mask serious underlying problems. Although Lazuli Buntings had been reported to be rare hosts of Brown-headed Cowbirds (*Molothrus ater*; Friedmann 1929, Friedmann et al. 1977, Friedmann and Kiff 1985), it has recently been discovered that parasitization levels are high in many populations (Greene et al. 1996). The demographic consequences of parasitization appear severe, and parasitization levels above about 20% are likely to reduce population growth rate below that required for replacement (Greene et al. 1996, Greene *this volume*). Thus, some Lazuli Bunting breeding populations may consist of source populations in which reproduction is good, and these sources may resupply sink populations.

We currently have no information on possible location of source and sink areas for Lazuli Buntings. Our objective is to predict the breeding distribution of Lazuli Buntings and Brown-headed Cowbirds for Montana. We estimate the amounts, locations, and spatial configurations of potential Lazuli Bunting breeding habitat that is at various degrees of risk from Brown-headed Cowbirds. This general approach may also serve as a model for other species of birds (Tucker et al. 1997), and may help inform management decisions (Thompson 1993, Doak and Mills 1994, Petit et al. 1995).

METHODS

We modeled the potential breeding habitats for Lazuli Buntings and Brown-headed Cowbirds using a GIS database containing information on types of land cover, elevation, slope, aspect, and hydrography for the entire state of Montana. We briefly describe the construction of this database, followed by descriptions of the specific habitat models for Lazuli Buntings and Brown-headed Cowbirds.

GIS DATABASE

A two stage, digital classification process was used to map vegetation and land cover across Montana. In the first stage, land cover patterns were derived from false-color composite images from Landsat Thematic Mapper (TM) channels 4, 5, and 3 (R, G, and B) using an unsupervised classification algorithm (www.wru.umt.edu/default.shtml). Thirty-three different Landsat TM scenes were used to map existing vegetation and land cover across the state. All scenes were recorded during the growing seasons (mid-June to mid-September) of 1991–1993. The scenes were obtained in terrain-corrected form and projected into an Albers Equal Area Conic projection (NAD27 datum). The final pixel size was 30 m². Adjacent pixels of the same spectral class were grouped into contiguous areas equal to or greater than 2 ha for upland cover types (Ma 1995, Ford et al. 1997). In riparian and woody draw areas,

pixels were merged to 0.4 ha minimum map units (MMU) in eastern Montana and 0.1 ha in western Montana. These spatial units were imported into ARC/INFO GIS as raster polygons (and were termed "regions").

The second stage involved a supervised classification (based on ground reference data) run within ARC/INFO to label all regions according to existing vegetation and land cover types (Ford et al. 1997). This process was carried out independently for each TM scene, then all 33 scenes were edge-matched to create a seamless raster database containing cover type attributes for each region. The resulting database contained more than 4 million regions labeled to one of 50 different land cover types. To reduce the file size for GIS modeling, the statewide land cover grid was resampled to 90 m², which still resulted in a very large database with over 4.232×10^9 pixels covering Montana (38,081,490 ha).

Information on elevation, slope, and aspect were derived from digital elevation data. U. S. Geological Survey (USGS) 7.5' Digital Elevation Models were used when available ($\approx$ 1,500). Some quadrangles, particularly in eastern Montana, were not available in digital form. Data for these quadrangles were estimated with 3-arc-second data from USGS (source scale 1:250,000), resampled to 30 m² cells, and co-registered to the TM scenes. Digital Elevation Models for each TM scene were appended to the state boundary and then resampled to the same 90 m² pixel size as the land cover data set. Data on rivers, streams, and lakes, in the form of USGS 1:100,000 scale digital line graphs were acquired for all Montana. These were merged to create a seamless, statewide hydrography database.

All analyses were conducted with ARC/INFO (version 7.11) and Erdas Imagine (version 8.1) on IBM RS/6000 workstations running AIX (version 4.1). In addition, customized software for many processing steps was written in FORTRAN and C, or scripts written in ARC Macro Language. Descriptions of the land cover types used the species habitat models are summarized in the Appendix. Additional information on the database, along with detailed descriptions and photographs of the 50 vegetation cover categories can be found at the University of Montana's Wildlife Spatial Analysis Lab's web site (www.wru.umt.edu/default.shtml).

HABITAT MODELS

We developed habitat models to predict the breeding distribution of Lazuli Buntings and Brown-headed Cowbirds by selecting combinations of variables from the statewide land cover, hydrography, and topography data sets. We selected the distributional rules based on both published sources, as well as our unpublished information on the distribution of Lazuli Buntings in western Montana. All GIS operations were done in raster format using the Grid Module in ARC/INFO. The selection rules described below produced distributional layers that corresponded closely with actual bunting and cowbird distributions in western Montana.

Lazuli Bunting Model

Lazuli Buntings breed in habitats that have thick shrubs, low trees, and/or dense herbaceous vegetation (Greene et al. 1996). These areas include arid brushy canyons, slopes of hills and escarpments, riparian edges, and thicketed swales. On the prairies east of the continental divide, Lazuli Buntings typically breed in riparian areas, vegetated gullies, thickets on hillsides, sagebrush, and along ravines and gullies (Dobkin 1994, Greene et al. 1996). In western Montana, Lazuli Buntings breed from the lowest valleys to at least 3,000 m on mountain slopes, alpine meadows, and in high elevation aspen forests with thick shrub cover. The highest breeding densities occur in recent post-fire areas, but lower breeding densities are typical in post-logged treatments such as group-selection cuts, seed-tree cuts, and clearcuts (Hutto 1995b, Greene et al. 1996). Lazuli Buntings also breed in open forests with low canopy closure.

To model potential Lazuli Bunting breeding habitat, the GIS database was queried to find suitable combinations of land cover, topography, and proximity to water. In the following query descriptions, numbers in parentheses refer to land cover type codes (descriptions and photographs are available at www.wru.umt.edu/default.shtml). All grassland (3110, 3130, 3150, 3170), agriculture (2010, 2020), and urban (1100) land cover types were selected, along with a 90-m wide buffer strip into adjacent shrub or forest lands (3200 through 4400). Similar 90-m wide buffer strips were selected along both sides of all streams if the land cover represented montane parkland and subalpine meadow (3180), grassland (3110, 3130, 3150, 3170), xeric forest (4290), or broadleaf-conifer forest (4300). Grassland cover types (3110, 3130, 3150, and 3170) were included if the associated slope was greater than 20%. Low canopy closure (10–39%) was selected for ponderosa pine (*Pinus ponderosa*) (4206), xeric forest (4290), and broadleaf forest (4140) within 90 m of streams and rivers. All burns (4400) were included.

Brown-headed Cowbird Model

Brown-headed Cowbirds have expanded their range into nearly all of Montana. They are common in a wide variety of areas within commuting distances of livestock, including agriculture areas, grasslands, riparian vegetation, woodlands and woodland edges, brushy thickets, and residential areas (Robinson et al. 1995a, Hutto 1995b). Brown-headed Cowbird females commute between separate breeding and feeding ranges, and typical commuting distances are in the range of 1–7 km, although females can travel longer distances to their foraging areas (Rothstein et al. 1980, 1984, 1986b; Dufty 1982a, Thompson 1994, Robinson et al. 1995a).

We predicted two different Brown-headed Cowbird distributional layers: (1) a High Risk layer included areas within 2700 m of cover types that contain suitable afternoon foraging areas for Brown-headed Cowbirds, and (2) a Low Risk layer that included areas 2700–4500 m from cover types suitable for afternoon foraging by Brown-headed Cowbirds. The High Risk layer included all vegetation along riparian cover types (6110–6400), plus all areas within 2700 m of all urban (1100), agricultural (2010, 2020), and grassland cover types (3110, 3130, 3150, and 3170). The Low Risk layer included areas that were farther than 2700 m but less than 4500 m from any of the cover types used to define the High Risk areas. These risk areas are conservative, because female Brown-headed Cowbirds can commute more than 4500 m from foraging areas to egg-laying areas (Rothstein et al. 1980, 1995a; Dufty 1982a).

Accuracy of Models

To assess the accuracy of the land cover map, the probability of misclassifying cover types was estimated using a bootstrap method, in which the training data were subsampled 50 times, randomly and with replacement; each time the bootstrap sample was used to classify the remaining reference data (details in Steele et al. 1998). Because the land cover classification scheme is complex, and some cover types were quite similar in terms of their constituent plant species, some types of misclassification were considered less serious than others. For example, confusion between sagebrush (3350) and xeric shrub-grasslands (3520) was considered to be acceptable, since sagebrush (*Artemesia* spp.) is a dominant component of each cover type. In contrast, a confusion between very low cover grassland (3130) and Douglas-fir forest (4212) was considered an absolutely wrong mismatch. The average classification accuracy at the acceptable level (i.e., the cover type was classified correctly, or classified as another cover type which shares the same dominant plant species) was 82.8% for the cover types used in the species habitat models (Appendix).

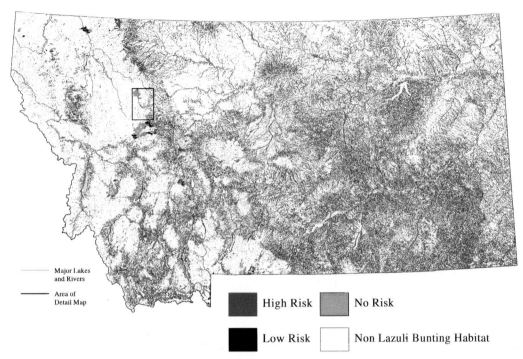

FIGURE 1.   GIS habitat model for potential Lazuli Bunting breeding habitat for Montana. Inset box in west-central part of state indicates location of area shown in more detail in Fig. 2.

The accuracy of the bird habitat models was assessed following the recommendations of Edwards et al. (1996). The predicted and observed occurrence of Lazuli Buntings and Brown-headed Cowbirds was compared at 14 validation sites around the state for which checklists were available. For Brown-headed Cowbirds, there was 100% agreement between the predicted and observed occurrence. For Lazuli Buntings, there was 86% agreement; in no case were buntings recorded where we did not predict them to occur (error of omission), but there were two areas where we predicted they would occur but they have not been recorded (errors of commission).

OVERLAPPING LAYERS

We intersected the predicted High Risk and Low Risk Brown-headed Cowbird layers with the Lazuli Bunting distribution. This predicted three different categories of potential Lazuli Bunting breeding habitat corresponding to three different levels of risk of Brown-headed Cowbird parasitization. We defined (1) High Risk Lazuli Bunting habitat as that within 2700 m of potential afternoon foraging areas for Brown-headed Cowbirds; (2) Low Risk Lazuli Bunting habitat as potential breeding habitat between 2700 and 4500 m away from potential afternoon foraging areas for Brown-headed Cowbirds; and

(3) No Risk areas as all potential Lazuli Bunting breeding habitat that was farther than 4500 m away from potential afternoon foraging areas for Brown-headed Cowbirds.

To obtain perimeter measurements for all the No Risk patches of potential Lazuli Bunting breeding habitat, we converted the patch boundaries from 90 m² raster format to smooth, vector lines (using ARC/INFO). For each No Risk bunting patch, we also estimated the distance to the nearest High Risk and Low Risk areas, measured from the centroid of each patch.

RESULTS

The model identified 8,070,163 ha as potential breeding habitat for Lazuli Buntings in Montana (Fig. 1). Of this habitat, over 97.2 % (7,846,315 ha) occurred in areas that are potentially at High Risk of Brown-headed Cowbird parasitization; 1.3 % (100,793 ha) occurs in areas of Low Risk; and only 1.5 % (123,055 ha) occurred in areas where Brown-headed Cowbirds are unlikely to occur.

The distribution of potential High Risk, Low Risk, and No Risk habitats for Lazuli Buntings varied across the state. East of the continental divide, all potential Lazuli Bunting breeding habitat was classified as High Risk. This is because Lazuli Bunting breeding habitat was main-

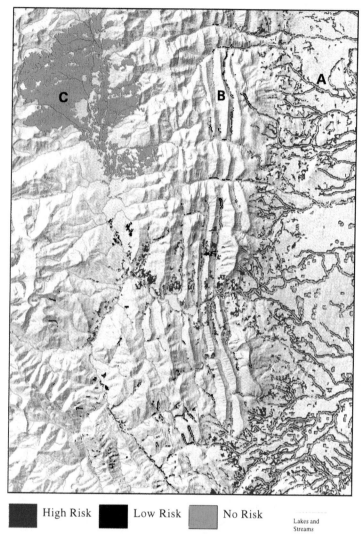

High Risk   Low Risk   No Risk   Lakes and Streams

FIGURE 2. Detail of inset area shown in Fig. 1 along the Rocky Mountain front, where prairies (to the east) meet the Rocky Mountains. Potential High Risk, Low Risk, and No Risk Lazuli Bunting breeding habitats are shown in relation to topographic relief.

ly restricted to riparian edges and small patches of vegetation that were close to areas that could be grazed by livestock. West of the continental divide, Brown-headed Cowbirds and Lazuli Buntings both occur in mountain valleys, and their overlap was predicted to be substantial at lower elevations. However, Lazuli Buntings also breed at higher elevations farther away from areas likely to support Brown-headed Cowbirds. Thus, west of the continental divide, patches of No Risk habitat were widely distributed on the slopes above the mountain valleys.

This analysis also suggested that there are three qualitatively and quantitatively different patterns of spatial configuration of Lazuli Bunting breeding habitat in Montana. All three spatial patterns are illustrated in Fig. 2, which is an enlargement of an area along the east front of the Rocky Mountains (shown as a rectangle in Fig. 1). First, east of the Rocky Mountain front, potential Lazuli Bunting breeding habitat occurred primarily in thin, highly-dissected strips along streams, gullies and rivers (A in Fig. 2). Second, west of the Rocky Mountain front, small, isolated patches of Low Risk or No Risk habitat were distributed mainly at mid-elevations above valley bottoms (B in Fig. 2). Third, extremely large patches of No Risk habitat were

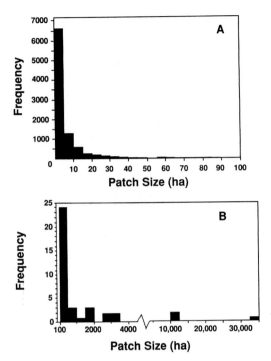

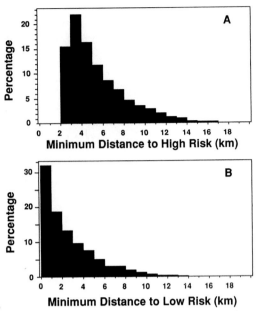

FIGURE 4.   Minimum distance from patches of No Risk Lazuli Bunting breeding habitat (N = 9,673 habitat patches) to (A) High Risk habitat, and (B) Low Risk habitat.

FIGURE 3.   A. Distribution of sizes of potential patches of No Risk breeding habitat of Lazuli Bunting. (N = 9,673 patches). Thirty eight patches are larger than 100 ha, but they do not show up at this scale. B. Distribution of patch size of potential breeding habitat larger than 100 ha; all patches larger than 1000 ha occurred in burns. Notice the different scales in panels A and B.

limited to burned areas in the western mountains (C in Fig. 2), and near Yellowstone National Park along the borders of Wyoming and Idaho.

In general, Lazuli Bunting breeding habitat occurred in small patches (Fig. 3). Of all habitat patches in No Risk areas, 72% were less than 5 ha, 85% were less than 10 ha, and 95% were less than 20 ha in size (Fig. 3A). Only 38 (0.29%) potential patches of No Risk breeding habitat in Montana were larger than 100 ha (Fig. 3B); 27 of these patches were between 100 and 1,000 ha. All patches larger than 1,000 ha occurred in old burns. The three patches larger than 10,000 ha were in the 1988 Scapegoat Wilderness burn (33,880 ha), visible as the largest green patch in west-central Montana in Fig. 1; part of the 1988 Yellowstone fire complex visible on the Montana-Wyoming border (10,998 ha in Montana); and the 1984 Charlotte Peak burn (10,387 ha), visible in Fig. 1 north of the Scapegoat burn, and shown in close-up at C in Fig. 2.

In addition to their small size, patches of No Risk breeding habitat were located fairly close to habitats that could support Brown-headed

Cowbirds (Fig. 4). Out of 9,673 patches of potential No Risk habitat, 38.5% were within 4 km of High Risk areas, and 76.1% were within 7 km of High Risk areas (Fig. 4A); 75.4% of patches were within 4 km of Low Risk areas, while 91.6% were within 7 km of Low Risk areas (Fig. 4B). There was no relationship between the size of No Risk habitat patches and the distance away from potential areas with Brown-headed Cowbirds (Fig. 5). This figure shows the

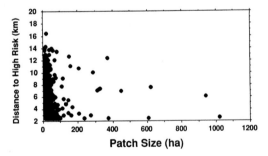

FIGURE 5.   Relationship between size of potential breeding habitat in No Risk areas and distance to the nearest High Risk area. This graph shows the relationship for the 1500 largest patches (N = 1500 patches, r^2 = 0.00026, ns). Ten largest patches omitted from this graph for scaling purposes; the relationship does not change when all patches included.

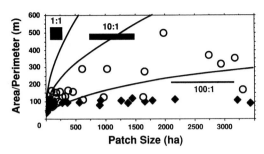

FIGURE 6. Shape indices for patches of potential breeding habitat. Lines show theoretical curves for area/perimeter ratios for patches of different shapes (square patches, rectangular patches ten times longer than wide, and rectangular patches 100 times longer than wide). Circles show area/perimeter ratios for 1,500 randomly selected patches of potential No Risk habitat in western Montana; diamonds show area/perimeter ratios for 500 randomly selected patches of potential High Risk habitat in eastern Montana.

relationship for the largest 1500 patches (the ten largest patches were omitted for scaling purposes; there was no change if all patches are included).

Potential breeding habitat of Lazuli Buntings occurred in long, thin strips or in highly dissected patches, with lots of edge relative to area (Fig. 6). The distribution of area-perimeter ratios for No Risk habitat patches (from west of the Rocky Mountain front) were clustered between the lines showing area-perimeter ratios for rectangles ten and 100 times longer than wide. Potential patches of breeding habitat were even more elongated in the eastern part of Montana, with most patches even more extreme than the 100:1 line (Fig. 6).

DISCUSSION

Our landscape-level GIS model is a first step towards a better understanding of the population dynamics of Lazuli Buntings on a large spatial scale; we present these results as testable hypotheses in need of ground-truthing. Our model identified a large proportion (97%) of potential Lazuli Bunting breeding habitat in Montana at high vulnerability to Brown-headed Cowbirds. This is especially true for eastern Montana. However, the Brown-headed Cowbird distributional model was based solely on land cover types, and did not incorporate any information on the actual spatial distribution of livestock (since such information is not currently available). This model assumes that all areas that could support livestock actually contain cattle. Although this assumption may be correct for some parts of the state, we need more information on the spatial and temporal distribution of

livestock, and thus Brown-headed Cowbirds, for many western locations. It is probable that cattle and Brown-headed Cowbirds are much more clumped in time and space than suggested by the red, High Risk areas identified in Fig. 1. If this is the case, there may be many more safe, No Risk or Low Risk habitats east of the Rocky Mountain front than was identified by this model. We are currently conducting ground-truthing studies to identify the spatial and temporal distribution of cows and Brown-headed Cowbirds, especially within areas identified as High Risk for Lazuli Buntings.

Potential Lazuli Bunting breeding habitat occurs in three quantitatively different spatial configurations. First, potential breeding habitat in non-mountainous areas tends to occur in long, linear, strips along streams and in gullies. These patches have low ratios of interior to edge, and are typically embedded in vegetation types that could support livestock, such as rangeland or grassland. Brown-headed Cowbirds are able to search vegetation with these characteristics extremely effectively (Robinson et al. 1995a). In the western part of Montana, most potential Lazuli Bunting breeding habitat that occurred in the valley bottoms was predicted to be at High Risk of parasitization. Many small (usually less than 20 ha) Low Risk and No Risk habitat patches occurred above the valley bottoms; a few extremely large patches of No Risk habitats occurred in old burns.

We defined High Risk and Low Risk Lazuli Bunting habitats as those occurring within 2.7 km, and 2.7–4.5 km, respectively, of potential habitats that could support livestock. This is a conservative choice of buffer distances, since radio-tracking studies indicate that female Brown-headed Cowbirds can commute up to 7 km between their morning breeding areas and afternoon feeding sites (Rothstein et al. 1984, Thompson 1994). However, most female cowbirds commute shorter distances than these maximum values, and parasitization levels typically fall off with increasing distance from afternoon feeding areas.

Lazuli Bunting populations appear to consist of spatially-separated subpopulations, interconnected by dispersal of individuals between patches (i.e., metapopulations). Realistic metapopulation models for Lazuli Buntings will require more information on the sizes, spatial relationships, and demographic characteristics (reproductive performance, survivorship) of bunting sub-populations, and dispersal behavior of buntings between sub-populations.

Dispersal abilities and recolonization behavior are unknown for most species of birds, including Lazuli Buntings. Dispersal distances for many species may be much larger than previously thought, and thus the appropriate spatial scale for metapopulation models may be large. Information on the dispersal of Lazuli Buntings is limited, but anecdotal evidence suggests that this species can disperse large distances and quickly colonize suitable areas. First, Lazuli Buntings breed in early successional vegetation that is created unpredictably in time and space. Forest fires (or other events such as draining reservoirs) create patches of suitable vegetation that are often a long way from other suitable areas; Lazuli Buntings typically colonize these areas rapidly and in large numbers (Greene et al. 1996). Second, banding studies suggest that natal philopatry by juvenile buntings is low, and that adults can disperse among suitable breeding habitats between years (Greene et al. 1996). Third, there does not appear to be any large-scale geographic structure to song dialects. Yearling males learn their song after they return to the breeding grounds (Greene et al. 1996). With local or regional philopatry, we would expect some hint of cultural evolution of song types, giving rise to some sort of geographic song dialects.

These issues of dispersal behavior aid in understanding the dynamics of interconnected populations, and in formulating ecologically realistic metapopulation models (Pulliam 1988, Robinson et al. 1995b, Brawn and Robinson 1996). The original formulation of metapopulation models consisted of habitat patches in which isolated subpopulations of about the same size exchanged migrants with each other (Levin 1974, Gilpin and Hanski 1991). Several variations on this theme have been proposed, and they differ mainly in the relative size of habitat patches and the spatial scale of dispersal relative to the spatial heterogeneity of the environment. The core-satellite model (Hanski 1982, Harrison 1991) refers to a population that is subdivided into a large, central population with smaller peripheral satellite populations. Most of the reproduction occurs in the core area, and it provides dispersers to the outlying satellite populations, but not vice versa. The dynamics and persistence of such a system is determined by events in the core area and does not depend upon the satellite populations. Such may be the case for Lazuli Buntings if it is found that reproductive success is high only in the large burns (source populations) and much lower in other areas (satellite populations).

Patchy population models describe individual patches that are separated from other patches, but the patches are close enough to each other so that dispersal of individuals among patches is extremely frequent. The spatial scale of dispersal is much larger than the spatial scale of habitat

heterogeneity (Harrison 1991). In this case, the relevant demographic unit is a larger network of interconnected patches that are isolated demographically from other networks of patches.

IDENTIFICATION OF RESEARCH PRIORITIES

This landscape analysis helps to focus attention on some research and management priorities.

Spatial and temporal distribution of Brown-headed Cowbirds in western landscapes

We currently have much less understanding of Brown-headed Cowbird movements and spatial relationships with livestock in western than in eastern and mid-western landscapes (Robinson et al. 1995a). Rather than isolated islands of undisturbed vegetation embedded in landscapes modified by human activities (e.g., agricultural and urban lands), many western landscapes consist of relatively large tracts of forested areas inset with smaller patches of disturbed areas. We need to document the spatial and temporal distributions of livestock and Brown-headed Cowbirds in these western landscapes.

Management implications

Once we have a better understanding of the relationship between the distribution of livestock and Brown-headed Cowbirds, it may be possible to suggest ways to modify grazing regimes that would result in large improvements in reproductive success for many species of Brown-headed Cowbird hosts (Robinson et al. 1993, 1995a; Thompson 1993, Petit et al. 1995). For example, cattle may be concentrated for short periods during the time when many species initiate nesting. Although areas surrounding the cattle might experience extremely high levels of parasitization, larger areas farther away from the cattle could be converted into source areas experiencing much lower levels of parasitization.

Ecological importance of burns

Ecologists recognize that fires play a critical role in western forest ecosystems. Their ecological effects can be different from other sorts of disturbances, such as different types of forest harvesting practices. The only large, No Risk habitats identified by our model were burned areas. Indeed, the highest breeding densities of Lazuli Buntings have been reported in post-burn areas (Hutto 1995b). These few, large burns may be significant source locations, producing excess buntings that disperse to other areas in which reproductive success is lower. The importance of large, post-burn areas for Lazuli Bunting reproduction needs to be determined.

Dispersal behavior and metapopulation models

Dispersal behavior remains one of the most poorly studied aspect of the ecology of many organisms. This information is crucial for constructing realistic metapopulation models, and for understanding the population dynamics of spatially-fragmented species.

ACKNOWLEDGMENTS

Our work has been generously supported by the US Fish and Wildlife Service. Special thanks to S. Jones of the US Fish and Wildlife Service for her continued encouragement and support. P. Thornton and P. McLaughlin helped construct the GIS models, and were invaluable with the computer analysis. J. Schumacher produced the final GIS figures. We thank L. Hall, R. Hutto, M. Morrison, J. Citta, and S. Mills for helpful discussion and comments.

APPENDIX. DESCRIPTIONS OF MONTANA GAP ANALYSIS LAND COVER TYPES USED IN GIS MODELS

Cover type code	Name	Area (ha)	Number of patches	% of state	Estimated Level 3 accuracy[a]
1100	Urban or developed lands	63,733	1,109	0.17	—
2010	Agricultural lands non-irrigated	3,632,611	96,092	9.54	—
2020	Agricultural lands	1,957,294	94,928	5.14	—
3110	Altered herbaceous	1,104,946	109,396	2.67	89.5
3130	Very low cover grasslands	1,104,361	139,493	2.90	97.8
3150	Low/moderate cover grasslands	10,427,464	432,016	27.38	95.1
3170	Moderate/high cover grasslands	1,236,660	196,470	3.25	88.5
3180	Montane parklands and subalpine meadows	528,201	59,185	1.39	79.6
3200	Mixed mesic shrubs	949,873	172,497	2.49	68.1
3300	Mixed xeric shrubs	1,227,852	184,013	3.22	81.1
3309	Silver sage	73,334	20,022	0.19	61.5
3310	Salt-desert shrub/dry salt flat	131,141	22,824	0.34	96.9
3350	Sagebrush	2,145,574	220,288	5.63	90.9
3510	Mesic shrub–grassland	280,075	64,714	0.74	83.6
3520	Xeric shrub–grassland	524,061	79,041	1.38	90.8
4000	Low density xeric forest	286,187	63,913	0.75	76.2
4140	Mixed broadleaf forest	357,539	72,262	0.94	76.2
4203	Lodgepole pine	1,286,156	98,028	3.38	96.3
4205	Limber pine	120,372	22,148	0.32	63.0
4206	Ponderosa pine	1,066,130	127,272	2.80	92.8
4207	Grand fir	22,017	3,328	0.06	94.5
4210	Western red cedar	36,339	4,551	0.10	88.9
4211	Western hemlock	20,940	1,990	0.05	94.8
4212	Douglas-fir	1,329,994	139,735	3.49	93.1
4214	Rocky Mountain juniper	80,379	17,669	0.21	75.6
4215	Larch	90,437	13,652	0.24	85.2
4216	Utah juniper	14,843	2,686	0.04	50.7
4223	Douglas-fir/lodgepole pine	451,332	50,494	1.19	93.8
4260	Mixed whitebark pine forest	394,340	38,963	1.04	81.3
4270	Mixed subalpine forest	1,582,611	83,658	4.16	96.2
4280	Mixed mexic forest	1,227,309	62,871	3.22	95.7
4290	Mixed xeric forest	542,049	79,625	1.42	89.9
4300	Mixed broadleaf and conifer forest	99,843	23,137	0.26	87.1
4400	Standing burnt forest	139,261	3,431	0.37	59.9
6100	Conifer riparian	85,004	71,033	0.22	83.8
6120	Broadleaf riparian	198,372	91,838	0.52	83.2
6130	Mixed broadleaf conifer riparian	34,932	29,923	0.09	60.9
6200	Graminoid and forb riparian	702,574	281,322	1.84	74.5
6300	Shrub riparian	363,596	200,240	0.95	74.0
6400	Mixed riparian	122,662	88,540	0.32	73.7

[a] Level 3 Acceptability was assigned if the cover type was classified correctly, or if the cover type was misclassified, but the dominant plant species were the same in the two cover types.

Studies in Avian Biology No. 18:144–152, 1999.

DEMOGRAPHIC CONSEQUENCES OF BROWN-HEADED COWBIRD PARASITIZATION OF LAZULI BUNTINGS

Erick Greene

Abstract. Lazuli Buntings (*Passerina amoena*) have a large breeding distribution throughout western United States and southwestern Canada. They are not currently considered to be a species at risk, and have been reported to be rare hosts of Brown-headed Cowbirds (*Molothrus ater*). At some locations in west-central Montana, however, the prevalence of cowbird parasitization is high, with over 70% of bunting nests parasitized. The cost of cowbird parasitization for Lazuli Buntings is severe: about 90% of parasitized nests that fledged a cowbird chick did not fledge any bunting chicks. The demographic consequences of parasitization by cowbirds were investigated with non-spatial, age-structured population models, using a range of values for survivorship, fecundity, and cost of parasitization. These demographic analyses suggest that isolated populations of Lazuli Buntings are more at risk than currently appreciated; deterministic models suggest that the threshold parasitization levels required for bunting populations to replace themselves ($\lambda = 1.0$) are relatively low (threshold levels are 17% of nests parasitized for intermediate survivorship estimates and 44% for high survivorship estimates). When realistic environmental and demographic stochastic variation is incorporated into the demographic models, Lazuli Bunting populations appear even more at risk than suggested by deterministic models. More research is needed on documenting the spatial and temporal patterns of cowbird parasitization, refining survivorship estimates, and understanding the metapopulation structure of Lazuli Buntings.

Key Words: age-structured model, brood parasitism, Brown-headed Cowbird, cost of parasitization, Lazuli Bunting, *Molothrus ater*, neotropical migrant, *Passerina amoena*, population dynamics.

The impact of parasitization by Brown-headed Cowbirds (*Molothrus ater*) on populations of passerine hosts has been a long-standing issue in conservation biology. There are some well-publicized cases in which populations of songbirds are threatened by cowbird parasitization (usually in conjunction with other anthropogenic changes, such as loss and fragmentation of breeding habitat, and high densities of nest predators; Robinson et al. 1995b): Kirtland's Warbler (*Dendroica kirtlandii*; Mayfield 1977), Black-capped Vireo (*Vireo atricapillus*; Grzybowski et al. 1986), and Least Bell's Vireo (*Vireo bellii pusillus*; Goldwasser et al. 1980). In spite of one view that many populations of songbirds are now threatened by cowbird parasitization (Brittingham and Temple 1983, Terborgh 1989), the magnitude of this problem remains unclear. This is largely because the abundance of a species does not necessarily reflect its reproductive success at a location; because of large total populations and high juvenile and adult dispersal, birds can continue to recolonize areas in which nesting success is extremely low (Brawn and Robinson 1996). Since abundance may mask serious underlying reproductive failures at a location, there is a need for more detailed demographic analyses of the impact of cowbird parasitization on the dynamics of songbird populations (Robinson et al 1995a).

Lazuli Buntings (*Passerina amoena*) are widespread breeding songbirds throughout western United States and southwestern Canada, and they can be very abundant in many different types of vegetation (Greene et al. 1996). Analysis of Breeding Bird Survey (BBS) data (Butcher et al. 1992) suggested that Lazuli Bunting populations were stable or perhaps increasing, and none of the monitoring criteria indicated that Lazuli Buntings were a species at risk.

However, other analyses of BBS data (Sauer and Droege 1992) suggested populations were declining in some central and western regions, although these decreasing trends were not statistically significant. More detailed analyses of BBS data that took into account magnitude of population changes (DeSante and George 1994) suggested that populations were declining in seven states, especially in Utah. These population analyses combined data from large geographic areas and many vegetation types, and therefore may mask some serious local reproductive failures and regional population declines.

If bunting populations are declining in some areas, the causes are unknown. Previous studies have suggested that Lazuli Buntings are rare hosts of Brown-headed Cowbirds (Friedmann et al. 1977, Friedmann and Kiff 1985). However, the prevalence of cowbird parasitization, the cost of parasitization on Lazuli Bunting reproductive success, and the impact of parasitization on Lazuli Bunting population dynamics are currently unknown.

The purpose of this paper is to (1) document levels of Brown-headed Cowbird parasitization on Lazuli Buntings in western Montana, and (2) model the demographic consequences of varying levels of cowbird parasitization on Lazuli Buntings.

METHODS

DEMOGRAPHIC MODELS

The demographic consequences of cowbird brood parasitization on Lazuli Buntings were modeled using age-structured, non-spatial matrix projection models. Such models summarize the survival and reproduction of different age classes in projection matrices, and they allow a wide variety of demographic analyses (e.g., Crouse et al. 1987, Burgman and Gerard 1990, Wooton and Bell 1992; for reviews of these methods see Caswell 1989 and McDonald and Caswell 1993).

Since the survival and fecundity of buntings differ between yearling birds and older birds, but is independent of age after the first year of life (Greene et al. 1996), I constructed a female-based model with two age classes, and with a projection interval of one year. This demographic model is summarized as a life cycle diagram (Caswell 1989), which shows the transition coefficients related to survivorship and reproduction of the two age classes (Fig. 1A). Note that the age categories span a year. Thus, the yearling category integrates information about birds from just after hatching until just after their first birthday (for details see Caswell 1989, McDonald and Caswell 1993).

I investigated the consequences of cowbird parasitization on the population dynamics of Lazuli Buntings with two types of models:

1) *Deterministic population models.* These models assume time-invariant transition probabilities, density independent population growth, and do not allow for stochastic variation in vital rates (Caswell 1989). The dominant eigenvalue of a projection matrix, λ, represents the geometric rate of population growth associated with the specific transition coefficients in the matrix; a value of $\lambda = 1.0$ indicates a population is exactly replacing itself, $\lambda > 1$ indicates a population is increasing, and $\lambda < 1$ indicates a population is declining. For example, a matrix that has an associated dominant eigenvalue of $\lambda = 1.054$ indicates that a population with those vital rates would grow at 5.4% per time interval. The break-even threshold values ($\lambda = 1.0$) presented in these analyses are equivalent to May and Robinson's (1985) maximum rate of parasitization sustainable by a host population. Although long-term projections of such models are undoubtedly suspect, they are useful for investigating the short-term potential of a population

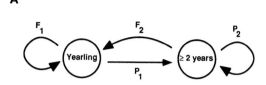

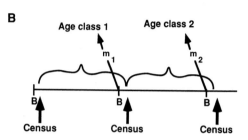

FIGURE 1. (A) Life cycle diagram of the age-structured matrix population model for Lazuli Buntings. The two nodes represent the two age classes, yearling females and females ≥ 2 years of age. Arrows indicate age-specific survivorship (P_i's) or age-specific fertilities (F_i's). The projection interval was one year. Specific values for the transition probabilities used in the analyses are shown in Table 2. (B) Schematic time line of a seasonally breeding bird, showing bookkeeping details used in a post-breeding census parameterization of projection matrices. B indicates the yearly pulse of breeding activity. The vertical arrows show the timing of the yearly censuses just after the breeding season. The chicks produced by females (m_i) are assigned to the age class before the birth event (Caswell 1989). See text for more details.

to grow (or decline), and to compare the effect of different vital rates on population growth rates.

The relative contribution of different transition coefficients to the overall population growth rate, λ, can be assessed through elasticity analyses. Elasticity coefficients, or proportional sensitivities, measure the relative change in λ in response to a proportional change in one transition coefficient (Caswell 1989, McDonald and Caswell 1993). Elasticity values are calculated for each matrix element independently (i.e., assuming all other transition coefficients do not change), and they represent the effect of infinitely small changes in each transition coefficient on λ (calculated as the partial derivative $\delta (\ln \lambda)/\delta (\ln a_{ij})$, where a_{ij} is the element in the ith row and j^{th} column of the transition matrix). Since elasticity values sum to 1, the relative contribution of matrix elements to overall population growth, λ, can be compared; a large elasticity coefficient associated with a particular vital rate suggests that a change in that transition will result in a relatively large change in the population growth rate, whereas a small elasticity coefficient indicates that a change in that vital rate will have a relatively small effect on the population growth rate. See Caswell (1989) and McDonald and Caswell (1993) for more detailed discussions on the calculation and interpretation of elasticity coefficients. Wisdom and Mills (1997) commented on limitations of the elasticity approach, and offered some methods of estimating the relative contribution of transitions on population growth rates over larger ranges of variation for each transition, and when all transition coefficients are allowed to vary at the same time (see also Citta and Mills *this volume*).

2) *Stochastic population models.* All species experience variation in life history characteristics, such as survivorship and fecundity. Incorporating variation in demographic models can provide additional important insights into the population dynamics of a species, and allows probabilistic statements about the distribution of population sizes over time (Caswell 1989, Burgman et al. 1993). Thus, in addition to the deterministic demographic models with fixed vital rates described above, I also ran stochastic Monte Carlo simulations of bunting populations that incorporated both demographic and environmental stochasticity. Demographic stochasticity refers to chance variation in population size when vital rates are applied to individuals in small populations (Burgman et al. 1993). For example, it is impossible to have 9.5 individuals, and so the population would have to be either 9 or 10; the chance difference of "half" an individual represents a large proportion of such a small population. Environmental stochasticity refers to variation in survivorship and fecundity arising from variation in environmental conditions (Caswell 1989, Burgman et al. 1993).

Each of the stochastic simulations started with 100 replicate bunting populations, each with an initial size of 100 females. Vital rates were randomly drawn from normal distributions with coefficients of variation (CV) of 10% of the mean value of the vital rates. These values of yearly variation are well within the range of variation for birds, and have been used in stochastic simulations for other species (e.g., Burgman et al. 1993). For example, a 10% CV for a mean yearly survivorship of 70% implies that 95 out of 100 populations would experience survivorship values between 56–84% (i.e., $\bar{x} \pm 2$ SD).

The models used in these analyses assume closed populations, and do not allow for dispersal among sub-populations. It is clear that most populations consist of metapopulations, in which isolated sub-populations are loosely connected by immigration and emigration of individuals. The population dynamics of a metapopulation depends upon the sizes and spatial relationships of sub-populations, variation in survivorship and reproduction among patches, and dispersal among patches (Gilpin and Hanski 1991, Harrison 1991, Brawn and Robinson 1996). Hence, the results of the non-spatial models presented here are meant only to address the question of how cowbird parasitization may influence isolated bunting populations. In essence, these analyses ask the questions: at what level of cowbird parasitization is a bunting population a potential sink population (i.e., $\lambda < 1$), and at what level of cowbird parasitization is a bunting population a potential source population (i.e., $\lambda > 1$)? Analyses of potential source and sink populations of Lazuli Buntings are the subject of another paper (Greene et al. *this volume*).

PARAMETRIZATION OF DEMOGRAPHIC MODELS

As part of other behavioral studies, populations of color-marked Lazuli Buntings have been monitored in west-central Montana since 1992 (Greene et al. 1996). Data on reproductive success, survivorship, incidence of parasitization, and the cost of parasitism from three main study locations (described below) were used to parameterize these demographic models. To gather information on age-related reproductive performance and survivorship, buntings were aged using plumage characteristics; yearling birds retain brown primary coverts, whereas birds in their second year or older have primary coverts that are tinged with blue edges (Young 1991, Greene et al. 1996).

SURVIVORSHIP

Over a six year period (1992–1997), an average of 43% of banded adult males returned to the study sites the following year. This estimate of annual survivorship is undoubtedly low, since there was dispersal off of and onto the study sites between years (Greene et al. 1996). The highest estimates of yearly adult male survivorship for the congeneric Indigo Buntings (*Passerina cyanea*) are about 0.70 (Payne 1992). Yearly survivorship for adult female Indigo Buntings are generally lower than those for adult males (Payne 1992). There is little information on survivorship of buntings during their first year of life since it is extremely difficult to distinguish between mortality and dispersal. However, first year survivorship for many passerines has been suggested to be roughly half that of adult birds (Ricklefs 1973). For these analyses I have assigned juvenile survival as half of adult survival. These estimates may be too low, and thus overestimate the impact of cowbird parasitism.

rized in Table 1. As pointed out by Pease and Grzybowski (1995), it can be misleading to estimate how brood parasites influence the seasonal reproductive success of hosts from individual nesting attempts. For example, if a female quickly renests after nest failure or parasitization, she may produce the same number of young during the entire breeding season as unparasitized females. However, Lazuli Buntings accept cowbird eggs (Greene et al. 1996), and they rarely renest in Palouse prairie areas in western Montana. The data used to parameterize these models were from intensive nest searching and monitoring of known birds over entire breeding seasons. Thus, these estimates of reproductive success were not adjusted using the methods of Pease and Grzybowski (1995).

TABLE 1. SUMMARY OF LIFE HISTORY PARAMETERS USED IN DEMOGRAPHIC ANALYSES

A. Yearly survivorship

	First year	Subsequent years
Low	0.20	0.40
Intermediate	0.45	0.65
High	0.50	0.70

B. Age-specific fertilities (# female offspring fledged per female per breeding season).

	Yearling female	Females two and older
No cowbird parasitization	0.61	1.13
Low effect of parasitization[a]	0.20	0.20
Severe effect of parasitization[b]	0.05	0.05

[a] Derived from congeneric Indigo Buntings (*Passerina cyanea*, Payne 1992; Payne and Payne 1998).
[b] Estimated from nest studies in western Montana.

To bracket a range of plausible survivorship values, three different estimates (low, intermediate, and high) were analyzed (Table 1A). The high survivorship schedule corresponds to the highest survivorship values estimated for *Passerina* buntings (Payne 1992).

REPRODUCTIVE SUCCESS

During six breeding seasons (1992–1997) near Missoula, Montana, the average number of young reared to fledging per breeding season per female in unparasitized nests was 1.87. However, the age of the female, but not the male, influenced fledging success; yearling females fledged an average of 1.22 chicks per breeding season, whereas older females fledged average of 2.26 chicks per breeding season (N = 60 females). The age-specific fertilities are summa-

COST OF PARASITIZATION

The effect of cowbird parasitization on Lazuli Buntings in western Montana is severe. Most cowbird chicks hatch slightly before or at same time as bunting chicks. When this happens, the cowbird chick obtains most of the food, and the bunting chicks usually starve within 2–3 days (Greene et al. 1996, Davison 1998). In a sample of 38 nests that fledged cowbird chick(s), 73.7% fledged only 1 cowbird chick, 15.8% fledged 2 cowbird chicks, and only 10.5% fledged 1 cowbird chick and 1 bunting chick.

To bracket a range of different costs of parasitization on bunting reproductive success, two different values were used (low and severe; Table 1B). The severe effect of parasitization is from reproductive success data from study sites in western Montana; the low cost is derived from Indigo Buntings in Michigan (Payne 1992, Payne and Payne 1998).

TABLE 2. LEFKOVITCH TRANSITION MATRICES FOR LAZULI BUNTINGS USED IN DEMOGRAPHIC ANALYSES, DERIVED USING LOW, INTERMEDIATE, AND HIGH SURVIVORSHIP ESTIMATES IN TABLE 1

To	From	
	Yearling	≥ 2 years
Low survivorship, no parasitization		
Yearling	0.122 (0.060)[a]	0.425 (0.230)
≥ 2 years	0.20 (0.230)	0.40 (0.479)
	$\lambda = 0.5922$[b]	
Intermediate survivorship, no parasitization		
Yearling	0.275 (0.089)	0.73 (0.256)
≥ 2 years	0.45 (0.256)	0.65 (0.400)
	$\lambda = 1.067$	
High survivorship, no parasitization		
Yearling	0.305 (0.092)	0.791 (0.258)
≥ 2 years	0.50 (0.258)	0.70 (0.392)
	$\lambda = 1.1617$	

[a] Elasticity coefficients associated with specific transition coefficients shown in brackets.
[b] The dominant eigenvalue, λ, is shown below each transition matrix.

TRANSITION MATRICES

The demographic parameters used in matrix-based models are different from the survivorship (l_x) and maternity (m_x) functions used in life table approaches. This is worth emphasizing, since these differences continue to be a source of confusion (McDonald and Caswell 1993). In particular, as pointed out below, the fertility elements (F_i's) of matrix-based models, unlike the m_x functions of life tables, contain terms relating to survival as well as fertility rates.

To derive the coefficients for a projection matrix model, we must define the projection interval and for birth-pulse organisms, such as buntings with concentrated, seasonal reproductive periods, the time of the census of individuals relative to the breeding period. For the projection matrix for Lazuli Buntings, the projection interval and the age class is defined as one year, and I have chosen to parameterize the model with a post-breeding census. The bookkeeping aspects of the model parameterization are shown schematically in Fig. 1B.

The survival and fertility coefficients are defined as follows (Caswell 1989, McDonald and Caswell 1993):

P_i = the probability that members of age class i survive to enter the next age class i + 1.

F_i = the number of individual females in age class 1 at time t + 1 per individual in age class i at time t.

As an example, the coefficients for the projection matrix using the low survivorship and no parasitism values from Table 1 are derived as follows. With a post-breeding census, we assign the offspring that are produced by females just before their first birthday to age class 1 (Caswell 1989). Thus, for F_1, we are concerned with how the newborn individuals in age class 1 survive to the next census period and then reproduce. By definition,

F_1 = (the probability that newly hatched individuals survive to the next census period) × (the number of female offspring produced by the surviving individuals on their first birthday).

For no parasitism and low survivorship values (from Table 1), $F_1 = 0.2 \times 0.61 = 1.22$, which is the value in the upper left of the top transition matrix in Table 2.

Similarly,

F_2 = (the probability that 1 year olds survive to the next census period) × (the number of female offspring produced by

those surviving females on their second birthday).

For no parasitism and low survivorship values (from Table 1), $F_2 = 0.4 \times 1.13 = 0.452$, which is the value in the upper right of the top transition matrix in Table 2. The age specific survivorship values are $P_1 = 0.2$ and $P_2 = 0.4$ (Caswell 1989). These are the values in the lower left and lower right, respectively, of the top matrix in Table 2.

Although I arbitrarily chose a post-breeding bookkeeping census, the model could be parameterized with any other arbitrarily chosen census time, such as a pre-breeding census. The transition coefficients in the resulting matrix would be different, but the resulting demographic analyses and conclusions would be identical. For more details on the construction and parameterization of matrix-based projection models, the interested reader is referred to the excellent treatments of Caswell (1989) and McDonald and Caswell (1993).

All demographic simulations were performed with Ramas/Age (Ferson and Akçakaya 1991) and Ramas/Stage software (Ferson 1994).

INCIDENCE OF PARASITIZATION

The prevalence of cowbird parasitization in Lazuli Bunting nests was determined at three main study sites in western Montana.

1) *Mount Sentinel and Mount Jumbo* are west-facing hillsides overlooking the city of Missoula, Montana (46° 50' N, 114° 10' W). This Palouse prairie grassland is dominated by several species of native bunch grasses, several invading weeds, with patches of bushes of ninebark (*Physocarpus malvaceus*), honeysuckle (*Lonicera utahenesis*), snowberry (*Symphoricarpos occidentalis*), wild rose (*Rosa woodsii*), and serviceberry (*Amelanchier alnifolia*) and chokecherry (*Prunus virginiana*) trees. During the 1995 breeding season, a communal cowbird roost was located in bushes at the base of Mount Jumbo and the north end of Mount Sentinel. This roost contained at least several hundred cowbirds. Spring floods during the 1996 and 1997 breeding seasons covered the cowbird roost sites, and they moved somewhere else.

2) *Bison Range National Wildlife Refuge* (47° 08' N, 114° 20' W) consists of Palouse Prairie vegetation, with steep gullies with dense patches of wild rose, ninebark, alder (*Alnus* spp.), hawthorn (*Crataegus* sp.), serviceberry, and chokecherry. Approximately 370 adult American bison (*Bison bison*) with 80–100 calves are kept on 7,492 ha, but are rotated through eight large grazing units. Ranches with large herds of cattle occur outside of the wildlife refuge. Flocks of

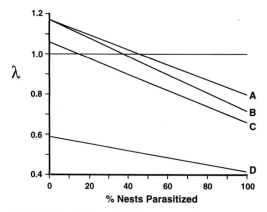

FIGURE 2. Effect of different parasitism rates and demographic characteristics on population growth rates of Lazuli Buntings in the deterministic model. The line λ = 1 indicates the break-even point at which a population exactly replaces itself; λ < 1 indicates a declining population, λ > 1 indicates a population with the potential to increase. The four different lines were calculated with the following combinations of survivorship and fertility shown in Table 3: (A) high survivorship, low effect of parasitism; (B) high survivorship, strong effect of parasitism; (C) intermediate survivorship, strong effect of parasitism; and (D) low survivorship, strong effect of parasitism.

cowbirds associate with the bison in the afternoon. I located and monitored Lazuli Bunting nests in Triskey Creek when bison were absent (the closest bison or cattle were about 4 km away), and near Indian Springs, where bison were present in large numbers throughout the breeding season.

3) *Along the Bitterroot River*, from Lee Metcalf National Wildlife Refuge (46° 40' N, 114° 20' W) and north to the town of Lolo, Montana. Riparian vegetation occurs in thin strips of black cottonwood (*Populus trichocarpa*) and Ponderosa pine (*Pinus ponderosa*) gallery forests and dense shrubby areas. These forests are generally less that 250 m wide. Cattle and horses are nu-

merous in the surrounding valley on farms and small "ranchettes."

RESULTS

DEMOGRAPHIC MODELS

The deterministic demographic models suggest that Lazuli Bunting populations are not self-sustaining in the face of low to modest levels of cowbird parasitization (Fig. 2). Even in the complete absence of cowbird parasitization, a bunting population experiencing the low survivorship values would decline by about 60% per year (λ = 0.59; Fig. 2, line D). For bunting populations experiencing intermediate survivorship values and severe parasitization, population growth is slightly above the break even point even in the absence of parasitization (λ = 1.066; Fig. 2, line C); the break-even point of λ = 1.0 would occur when 17% of the bunting nests were parasitized (Fig. 2, line C). Even with the highest estimates of survivorship and low effect of parasitism on bunting reproductive success, parasitism levels of higher than 44% would lead to growth rates that could not sustain the local population (λ < 1.0; Fig. 2, line A).

The elasticity coefficients associated with different transition coefficients (shown in brackets in Table 3) suggest that population growth rate is most sensitive to changes in adult survivorship, less sensitive to changes in yearling survivorship, and least sensitive to changes in fertility. These general results are illustrated graphically when adult survivorship and the effect of cowbird parasitization were independently varied (Fig. 3). For example, a 10% increase in the effect of cowbird parasitization had almost negligible demographic consequences; this change resulted in only a 0.10% change in the percentage of nests parasitized required for exact population replacement (Fig. 3, lines C to D). Furthermore, a 400% increase in the effect of parasitization resulted in only 3.5% increase in the percentage of nests parasitized required for exact population replacement (Fig. 3, lines D to B). In

TABLE 3. PERCENT OF LAZULI BUNTING NESTS PARASITIZED IN WESTERN MONTANA

Location	Percent parasitized		
	1995	1996	1997
Bison Range NWR			
Indian Springs (bison present)	100.0 (3)[a]	87.5 (8)	100.0 (5)
Triskey Creek (bison absent)	5.9 (17)	16.6 (12)	12.5 (8)
Missoula			
Mt Jumbo and Mt Sentinel (north)	95.8 (24)	25.0 (12)	44.4 (9)
Mt Sentinel (south)	6.2 (48)	13.3 (15)	20.0 (5)
Bitterroot River			
Cottonwood forests	100.0 (4)	83.3 (12)	72.2 (18)

[a] Sample size in parentheses.

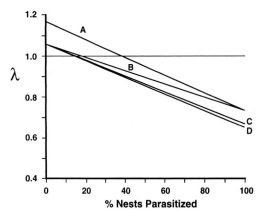

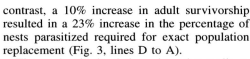

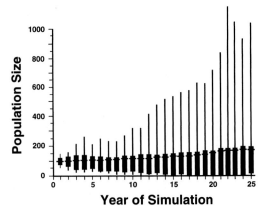

FIGURE 3. Sensitivity of population growth rate to changes in survivorship and effect of parasitism for Lazuli Buntings in western Montana. The four lines were calculated with the intermediate survivorship transition matrix (Table 3), with the following changes: (A) Intermediate adult survivorship + 10% (i.e., $P_{2,2}$ = 0.715), strong effect of parasitism; (B) Low effect of parasitism; (C) Strong effect of parasitism + 10%; and (D) Strong effect of parasitism.

FIGURE 4. Example of a stochastic simulation of Lazuli Bunting population growth, using $\lambda = 1.0186$ (high survivorship and strong effect of parasitism, with 36% of population parasitized). Simulations run with 100 populations for 25 years, with 10% coefficient of variation on vital rates. Horizontal bars indicate mean population size; vertical bars indicate range; thick bars bracket 75% of all population values for each time step.

contrast, a 10% increase in adult survivorship resulted in a 23% increase in the percentage of nests parasitized required for exact population replacement (Fig. 3, lines D to A).

The stochastic simulations show that replicate populations exposed to variation in vital rates become increasingly skewed around the average population size, with many populations smaller than the mean, and only a few populations much larger than the mean population size. This point is illustrated with the simulations for populations with a deterministic $\lambda = 1.019$; although the mean population size increased about 2% per year, the distribution of population sizes around the mean became quickly skewed over time (Fig. 4). Indeed, 82 of the original 100 populations in the stochastic simulation had decreased in size, even though the overall mean of all 100 populations increased (Fig. 4).

This result is a general one, in which the distribution of population sizes in stochastic environments became grossly skewed around the mean, with most populations much smaller than the overall mean.

INCIDENCE OF PARASITISM

There was considerable variation between sites and across years in the incidence of parasitization (range 5.9–100% of nests parasitized; Table 3). However, bunting breeding habitats that were close to agricultural land with livestock (Bitterroot River sites) or bison (Bison Range NWR, Indian Spring site), or close to

cowbird roosts (Mount Jumbo and Mount Sentinel north in 1995) had high levels of parasitization (72–100% of nests parasitized; Table 3).

DISCUSSION

These analyses suggest that Lazuli Bunting populations may be adversely effected by relatively low levels of cowbird parasitization. Even with high estimates of survivorship and reproductive success, the deterministic demographic analyses suggest that parasitization levels above about 40% of nests would cause populations to decline. Analyses for White-crowned Sparrows in the San Francisco Bay area suggested that populations can not be maintained when parasitization rates exceed about 20% (Trail and Baptista 1993).

The stochastic population models suggest that there may be even more cause for concern than suggested by the deterministic analyses; even though a λ value may be well above the break-even point of 1.0, replicate populations experiencing realistic levels of stochastic variation in vital rates become skewed around the mean population size. These results are in concordance with theoretical models of stochastic population growth, which indicate that the probability distribution of population sizes are asymptotically lognormal (stochastic ergodic theorems; Tuljapurkar and Orzach 1980, Caswell 1989). The most important implication of this result is that the lognormal distribution is skewed around its mean, with most populations below the mean, and few populations above the mean; the mean population size, and the geometric growth rate λ, become poor measures of population dynamics in stochastic environments (Caswell 1989). Indeed, λ or the mean population size can be dangerously misleading in stochastic environments; even though the average population size can increase over time for replicate populations exposed to stochastic variation in vital rates (i.e., λ > 1), most of the original populations may have gone extinct (Caswell 1989).

Intensive monitoring of Lazuli Bunting nests at several locations revealed previously unsuspected high levels of cowbird parasitization in western Montana. Although there was substantial spatial and yearly variation in parasitism levels, generally more than 70% of buntings breeding close to livestock or cowbird roosts were parasitized. These high parasitism levels are comparable to those reported for Lazuli Buntings breeding in riparian vegetation along the Sacramento River in California (87% of 45 nests parasitized over four years, annual variation ranged from 71–100%; Gardali et al. 1998). Lazuli Bunting populations experiencing such high levels of parasitism are unlikely to be self-sustaining, and are most likely sink populations that are continually recolonized by individuals from other source populations (Robinson 1992, Brawn and Robinson 1996).

The cost of parasitization was high for Lazuli Buntings in west-central Montana. Congeneric Indigo Buntings are common cowbird hosts, but they appear to be able to commonly fledge some of their own chicks as well as a cowbird chick (Payne 1992, Payne and Payne 1998). For example, Payne (1992) found that 67% of 76 parasitized nests that fledged a cowbird also fledged an Indigo Bunting chick; the immediate cost of parasitization was about 1.2 fewer bunting chicks fledged per parasitized nest than unparasitized nests (Payne and Payne 1998). It is not clear how these differences arise; food may be less abundant in the more xeric Lazuli Bunting breeding habitat in western Montana than the more mesic areas used by Indigo Buntings. Observations at Lazuli Bunting nests indicate that cowbird chicks receive most of the food brought in by the Lazuli Bunting adults, and that bunting chicks in parasitized nests typically starve to death in a few days (Greene et al. 1996, Davison 1998). Nestling provisioning rates may be higher in more mesic areas if food is more plentiful. If this is the case, cowbird chicks may become satiated, allowing bunting chicks to obtain food after that.

It is best to view the results of these demographic analyses as cautionary. I have made a

number of demographic assumptions that are undoubtedly biased on the pessimistic side.

1) *Survivorship estimates.* Juvenile survivorship was estimated as half the adult survivorship (Table 1). Survivorship is extremely difficult to estimate, especially for species, such as Lazuli Buntings, that breed in early successional vegetation and appear to have good dispersal abilities (Greene et al. 1996). Thus, both adult and juvenile survivorship may be higher than the values used in these analyses.

2) *Fecundity estimates.* Although the fecundity values used in these analyses were estimated from field data, the estimates for yearlings may be too low. Most passerines show weak age effect on reproductive success (Saether 1990). In addition, estimates of reproductive success from unparasitized nests may underestimate the true reproductive success in areas where cowbirds are common, since undetected egg destruction and egg removal by cowbirds at unparasitized nests also reduces host fecundity (Arcese and Smith in press, Pease and Grzybowski 1995).

3) *Parasitization frequency.* The estimates of parasitization frequency were from a small geographic area (all were within 50 km of Missoula, Montana). It may be that these locations happen to be cowbird "hotspots" that are unrepresentative of parasitization pressures in other places. In addition, there was considerable fluctuations in parasitization frequencies between years.

IDENTIFICATION OF RESEARCH PRIORITIES

These demographic analyses, and the uncertainties in these analyses outlined above, help focus attention on some research and management priorities. The issues outlined below are poorly understood, not only for Lazuli Buntings, but for many other species of birds as well.

Incidence of parasitization

This study has documented previously unsuspected high levels of cowbird parasitization in populations of Lazuli Buntings in west-central Montana. With the exception of similarly high parasitism levels reported in the Sacramento Valley of California (Gardali et al. 1998), there are few other estimates of the incidence of parasitization in other areas of the breeding range of Lazuli Buntings. Thus it is unclear if these results are representative of other areas. We need more information on the geographic structure of reproductive success and parasitization for Lazuli Buntings (as well as other species of birds).

Dispersal and survivorship

These life history parameters are difficult to estimate, since mortality is difficult to distinguish from dispersal. The demographic analysis indicate that population growth rate λ is most sensitive to changes in survival estimates. How good were the ranges of survivorship values used in these analyses? Although I used a wide a range of survivorship values (0.2–0.5 for birds in their first year of life; 0.4–0.7 for older birds), Lazuli Bunting populations may be more resilient to cowbird parasitization than suggested by these demographic analyses if they tend to live longer than suggested by our current estimates. These problems are especially problematic for species, such as Lazuli Buntings, that breed in early successional vegetation types, and thus may have good dispersal abilities.

Metapopulation structure

These analyses investigated the demographic consequences of parasitization of isolated populations. However, bunting populations are connected by dispersal, and the dynamics of these interconnected populations depend on the details of the sizes and distances between populations, the geographic structure of survivorship, repro-ductive success, parasitization, and patterns of dispersal of buntings among patches. Better data on these life history characteristics will be important to construct biologically realistic metapopulation models.

ACKNOWLEDGMENTS

This work has been generously supported by the US Fish and Wildlife Service. S. Jones of the US Fish and Wildlife Service has been especially supportive. Comments by J. N. M. Smith, M. Morrison, S. Mills, and J. Rotenberry have improved the manuscript. M. Bishop, L. Clark, P. Jamieson (of the Bison Range National Wildlife Refuge), P. Gonzales (of the Lee Metcalf Wildlife Refuge), J. Davis, S. Jones, and P. Wright have all provided assistance for this project. Special thanks to all the assistants who helped with all the field work: A. Agather, J. Carlson, W. Davison, R. Domenech, A. Edmonds, K. Gray, D. Gryskiewicz, J. Haskell, Q. Hodgson, K. Horst, K. Karwacky, L. Keeton, A. M. Lareau, J. Laws, L. Leroux, J. Lloyd, N. Marlenee, M. Miller, C. Minch, M. Miyai, V. Muehter, S. Oliver, A. Rapone, T. Redman, C. Richardson, J. Roach, J. Root, R. Sacco, R. Scholl, Y. Tamanda, A. Tomon, L. Whitney, B. Winter, K. Wood, and J. York.

Studies in Avian Biology No. 18:153–159, 1999.

ASSESSING THE IMPACT OF BROWN-HEADED COWBIRD PARASITISM IN EIGHT NATIONAL PARKS

MARY D. HALTERMAN, SARAH ALLEN, AND STEPHEN A. LAYMON

Abstract. In 1995 and 1996 we conducted point count surveys and nest searches to examine the need to manage Brown-headed Cowbird (*Molothrus ater*) populations in eight western national parks. Our goal was to examine what impact, if any, Brown-headed Cowbird parasitism was having on passerines in the parks, and how current management practices might be affecting cowbird activity. The parks selected for this study were: Golden Gate National Recreation Area, Great Basin National Park, Lake Mead National Recreation Area, Montezuma Castle National Monument, Organ Pipe Cactus National Monument, Point Reyes National Seashore, Sequoia-Kings Canyon National Parks, and Yosemite National Park. We located and monitored 1295 nests of potential cowbird hosts. Parasitism had a significant impact on host reproduction in four of the eight parks: Golden Gate, Great Basin, Lake Mead, and Montezuma Castle. All of the parks had some form of livestock within or adjacent to their boundaries (cattle or horses), and proximity to grazing was significantly correlated with parasitism rates.

Key Words: brood parasitism, Brown-headed Cowbird, *Molothrus ater,* National Parks.

Birds are recognized as an important component of the biological resources protected and managed by the National Park Service. Park units provide vital breeding areas for a variety of avian species, including many neotropical migrants. Neotropical migrant birds (NTMB) are receiving much attention from international, federal, and state resource agencies and conservation organizations because many species have shown significant declines in all or part of their range (Ehrlich et al. 1992). Declines in the populations of some neotropical migrant bird populations have been documented by Breeding Bird Surveys over the past forty years in eastern North America and the past several decades in western North America (Askins et al. 1990, Sauer and Droege 1992).

The primary factors contributing to the recent declines of NTMBs are loss and fragmentation of habitat on breeding grounds in North America and deforestation and pesticides on Latin American wintering grounds. More recently, declines in the populations of some species have been linked to the range expansion of the parasitic Brown-headed Cowbird (*Molothrus ater*; Gaines 1974, Laymon 1987). Robinson et al. (1993) suggest that brood parasitism by cowbirds has become one of the major threats to neotropical migrants on the breeding grounds. Cowbirds are the only obligate brood parasite in North America, they have a large number of potential hosts, and they often remove or damage the host eggs (Friedmann and Kiff 1985). Populations of cowbirds have increased throughout North America over the last eighty years (Brittingham and Temple 1983, Laymon 1987). A number of NTMBs, including several species of flycatchers, vireos, warblers, tanagers, and grosbeaks are suffering

heavy losses in productivity and population decreases at least partially due to cowbird parasitism (Brittingham and Temple 1983, Laymon 1987, Whitfield 1990). Freidmann and Kiff (1985) reported that cowbirds have been recorded parasitizing 220 species of birds, of which 144 species have successfully raised young cowbirds. Studies done by Gaines (1974) on riparian songbirds breeding in the Sacramento Valley of California indicated that virtually all of the species that declined this century are highly parasitized by the Brown-headed Cowbird.

Many of the NTMB species impacted are riparian obligate species. Riparian areas support the highest breeding bird diversity and density of any habitat type, and they often have the highest proportion of species of management concern (Thomas et al. 1979, Laymon 1987). Cowbird parasitism in riparian zones can therefore affect a major part of the bird community in an area. As human populations outside the National Parks have expanded and caused alteration of riparian habitats, the remaining riparian areas within the parks have increased in importance as neotropical migrant habitat.

There are several Park Service-wide issues and park-specific Resource Management Plans that are directly addressed by this study. The most important service-wide resource management issues are: (1) impacts on threatened, endangered and other sensitive species; (2) degradation of park resources due to non-native animals; and (3) disruption of natural ecosystems.

The threats to neotropical migrant birds within the National Park System are broad, immediate, and complex. The magnitude of the resource threat is demonstrated by the number of park units with riparian habitats that have been damaged by cattle, erosion, and the presence of parasitic cowbirds, and the number of bird species that are involved. Parasitic cowbirds have expanded their range in the West in association with livestock grazing both in and adjacent to park units. Horse stables in the parks and other external developments have also aided the cowbird by providing concentrated sources of food (Rothstein et al. 1980). The threat is immediate because many NTMBs are listed or are proposed for listing as state and federal endangered species (Cunningham 1993). The impacts of cowbird parasitism are complex because cowbirds can affect neotropical migratory birds in several ways: (1) removal of host eggs results in lowered clutch size; (2) competition for food by the aggressive cowbird chicks may result in mortality of host young; and (3) the effort to feed the fledgling cowbird may adversely affect multiple nesting attempts. Neotropical migrants are especially vulnerable to parasitism because: (1) many build open-cup nests, which are the most frequent target of cowbirds (Friedmann 1929); (2) the cowbird egg-laying season generally coincides with the peak egg-laying season of most neotropical migrants; and (3) cowbirds usually parasitize hosts that are smaller (cowbirds weigh 30–60 grams, while most warblers, vireos and flycatchers weigh less than 20 grams) and have a smaller egg size. This interaction results in nest failure or reduced reproductive output for the host species (Best and Stauffer 1980, Robinson et al. 1993).

In addition to a general mandate to protect endangered species and other resources within parks, the Park Service should be concerned with determining how park actions may be contributing to the local and regional cowbird problem. For example, cowbirds are known to concentrate at, and benefit from, pack mule stations and horse corrals at Grand Canyon National Park (Johnson and Sogge 1995). In Yosemite National Park and Sequoia-Kings Canyon National Park, cowbirds concentrate at stock areas, as well as at campgrounds (Beedy and Granholm 1985). Cowbirds are common in riparian zones in these parks, but these numbers may be influenced by the presence of park-provided, concentrated food sources. Thus, the parks need to determine the extent to which they are contributing to the problem and decide on remedies to the situation.

We examined what impact, if any, Brown-headed Cowbirds were having on passerines in eight western National Parks, and how current management practices might be affecting cowbird activity. The objectives of the project were to: (1) survey neotropical migratory bird populations; (2) monitor neotropical migratory bird

nesting success and cowbird parasitism; (3) survey cowbird populations; and (4) determine if cowbirds were having enough of an impact on host populations to initiate a removal program. Because many NTMB species are riparian obligates, we focused on riparian habitats for this study. We spent two seasons studying the level of parasitism in these eight parks.

This study was intended to give an overview to determine problem areas within the parks studied. It was intended to develop a methodology to allow managers to determine problems in their area and at what parasitism level they will need to respond to cowbird presence to protect adequately the species in their parks. We wished to develop readily measurable parameters to detect a certain level of cowbird parasitism that may require intervention on the part of managers. It should be considered a preliminary study, intended to gather data necessary for management decisions, and identify those host species which should be the subject for future studies.

METHODS

The parks selected for this study were chosen because they have extensive riparian habitat, the presence of Brown-headed Cowbirds has been documented, and they represent a range of habitats and elevations. The project was conducted for two years (1995 and 1996) and focused on all potential cowbird hosts, with particular focus on neotropical migrant land birds. The following parks were selected for the study: Golden Gate National Recreation Area, Great Basin National Park, Lake Mead National Recreation Area, Montezuma Castle National Monument, Organ Pipe Cactus National Monument, Point Reyes National Seashore, Sequoia-Kings Canyon National Parks, and Yosemite National Park (Table 1).

Point counts were conducted to assess the size of both host and cowbird populations. Point counts were timed to coincide with host breeding season in each park, rather than Brown-headed Cowbird presence. Each point was surveyed 6–8 times each year at 2-week intervals in each park. Each point count lasted 10 min, and detections were categorized as flyovers, <50 m of the point, or >50m from the point. We also noted if species detected were within the riparian habitat. Surveys were conducted between 10 min before sunrise to 5 hr after sunrise. One technician worked in each park, and this person conducted all of the point counts and most or all of the nest searches in a given park. In the low desert and coastal parks we began surveying in early March, and in the mountain parks we began surveys in late April or early May.

TABLE 1. LOCATION AND CHARACTERISTICS OF THE EIGHT NATIONAL PARKS IN WHICH SURVEYS AND NEST-SEARCHING WERE CONDUCTED

Park	Location	Type of Brown-headed Cowbird habitat in each park	Timing of point counts
Golden Gate National Recreation Area	2 km N of San Francisco, CA	Horse stable, riding trails, and picnic grounds	mid-March to mid-June.
Great Basin National Park	On Utah border 130 km E of Ely, NV	Extensive livestock grazing	early May to early August.
Lake Mead National Recreation Area	45 km SE of Las Vegas, NV	Wild burros & cattle within park; bordered by agriculture	mid-March to mid-June.
Montezuma Castle National Monument	100 km N of Phoenix, AZ	Surrounded by livestock grazing and agriculture	late March to early July.
Organ Pipe Cactus National Monument	15 km S of Ajo, AZ	Agriculture and low-intensity livestock grazing adjacent	early March to early June.
Point Reyes National Seashore	30 km N of San Francisco, CA	Cattle pasture and horse stables within and adjacent to park	late March to late June.
Sequioa-Kings Canyon National Parks	In the Sierra Nevada Mountains, CA	Campgrounds, horse stables and trails in the parks	late April to late July.
Yosemite National Park	In the Sierra Nevada Mountains, CA	Campgrounds and horse stables and trails in the park	late April to late July.

A qualitative survey of the vegetation of each site was conducted during 1995. From this information we determined average width and length of the riparian habitat in each survey area.

A total of 584 separate point count sites were surveyed during both 1995 and 1996. Sites were located at 200-m intervals in riparian habitat. Each park had 65–90 points, with the exception of MOCA, which had only 22 sites. In GRBA, for example, we had 90 points in 5 drainages, and we had 16–19 points in each drainage. Each year we surveyed a combined total for all eight parks of 126 km of streams and meadows. All sites were located within 3 km of a road. We used point count data to determine mean detections/point and frequency of detection for each park.

From the point count data we calculated overall Brown-headed Cowbird frequency. This is the percentage of points at which cowbirds are encountered at least once during the point count surveys. Cowbird frequency through time is the percentage of points at which cowbirds are encountered during a given survey period.

Nest searching and monitoring were conducted to determine the level of parasitism and what, if any, impacts cowbirds were having on host species reproductive success. We also assessed the relationship between the number of cowbirds detected and the level of parasitism observed. Nest searches were conducted for potential cowbird host nests (any open-cup nesting passerine) within the riparian corridor at a subset of the point count areas. Because of the distances between survey areas it was not possible to effectively search for and monitor nests in all areas. Due to time and personnel constraints, only approximately 80% of the survey areas within each park were included in this part of the project, rather than all sites. We therefore selected sites with the best habitat and with good access (less than 1 hr driving time). When possible, some sites within a park were near potential cowbird foraging areas while other sites were more isolated from cowbird foraging areas.

Nest searching was conducted during the same time period as the point counts, and continued for 1–2 months after completion of the point counts. We used standard practices to search for and mark the nests (Ralph et al 1993). Between 25 and 40 hr/week were spent conducting nest searches. Emphasis was placed on finding nests of species that are known to be preferred hosts of cowbirds. Nests were checked every 3–7 days.

A nest was considered successful if it fledged at least one host young. Determination of this was based on observation of fledglings in the area of the nest and the condition of the nest.

TABLE 2. RESULTS OF COWBIRD HOST NEST SEARCHING FOR EIGHT NATIONAL PARKS, 1995–1996

Park	Total # of nests	Total # successful (%)	Total # parasitized (%)
Golden Gate	209	118 (56.5%)	9 (4.3%)
Great Basin	180	108 (60.0%)	13 (7.2%)
Lake Mead	113	62 (54.9%)	15 (13.3%)
Montezuma Castle	52	26 (50.0%)	14 (26.9%)
Organ Pipe Cactus	195	115 (59.0%)	1 (0.5%)
Point Reyes	282	129 (45.7%)	26 (9.2%)
Sequioa-Kings Canyon	134	85 (63.4%)	4 (2.9%)
Yosemite	131	96 (73.3%)	3 (2.2%)
Total	1296	739 (57.0%)	85 (6.6%)

This is a simplified method of determining nest success, but the broad scope of the project and limited personnel (one researcher per park) forced us to use this method. We were unable to use the more detailed Mayfield method (Mayfield 1975) due to this lack of personnel, and also due to variation in nest-check interval between the parks. We included only potential host nests for which both nest success and parasitism were known in all analyses.

We used two different methods to determine if Brown-headed Cowbird parasitism was having a significant impact on host populations. First, we evaluated whether the level of parasitism at each park was severe enough to threaten host species. For the first test we set an overall 30% level of parasitism to indicate a significant impact, because Mayfield's (1977) and Laymon's (1987) results indicate that a parasitism rate of 30% may lead to an unstable host population. Secondly, we did a Chi-square analysis to determine if parasitized nests were significantly less successful than unparasitized nests. Success was defined as a nest fledging at least one host young.

We conducted surveys of surrounding areas that had potential cowbird foraging habitat. This information was used to determine the direct-flight distance between the riparian survey areas and known cowbird foraging sites. These sites included cattle feedlots, dairies, active livestock pastures, and horse stables. We determined width and length of the riparian habitat at the survey points from visual examination of the sites and topographic maps.

RESULTS

We combined the data from both years to examine host success and cowbird parasitism level (Table 2). Overall nest success in the parks was 57%. A total of 15 different species were parasitized. Parasitism frequencies ranged from 0.5% to 26.9%, with an overall park average of 6.6%.

The four most commonly parasitized hosts were Song Sparrow, Wilson's Warbler, Bell's Vireo, and Warbling Vireo (Table 3). The parasitization of Bell's Vireos are of particular interest. We found a total of 91 nests, 12 of which were parasitized, although none of the 53 nests found in Organ Pipe were parasitized.

In our first evaluation of the significance of parasitism, no parks met the criterion of an overall 30% parasitism rate to indicate a significant negative impact of cowbird parasitism. In our second evaluation, comparing fledging success of parasitized versus non-parasitized nests, we found that in four of the parks Brown-headed Cowbirds were having a significant impact on overall host reproductive success (Table 4). Additionally, we found that, when compared by individual drainages, a higher average success rate at a park was significantly correlated to a lower parasitism rate (Pearson r = −0.44, N = 79, P < 0.05).

We next combined the data from all the parks to do regression analysis on parasitism rates for each site within the parks for the following variables: overall Brown-headed Cowbird frequency, nest success, distance to cowbird foraging habitat, and width and length of riparian habitat (Table 5). The following variables were identified as significant correlates of parasitism by the regression analysis: (1) frequency of occurrence of Brown-headed Cowbirds within each area (Pearson r = 0.32, N = 79, P < 0.05); (2) nest success (Pearson r = −0.44, N = 79, P < 0.05); (3) distance to cowbird foraging sites (Pearson r = −0.30, N = 76, P < 0.05); (4) length of the habitat (Pearson r = 0.23, N = 76, P < 0.05); and (5) width of the riparian corridor (Pearson r = 0.42, N = 76, P < 0.05). Average host occurrence was not significant (Pearson r = 0.05, N = 79, P > 0.05). This last finding is somewhat surprising, since other studies have found that cowbird frequency does increase in response to host abundance (Barber and Martin 1997).

We next looked at the number of nests found during each survey period as an indication of nesting activity. This was not significant (Pearson r = 0.13, N = 111, P > 0.05), indicating

TABLE 3. COMPARISON OF SPECIES OCCURANCE AND COWBIRD PARASITISM IN EIGHT NATIONAL PARKS, 1995–1996

Host species	Number of parks		Number of nests	
	Occurred	Parasitized	Total	Parasitized
Dusky Flycatcher *Empidonax oberholseri*	3	2	24	3
Blue-gray Gnatcatcher *Polioptila caerulea*	1	1	11	3
Black-tailed Gnatcatcher *Polioptila melanura*	2	1	40	5
Warbling Vireo *Vireo gilvus*	6	1	76	8
Solitary Vireo *Vireo solitarius*	3	1	10	1
Bell's Vireo *Vireo bellii*	3	2	91	14
Lucy's Warbler *Vermivora luciae*	2	1	19	1
Yellow-rumped Warbler *Dendroica coronata*	3	1	11	1
Common Yellowthroat *Geothlypis trichas*	3	1	28	2
Yellow-breasted Chat *Icteria virens*	2	1	13	1
Wilson's Warbler *Wilsonia pusilla*	6	3	76	8
Brewer's Blackbird *Euphagus cyanocephalus*	5	3	85	4
Northern Cardinal *Cardinalis cardinalis*	2	1	12	1
Blue Grosbeak *Guiraca caerulea*	2	1	6	2
American Goldfinch *Spinus tristis*	2	1	22	1
Canyon Towhee *Pipilo fuscus*	2	1	9	1
Chipping Sparrow *Spizella passerina*	3	1	20	1
Song Sparrow *Melospiza melodia*	5	5	182	22

that we were locating nests at a similar rate throughout the time period examined. We also compared the number of nests found vs. host abundance. Not surprisingly, the number of

TABLE 4. RESULTS OF CHI-SQUARE ANALYSIS ON NEST SUCCESS IN PARASITIZED VS. UNPARASITIZED NESTS IN EIGHT NATIONAL PARKS, 1995–1996

Park	Chi-square (df = 1)	P-value	N
Golden Gate	4.09	0.043	209
Great Basin	9.85	0.002	180
Lake Mead	15.96	<0.001	113
Montezuma Castle	8.38	0.004	52
Organ Pipe Cactus	1.43	0.232	195
Point Reyes	1.19	0.275	282
Sequoia-Kings Canyon	0.3	0.583	134
Yosemite	2.34	0.126	131

nests detected increased as host abundance increased (Pearson r = 0.21, N = 85, P < 0.05). The percentage parasitism was not significantly correlated with the number of nests found (Pearson r = 0.03, N = 95, P > 0.05). This indicates that an increase in parasitism is not simply a result of finding more nests. In each park a small peak in nest detections occurred before the peak in cowbird frequency.

We compared survey period to percentage parasitism and percent success through time. The percentage did increase through time (Pearson r = 0.38, N = 99, P < 0.05), no doubt a reflection of the increase in cowbird abundance through time. Nest success did not change significantly with the passage of time (Pearson r = 0.13, N = 99, P > 0.05).

We found that the following variables were significantly correlated with cowbird frequency

TABLE 5. COWBIRD PARASITISM RATE, FREQUENCY OF OCCURRENCE, AND LANDSCAPE VARIABLES IN EIGHT NATIONAL PARKS, 1995–1996

Park	Overall parasitism (%)	Cowbird frequency (%)	Distance to foraging sites (m)	Habitat width (m)	Habitat length (km)	Livestock nearby
Golden Gate	4	26	733	39.5	2.6	yes
Great Basin	6	31	1000	60.7	10.9	yes
Lake Mead	12	95	512	240	3.7	yes
Montezuma Castle	22	90	200	300	1.8	yes
Organ Pipe Cactus	1	22	575	137	5.3	no
Point Reyes	9	87	330	81.7	3	yes
Sequoia-Kings Canyon	3	50	500	23.7	2.5	no
Yosemite	2	24	1083	34	1.6	no

through time: survey period (Pearson r = 0.44, N = 99, P < 0.05), percentage parasitism through time (Pearson r = 0.40, N = 99, P < 0.05), and percent nest success through time (Pearson r = −0.23, N = 99, P < 0.05). These indicate that as time progressed, cowbird frequency and parasitism increased while nest success decreased.

DISCUSSION

We scheduled the survey periods to coincide with the host breeding season in each park, ranging from early March to May, and we observed that cowbirds began to arrive in late April in most of the parks. The overall low parasitism rates found on this study may be partially attributable to timing of nesting rather than overall parasitism.

The parasitism rates found during this study were relatively low compared to those in other riparian systems reported by researchers at the Sacramento, California, Partners in Flight symposium (October 1997: G. R. Geupel, unpubl. data; C. P. Ortega, unpubl. data; M. J. Whitfield, unpubl. data; E. Greene *this volume*). In the four parks with a significant impact of parasitism on host nest success (Golden Gate, Great Basin, Lake Mead, and Montezuma Castle) there is either livestock grazing within the park or agriculture contiguous with the park boundary. Thompson (1994) found that cowbirds in the Midwest were foraging primarily in short grass or agricultural areas and breeding in forested areas, which should account for our findings. Three of the other four parks (Organ Pipe, Sequoia-Kings Canyon, and Yosemite) are all somewhat isolated from agricultural impacts.

One anomaly in our findings is that Point Reyes, with grazing both in and adjacent to the park, did not show a significant impact on reproduction from parasitism. It is possible the data may have been heavily affected because two nest search sites at this park were over one km from grazing land, and both of these sites

experienced lower parasitism than other sites in the park.

Our survey did not find did that certain management practices, such as horse packing stations, camping, and picnic areas, encourage Brown-headed Cowbirds enough to be a significant factor in the level of cowbird parasitism. We also did not find a widespread impact of parasitism on host populations in the parks studied. We did find, however, that for some species parasitism rates were very high, and could be having a negative impact on those host populations. A more in-depth study focusing on those species used as hosts in this study, and attempting to find nests at earlier stages and following them more closely, may clarify the severity of the threat to these hosts.

There were a number of biases in our data set. For example, most of our nests were found during incubation or nestling stages. We therefore very probably missed parasitism events that occurred before incubation began if the nest was abandoned or depredated. We did not check nests with enough frequency to employ the more complex methods of determining the impact of parasitism on nest success, such as those suggested by Pease and Grybowski (1995). Our estimate of success does not take into account the differences between abandonment, depredation, and loss specifically due to parasitism. Also, it does not account for the fact that an individual female may re-nest several times during the breeding season after loss of a nest. Few nests were found during nest-building. This may well result in an underestimate of the effects of parasitism on nests, since they are usually parasitized during the egg-laying stage. It was unlikely that we would detect those nests which were abandoned early as a direct result of parasitism. Additionally, we had fewer than 10 nests for most species, so sample size was also a factor in our ability to determine the impacts in a given park on a given species.

This study presents an overview of parasitism

in several western National Parks. Cowbirds do appear to be negatively impacting several host species in Golden Gate, Great Basin, Lake Mead, and Montezuma Castle. None of the species with high parasitism rates in this study are either state or federally listed as endangered. The Park Service may decide that they do not need to alter their current management practices. Also, few of the factors affecting cowbird densities are under the control of the National Park Service. They may, however, wish to reconsider the policy of allowing livestock grazing within parks, since this seems to be an important factor contributing to cowbird parasitism which is within the parks control. The factors affecting parasitism in the parks could be clarified with a study which focused on the hosts identified by this project, particularly one which attempted to find nests in very early stages, and monitored cowbird abundance throughout the entire study.

ACKNOWLEDGMENTS

This project was a cooperative venture between the National Park Service and the Kern River Research Center. We would like to thank the National Park Service for supporting this project, and also the numerous park biologists and field assistants without whose hard work this project would not have been possible. In Golden Gate we were assisted by D. Hatch, N. Chow, F. Berghout, and D. Kisner; in Great Basin by V. Davala and J. Burnett; in Lake Mead by K. Turner, B. Pelle, A. Spaulding, and S. Schmidt; in Montezuma Castle by M. Sogge, M. Johnson, D. Greenwood, and R. Miller; in Organ Pipe by T. Tibbits and L. Dickson; in Point Reyes by S. Koenig, S. Allen, T. Gardali, S. Small, and N. Christy; in Sequoia-Kings Canyon by D. Graber, M. Mercurio, and S. Baillie; and in Yosemite by S. Thompson, M. Anderson, and A. French. Also, many thanks to the reviewers of this manuscript for their invaluable assistance and comments.

Studies in Avian Biology No. 18:160–166, 1999.

IMPACTS OF BROWN-HEADED COWBIRD PARASITISM ON PRODUCTIVITY OF THE ENDANGERED LEAST BELL'S VIREO

BARBARA E. KUS

Abstract. The Least Bell's Vireo (*Vireo bellii pusillus*) is an obligate riparian breeder brought to the brink of extinction in the last 50 years by habitat loss and Brown-headed Cowbird (*Molothrus ater*) parasitism. Although cowbird removal programs have effectively reversed the species' decline and promoted a rangewide population rebound, limitations on the timing, duration, location, and scope of trapping efforts permit parasitism to continue in some vireo populations. We quantified the impact of cowbirds on vireo productivity during a 9-yr study of one such population at the San Luis Rey River, California, where trapping of adults and removal of cowbird eggs from vireo nests were conducted annually to control parasitism. Cowbird parasitism occurred in every year of the study, and extended throughout the entire breeding season (April–August). Nineteen to 43% of nests (N = 667), and 19–56% of pairs (25–66), were parasitized at least once during a given year. On average, 29% of parasitized nests (N = 207) were abandoned before cowbird eggs could be removed, and parasitism was responsible for up to 29% of all nest failures. Of 139 nests from which cowbird eggs were removed, 99% remained active, and half eventually fledged vireo young. However, reduced clutch size and hatch rate in these "rescued" nests resulted in the production of up to four times fewer young per nest, and half as many young per egg, than non-parasitized nests. Nevertheless, nest monitoring and cowbird egg removal enhanced annual productivity by 11–44% over that expected in the absence of monitoring and removal. While monitoring and egg removal are effective tools in reducing impacts of parasitized nests, it is essential that appropriate trapping protocol be implemented to prevent access of cowbirds to nests and thus eliminate the impacts that monitoring cannot control. Long-term plans for management of cowbirds and their hosts should emphasize controlling landscape level factors influencing cowbird abundance as opposed to reliance solely on localized trapping programs.

Key Words: brood parasitism, Brown-headed Cowbird, endangered species, Least Bell's Vireo, *Molothrus ater,* reproductive success, species management, *Vireo bellii pusillus.*

Brood parasitism by Brown-headed Cowbirds (*Molothrus ater*) has been implicated in the declines of many sensitive species of the western United States (Hanna 1928, Gaines 1974, Goldwasser et al. 1980, Laymon 1987, Unitt 1987, Harris 1991; U.S. Fish and Wildlife Service 1991, 1992; Brown 1994) . Among these is the Least Bell's Vireo (*Vireo bellii pusillus*), an obligate riparian breeder once abundant throughout the coastal and interior lowlands of California and Baja California, but currently restricted in the U.S. to a few drainages in southern California (Cooper 1861; Anthony 1893, 1895; Fisher 1893a, Grinnell and Swarth 1913, Grinnell and Storer 1924, Grinnell and Miller 1944) . The vireo, a state and federally listed endangered species, was extirpated from most of its historic range by widespread habitat loss and, secondarily, cowbird parasitism, the impact of which was evidently greater than the resultant small, fragmented populations could withstand (Franzreb 1989a). Like other vireos (Graber 1961, Friedmann 1963), the Least Bell's Vireo is particularly susceptible to parasitism, which is currently the most immediate threat to the vireo's persistence. In light of this, recovery efforts have focused on implementing cowbird removal programs in vireo breeding areas to control parasitism. Cowbird trapping, coupled with nest monitoring to detect and remove cowbird eggs from vireo nests, has virtually eliminated parasitism from many populations (Griffith and Griffith in press; B. Kus unpubl. data), and in the dozen years since listing has reversed the vireo's decline and brought about a 6-fold increase in population size (L. Hays, pers. comm.).

Although cowbird trapping has been successful in promoting a rangewide population increase, programs in some areas have been unsuccessful, allowing parasitism of vireos to continue. While undesirable within the context of short-term management goals, such circumstances afford a rare and important opportunity to quantify the impacts of cowbirds on vireos with the aim of evaluating long-term management options through an understanding of cowbird-host dynamics. One site where such an investigation has been feasible is the San Luis Rey River in northern San Diego County, California. This 80-km drainage, bordered by agricultural, residential, commercial, recreational (golf course, equestrian centers), and other types of lands attractive to cowbirds, has traditionally been difficult to manage with regard to cowbird control. Limited access to properties, vandalism of traps, and other obstacles have prevented deployment of an adequate number of cowbird traps in suitable locations within the appropriate

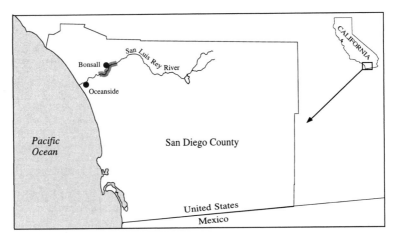

FIGURE 1.　Location of study area (shaded region) along the San Luis Rey River in San Diego County, California.

time frame (1 April–15 July) to effectively remove cowbirds from vireo breeding habitat and thereby eliminate parasitism (G. Collier, pers. comm.). Consequently, the San Luis Rey River supports one of the most heavily parasitized populations of Least Bell's Vireos in the state (B. Kus, unpubl. data).

In this paper, I document the effect of cowbird parasitism on Least Bell's Vireos by drawing from the results of a 9-yr nest monitoring study of vireos at the San Luis Rey River, which at the outset of the project supported the third largest vireo population in California. I quantify the impact of parasitism on vireo productivity by comparing several reproductive parameters of parasitized and non-parasitized pairs, and conclude with an assessment of management alternatives for controlling parasitism in vireos and other species.

STUDY SITE AND METHODS

We studied vireos from 1988–1996 along a 16-km reach of the San Luis Rey River between College Avenue in Oceanside and Gird Road in Bonsall, California (Fig. 1). Cowbird trapping and vireo nest monitoring have been conducted within this portion of the drainage since 1988 as mitigation for the impacts of highway construction on vireo habitat along the river, and have been summarized in annual technical reports prepared for the California Department of Transportation, District 11, by B. Kus, G. Collier, and J. T. and J. C. Griffith. Cowbirds were captured using modified Australian crow traps baited with seed and live decoys and positioned near riparian habitat and cowbird feeding areas. Traps were serviced daily to remove cowbirds, release non-target birds, and replenish food and water.

On average, 12 traps were deployed each year (range 8–15) for various lengths of time between 23 March and 1 August, with an average of 1,230 ± 444 trap-days of coverage per yr.

We studied the vireos at our site between March 15 and August 31 each year. Surveys were conducted to locate vireo territories and determine the breeding status (paired or unpaired) of all males in the study area. Pairs were visited weekly to monitor nesting activity and locate nests, which typically are placed <1m high in dense shrubby vegetation. Nests were visited according to a schedule designed to facilitate detection and removal of cowbird eggs from nests, as well as allow determination of clutch size, date of initiation, hatch rate, and fledge rate. Investigators used small automotive mirrors extendable to 1 m to examine nest contents from a distance and thereby avoid creating trails to nests. Nests were not approached if cowbirds or potential predators (e.g., Western Scrub-Jays [*Aphelocoma californica*], American Crows [*Corvus brachyrhynchos*], or Common Ravens [*C. corax*]) were in the vicinity. All cowbird eggs found in vireo nests were removed with adhesive tape to minimize disturbance to the rest of the clutch. Vireo eggs that did not hatch were examined for damage and deposited with the U.S. Fish and Wildlife Service. An attempt was made to document the fate of all nests produced by pairs in the study area.

One-tailed t-tests assuming equal variances were used to test the prediction that parasitized nests were less productive than non-parasitized nests. Correlations involving proportions were calculated using arcsine-transformed values. Variance associated with means is reported as standard deviations.

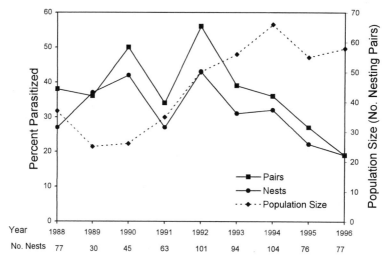

FIGURE 2. Least Bell's Vireo population size, and % of nests and pairs parasitized at the San Luis Rey River, 1988–1996. Number of trap-days = 763, 1,973, 1,784, 1,129, 1,018, 863, 820, 1,125, and 1,596 for 1988–1996, respectively.

RESULTS

LEVELS AND TIMING OF PARASITISM

Despite removal of several hundred cowbirds annually ($\bar{x}$ = 623 ± 258 [SD]), parasitism of Least Bell's Vireos occurred during every year of the study. The incidence of parasitism was highly variable across years, ranging from a high

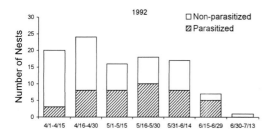

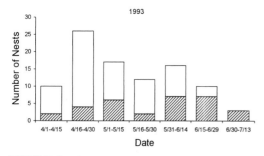

FIGURE 3. Seasonal pattern of Least Bell's Vireo nest initiations and Brown-headed Cowbird parasitism at the San Luis Rey River, 1992–1993.

of 56% of pairs and 43% of nests in 1992, to a low of 19% of pairs and nests in 1996 (Fig. 2). Neither the proportion of pairs (r = −0.35, 7 df, P > 0.20) nor nests (r = −0.43, 7 df, P > 0.20) parasitized was related to vireo population size in a density-dependent manner.

Parasitism occurred throughout the entire vireo nesting season, as shown by two representative years (Fig. 3). Vireos begin arriving at their southern California breeding grounds by as early as mid-March, and typically 80% of pairs have initiated nests by the end of April, although some pairs initiate first nests as late as June (B. Kus, unpubl. data). Most nests initiated after April are re-nesting attempts following unsuccessful previous attempts. Proportionately fewer vireo nests were parasitized in early April, when most cowbirds in San Diego County are migrants en route to breeding areas elsewhere (J. Wells and J. Turnbull, unpubl. data), than during the rest of the season. Parasitism subsequently increased with the arrival of locally breeding cowbirds, occurring in 25–50% of nests initiated during 2-wk periods prior to mid-June, and 75–100% of nests initiated after that date.

VIREO RESPONSE TO PARASITISM

Of the 207 parasitized nests located during the study, an average of 29% (range = 12–52%, N = 9 years) were abandoned per year (Fig. 4). Of these, 97% (60/62) were abandoned by the time nest monitors detected cowbird eggs in nests, and 3% (2/62) were abandoned following removal of cowbird eggs from nests. In the latter two instances, cowbird egg removal left clutches

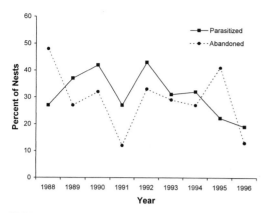

FIGURE 4. Percent of Least Bell's Vireo nests parasitized and abandoned at the San Luis Rey River, 1988–1986.

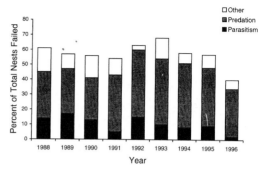

FIGURE 5. Sources of failure of Least Bell's Vireo nests at the San Luis Rey River, 1988–1996.

of two or fewer vireo eggs. The probability of abandonment (prior to egg removal) was unrelated to the rate of parasitism (r = 0.14, 7 df, P > 0.50), with pairs differing by as much as 4-fold in the likelihood of abandonment between years with similar parasitism frequencies (e.g., 1995 and 1996, 1988 and 1991; Fig. 4). Rather, abandonment appeared to be determined by clutch size (number of vireo eggs) and degree of clutch reduction by cowbirds. Clutch size reduction, presumably the result of cowbirds ejecting vireo eggs from nests at the time of laying, was particularly severe in abandoned nests. Of 31 nests for which clutch size was known prior to parasitism, clutch size reduction was documented in 90%, reducing the number of vireo eggs per nest from an average of 2.5 ± 1.1 in initial clutches to 0.5 ± 0.9 in reduced clutches (t = 7.6, 54 df, P < 0.001). Consequently, clutch size at the time of discovery of cowbird eggs was significantly smaller in abandoned nests (x̄ = 0.8 ± 1.0, N = 60) than in non-abandoned nests (x̄ = 2.8 ±0.9, N = 137; t = −14.6, 195 df, P < 0.001; see below).

Eight parasitized nests still active by the time nest monitors discovered the parasitism contained only broken, dead, or no vireo eggs where eggs had been previously documented. These nests, while not abandoned, were consequently considered failures in that they had no potential to fledge vireo young. Adding these to failures resulting from abandonment, parasitism accounted for 2–17% of all nest failures in a given year (Fig. 5), adding to nest losses attributable to predation and other sources such as human disturbance and infertile clutches. The contribution of parasitism to overall nest failure was highest in years when the frequency of parasit-

ism and the probability of abandonment of parasitized nests were simultaneously high.

RESCUED NESTS

Although up to half of the parasitized nests in a given year were abandoned and failed outright, the majority (137/207) of parasitized nests were "rescued" through the removal of cowbird eggs by nest monitors (Table 1). A fraction of these rescued nests subsequently failed as a result of predation, but with the exception of one year (1996), there was no evidence that predation rates of rescued nests were any higher than those of non-parasitized nests (Table 2). Between 36–70% (x̄ = 48%, N = 9) of rescued nests successfully fledged vireo young, increasing annual population productivity by as much as 44% over that predicted in the absence of cowbird egg removal, where parasitized nests would either be abandoned or yield only cowbird fledglings.

Although cowbird egg removal was effective in rescuing parasitized nests, the productivity of rescued nests was significantly lower than that of non-parasitized nests as a result of the behavior of female cowbirds when depositing eggs. Vireo clutch size, calculated for nests observed

TABLE 1. LEAST BELL'S VIREO NESTS REMAINING ACTIVE FOLLOWING COWBIRD EGG REMOVAL

Year	% rescued[a]	% successful	# fledglings	Increase in productivity
1988	48 (21)	70	13	24%
1989	55 (11)	50	5	18%
1990	63 (19)	50	15	37%
1991	82 (17)	36	8	11%
1992	63 (43)	55	31	44%
1993	71 (31)	41	21	38%
1994	76 (33)	44	25	27%
1995	53 (17)	44	11	12%
1996	87 (15)	39	14	10%

[a] Parasitized nests remaining active; N (total number of parasitized nests) in parentheses.

TABLE 2. PREDATION RATES OF RESCUED PARASITIZED NESTS AND NON-PARASITIZED NESTS

Year	Parasitized nests		Non-parasitized nests		P[a]
	N	% depredated	N	% depredated	
1988	10	30	43	51	0.23
1989	6	50	16	44	0.84
1990	11	45	20	35	0.34
1991	13	62	40	40	0.20
1992	27	41	56	61	0.09
1993	21	57	48	60	0.88
1994	24	54	65	49	0.70
1995	9	56	56	48	0.70
1996	13	62	57	33	0.06

[a] Chi-squared tests, 1 df.

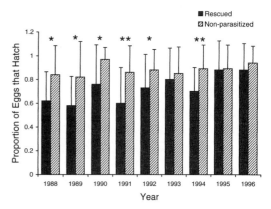

FIGURE 7. Proportion of eggs ($\bar{x}$, SD) in parasitized and non-parasitized nests that hatched at the San Luis Rey River, 1988–1996. * P < 0.06; ** P < 0.01.

with complete clutches, was significantly lower in rescued parasitized nests than in non-parasitized nests in six of the study years (Fig. 6). This was presumed to be the result of clutch size reduction by cowbirds, which was documented in 80% (8/10) of instances where it would have been possible to detect (initial clutch size: $\bar{x}$ = 3.6 ± 0.52, reduced clutch size: $\bar{x}$ = 2.3 ± 0.52; t = 4.83, 14 df, P < 0.001). In addition to, or possibly instead of, removing host eggs from nests, cowbirds frequently punctured or otherwise damaged vireo eggs, destroying egg viability and reducing hatch rates within parasitized as compared to non-parasitized clutches (Fig. 7). The difference in hatch rate between parasitized and non-parasitized nests was greatest in years when clutch size did not differ significantly between the two nest types (1988, 1989, 1991; Figs. 6 and 7).

IMPACT OF PARASITISM ON VIREO PRODUCTIVITY

The cumulative impact of cowbird parasitism on vireo productivity, produced by nest aban-

donment, and reduced clutch size and egg viability in non-abandoned nests, was that parasitized pairs fledged on average a half to a third as many young per nesting attempt as did non-parasitized birds (Fig. 8). Moreover, parasitized birds fledged only half as many young per egg (Fig. 9), an index of productivity reflecting reproductive effort and thus a more appropriate measure of relative fitness. This latter impact is likely underestimated in that it does not take into account undetected eggs ejected from vireo nests by cowbirds.

The predicted differences in productivity between parasitized and non-parasitized nests were observed in all years of the study, although not all differences were statistically significant (Figs. 6–9). It is likely that failure to identify significant differences in some years is due to small sample sizes, high variability, and, in

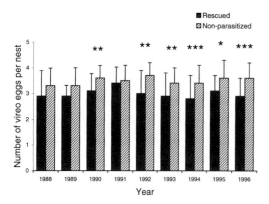

FIGURE 6. Clutch size ($\bar{x}$, SD; based on completed clutches) of parasitized and non-parasitized Least Bell's Vireo nests at the San Luis Rey River, 1988–1996. * P < 0.05; ** P < 0.01; *** P < 0.001.

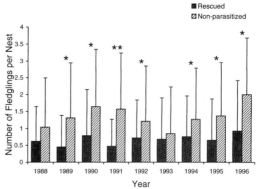

FIGURE 8. Number of fledglings per nest ($\bar{x}$, SD) in parasitized and non-parasitized Least Bell's Vireo nests at the San Luis Rey River, 1988–1996. * P < 0.06; ** P < 0.01.

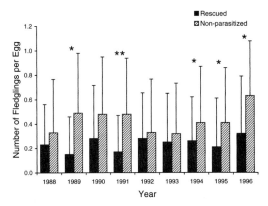

FIGURE 9. Number of fledglings per egg ($\bar{x}$, SD) in parasitized and non-parasitized Least Bell's Vireo nests at the San Luis Rey River, 1988–1996. * P < 0.05; ** P < 0.01.

some cases (e.g., clutch size in 1991, hatch rate in 1995), the lack of a true difference.

DISCUSSION

The rate of parasitism of Least Bell's Vireos in this managed population was only marginally lower than that of vireos in areas without cowbird removal programs (Gray and Greaves 1984; S. Goldwasser, unpubl. data; L. Salata unpubl. data), and varied considerably from year to year. It is likely that part of this variability stemmed from differences between years in the scope and duration of the trapping effort, with declines in recent years the result of broadening the trapping area and increasing the number of traps operated. However, environmental variables probably also contributed to annual fluctuations in parasitism, and identification of those variables is important to our understanding of cowbird-host dynamics. Clearly, a site-specific approach is necessary for properly evaluating and managing cowbird impacts on hosts, particularly in regions such as southern California that are characterized by high spatial and temporal variability.

Least Bell's Vireos in this study exhibited a strong propensity for deserting parasitized nests, at least in part a response to clutch size reduction by cowbirds. Although clutch reduction occurred in both abandoned and non-abandoned nests, the degree of reduction was significantly greater in the former, leaving vireos with clutches of fewer than one vireo egg on average as opposed to over two in non-abandoned nests. These data suggest that vireos are more likely to persist in nesting attempts where the "perceived" clutch size (vireo and cowbird eggs combined) at the time of parasitism is three or greater. Factors associated with clutch size re-

duction below this threshold, such as timing of parasitism and competition leading to multiple parasitism of nests, warrant further investigation to minimize abandonment of parasitized nests. Although vireos readily re-nest following nest failures, the effect of abandonment is to delay the fledging of young to the latter part of the season when post-fledging survival may be reduced by inadequate time to prepare physiologically for migration or by other factors. Parasitism during May and June, although generally less common than in April, may in fact exert a greater impact on the population in that it further delays the potential for as-yet unsuccessful pairs to fledge young within the narrowing window of time available to them. Late season parasitism may be particularly harmful; although proportionately few vireo nests are initiated after mid-June, nearly all are parasitized, preventing re-nesting pairs and late first-time breeders from producing any young at all and thus reducing effective population size, an important determinant of the survival of rare species.

Even if nest abandonment is averted by cowbird egg removal, parasitism reduces the potential for population growth through its effects on clutch size and hatch rate, which, combined, result in lower productivity of parasitized nests. Although pairs may ultimately succeed in fledging young, the reproductive effort required to do so exceeds that of pairs rearing young in non-parasitized nests. This is particularly so for females, which bear the cost of egg production, but also applies to males which assist with every aspect of nest-building, incubation, and rearing of young. Although spared the consequences of desertion, pairs fledging young from rescued parasitized nests realize a lower fitness return relative to investment than do non-parasitized pairs, both during the immediate season, and perhaps over their lifetimes.

An unanswered question bearing on whether rescued pairs actually experience reduced fitness is whether young fledged from rescued nests survive less well than those from non-parasitized nests. If clutch size reduction leads to reduced competition among nestlings, post-fledging survival may actually be higher in parasitized nests, offsetting part or all of the energetic costs associated with production of young. Research addressing this question will further our understanding of the costs of parasitism and the efficacy of current management techniques.

One can extrapolate from the results of this investigation and speculate on the impacts that cowbird parasitism has had on unmanaged vireo populations during the last two decades. Reports prior to the implementation of cowbird management programs indicate that cowbirds parasitized 33–100% of vireo nests (Goldwasser et al. 1980, Gray and Greaves 1984; L. Salata, unpubl. data; B. Jones, unpubl. data; L. Hays, unpubl. data), and regardless of the role that cowbirds played in the initial decline of the vireo, we know from history that parasitism interacted with habitat loss to produce a precipitous and rapid decline in what was once one of California's most abundant species (Franzreb 1989a and references therein). Now well into the species' recovery, we also know that eliminating parasitism has produced an impressive population rebound. Cowbird trapping is likely to continue in the foreseeable future as a tool for promoting vireo range expansion and establishment of viable populations throughout California, and it is appropriate as we move beyond crisis management of the vireo that we consider the most biologically and economically effective options available. One option is to divorce cowbird trapping from vireo nest monitoring and apply the monetary savings to increasing the scope of the cowbird removal effort. This proposal has advantages and disadvantages; done properly, trapping is less expensive than nest monitoring, does not require specialized personnel and the same degree of state and federal permitting, and benefits all potential hosts in the area rather than just a single species. However, it results in the capture and holding of many non-target species (on average $1,285 \pm 1,238$ capture-events per year in this study), contributing to non-target mortality and potentially reducing reproductive success by keeping breeding birds from their nests. If not done adequately with regard to dates of operation and number and placement of traps, trapping permits parasitism to occur, which, if the trapping is performed as mitigation, is unsatisfactory, and which under any circumstances is not fully accomplishing its objective. Although trapping alone can reduce the incidence of parasitism, it cannot prevent any of the subsequent impacts on nests that are parasitized. In contrast, nest monitoring and cowbird egg removal can rescue parasitized nests by preventing total loss of vireo productivity, and do not affect non-target species. But, although it can enhance population productivity, nest monitoring cannot prevent the impacts created by egg ejection and damage done by cowbird females. Monitoring is probably the most efficient means for controlling parasitism in very small (<10 pairs) or remote populations where daily visits to check traps are prohibitively costly and time-consuming.

Presently, the most valuable use of nest monitoring within the context of cowbird control is to gauge the effectiveness of trapping programs, particularly large scale ones, and guide improvement as necessary. Once successful trapping protocols have been established, follow-up monitoring can be effectively accomplished on a 2–3 yr cycle as opposed to the annual schedule followed up to this point. Trapping by itself should suffice to eliminate parasitism in the intervening years.

Ultimately we need to develop ways to protect native birds from parasitism that do not rely on continued and invasive "topical" (localized) treatments. From a biological perspective, species like the Least Bell's Vireo will never be recovered as long as they are reliant on human intervention for their survival. Long-term funding for wildlife management is unpredictable, and it is imperative that we make progress in identifying more permanent means for controlling cowbirds and their impacts. Considerable progress has been made recently in identifying habitat and landscape features influencing cowbird densities and parasitism rates (e.g., Howe and Knopf in press, Uyehara and Whitfield in press, Petit and Petit in press, Thompson et al. in press, Robinson et al. in press, Yamasaki et al. in press, several papers in this volume). Habitat restoration to achieve conditions less conducive to cowbirds, such as enlarging or reconnecting remnants of habitat, should be pursued. Biologists should also promote changes in land use policy that discourage or restrict siting feedlots, dairies, and other operations attractive to cowbirds adjacent to host breeding habitats. Research on cowbird-host dynamics and determination of species-specific tolerable levels of parasitism should be initiated with an eye towards "weaning" sensitive species from intensive cowbird management. Only through such a long-term view can we hope to restore the native avifauna in regions where the future survival of many species is uncertain.

ACKNOWLEDGMENTS

I am grateful for the effort and dedication of the small army of field assistants that monitored vireos over the years: P. Ashfield, P. Beck, J. Bennett, E. Berryman, M. Caruana, J. Newman, R. Owens, D. Parker-Chapman, J. Rombouts, M. Spiegelberg, G. Waayers, and J. Wells. G. Cox, C. Hahn, K. Purcell, and J. Uyehara provided valuable comments on the manuscript, and their suggestions helped improve the final product. B. Collier, D. Deutschman, and S. Hurlburt provided statistical advice. This research was funded by the California Department of Transportation, District 11.

Studies in Avian Biology No. 18:167–181, 1999.

COSTS OF BROWN-HEADED COWBIRD PARASITISM TO WILLOW FLYCATCHERS

JAMES A. SEDGWICK AND WILLIAM M. IKO

Abstract. The costs of Brown-headed Cowbird (*Molothrus ater*) brood parasitism to Willow Fly-catcher (*Empidonax traillii adastus*) seasonal fecundity and lifetime reproductive success were assessed in a long-term study conducted from 1988–1997 at Malheur National Wildlife Refuge, Oregon. Parasitism rates of Willow Flycatcher pairs (N = 882) among three study areas averaged 23.4%, ranging from 10.9–40.7% over 10 years (all study areas combined) and from 15.4–41.5% across the three study areas (all years combined). The lowest (0.0%, Dredger South, 1997) and highest (87.1%, Bridge Creek, 1991) parasitism rates underline the high variability of cowbird parasitism across time and space. Nest success (pairs fledging ≥ 1 young) of parasitized pairs was 50.3% less than that of unparasitized pairs; parasitized pairs had fewer eggs survive to fledging (17.3 vs. 51.4%), lost more eggs (3.08 vs.1.28) and nestlings (1.18 vs. 0.79), and reared fewer offspring (0.80 vs. 2.11) in a season compared to unparasitized pairs. Parasitized females also incurred higher costs by spending more time attending nests (2–4.5 days), building more nests (1.83 vs. 1.38), laying more eggs (4.72 vs. 4.12), and fledging young later (4 days) within a season compared to unparasitized females. Return rates and survival varied by age and sex; although there was no difference in the overall return rates or survival of parasitized vs. unparasitized females or of their young, males of parasitized pairs tended to survive longer than unparasitized males (1.29 vs. 1.01 years). Among successful pairs, the return rate of females parasitized in their initial year of capture was greater than that of unparasitized females, but survival did not differ between these groups. There were no differences in return rates and survival between parasitized and unparasitized successful males. Lifetime reproductive success of females depended on their parasitism and first-year success status; parasitized females reared significantly fewer young over their lifespans than unparasitized females (2.25 vs. 4.09 young), but there was no difference in lifetime output between these groups in years subsequent to their first breeding season (2.84 vs. 3.49 young). Whether females were successful or not, or parasitized or not, did not significantly affect reproductive success in subsequent years. Seasonal fecundity losses due to predation (0.74 young/pair) were greater than losses to parasitism (0.30 young/pair); lifetime reproductive losses displayed similar trends (predation vs. parasitism losses: 0.70 young/pair vs. 0.37 young/pair). Our results suggest that: (1) robustness of Willow Flycatcher reproductive strategies in response to cowbird parasitism is evident; (2) cowbird parasitism appears to exact the greatest toll on first-year birds; (3) similarities across parasitism and success classes for lifetime reproductive success in years subsequent to their first breeding year suggest that older Willow Flycatchers may learn improved anti-parasite strategies over time; and (4) similar return rates, survival, and lifetime reproductive success (subsequent to first-year) of parasitized vs. unparasitized pairs suggest that female cowbirds may be selecting for superior host parents.

Key Words: brood parasitism, Brown-headed Cowbird, *Empidonax traillii adastus,* lifetime reproductive success, *Molothrus ater,* seasonal fecundity, spatial and temporal variability, Willow Flycatcher.

Brown-headed Cowbirds (*Molothrus ater*) are known to parasitize over 200 species of birds (Friedmann et al. 1977) and have dramatically increased in distribution and abundance over the last 100 years (Rothstein 1994). Historically thought to occupy primarily the short-grass prairie regions of central North America, cowbird populations have spread both eastward and westward at a rapid rate (DeSante and George 1994). Most host species and populations are believed to be able to withstand some level of brood parasitism, but if parasitism rates are high and defense mechanisms poorly developed, parasitism could threaten population viability. Recent contact with this brood parasite poses a serious problem for a number of species, including the Willow Flycatcher (*Empidonax traillii*) (Rothstein 1994).

In the western United States, the Willow Flycatcher is composed of a mosaic of healthy and threatened populations. Many appear to be reproductively stable, but in some parts of the West, Willow Flycatchers have shown significant declines, including Washington, Oregon, California, and Arizona (DeSante and George 1994, Sauer et al. 1997). The high levels of reported cowbird parasitism of Willow Flycatchers (Trautman 1940, Sedgwick and Knopf 1988), especially of the endangered subspecies, *E. t. extimus* (Brown 1988, 1994, Rothstein 1994), have made parasitism a topic of concern regarding the conservation of both the endangered subspecies and other subspecies of Willow Flycatchers in North America (Robinson et al. 1995a).

Small passerine hosts such as the Willow Flycatcher often incur a variety of costs as a result of brood parasitism. These costs are usually expressed in terms of information collected on individual nests, such as reduced nest success, the number of host eggs removed by cowbirds, lower hatching success, and fewer fledglings produced. Primarily because of nest abandonment and renesting following some instances of parasitism, and variation in the length of the breeding season, brood reduction per nest and lower nest success are only indirect measures of the costs of parasitism (Pease and Grzybowski 1995, Payne 1997). The decrease in seasonal fecundity per pair (or female) is a more direct measure of the consequences of brood parasitism and a better measure of fitness of host populations. Because information on seasonal fecundity requires following individual females throughout an entire breeding season, most studies report data from individual nesting attempts. Only a few studies (e.g., Nolan 1978, Smith 1981, Payne 1989) have measured the costs of parasitism in terms of seasonal fecundity.

Even fewer studies have examined the costs of parasitism over the lifespan of a group of marked individuals (Newton 1989). This requires long-term, or longitudinal, studies that track the breeding success of animals throughout their lifespans. Such studies combine survival and the seasonal fecundities of an individual into one measure of performance–lifetime reproductive success. Thus, a comparison of lifetime reproductive success of parasitized and unparasitized animals is a comparison of approximations of biological fitness, and may be a better indicator of the effects of parasitism on the population as a whole (May and Robinson 1985, Newton 1989). Longitudinal studies have the additional advantages of reducing variability due to short-term environmental variation and accounting for annual variation in the distribution of animal samples.

In addition to the costs of parasitism directly associated with reproductive output, hosts may incur a number of other, less obvious costs affecting their long-term survival. Energetic costs may be higher for parasitized females because they may ultimately build more nests, spend a greater portion of the breeding season attending nests, and lay a greater number of eggs than unparasitized females. In turn, adult survival, particularly that of females, may be lower for parasitized birds because of these higher energy demands imposed on them as a consequence of abandoning previously parasitized nests and renesting (Drent and Daan 1980, Gowaty 1996). The potentially high energy costs of feeding a brood parasite that is often three to four times larger than host nestlings may reduce adult survival and return rates as well (Rosa and Murphy 1994). Finally, direct costs to fitness may arise due to phenology shifts. Because of multiple nest abandonment of parasitized nests and subsequent renesting, fledging of host young may be set back, resulting in lower return rates and increased mortality of late-born young (Perrins 1965, Morton 1992).

Whereas most field biologists would agree that parasitism can have negative consequences for a host population, the way in which such information is presented often overstates the costs of parasitism. Most studies report comparisons between parasitized and unparasitized classes, and the differences between these two classes are often quite dramatic, with unparasitized nests, for example, often fledging many more young than parasitized nests. This comparison can be somewhat misleading, however, if only a small portion of the population is parasitized (Payne 1997). In such cases, the overall costs of parasitism to the population will be smaller than the parasitized-unparasitized comparison suggests, and may even be relatively minor, especially in comparison to other factors, such as predation (Davies and Brooke 1988). Comparisons of the entire population to an unparasitized subgroup provide a more realistic view of the consequences of parasitism to a population (Nolan 1978:390). This latter comparison asks the question: How well did the entire population actually do compared to how well the population would have done if unparasitized?

To assess the consequences of cowbird parasitism on Willow Flycatcher populations, we established a long-term study at Malheur National Wildlife Refuge in southeastern Oregon. Our objectives were to examine the effects of cowbird parasitism on a large and stable host population to provide insights for evaluating ecological limiting factors at locations where the species is declining. In this paper, we focus on the costs of parasitism in terms of seasonal fecundity, lifetime reproductive success, energetic demands, and survival. In addition, we evaluate the population-level effects of parasitism by comparing the entire population to an unparasitized subgroup.

STUDY AREA AND METHODS

STUDY AREA

Our study was conducted at Malheur NWR, which lies at the northern extremity of the Great Basin in Harney County, southeastern Oregon (42°52′N, 118°53′W). It is one of the largest wildlife refuges in the lower 48 states (73,250 ha) and comprises one of the largest wetland complexes in North America. Dominant features of the refuge include rimrocks, freshwater marshes, lakes, meadows, alkali flats, shrub uplands, and shrub-willow riparian areas. We selected three riparian reaches (spanning 5 km) of the Blitzen River at the southern end of the refuge based on habitat suitability and presence of Willow Flycatchers. The three study areas, Bridge Creek (BC), Dredger South (DS), and Dredger North (DN) were 1.5 km, 1.5 km, and 2.0 km in length and were interrupted by gaps of 1.5 km and 2.0 km between study sites.

Stringer shrub willow (*Salix exigua* and *S. lutea*) occurs along a channelized portion of the Blitzen River in approximately linear arrangements. Willow stringers along the Blitzen River in these areas range from 5–10 m in width, but often extend laterally for short distances (5–100 m) into adjacent management units (i.e., fields, meadows, and wetlands). Other common riparian shrubs include currant (*Ribes* sp.), wild rose (*Rosa* sp.), and chokecherry (*Prunus* sp.).

FIELD METHODS

Productivity of Willow Flycatchers was evaluated by locating and monitoring nests to determine clutch size, hatching success, fledging success, incidence of cowbird parasitism, and mortality patterns occurring during the breeding season. Nearly all nests and renests of approximately 100 pairs per year breeding on the three study sites were located and monitored from 1988 to 1997 (N = 1,168 total nests). The majority of nests were found before the first egg was laid and were checked every other day, which enabled more precise estimates of laying patterns and egg removal by cowbirds.

Willow Flycatcher adults, and nestlings near fledging (8–10 d of age), were banded to evaluate survival, differential productivity, and fecundity per pair. Adults were captured using mist nets placed near nests and young were captured on the nest prior to fledging (8–10 d after hatching). Adult flycatchers were banded with both a US Fish and Wildlife Service (USFWS) band and either one or two color bands; thus each adult carried up to three bands (two on one leg and one on the other). Nestlings were banded with a USFWS band, and in the first 2 years of the study (1988 and 1989) were also color-banded. Birds returning to the study areas as adults but originally banded as nestlings or hatching-year birds (USFWS band only), were then banded with color bands as well. Adults were sexed by cloacal protuberance (males) and brood patch (females), and in a few instances by a combination of wing length, tail length (longer in males), and the above characters (Pyle et al. 1987). Locals and hatching-year birds could not be sexed. There is no known method of aging adults; all adults were categorized as after-hatching-year birds.

Each year, identities of adults were determined by initial capture (and banding, if necessary) of territorial occupants. We subsequently verified the identity of territory holders by visual determination of color band combinations through binoculars or spotting scopes. Not all birds could be captured, nor could the identities of all adults associated with particular territories be determined with certainty (i.e., of 882 pairs, we positively identified 76.8% of the males and 85.6% of the females). But because most of the population was marked and positively associated with a territory, we were able to assess seasonal fecundity for most pairs.

DATA ANALYSIS

Because one of our primary objectives was an examination of the impacts of parasitism on seasonal fecundity and lifetime reproductive success, we restricted our analysis of return rates and survival to birds returning to the study areas and occupying a territory. Thus, individuals that may have been captured in one or more years subsequent to the year of initial capture, but that were not positively associated with a nest, were not considered to have returned or to have survived for the purposes of the analyses in this paper. Only a small proportion of adults recaptured in subsequent years were not associated with nests, and thus our somewhat restrictive analysis reflects a reasonable estimate of actual return rates and survival for adults. Restricting our analysis to birds returning and nesting for birds originally banded in their first year of life (as nestlings or hatching-year birds) reduced our sample by about one half. About 15% of nestlings ultimately returned, but only about half that many returned and nested on our study areas. We define a return as a bird returning to one of the study areas and nesting at least once after its initial year of capture. Survival data consider the age of individuals and take into account how many times a bird returned to the study areas and how many years it survived.

To assess the effects of parasitism, we compared reproductive output and effort between pairs that had and had not been parasitized. This comparison generated estimates of difference in reproductive effort between these two groups. Another way to characterize the impact of cowbirds on a population would be to compare reproductive effort of females from unparasitized nests to that of all females in the population (Nolan 1978). The average reproductive effort of the unparasitized subgroup gives a baseline estimate of how the population would do (under the environmental conditions within that given breeding season) if no parasitism were occurring. However, statistical analyses of these comparisons are limited due to the non-independence of the data sets being compared. We report comparisons between unparasitized pairs vs. all (unparasitized and parasitized combined) pairs in an effort to demonstrate a more direct and simple measure of the effects of parasitism on Willow Flycatchers, and to contrast with the more conventional comparison.

We estimated reproductive success in a number of ways. Basic measures of the consequences of parasitism are comparisons between parasitized and unparasitized pairs of the number of eggs surviving to the nestling stage and the number of eggs and nestlings surviving to fledging. Another measure of the cost of parasitism is clutch and brood reduction. We include seasonal egg and nestling losses as well as any reductions in seasonal fecundity or reproductive output in this category. We further incorporated into our analysis fecundity losses that occurred within the following six success and parasitism classes to determine the effects of parasitism on each of these sub-groups: (1) successful, unparasitized pairs; (2) successful, parasitized pairs that reared one cowbird and at least one flycatcher young; (3) successful, parasitized pairs that reared only flycatcher young; (4) unsuccessful, parasitized pairs that reared only cowbird young; (5) unsuccessful, unparasitized pairs with no young; and (6) unsuccessful, parasitized pairs with no young.

Parasitism may have less obvious costs to the reproductive success of the host female in the additional time and energetic costs spent building more nests, laying additional numbers of eggs, increased nest attentiveness, and phenology shifts caused by these delays in the breeding cycle. In turn, adult survival (particularly that of females) and survival of their young may be lower. We estimated these increased time and energetic costs by estimating parental investment in days occupied attending active nests (from egg 1 of the first nest to fledging or failure of last nests of the season), total number of nests built per season, and total number of eggs laid per season. We also compared the return rates and survival of young by three fledging classes: early fledges (1–15 July), mid-season fledges (16–31 July), and late fledges (after 1 August). Finally, we compared return rates and survival across the parasitism classes for adults by categorizing adults as either parasitized or unparasitized in their initial year of capture.

We analyzed lifetime reproductive success of Willow Flycatcher females (the number of flycatcher young fledged in their lifetime) in several different ways. First, we compared lifetime output based on parasitism class (parasitized vs. unparasitized) in the initial year of capture. That is, we compared lifetime reproductive success of females that were, or were not, parasitized in their first year. We subdivided these groups further by comparing the number of offspring produced in the six success and parasitism classes simultaneously. We then calculated the reproductive success of parasitized and unparasitized females for the years following their first breeding season to test whether or not parasitism in a bird's first year had an effect on subsequent lifetime output.

To evaluate the relative costs of parasitism versus predation, we compare the seasonal fecundity and lifetime reproductive success of three different success classes: (1) unparasitized, successful pairs; (2) all unparasitized pairs; and (3) all pairs. When comparing between all pairs and all unparasitized pairs, differences in fecundity, for example, are due to the effects of parasitism. The comparison is of fecundity of the entire population to a subgroup not under the constraints of parasitism and so is a population-level estimate of the consequences of parasitism. Comparisons between all unparasitized pairs and successful, unparasitized pairs account for the effects of predation. The difference in fecundity, for example, between these two classes is largely a measure of predation on fecundity (but may also include losses due to infertile eggs and weather), as all instances of parasitism are excluded from each class.

Statistical procedures were conducted using the Statistical Analysis System (SAS Institute 1985). We used the Chi-square test of homogeneity to test simple measures of nest success, egg success, and return rates between classes of flycatchers. We used the General Linear Models Procedure (SAS Institute 1985) to test means of continuous variables (e.g., egg and nestling losses/pair, brood reduction, survival) across classes. Statistical tests were not possible for some comparisons (e.g., all pairs vs. unparasitized pairs) because of a lack of independence between classes (i.e., the class "all pairs" includes the class "unparasitized pairs"). Null hypotheses were rejected at $\alpha \leq 0.05$.

RESULTS

PARASITISM RATES

Parasitism of Willow Flycatcher pairs (N = 876) averaged 23.4% and ranged from 10.9–40.7% over 10 years (all study areas combined) and from 15.4–41.5% across three study areas (all years combined; Table 1). A prescribed fire in the early spring of 1991 resulted in the accidental burning of approximately 50% of the ri-

TABLE I. Spatial and temporal variability of cowbird parasitism of Willow Flycatcher pairs, Malheur National Wildlife Refuge, Oregon (1988–1997)

	Study area							
	Bridge Creek		Dredger South		Dredger North		Total	
Year	%	(N)	%	(N)	%	(N)	%	(N)
1988	11.1	(9)	25.0	(16)	8.8	(34)	13.6	(59)
1989	55.0	(20)	53.1	(32)	13.5	(37)	37.1	(89)
1990	51.6	(31)	17.7	(34)	19.6	(56)	27.3	(121)
1991	87.1	(31)	15.4	(26)	25.5	(51)	40.7	(108)
1992	34.6	(26)	15.6	(32)	6.4	(47)	16.2	(105)
1993	34.6	(26)	20.0	(30)	22.2	(36)	25.0	(92)
1994	40.0	(30)	14.7	(34)	14.6	(41)	21.7	(105)
1995	12.0	(25)	13.5	(37)	9.5	(42)	11.5	(104)
1996	13.3	(15)	15.6	(32)	—[a]		14.9	(47)
1997	31.3	(16)	0.0	(30)	—[a]		10.9	(46)
Total	41.5	(229)	18.8	(303)	15.4	(344)	23.4	(876)

[a] No data.

parian stringers in the BC study area and may have been the apparent cause of an explosive increase in parasitism there in 1991 (51.6% in 1990 vs. 87.1% in 1991 and 34.6% in 1992). The lowest (0.0%, DS, 1997) and highest (87.1%, BC, 1991) rates of parasitism underline the high variability in parasitism rates across both time and space.

EGG SUCCESS AND PAIR SUCCESS

The percentage of eggs surviving to the nestling stage for parasitized pairs (34.6%) was significantly less than that for eggs of unparasitized pairs (69.1%; $\chi^2_{1df} = 334.5$, P < 0.001; Table 2). The number of eggs surviving to fledging was also lower for parasitized pairs (17.3%) than for unparasitized pairs (51.4%; $\chi^2_{1df} = 321.2$, P < 0.001) as was the number of nestlings surviving to fledging (parasitized: 50.0%; unparasitized: 74.4%; $\chi^2_{1df} = 77.6$, P < 0.001).

Flycatcher success (pairs fledging ≥ 1 young) of unparasitized pairs (74.1%) was more than twice that of parasitized pairs (36.8%; $\chi^2_{1df} =$ 96.2, P < 0.001) yielding a 50.3% reduction in pair success. However, when comparing pair success of unparasitized pairs (74.1%) to all (parasitized and unparasitized) pairs (65.4%) in the population, the cost of parasitism was a reduction of 11.7% in pair success ($\chi^2_{1df} = 13.5$, P < 0.001). This is a more direct estimate of the consequences of parasitism to the population as it compares the nest success of a subgroup not under the constraints of parasitism to that of the entire population. This comparison effectively accounts for the fact that only 23.4% of all pairs were parasitized (Table 1).

Of the 204 parasitized pairs, 81 (39.7%) failed to produce any fledglings. The remaining 123 parasitized pairs produced either a cowbird (48 pairs, 23.5%), Willow Flycatcher(s) (57 pairs, 27.9%), or both (18 pairs, 8.8%). Thus, although only 36.8% of parasitized pairs produced flycatchers, more parasitized pairs fledged flycatchers (N = 75) than cowbirds (N = 66), with Willow Flycatchers raising 0.32 cowbirds/parasitized pair.

TABLE 2. Eggs laid, eggs surviving to the nestling stage, eggs surviving to fledging, and nestlings surviving to fledging in parasitized and unparasitized Willow Flycatcher pairs, Malheur NWR, Oregon (1988–1997)

	No. eggs laid	Eggs surviving to nestling stage		Δ related to parasitism (%)[a]	Eggs surviving to fledging		Δ related to parasitism (%)[a]	Nestlings surviving to fledging		Δ related to parasitism (%)[a]
	N	%	N		%	N		%	N	
Parasitized	907	34.6	314		17.3	157		50.0	157	
				−50.0[b]			−66.3[b]			−32.8[b]
Unparasitized	2630	69.1	1817		51.4	1353		74.4	1353	
				−8.9[c]			−16.9[c]			−4.7[c]
All	3537	60.2	2131		42.7	1510		70.9	1510	

[a] Comparison of parasitized and unparasitized pairs, and unparasitized and all (parasitized + unparasitized) pairs.
[b] Significant difference at P < 0.001.
[c] No statistical tests possible (see Methods).

STUDIES IN AVIAN BIOLOGY

TABLE 3. SEASONAL CLUTCH AND BROOD REDUCTION, AND FECUNDITY OF PARASITIZED AND UNPARASITIZED WILLOW FLYCATCHER PAIRS (N), MALHEUR NWR, OREGON (1988–1997)

	Eggs lost			Δ related to parasitism (eggs)[a]	Nestlings lost			Δ related to parasitism (nestlings)[a]	Young fledged			Δ related to parasitism (young)[a]
	N	x̄	SE		N	x̄	SE		N	x̄	SE	
Parasitized	194	3.08	0.16		122	1.18	0.12		204	0.80	0.08	
				+1.80[b]				+0.39[c]				−1.31[b]
Unparasitized	642	1.28	0.06		579	0.79	0.05		670	2.11	0.06	
				+0.41[d]				+0.07[d]				−0.30[d]
All	836	1.69	0.07		701	0.86	0.05		874	1.81	0.05	

[a] Comparison of parasitized and unparasitized pairs, and unparasitized and all (parasitized + unparasitized) pairs.
[b] Significant difference at P < 0.001.
[c] Significant difference at P = 0.003.
[d] No statistical tests possible (see Methods).

SEASONAL CLUTCH AND BROOD REDUCTION

Parasitized pairs lost 3.08 ± 0.16 eggs over the course of a season compared to only 1.28 ± 0.06 eggs lost for unparasitized females (P < 0.001; Table 3). Parasitized females lost more nestlings (1.18 ± 0.12) as well, compared to unparasitized females (0.79 ± 0.05; P = 0.003). Seasonal fecundity was reduced by 1.31 young/pair, with parasitized pairs fledging only 0.80 ± 0.08 young and unparasitized pairs fledging 2.11 ± 0.06 young (P < 0.001).

As in the case of pair success, brood reduction was much less severe (0.30 young/pair) when comparing seasonal fecundity of unparasitized pairs (2.11 ± 0.06) with that of the entire population (1.81 ± 0.05, parasitized and unparasitized pairs combined; Table 3). Similarly, unparasitized pairs lost fewer eggs (0.41 egg/pair; 1.28 ± 0.06 vs. 1.69 ± 0.07) and fewer nestlings (0.07 nestlings/pair; 0.79 ± 0.05 vs. 0.86 ± 0.05) in comparison with the entire population.

In comparison of success-by-parasitism classes, successful, unparasitized pairs reared more flycatchers annually than either parasitized pairs raising only flycatchers or parasitized pairs rearing both cowbirds and flycatchers (P < 0.001; Table 4). Seasonal egg losses were least for successful, unparasitized pairs (0.88 ± 0.04) and greatest for unsuccessful pairs rearing only cowbird(s) (3.14 ± 0.33) and unsuccessful, parasitized pairs rearing neither flycatchers nor cowbirds (3.77 ± 0.24; P < 0.001). Seasonal nestling losses were least for successful flycatcher pairs (0.41–0.75) and greatest for unsuccessful pairs (1.81–2.58).

TIME AND ENERGETIC COSTS

Successful, parasitized females spent more time attending nests (35.12 ± 0.90 d) than successful, unparasitized females (33.03 ± 0.35 d, P = 0.012; Table 5). This trend was also the case for unsuccessful, parasitized females (25.92 ± 1.31 d) compared to unsuccessful, unparasitized females (21.25 ± 0.79; P = 0.002). Parasitized females built more nests (1.83 ± 0.06) in a season than unparasitized females (1.38 ± 0.02; P < 0.001) and also laid more eggs (4.72 ± 0.15) in a season than unparasitized females (4.12 ± 0.05; P < 0.001). This difference in the number of eggs laid understates the actual difference between parasitized and unparasitized females because of presumed undetected egg removal by cowbirds. We estimated undetected egg removal as the difference between the number of eggs laid by unparasitized females who had only one nest in a season (3.66 ± 0.03) and the number laid by parasitized females that had only one nest (3.31 ± 0.12; P = 0.001). We assumed that an undetected 0.35 eggs (3.66–3.31) were removed by cowbirds between nest checks, and so 0.35 could be added to the 4.72 eggs laid in a season by parasitized females.

Direct costs (comparing unparasitized pairs to all pairs) were as follows: (1) time invested attending active nests by successful females: 33.03 ± 0.35 d (unparasitized) vs. 33.44 ± 0.33 d (all); (2) time invested by unsuccessful females: 21.25 ± 0.79 d (unparasitized) vs. 22.73 ± 0.69 d (all); (3) nests built: 1.38 ± 0.02 (unparasitized) vs. 1.49 ± 0.02 (all); and (4) total eggs laid: 4.12 ± 0.05 (unparasitized) vs. 4.26 ± 0.05 (all). As with our earlier comparisons, the effects of brood parasitism on measures of seasonal fecundity are diminished when compared to the entire population as a whole.

PHENOLOGY SHIFTS

The mean (julian) fledging date of young from nests of successful parasitized pairs (211.4 ± 1.0) differed from that of young from nests of successful unparasitized pairs (207.5 ± 0.4, P < 0.001; Table 6). Thus, young of parasitized pairs fledged nearly 4 d later than young produced by unparasitized pairs. Initiation dates of first nests were nearly identical by parasitism class, and so the investment of parasitized fe-

TABLE 4. SEASONAL CLUTCH AND BROOD REDUCTION AND FECUNDITY OF WILLOW FLYCATCHER PAIRS (N), BY SUCCESS-BY-PARASITISM CLASSES, MALHEUR NWR, OREGON (1988–1997)

	Seasonal fecundity			Duncan's multiple range test[c]	Eggs lost			Duncan's multiple range test[d]	Young lost			Duncan's multiple range test[e]
	N	x̄	SE		N	x̄	SE		N	x̄	SE	
Successful, unparasitized, flycatcher only	497	2.85	0.04	A[f]	472	0.88	0.06	C[f]	474	0.41	0.04	C[f]
Successful, parasitized, rearing both[a]	18	1.39	0.14	B	15	2.20	0.55	B	16	0.75	0.23	C
Successful, parasitized, flycatcher only	58	2.40	0.12	C	57	2.32	0.25	B	56	0.41	0.12	B
Unsuccessful, parasitized, cowbird only	48	1.06[b]	0.04[b]	—	43	3.14	0.33	A	26	1.81	0.24	B
Unsuccessful, unparasitized, no young	173	—	—	—	170	2.37	0.15	B	105	2.51	0.12	A
Unsuccessful, parasitized, no young	80	—	—	—	79	3.77	0.24	A	24	2.58	0.22	A

a Females that successfully reared one cowbird and at least one Willow Flycatcher young.
b Number of cowbirds reared per pair that successfully fledged cowbirds.
c $F = 525.58$, $P < 0.001$.
d $F = 62.37$, $P < 0.001$.
e $F = 97.79$, $P < 0.001$.
f Values sharing the same letter are not significantly different ($P > 0.05$).

males was also about 4 d longer than that of unparasitized females. The later mean fledging date can be attributed to the greater number of nests built by successful, parasitized females (1.81 ± 0.09) compared to successful, unparasitized females (1.30 ± 0.02; $P < 0.001$) and more eggs laid (5.01 ± 0.23 parasitized vs. 4.17 ± 0.06 unparasitized; $P < 0.001$), because of renesting and further egg laying following abandonment of some parasitized nests.

RETURN RATES, SURVIVAL, AND PARASITISM

Return rates of parasitized adult females (48.9%) and unparasitized adult females (55.3%) were similar ($\chi^2_{1df} = 1.11$, $P = 0.29$); there was no significant difference in female survival rates (parasitized: 0.967 ± 0.07 yr; unparasitized: 0.969 ± 0.14 yr; $P = 0.99$; Table 7). Return rates of parasitized males (55.6%) and unparasitized males (51.2%) were also similar ($\chi^2_{1df} = 0.36$, $P = 0.55$). Parasitized males tended to survive longer (1.29 ± 0.23 yr) than unparasitized males (1.01 ± 0.09 yr), but the difference was not significant ($P = 0.18$).

Successful, parasitized adult females were more likely to return to the study area in subsequent years than successful, unparasitized females (Table 7). The return rate of successful, parasitized (in their initial year of capture) females (72%) was greater than that of successful, unparasitized females (56.5%; $\chi^2_{1df} = 3.92$, $P = 0.048$) but survival did not differ (successful, parasitized: 1.20 ± 0.16 yr; successful, unparasitized: 0.99 ± 0.09 yr; $P = 0.271$). Return rates for successful, parasitized males (60.0%) were similar to those of successful, unparasitized males (50.7%; $\chi^2_{1df} = 0.75$, $P = 0.385$) as was survival (successful, parasitized: 1.08 ± 0.24 yr; successful, unparasitized: 1.08 ± 0.12 yr; $P = 0.99$).

There was no difference in the return rates of young produced by parasitized (5.4%) vs. unparasitized (7.7%) pairs ($\chi^2_{1df} = 0.81$, $P = 0.367$) nor was there a difference in survival of young produced by parasitized (0.116 ± 0.05 yr) vs. unparasitized (0.169 ± 0.02 yr) pairs ($P = 0.42$; Table 7). The return rate of early fledges (29.1%) was much greater than that of mid-season fledges (4.8%) and late fledges (5.4%; $\chi^2_{2df} = 97.46$, $P < 0.001$; Table 8). Survival also differed across these three classes (early: 0.70 ± 0.13 yr; mid-season: 0.10 ± 0.02 yr; late: 0.10 ± 0.10 yr; $P < 0.001$). However, survival of birds returning to the study area at least one time was not significantly different (early: 2.41 ± 0.29 yr; mid-season: 2.15 ± 0.23 yr; late: 1.94 ± 0.33 yr; $P = 0.55$).

TABLE 5. ANNUAL ENERGETIC COSTS TO PARASITIZED AND UNPARASITIZED WILLOW FLYCATCHER FEMALES (N) IN TERMS OF TIME INVESTMENT, NUMBER OF NESTS BUILT AND EGGS LAID, MALHEUR NWR, OREGON (1988–1997)

	Investment (days), successful females			Δ related to parasitism (days)[a]	Investment (days), unsuccessful females			Δ related to parasitism (days)[a]	Nests built			Δ related to parasitism (nests)[a]	Eggs laid			Δ related to parasitism (eggs)[a]
	N	x̄	SE		N	x̄	SE		N	x̄	SE		N	x̄	SE	
Parasitized	121	35.12	0.90	+2.09[b]	78	25.92	1.31	+4.67[c]	188	1.83	0.06	+0.45[d]	192	4.72	0.15	+0.60[d]
Unparasitized	489	33.03	0.35	+0.41[e]	168	21.25	0.79	+1.48[e]	594	1.38	0.02	+0.11[e]	639	4.12	0.05	+0.14[e]
All	610	33.44	0.33		246	22.73	0.69		782	1.49	0.02		831	4.26	0.05	

[a] Comparison of parasitized and unparasitized pairs, and unparasitized and all (parasitized + unparasitized) pairs.
[b] Significant difference at P = 0.001.
[c] Significant difference at P = 0.002.
[d] Significant difference at P < 0.001.
[e] No statistical tests possible (see Methods).

LIFETIME REPRODUCTIVE SUCCESS

Females parasitized in their first year reared significantly fewer flycatcher young (2.25 ± 0.28) over their lifespans compared to unparasitized females (4.09 ± 0.20 young, P < 0.001; Table 9). Unparasitized, successful females had the highest lifetime output (4.79 ± 0.21 young), followed by parasitized females that raised both flycatchers and a cowbird in their first year (3.89 ± 0.84 young), and parasitized females that successfully reared only flycatchers (3.76 ± 0.48 young; Table 9). The other three classes (those raising [1] only a cowbird, [2] unsuccessful, unparasitized females, and [3] unsuccessful, parasitized females) reared significantly fewer flycatchers over their lifespans (P < 0.001). Thus, the three classes rearing flycatchers in their first year also had the highest lifetime output, whereas the three classes raising only a cowbird, or neither flycatchers nor cowbirds, had the lowest lifetime reproductive success. Females unparasitized in their first year did not rear significantly more young over the remainder of their lifespans (3.49 ± 0.26) compared to females parasitized in their first year (2.84 ± 0.43) (P = 0.214; Table 10). A comparison of overall and after-first-year lifetime reproductive success (compare Tables 9 and 10) suggests that females that were parasitized in their first year and returned closed the gap with females that were unparasitized in their first year by increasing lifetime output. Combining parasitism and success classes as above, reproductive outputs were similar across all six success-by-parasitism classes (F = 0.64, P = 0.67; Table 10). Previously unparasitized females tended to rear more young in subsequent years than parasitized females, but those females rearing a cowbird in their first year subsequently reared about as many flycatchers (3.56 ± 1.14) as unsuccessful (4.04 ± 0.74) and successful (3.38 ± 0.27) unparasitized females. But whether birds were successful or not, or parasitized or not, did not significantly affect reproductive success in years subsequent to their first breeding effort (Table 10).

RELATIVE COSTS OF PARASITISM AND PREDATION

For Willow Flycatchers, the costs of parasitism were relatively minor compared to the costs of predation. Losses in seasonal fecundity due to predation were 0.74 young/pair when comparing fecundity of unparasitized, successful pairs (2.85 ± 0.04 young) to all unparasitized pairs (2.11 ± 0.06 young). Fecundity losses due to parasitism were only 0.30 young/pair, or less than half the cost of predation, when comparing reproductive output of unparasitized (2.11 ± 0.06) vs. all (1.81 ± 0.05) pairs. Comparisons

TABLE 6. PHENOLGY SHIFT IN FLEDGING DATE AND ASSOCIATED VARIABLES FOR SUCCESSFUL PARASITIZED AND UNPARASITIZED WILLOW FLYCATCHER PAIRS, MALHEUR NWR, OREGON (1988–1997)

	Successful parasitized			Successful unparasitized			
	N	x̄	SE	N	x̄	SE	Pa
Fledging Date (Julian Date)	76	211.43	1.01	496	207.47	0.42	0.001
Nest Initiation Date (Julian Date)	76	174.28	0.67	489	174.33	0.30	0.943
Investment (days)	76	37.16	1.00	489	32.97	0.35	0.001
No. of Nests	75	1.81	0.09	457	1.30	0.02	0.001
Eggs laid	72	5.01	0.23	471	4.17	0.06	0.001

[a] One-way analysis of variance (ANOVA).

of the lifetime reproductive success of females yielded similar results. The estimate of the cost of parasitism to lifetime output was 0.37 young/female (lifetime reproductive output of all unparasitized pairs: 3.96 ± 0.20 young/female vs. lifetime reproductive output of all pairs: 3.59 ± 0.17 young/female). The cost of predation to lifetime reproductive output (0.70 young/female) was nearly twice that of parasitism (lifetime reproductive output of successful unparasitized pairs: 4.66 ± 0.20 young/female vs. lifetime reproductive output of all unparasitized pairs: 3.96 ± 0.20 young/female).

DISCUSSION

PARASITISM RATES

The overall parasitism rate (23.4%) on the three study areas during the 10 years of this study was somewhat lower than that reported for most other populations of Willow Flycatchers. Prior to cowbird trapping in California, parasitism of *E. t. extimus* averaged 66% (Whitfield and Sogge *this volume*). Brown (1994) reported a 50% rate in the Grand Canyon of Arizona for *E. t. extimus,* and Sedgwick and Knopf (1988) reported a rate of 40.7% for *E. t. adastus* in Colorado. Lower rates (<25%) are reported for most sites in Arizona (*E. t. extimus*) but range from 3% to 48%; parasitism rates in New Mexico ranged from 18% to 40% (Whitfield and

Sogge *this volume*). For the eastern subspecies (*E. t. traillii*; 6 studies) rates were <17% (Friedmann 1963), although one eastern study reported a higher rate of parasitism (56.3%; Trautman 1940). Variability at the local scale was high (15.4–41.5%) in this study, and this pattern repeats itself at broader geographical scales in other regions of the country.

Temporal variability of parasitism rates was equally dramatic at Malheur NWR (10.9–40.7% from 1988 to 1997, all study areas combined) and is typical of patterns at broader geographic scales throughout the West. Whitfield and Sogge (*this volume*) summarized annual variability in parasitism rates of *E. t. extimus* in three states: Arizona, 8–40%; California, 50–80%; and New Mexico, 14.7–27%. Variability in parasitism rates across time is not difficult to understand, and is almost to be expected, because of large annual fluctuations in densities of both parasites and hosts (Trail and Baptista 1993). Long-term, longitudinal studies address this problem by including both average years and extreme years of environmental variation and the distribution of animal samples.

Variability in parasitism rates across space, especially at the local scale, is more difficult to explain. At Malheur NWR, our three study areas were all in the same drainage, vegetation types were similar, and the three areas were each sep-

TABLE 7. RETURN RATES (%) AND SURVIVAL (YR) OF PARASITIZED AND UNPARASITIZED WILLOW FLYCATCHERS, MALHEUR NWR, OREGON (1988–1997)

	Parasitized				Unparasitized			
		No. birds returned	Survival			No. birds returned	Survival	
	N	%	Yr	SE	N	%	Yr	SE
Juveniles	129	5.4	0.116	0.05	1142	7.7a	0.169	0.02a
All females	92	48.9	0.967	0.14	255	55.3a	0.969	0.07a
All males	63	55.6	1.29	0.23	201	51.2a	1.01	0.09b
Successful females	50	72.0	1.20	0.16	184	56.5c	0.99	0.09a
Successful males	25	60.0	1.08	0.24	154	50.7a	1.08	0.12a

[a] No significant difference (P > 0.05).
[b] Significance between survival of parasitized and unparasitized males: P = 0.18.
[c] Significance between return rates of parasitized and unparasitized successful females: P = 0.048.

TABLE 8. RETURN RATES AND SURVIVAL OF WILLOW FLYCATCHER YOUNG BY FLEDGING DATE CATEGORIES, MALHEUR NWR, OREGON (1988–1997)

	Returning young[a]		Overall survival (yr)[b]			Survival of returning birds (yr)[c]		
	N	%	N	x̄	SE	N	x̄	SE
Early (1–15 July)	127	29.1	127	0.70	0.13	37	2.41	0.29
Middle (16–31 July)	828	4.8	828	0.10	0.02	40	2.15	0.23
Late (1–26 Aug)	316	5.4	316	0.10	0.03	7	1.94	0.33

[a] Difference among return rates: $P < 0.001$.
[b] Difference among overall survival: $P < 0.001$.
[c] Difference among survival of returning birds: $P = 0.55$.

arated from one another by ≤ 2 km. Other researchers have also reported a patchy distribution of parasitism rates, even at the local level. These differences in rates are sometimes explained by habitat variability, such as the availability of tall perches, which may enhance the ability of cowbirds to locate and parasitize nests (Anderson and Storer 1976, Freeman et al. 1990). The availability of nearby foraging areas for cowbirds has also been linked to differences in parasitism rates, but at geographic scales broader than those considered at Malheur NWR (Verner and Ritter 1983). Because of the proximity of our three study areas and their similar vegetation structures, we believe that any differences in parasite densities, flycatcher densities, or densities of alternate hosts (sensu Barber and Martin 1997) are insignificant and are not causal factors in differences in parasitism rates among areas at Malheur NWR. Thus, the large differences in rates of parasitism across the three study areas at Malheur NWR remain an enigma, but may not be unusual as others have also reported pockets of parasitism in areas of uniform vegetation (Marvil and Cruz 1989). Variability in rates of parasitism, both locally and regionally, demonstrates that a direct estimate of the number of nests parasitized may not be adequate in assessing the true impact of parasitism. More intensive studies from a number of locations may be required to get an averaging for regional, and local, parasitism rates. Variability in cowbird parasitism at the broad, and especially at the local, geographic scale suggests the need for carefully designed, long-term studies to fully assess parasitism rates across time and space.

EGG AND PAIR SUCCESS AND SEASONAL FECUNDITY

Fewer eggs and nestlings survived to fledging, and nest success of parasitized pairs was far less than that of unparasitized pairs at Malheur NWR. Generalized costs such as these have been reported for a number of host species throughout North America (May and Robinson 1985). Parasitized Willow Flycatcher pairs also lost significantly more eggs and nestlings over the course of a season and fledged an average of 1.31 fewer young (61.6% fewer) than unparasitized pairs. Seasonal fecundity of successful, unparasitized pairs was greater, and seasonal egg losses fewer than for pairs of either of two parasitized classes: those raising both flycatchers and cowbirds, or those rearing only flycatchers.

TABLE 9. LIFETIME REPRODUCTIVE SUCCESS OF FEMALE WILLOW FLYCATCHERS (N), BY PARASITISM AND SUCCESS-BY-PARASITISM CLASSES, MALHEUR NWR, OREGON (1988–1997)

	Flycatcher young fledged			Duncan's multiple range test[a]	
	N	x̄	SE		
Overall					
Parasitized	92	2.25	0.28	A	
Unparasitized	257	4.09	0.20	B	} $F = 23.63, P < 0.001$
Success-By-Parasitism Class					
Successful, Unparasitized, Flycatcher Only	200	4.79	0.21	A	
Successful, Parasitized, Rearing Both[b]	9	3.89	0.84	A	
Successful, Parasitized, Flycatcher Only	29	3.76	0.48	A	} $F = 20.76, P < 0.001$
Unsuccessful, Parasitized, Cowbird Only	18	1.78	0.70	B	
Unsuccessful, Unparasitized, No Young	57	1.63	0.40	B	
Unsuccessful, Parasitized, No Young	36	0.86	0.32	B	

[a] Values sharing the same letter are not significantly different ($P > 0.05$).
[b] Females that successfully reared one Cowbird and at least one Willow Flycatcher young.

TABLE 10. LIFETIME REPRODUCTIVE SUCCESS OF FEMALE WILLOW FLYCATCHERS (N), BY PARASITISM AND SUCCESS-BY-PARASITISM CLASSES, SUBSEQUENT TO THEIR FIRST YEAR, MALHEUR NWR, OREGON (1988–1997)

	Flycatcher young fledged			Duncan's multiple range test[a]	
	N	x̄	SE		
Overall					
Parasitized	44	2.84	0.43	A	} $F = 1.55$, $P = 0.214$
Unparasitized	141	3.49	0.26	A	
Success-By-Parasitism Class					
Successful, Unparasitized, Flycatcher Only	118	3.38	0.27	A	
Successful, Parasitized, Rearing Both[b]	7	3.00	0.72	A	
Successful, Parasitized, Flycatcher Only	16	2.56	0.82	A	} $F = 0.64$, $P = 0.67$
Unsuccessful, Parasitized, Cowbird Only	9	3.56	1.14	A	
Unsuccessful, Unparasitized, No Young	23	4.04	0.74	A	
Unsuccessful, Parasitized, No Young	12	2.58	0.74	A	

[a] Values sharing the same letter are not significantly different ($P > 0.05$).
[b] Females that successfully reared one cowbird and at least one Willow Flycatcher young.

Seasonal nestling losses were similar for the above three successful groups indicating that most of the consequences of parasitism to seasonal fecundity were due to egg, and not nestling, losses.

Only a few studies have examined seasonal reductions in fecundity: Nolan (1978) reported only a 13.3% reduction in seasonal fecundity for Prairie Warblers (*Dendroica discolor*); Trail and Baptista (1993) presented data from Petrinovich and Patterson (1978, 1983) from which we calculated a reduction of 44.3% in seasonal fecundity for Nuttall's White-crowned Sparrows (*Zonotrichia leucophrys nuttalli*); and Smith (1981) found that parasitized female Song Sparrows (*Melospiza melodia*) raised as many young to independence as unparasitized female Song Sparrows.

There are numerous studies that report reductions in the average number of young produced on a per nest basis, with reductions typically most pronounced for hosts that have longer incubation periods and are smaller than cowbirds (Friedmann 1963, Rothstein 1975a). For example, Marvil and Cruz (1989) reported a significant reduction in per nest fledgling production between unparasitized (2.35) and parasitized (0.50) nests for Plumbeous Vireos (*Vireo plumbeus*); 1.2–1.9 fewer Dickcissels (*Spiza americana*) fledged in parasitized than unparasitized nests in a Kansas study (Zimmerman 1983); Yellow Warblers (*Dendroica petechia*) with unparasitized nests fledged significantly more young (2.28) than those with parasitized (1.64–1.90) nests (Weatherhead 1989); and parasitism by Shiny Cowbirds (*Molothrus bonariensis*) reduced by 84% the number of young fledged per active Puerto Rican Vireo (*Vireo latimeri*) nest (Woodworth 1997). Brood reductions on a per nest basis, however, are only indirect measures of the consequences of brood parasitism on seasonal fecundity because of multiple nesting (due to abandonment of parasitized nests and subsequent renesting) and some nesting of hosts before or after the egg-laying period of cowbirds (Pease and Grzybowski 1995, Robinson et al. 1995a).

From the above examples, it seems clear that at least on a per nest basis, parasitism can dramatically reduce the fecundity of small hosts. And seasonal fecundity reductions (parasitized pairs vs. unparasitized pairs) for Willow Flycatchers (1.31 young/pair, our study) also suggest significant costs as a consequence of parasitism. The population-level cost of seasonal fecundity (comparing seasonal fecundity of unparasitized pairs [2.11] to that of all pairs [1.81]) is not as severe (0.30 young/pair) because only 23.4% of all flycatcher pairs were parasitized. But no matter how the cost of parasitism is expressed, it still begs the question: Can Willow Flycatcher populations persist in the face of this level of reduction in seasonal fecundity?

ENERGETIC COSTS

Parasitism may increase adult mortality if parasitized females expend more energy during the breeding season than unparasitized females (Robinson et al. 1995a). We found that parasitized females spent more time attending nests, built more nests, and laid more eggs than unparasitized females. Return and survival rates of parasitized and unparasitized females were similar, however, suggesting that increased energetic costs as a consequence of parasitism do not increase female mortality in Willow Flycatchers. Smith (1981) also found no differences in survival of parasitized and unparasitized female Song Sparrows. However, energetic costs, or other factors associated with parasitism, may be linked to return rates for some species. Return rates of Black-capped Vireos (*Vireo atricapillus*), for example, were low following years of high rates of parasitism and were higher following years of low rates of parasitism (Gryzbowski 1991).

PHENOLOGY SHIFTS

Phenology shifts in fledging date may diminish reproductive output and be an additional, hidden cost of parasitism. Lowered reproductive output as a result of phenology shifts has been shown for a number of species, and is often corroborated by lower return rates and increased mortality in late-born young (Perrins 1965, Morton 1992). In our study, young produced by parasitized pairs fledged only 4 d later than young produced by unparasitized pairs. It seems clear that there is a direct link between this phenology shift and cowbird parasitism: fledging is delayed because of the greater number of eggs laid and nests built by parasitized female Willow Flycatchers. The delay in fledging is less than one might expect and, indeed, is less than the phenology shift (11 d) due to parasitism found by Whitfield and Sogge (*this volume*) for *E. t. extimus* in California. Neither shift (4 d or 11 d) would seem great enough to diminish seasonal fecundity; it is unlikely that females feeding nestlings only 4–11 d later in the season would be far enough out of phase with the foraging resource to affect reproductive success (Immelmann 1971). Because Willow Flycatchers rarely attempt to raise two broods in a season (J. Sedgwick, unpubl. data), phenology shifts cannot result in lost opportunities for fecundity enhancements from second broods. Greater phenology shifts, such as those for Common Flickers (*Colaptes auratus*) (21 d; Ingold 1996; D. Ingold, pers. comm.) and for Great Tits (*Parus major*) (49 d; Perrins 1965), have been shown to lower reproductive success, however.

The phenology shift at Malheur NWR was apparently not enough to affect return rates or survival. Larger differences in fledging dates do affect return rates in Willow Flycatchers, however, as the earliest fledging young (1–15 July) had return rates (29.1%) more than 5 times greater than for later fledging young (4.8–5.4%). Similarly, Whitfield and Sogge (*this volume*) reported significantly higher return rates for early-fledged compared to late-fledged *E. t. extimus,* and Morton (1992) and Drilling and Thompson (1988) documented higher return rates for early-fledged White-crowned Sparrows and House Wrens (*Troglodytes aedon*), respectively. Under certain circumstances, phenology shifts as a result of parasitism could conceivably be large enough to diminish return rates.

RETURN RATES, SURVIVAL, AND PARASITISM

Return rates and survival were low for juvenile Willow Flycatchers, due presumably to high juvenile mortality and/or dispersal, common in passerines (Horn and Rubenstein 1984, Plissner and Gowaty 1996). There were no significant differences in return rates or survival between juveniles from parasitized and unparasitized pairs in our study, even though juveniles from parasitized nests fledged on average four days later than offspring from unparasitized nests. Because later fledging potentially reduces the ability of young produced by parasitized pairs to survive to the following breeding season (Sullivan 1988), we expected a lower return rate among flycatcher young from parasitized nests. The greatest costs of parasitism incurred by juveniles probably occur during the post-fledging period. Several studies have found that late-fledging birds have increased mortality rates, especially in species where foraging skills and attainment of pre-migratory condition are essential for over-winter survival (Heinsohn 1987, 1991). However, our data indicated that once juveniles from parasitized nests pass through the bottleneck of post-fledging, their chances of overwinter survival and return to their natal areas were as good as offspring from unparasitized nests.

The return rates and survival of all parasitized and all unparasitized females did not differ. Among successful females, parasitized birds returned to the study area at a significantly higher rate than unparasitized females, but survival did not differ. Parasitized females incur a number of costs, including lower pair success, increased time investment, construction of more nests and laying more eggs, as well as feeding large parasite young (Payne 1977). Despite these costs, parasitized females still returned and survived at roughly the same rates as females from unparasitized nests. We offer these possible interpretations: (1) increased time and energy costs, while statistically significant, are simply of no biological consequence; or (2) parasitized Willow Flycatcher females may be superior in some way compared to average flycatchers and may return at the same (or better) rate as unparasitized females because they are better host parents and are able to bear the added energetic costs incurred as a result of parasitism (sensu Smith 1981). If cowbirds are selecting superior females to parasitize, then we might reasonably expect them to have higher return rates.

Neither return rates nor survival of parasitized and unparasitized male Willow Flycatchers differed; in fact, survival of parasitized males tended to be higher (Table 7). This was counter to what we anticipated, given that parasitized males probably invest more time defending territories (because their females attend nests longer) than unparasitized males, and are ultimately less successful because of parasitism. As with female flycatchers, cowbirds may be parasitizing those males that are deemed better host parents. Both the slightly higher survival of parasitized males and similar survival and return rates for females intimate that parasitized pairs may be superior individuals (Smith 1981, Smith and Arcese 1994). Hahn et al. (*this volume*) found that female cowbirds have home range fidelity over successive breeding seasons and concluded that cowbirds know their hosts and the quality of care their hosts provide. This seems to lend support to the argument that female cowbirds may select flycatcher pairs that are outstanding candidates to raise young under the burden of parasitism.

The differences we observed in the effects of parasitism on return and survival rates of female vs. male Willow Flycatchers may be related to the differences in energetic costs of breeding for females and males (Nur 1988). Despite the energetic expense of territorial defense and parasite-predator detection, males do not incur the same level of energetic costs as females, because they are only occasional participants in feeding offspring (J. Sedgwick, pers. obs.). This may explain their slightly higher survival rates. Parasitized females may have likewise returned more frequently than unparasitized females (as the parasitized males do), but do not do so because of their higher energetic costs (relative to males) imposed by parasitism.

LIFETIME REPRODUCTIVE SUCCESS

The consequences of parasitism to lifetime reproductive success of females supported our prediction: parasitized females fledged fewer young than unparasitized females, with an expected gradient of reproductive success from high (successful, unparasitized females) to low (unsuccessful, parasitized females). Notably, females that were parasitized and successfully reared a cowbird and at least one flycatcher had a lifetime output similar to those females that were parasitized and successfully raised only flycatchers. Given the increased energetic burden of rearing a large cowbird young (Payne 1977) and the associated loss a parasitic offspring represents to Willow Flycatcher fecundity, this is contrary to expectation. But if these females tend to be better host parents because cowbirds are selecting superior pairs, then the increased energetic costs of rearing a cowbird may be inconsequential. If parasitized females rearing both a cowbird and flycatcher(s) do not recognize that they have been parasitized, they may return in

subsequent years based on past reproductive success, regardless of whether the offspring were their own or cowbirds. So the combination of (1) being superior parents and (2) past reproductive success based on number of offspring fledged, not species, may explain the high lifetime reproductive success of parasitized Willow Flycatcher females raising both cowbirds and flycatchers. Similarly, Smith (1981) presented evidence that female Song Sparrows, despite being parasitized, were able to rear as many young to fledging as unparasitized females and suggested that female cowbirds may be actively selecting host individuals with the greatest chance of successfully rearing cowbird young.

If host selection is occurring, what criteria do female cowbirds use to select superior parents? For the parasitic female, these criteria may be relatively simple, e.g., the intensity of anti-parasite behavior displayed by the host territorial male (Robertson and Norman 1977, Uyehara and Narins 1995); the foraging behavior of host males within their territories, especially during courtship (Payne 1977); host density (Verner and Ritter 1983, Rothstein et al. 1986a); or the characteristics of the individual host birds nesting in the cowbird's home range (D. C. Hahn, pers. comm.).

Given the similar return rates and survival of parasitized pairs, we asked if the overall lifetime reproductive success that we observed for females may be affected by parasitism incurred during their first breeding attempt. The greatest impact to the lifetime reproductive success of female Willow Flycatchers may occur during their first year of reproduction, when inexperienced breeders may be most susceptible to cowbird parasitism (Payne 1997). If Willow Flycatcher adults are more naive to cowbird parasitism in their first breeding season but able to learn better evasion techniques in subsequent breeding attempts, we would expect that lifetime reproductive success may increase in the years subsequent to parasitism (Payne 1997). To evaluate this first-year effect, we examined the lifetime reproductive success of female Willow Flycatchers in years subsequent to their first year of reproduction.

Two trends emerge from these data. First, Willow Flycatcher females that are successful in their first year fledged no more young over the remainder of their lifespans than females that were unsuccessful in their first year. Thus, successful females do not appear to improve in subsequent performance as a result of their success. This suggests that successful females may be taking advantage of their unparasitized state in their first year and maximizing chick production when they can, but may pay a cost in diminished lifetime output after this first year. Unparasitized Willow Flycatcher females may be peaking in their reproductive success within their first year in this short-lived species.

Second, subsequent lifetime reproductive success was similar for all classes whether birds were parasitized or not, or successful or not, in their first year. This suggests that unsuccessful females may learn from experience how to become successful, and that parasitized females may learn how to avoid parasitism. Females that were parasitized were certainly not inferior, because they were just as successful in subsequent years as unparasitized females. They may have been more naive to cowbirds in their first year and more easily duped into raising a cowbird, however. Thus, cowbirds may be selecting the most naive host individuals, but not individuals that are reproductively inferior. Similarly, females that were successful and unparasitized in their first year, and had high lifetime reproductive success, may have been more experienced and less naive to cowbirds. Thus, they may have not been parasitized because they did not fit the criteria for cowbird selection of good host parents.

Our data suggest that although parasitism in the first year of breeding is detrimental to the reproductive success of Willow Flycatcher females over their lifespans, other factors, such as learning anti-parasite behaviors (Hobson and Sealy 1989, Payne 1997) or how to become better parents (Drent and Daan 1980), need to be considered in addressing lifetime reproductive success. It may not be just a matter of being parasitized, but also when parasitism occurs and learning from the experience to increase lifetime reproductive success.

RELATIVE COSTS OF PARASITISM AND PREDATION

Predation is thought to be one of the most important selective pressures shaping reproductive and survival strategies of prey species (Wittenberger 1981). The greatest threat from predators occurs during nesting and shortly after fledging when progeny are most vulnerable. At Malheur NWR, predation accounted for a greater proportion of the loss of potential progeny (0.74 young/season; 0.70 young/lifetime) than parasitism (0.30 young/season; 0.37 young/lifetime); therefore, we conclude that local predators must exert greater selective pressure on Willow Flycatchers at Malheur NWR than do cowbirds. The greater influence of predation has been reported for numerous species, such as California Gnatcatcher (*Polioptila californica*; Braden et al. 1997b), Prairie Warbler (Nolan 1978), Indigo Bunting (*Passerina cyanea*; Best and Stauffer 1980), Kirtland's Warbler (*Dendroica*

kirtlandii; Mayfield 1960), and Yellow-breasted Chat (*Icteria virens*; Thompson and Nolan 1973). Fewer studies have found that parasitism accounted for higher proportions of nest losses, for example, Plumbeous Vireo (Marvil and Cruz 1989), Red-eyed Vireo (*Vireo olivaceus*; Southern 1958), Black-capped Vireo (Graber 1961), and Yellow Warbler (Burgham and Picman 1989). If parasitism proves to be relatively less important than predation for a given species, then the selective pressures to evolve anti-parasite strategies may be lower than those to reduce predation. But regardless of the level of parasitism, if a heretofore unparasitized species is in equilibrium with historic levels of predation, then the additional reproductive costs of parasitism may lower productivity below that needed to replace adult mortality.

IMPLICATIONS FOR PERSISTENCE OF THE WILLOW FLYCATCHER

Of the small hosts with incubation periods longer than that of the cowbird, Willow Flycatchers appear to be fairly typical in terms of the costs of parasitism. Parasitized pairs hatch fewer eggs, fledge fewer young, have far fewer successful nests, and suffer reductions in seasonal fecundity and lifetime reproductive success. In addition, parasitized females expend more energy, and nestlings of parasitized females fledge slightly later than those of unparasitized females. Thus, in spite of nest abandonment, cowbird egg burial, and aggressive attempts to thwart cowbirds at the nest (Sedgwick and Knopf 1988), parasitized pairs have substantially lower fecundity than unparasitized pairs. However, a relatively small percentage of the population we studied was parasitized, and the population level consequences of parasitism do not appear to be severe. Furthermore, return rates of both sexes of parasitized adults and young of parasitized pairs are at least as high as those of unparasitized birds. Similar return rates for females suggest that the energetic costs they incur are not pivotal and similar return rates for young suggest that the slight delay in fledging is of no consequence. Compared to parasitism, predation would appear to be a much more significant selective force. In situations where there are pockets of parasitism, and especially where populations are small and fragmented, as is the case for most populations of *E. t. extimus,* parasitism may have more of a negative impact and reproductive success may not be sufficient to balance mortality. We believe we have reasonable estimates for most of the demographic parameters (seasonal fecundity, parasitism rates, and female mortality) for Willow Flycatchers at Malheur, all of which are necessary to assess effects of parasites on host populations (May and Robinson 1985). However, we lack a credible estimate of annual juvenile mortality. We again ask the question: Can Willow Flycatcher populations persist in the face of the levels of reduction in seasonal fecundity due to cowbird parasitism at Malheur? Using the equation for the critical probability of parasitism (p_c) in May and Robinson (1985),

$$p_c = \{\lambda - [2\mu/(1 - \mu_0)]\}/(\lambda - \lambda')$$

and using values from our study for the Malheur population (the probability of parasitism [p_c = 0.234], female mortality [μ = 0.464; J. Sedgwick, unpubl. data], and seasonal fecundity of unparasitized [λ = 2.11] and parasitized [λ' = 0.80] females), and solving for the annual mortality of juveniles (μ_0, the only unknown), we calculate that μ_0 = 0.49. This means that juvenile survival from fledging to breeding in the next year must be 0.51. Because of presumed low site fidelity and dispersal of juveniles, our return rates (5.4–7.7%; Table 7) are far below the calculated μ_0, but the latter is what they must be if the population is to persist. Therefore, the implication may be that the Malheur Willow Flycatcher population is in decline or is a sink population maintained only by immigration from other areas. However, given unknown rates of overwinter juvenile mortality and unknown rates of juvenile dispersal to and from respective natal areas, no reliable conclusions can be drawn. Information is lacking, as it is for virtually all other passerines, on juvenile survival rates, and until we have a better grasp of juvenile survival to first year of breeding, our estimates of the demographic consequences of parasitism are severely limited.

ACKNOWLEDGMENTS

We thank E. Anderson, R. Clemens, R. Corcorin, N. Darnall, L. Dent, J. Hovis, J. Jorgensen, R. Klus, P. Loafman, S. Marsh, S. Merrill, B. Moyer, S. Muschenheim, B. Petersen, C. Rupert, and J. Rupert for invaluable field assistance. Special thanks to G. Ivey and Malheur NWR for logistic and financial support and for Malheur NWR volunteer assistance. Additional financial support was provided by the U.S. Fish and Wildlife Service, Regions 2 and 6. Earlier drafts of the manuscript were reviewed and improved by M. L. Morrison, L. S. Hall, J. N. M. Smith, J. A. Gryzbowski, and D. C. Hahn. The senior author dedicates this paper to P. L. Wright, who inspired his original interest in *Empidonax* flycatchers.

Studies in Avian Biology No. 18:182–190, 1999.

RANGE-WIDE IMPACT OF BROWN-HEADED COWBIRD PARASITISM ON THE SOUTHWESTERN WILLOW FLYCATCHER (*EMPIDONAX TRAILLII EXTIMUS*)

MARY J. WHITFIELD AND MARK K. SOGGE

Abstract. We present datasets from long-term studies of brood parasitism of Southwestern Willow Flycatcher (*Empidonax traillii extimus*) populations at the South Fork Kern River (SFKR), California, the Grand Canyon, Arizona, and from other intensive flycatcher studies in Arizona. In the two main study areas, we recorded high parasitism rates for the flycatcher. We found that 75 % of Willow Flycatcher nests failed completely when parasitized and that an extremely low percentage of Willow Flycatcher eggs survived to fledging in parasitized nests (11% vs. 47% in unparasitized nests). Our data show that cowbird parasitism also delayed the fledging of young flycatchers. However, contrary to our expectations, we did not find a significant difference between the return rates of "early" versus "late" fledged birds. To evaluate how important cowbird parasitism is to the population decline of the endangered Southwestern Willow Flycatcher, we reviewed the current level of parasitism on this species throughout its range in six states using a large number of datasets from different sites. We also reviewed the historic pattern of increase in Brown-headed Cowbird (*Molothrus ater*) populations in the southwest between 1872–1997 using both nest record and egg collections and documentary evidence. Given the level of impacts to flycatcher productivity inflicted by cowbird parasitism that we observed at SFKR and Grand Canyon, it is likely that cowbirds played a role historically in reducing many local Southwestern Willow Flycatcher populations. Also, cowbirds continue to play a role in slowing or preventing the recovery of this subspecies.

Key Words: brood parasitism, Brown-headed Cowbird, *Empidonax traillii*, *Molothrus ater*, reproductive success, Willow Flycatcher.

The Southwestern Willow Flycatcher (*Empidonax traillii extimus*) once commonly bred in riparian thickets throughout the Southwest (Fig. 1; Unitt 1987). Although the flycatcher is still found in most of its former range, its numbers have been severely reduced in the last 60 years, prompting the US Fish and Wildlife Service to list this Willow Flycatcher subspecies as endangered (Unitt 1987, USFWS 1995).

Johnson and Haight (1984) estimated that only 5% of the original lowland riparian habitat in the Southwest remains, and destruction of this habitat is regarded as the main cause of the decline of this subspecies (Gaines 1974, Harris et al. 1987, Unitt 1987, Garrett and Dunn 1981, USFWS 1995). In addition, Brown-headed Cowbird (*Molothrus ater*) parasitism is considered a major factor in the subspecies' decline (Gaines 1974, Unitt 1987, Harris 1991, USFWS 1995).

Southwestern Willow Flycatchers suffer from high parasitism rates in at least two areas for which long-term data are available: the South Fork of the Kern River, California (SFKR), and in the Grand Canyon, Arizona (Brown 1988, 1994; Sogge et al. 1997, Whitfield in press). However, is cowbird parasitism a problem throughout the flycatcher's range? In this paper, we use long-term datasets to examine the impacts of cowbird parasitism on the flycatcher's reproductive success. We also review both the current and historical parasitism rates of South-

western Willow Flycatchers in different parts of its range, as well as the pattern of increase in cowbird populations, to evaluate the contribution of cowbird parasitism to the population decline of this subspecies.

METHODS

LONG-TERM STUDY AREAS

Grand Canyon, AZ.

Data were collected from 1992 to 1996 in riparian habitat patches along the Colorado River in the Grand Canyon from just below Glen Canyon Dam, downstream to the boundary between Grand Canyon National Park and Lake Mead National Recreation Area. Some data were also collected by B. Brown from 1982 to 1986 (see Brown 1988 and Sogge et. al 1997 for more details).

South Fork Kern River, CA.

The study area is located on The Nature Conservancy's Kern River Preserve (now managed by Audubon California) and the adjoining South Fork Wildlife Area in Kern Co., California. It encompasses 500 ha of cottonwood-willow riparian forest dominated by three tree species: red willow (*Salix laeviagata*), Gooding's black willow (*Salix gooddingii*) and Fremont cottonwood (*Populus fremontii*). Data were collected in 1987 by J. Harris and from 1989 to 1997 by

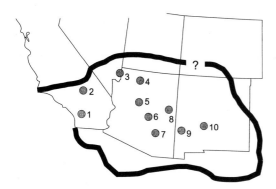

FIGURE 1. Approximate breeding range distribution (thick black line) of *Empidonax traillii extimus,* adapted from Unitt (1987) and Browning (1993). Shaded circles are approximate locations of breeding sites for which cowbird parasitism data are presented in the text. 1= San Luis Rey River, 2 = South Fork Kern River, 3 = Mesquite, Virgin River Delta, and Mormon Mesa, 4 = Grand Canyon, 5 = Verde River, 6 = Roosevelt Lake, 7 = San Pedro River, 8 = White Mtns., 9 = Gila River, 10 = Rio Grande.

M. Whitfield (see Harris 1991 and Whitfield et. al. *this volume* for more details).

OVERVIEW OF CURRENT PARASITISM RATES

We obtained data on current parasitism rate and cowbird presence at Willow Flycatcher breeding locations across the subspecies range from various sources (Fig. 1, Table 1).

LONG-TERM DATASETS: IMPACT OF PARASITISM ON FLYCATCHER REPRODUCTIVE SUCCESS

We used data from our own long-term studies and four other sources (Table 1) to analyze nest outcome of parasitized nests. We used only active nests (defined as nests with at least one egg or young, cowbird or flycatcher), with known outcome, in our analyses. A successful nest was one that fledged at least one Willow Flycatcher.

Egg success data were collected at SFKR from 1989 to 1997. We used a t-test and a Mann-Whitney U test for comparing hatching success and fledging success of parasitized and unparasitized nests.

We used six sources (Table 1) for the nest success analysis. Nest success was defined as the total number of successful nests divided by the total number of active nests. We used the Chi-square test of homogeneity for comparing nest success in parasitized and unparasitized nests in California, Arizona, and New Mexico.

Return rates of early versus late nesters.

Data were collected using banded birds on the SFKR from 1989 to 1997. All nestlings used in

TABLE 1. DATA SOURCES FOR THE VARIOUS ANALYSES CONDUCTED IN THIS PAPER

State(s)	Region	Author	Citation	Parasitism rates and cowbird presence	Parasitism rates by habitat types	Nest outcome	Nest success
AZ	Grand Canyon	Brown	1988	X		X	
AZ	Grand Canyon	Sogge et al.	1997 and this study	X		X	X
AZ	Various sites throughout the state	Muiznieks et al.	1994	X	X	X	X
AZ	Various sites throughout the state	Sferra et al.	1995, 1997	X	X	X	X
AZ	Various sites throughout the state	Spencer et al.	1996	X	X		X
CA	South Fork Kern River	Harris	1991	X		X	X
CA	South Fork Kern River	Whitfield	this study	X			
CA	San Luis Rey River	W. Haas	Unpubl. data	X		X	
CO, NV and UT	Various sites in these states	Sogge	this study	X			
NM	Various sites throughout the state	Maynard	1994	X			
NM	Various sites throughout the state	Cooper	1996, 1997	X			
NM	Rio Grande River	Ahlers and White	1995	X			
NM	Gila River Valley	Skaggs	1996	X			X
NM	Gila River Valley	S. Stoleson	Unpubl. data	X			
NV	Virgin River	R. McKernan	Unpubl. data	X			

the analysis were banded with a USFWS band. Due to heavy cowbird parasitism and the resultant low productivity, and low return rates, we did not have a large enough sample size to test directly whether breeding delays caused by cowbirds resulted in lower fledgling survival. However, we could indirectly test whether cowbirds decreased the survivorship of fledged young by investigating differences in return rates of young fledged from early vs. late nests. The first step was to determine whether cowbird parasitism caused significant delays in Willow Flycatcher fledging dates. To do this, we standardized laying dates in relation to arrival dates by designating the date when the first Willow Flycatcher egg was laid for the breeding season as day one for that year. This method helps reduce bias due to yearly variation in arrival dates (Perrins and McCleery 1989). For nests that were found after its first egg was laid, we estimated the first egg laid date by counting backwards the appropriate number of days (15 to 17 days depending on clutch size) from the hatching date.

The comparison of return rates of early versus late nesters was made by comparing the first egg dates of successful parasitized females with successful unparasitized females. A successful female was defined as a female that fledged at least one flycatcher young. Females that had nests in which we addled cowbird eggs or removed cowbird chicks were not used in the analysis. Because the data were not normally distributed, we tested for the difference in first egg dates between parasitized and unparasitized females using the Mann-Whitney U test.

To determine if there was a difference in survivorship of young that fledged early in the breeding season versus young that fledged late, we recorded the first egg dates of recaptured Willow Flycatchers that had been banded in earlier years as nestlings. Because the return rates of hatching years birds were unusually high (averaged 32% for eight years), we assumed that recapture rates would be a good index for survivorship (Uyehara et al. in press). To mimic the delay that parasitism has on successful parasitized females, a bird was categorized as "early fledged" when the first egg date of its natal nest was before the average first egg date of successful parasitized females. A bird was categorized as "late fledged" when the first egg date of its natal nest was on or later than the average first egg date of successful parasitized females.

HISTORICAL DATA ON INCREASE IN COWBIRD ABUNDANCE AND PARASITISM RATES

To estimate historical parasitism rates of the Southwestern Willow Flycatcher, we looked through records of nest collections sent to us from 50 North American natural history museums. We classified records as *E. t. extimus* if they came from a site that was within the known *E.t. extimus* range as reported by Unitt (1987) and Browning (1993). The following museums had *E.t. extimus* nest records: Cornell University (1 record); California State University, Long Beach (1 record); Delaware Museum of Natural History (5 records); Denver Museum of Natural History (1 record); New York State Museum, Albany (1 record); Peabody Museum of Natural History (5 records); Provincial Museum of Alberta (1 record); Royal Ontario Museum (3 records); San Bernardino County Museum (16 records); Santa Barbara Museum of Natural History (12 records); Slater Museum of Natural History at the University of Puget Sound, Washington (2 records); Smithsonian National Museum of Natural History (20 records); University of Arizona Museum Collection (35 records); University of California, Berkeley (3 records); University of Nevada, Las Vegas (1 record); Western Foundation of Vertebrate Zoology (147 records).

Information on historical presence and distribution of cowbirds in California was found in Unitt (1987), Laymon (1987), and Rothstein (1994). Estimates of historical abundance elsewhere in the Southwest were derived from sources listed in Table 9.

RESULTS

OVERVIEW OF CURRENT PARASITISM RATES

During the past five years, cowbirds have been detected at all known Southwestern Willow Flycatcher breeding locations in California, Arizona, New Mexico, southwestern Colorado, Utah, and Nevada. As is typical of all host species, cowbird parasitism rates of Southwestern Willow Flycatchers varied both geographically and temporally (Tables 2 and 3). In California, pre-trapping parasitism rates are known only for SFKR (1987, 1989–1992), where the rates averaged 66%. Post-trapping parasitism rates on SFKR (1993–1997) range from 11% to 38%. In Arizona, cowbird parasitism at most sites is below 25%, with a few of the smaller sites (< 5 pairs) experiencing parasitism of 100% in a given year and as much as 50% over 5–10 year periods. New Mexico parasitism data are limited to a few sites, where rates range from 18–40%. Although parasitism data are very limited or absent for Willow Flycatchers in Nevada, southern Utah, and southwest Colorado, cowbird parasitism has been documented at sites in each of these states.

LONG-TERM DATASETS: IMPACT OF PARASITISM ON FLYCATCHER REPRODUCTIVE SUCCESS

The data from our long-term studies of Willow Flycatcher populations at the SFKR and the

TABLE 2. GEOGRAPHIC VARIATION IN PARASITISM RATES OF THE SOUTHWESTERN WILLOW FLYCATCHER AT SE-LECTED LOCATIONS IN CALIFORNIA, NEVADA, ARIZONA, AND NEW MEXICO

Region	Years covered	No. nests	Mean annual parasitism rate[a]	SD
South Fork Kern River, CA	1987, 1989–1992	163	66%	0.11
Mesquite, NV	1997	5	40%	n/a
Virgin River Delta, NV	1997	14	21%	n/a
Mormon Mesa, NV	1997	3	0%	n/a
Grand Canyon, AZ	1982–1986, 1992–1996	25	48%	n/a 0.50
White Mountains, AZ	1993–1996	36	19%	0.19
San Pedro River, AZ	1995–1996	61	3%	0.03
Roosevelt Lake, AZ	1995–1996	17	18%	0.04
Verde River, AZ	1996	13	46%	n/a
Gila River Valley, NM	1995, 1997	49	18%	0.09
other sites, NM	1995	10	40%	n/a

[a] No cowbird trapping was done at these sites for these dates.

Grand Canyon, and from other extensive studies in Arizona, reflect the severe impacts that parasitism has on three parameters of reproductive success: nest failure rate, hatching success, and fledging success. Nest data from Arizona and SFKR show that the majority of parasitized Willow Flycatcher nests failed (Table 4). Nests fledged cowbird young two to three times more often than flycatcher young, and fewer than 2% of the nests fledged both a cowbird and a flycatcher. In addition, SFKR egg success data show that for all years (though it is only significant in 5 of the 7 years tested), the percentage of eggs hatched per nest is lower in parasitized than unparasitized nests (Table 5). When the data are pooled, the average hatching rate for parasitized nests (20%) is significantly lower than the hatching rate for unparasitized nests (61%) ($t_{279} = 8.21$, p < 0.001). The number of flycatcher eggs that hatched and subsequently produced fledglings followed the same pattern as hatching success, with all years showing lower fledging rates in parasitized nests than unparasitized nests (Table 6). When the data are pooled, the fledging rate is significantly lower most years in parasitized nests (11%) than unparasitized nests (47%) ($t_{279} = 7.51$, p < 0.001). Nest success data showed a similar pattern as

the egg success data in which the success of parasitized nests was lower than unparasitized nests in every year. An ANOVA showed that the yearly (MS error) variation was insignificant when compared to the difference between parasitized and unparasitized nests (MS effect) (AZ: ANOVA, MS effect =0.236, MS error = 0.037; CA: MS effect = 0.845, MS error = 0.018). Therefore, we pooled the data and found that nest success is significantly lower in parasitized nests than in unparasitized nests in California ($\chi^2_1 = 54.01$, p < 0.001), Arizona ($\chi^2_1 = 22.46$, p < 0.001), and New Mexico ($\chi^2_1 = 8.13$, p = 0.004) (Table 7).

Return rates of early versus late nesters

First egg dates of successful parasitized females were significantly later (day 27) than first egg dates of successful unparasitized females (day 16) ($Z = -3.60$, P = 0.003, Mann-Whitney U test). However, we did not find any significant differences in return rates of the "early fledged" (first egg date < day 27) birds when compared to the "late fledged" (first egg date ≥ 27) young) in any single year (Table 8). We did not pool the data and analyze the results, because of the substantial annual differences in the relative

TABLE 3. ANNUAL VARIATION IN COWBIRD PARASITISM RATES OF SOUTHWESTERN WILLOW FLYCATCHERS IN ARIZONA, CALIFORNIA, AND NEW MEXICO

Region	Years	Mean no. nests per year	Range of annual parasitism rates	
			No trapping	Trapping
Various sites, AZ[a]	1994–1996	76	8%–21%	
South Fork Kern River, CA	1989–1997	35	50%–80%	11%–38%
San Diego Co., CA	1994–1997	24	Unknown	0%–10%
Gila River Valley, NM	1995, 1997	24.5	14.7%–27%	

[a] Parasitism rates of Arizona were calculated from data pooled from all sites.

TABLE 4. NEST OUTCOME OF SOUTHWESTERN WILLOW FLYCATCHER NESTS PARASITIZED BY BROWN-HEADED COWBIRDS IN CALIFORNIA AND ARIZONA

Region	Years	Number of nests	Fledged cowbird	Fledged flycatcher	Fledged both	Failed
South Fork Kern River, CA	1989–1997	72	14%	9.7%	1.4%	75%
Various sites, AZ	1992–1996	40	30%	7.5%	0%	62.5%

return rate patterns for "early fledged" vs. "late fledged" birds.

HISTORICAL DATA ON INCREASE IN COWBIRD ABUNDANCE AND PARASITISM RATES

We found 254 *E. t. extimus* nest records from 16 of the 50 collections of nest records examined. None of the 36 Southwestern Willow Flycatcher nests collected between 1872 and 1899 were parasitized (Fig. 2). The first recorded parasitized Southwestern Willow Flycatcher nest was found by Herbert Brown near Yuma, Arizona, in 1900 (nest record collection of University of Arizona). The nest records show that the number of parasitized nests collected, and hence the inferred rate of parasitism increased gradually from zero before 1900 to 40% by 1997.

Our search of the literature indicated that although cowbirds were in the southwest much earlier than 1860, they apparently did not start to increase until after the 1860s or 1870s (Table 9).

DISCUSSION
THE CURRENT EXTENT AND ROLE OF PARASITISM

Observations from recent flycatcher surveys (sources listed in Table 1) indicated that cowbirds are present at all known Southwestern Willow Flycatcher breeding sites. Thus, the potential for parasitism of flycatcher nests is widespread and pervasive. Although cowbirds must obviously be at a site for parasitism to occur, mere cowbird presence does not mean that flycatchers are being parasitized at that site nor that parasitism rates are high. Indeed, we found enough geographic, temporal, and habitat-based variation in flycatcher parasitism rates to make it impossible to predict parasitism rates based simply on the presence of cowbirds.

However, Southwestern Willow Flycatchers are being parasitized throughout their range (Table 2). In southern California, pre-cowbird trapping parasitism rates are known only for the SFKR, which suffered from heavy parasitism (>50%) (Harris 1991, Whitfield 1990, in press).

TABLE 5. PERCENT EGGS HATCHED IN PARASITIZED AND UNPARASITIZED SOUTHWESTERN WILLOW FLYCATCHER NESTS ON THE SOUTH FORK KERN RIVER, CA, 1989–1997

Year	Unparasitized nests			Parasitized nests[a]			Difference	
	Number of nests	Mean percent eggs hatched per nest	SE	Number of nests	Mean percent eggs hatched per nest	SE	t-value	P-value
1989	15	68%	0.12	14	20%	0.10	3.06	0.005
1990	14	52%	0.13	17	27%	0.08	1.71	0.09
1991	9	70%	0.12	26	11%	0.05	5.60	<0.001
1992	11	54%	0.12	19	32%	0.10	1.34	0.19
1993	19	71%	0.09	11	32%	0.12	2.61	0.014
1994	25	64%	0.09	5	0%	0.00	2.62[b]	0.009
1995	21	51%	0.10	3	17%	0.17	n/a[c]	
1996	24	82%	0.08	2	0%	0.00	n/a[c]	
1997	36	45%	0.07	10	12%	0.10	2.17	0.04
Unmanipulated nest totals	n/a			57	18%	0.04		
Manipulated nest totals	n/a			50	23%	0.05		
Total	174	61%	0.03	107	20%	0.04	8.21	<0.001

[a] 1989–1991-no test manipulation (i.e. no addling of cowbird eggs or removal of cowbird chicks from nests), 1992–1997: nests manipulated.
[b] Z-value; Mann-Whitney U test used instead of t-test due to unequal variances and small sample size.
[c] Sample size too small to test.

TABLE 6. PERCENT EGGS THAT HATCHED AND FLEDGED IN PARASITIZED AND UNPARASITIZED SOUTHWESTERN WILLOW FLYCATCHER NESTS ON THE SOUTH FORK KERN RIVER, CA, 1989–1997

Year	Unparasitized nests			Parasitized nests[a]			Difference	
	Number of nests	Mean percent eggs to fledglings per nest	SE	Number of nests	Mean percent eggs to fledglings per nest	SE	t-value	P-value
1989	15	53%	0.13	14	2%	0.02	3.81	<0.001
1990	14	36%	0.14	17	13%	0.07	1.61	0.117
1991	9	58%	0.16	26	10%	0.05	4.05	<0.001
1992	11	54%	0.12	19	20%	0.09	2.27	0.031
1993	19	49%	0.11	11	16%	0.08	2.14	0.041
1994	25	51%	0.10	5	0%	0.00	2.08[b]	0.037
1995	21	46%	0.10	3	17%	0.17	n/a[c]	
1996	24	73%	0.09	2	0%	0.00	n/a[c]	
1997	36	26%	0.06	10	2%	0.03	1.88	0.067
Unmanipulated nest totals	n/a			57	9%	0.03		
Manipulated nest totals	n/a			50	13%	0.04		
Totals	174	47%	0.04	107	11%	0.02		

[a] 1989–1991-no nest manipulation (i.e. no addling of cowbird eggs or removal of cowbird chicks from nests), 1992–1997: nests manipulated.
[b] Z-value; Mann-Whitney U test used instead of t-test due to unequal variances and small sample size.
[c] Sample size too small to test.

The Santa Margarita River Willow Flycatcher population in San Diego County has increased from 5 birds to 24 birds after cowbird trapping started (Griffith and Griffith in press). Currently, all known southern California Willow Flycatcher populations of more than 10 pairs occur in areas where cowbirds are trapped (Unitt 1987, USFWS 1995), and mean parasitism rates of these Willow Flycatcher populations are 22% or lower. In Arizona and New Mexico, the statewide parasitism rates average 20% and 22% respectively. The overall picture that emerges in every state with intensive flycatcher monitoring is that parasitism is occurring throughout the range, often at rates exceeding those considered acceptable to most host species (Mayfield 1977, Brittingham and Temple 1983, Trail 1992).

When parasitism does occur, data from the SFKR and Arizona show that it negatively impacts the flycatcher at many different levels. Most parasitized Willow Flycatcher nests fail, and few fledge flycatchers. Cowbird parasitism significantly reduces hatching success and fledg-

ling success leading to significantly lower reproductive success. Harris (1991) noted that some parasitized Willow flycatcher pairs on the SFKR renested several times, one as many as five times, before successfully fledging flycatcher young. He hypothesized that these cowbird-caused delays in fledging could negatively affect survival of the young. Our data show that cowbird parasitism does indeed cause delays in fledging, on average an 11-day delay in first egg dates of successful parasitized pairs when compared to successful unparasitized pairs. However, unlike other studies (e.g., Perrins and McCleery 1989, Hochachka 1990, Verhulst et al. 1995), we did not find any significant differences in the return rates of nestlings from early nests when compared to nestlings from late nests.

Although these negative impacts are widespread, it is difficult to quantify the population-level effects of this loss of productivity, and the long-term effects of parasitism will vary between sites. Parasitism rates averaging 50% in

TABLE 7. NEST SUCCESS OF PARASITIZED AND UNPARASITIZED SOUTHWESTERN WILLOW FLYCATCHER NESTS IN DIFFERENT PARTS OF ITS RANGE

Region	Years	Parasitized		Unparasitized	
		N	Nest success	N	Nest success
South Fork Kern River, CA	1989–1997	133	14%	190	54%
Various sites, AZ	1994–1996	31	13%	133	60%
Gila River Valley, NM	1997	6	0%	61	61%

TABLE 8.   Return rates of banded nestling Southwestern Willow Flycatchers from early versus late nests on the South Fork Kern River, Kern Co., CA

Year	Early			Late			Fisher's exact P
	No. banded	No. returned	Percent returned	No. banded	No. returned	Percent returned	
1989	16	5	31.0%	0	0	n/a	n/a
1990	8	0	0.0%	10	1	10.0%	0.56
1991	0	0	n/a	9	0	0.0%	n/a
1992	14	4	28.6%	16	1	6.0%	0.13
1993	17	5	29.4%	11	4	36.4%	0.50
1994	24	7	29.2%	11	3	27.3%	0.62
1995	23	10	43.5%	6	1	16.7%	0.24
1996	38	12	31.6%	0	0	n/a	n/a
Total	140	43	30.7%	63	10	15.8%	n/a

the Grand Canyon have created a "population" that is not stable, but is maintained only by an influx of individuals from other areas (Sogge et al. 1997). A demographic analysis conducted on the SFKR Willow Flycatcher population by Uyehara et al. (in press) suggests that parasitism levels over 10% reduce population growth. On the other hand, the Gila River Valley population in New Mexico appears to be stable or increasing over the last few years while experiencing on average an 18% parasitism level (Skaggs 1996, S. Stoleson, pers. comm.). However, this population of flycatchers appears to be well over 100 pairs and thus may be able to tolerate higher levels of parasitism than the smaller SFKR population (Hall and Rothstein *this volume*). Although population-level effects vary and are not widely studied, high rates of parasitism threaten the stability of at least some Willow Flycatcher populations and probably limit potential rates of increase for others.

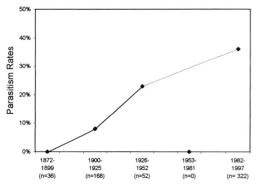

FIGURE 2.   Historical cowbird parasitism rates of Southwestern Willow Flycatchers in Arizona and California, 1872–1997 (no data available 1953–1981).

THE ROLE OF PARASITISM IN THE FLYCATCHER'S DECLINE

Cowbird parasitism may have contributed to the Southwestern Willow Flycatcher's population decline, but because cowbird parasitism is strongly influenced by habitat destruction and degradation, as well as nearby human land-use patterns, it is not possible to show how much of the decline was due to cowbird parasitism as opposed to habitat destruction (Rothstein 1994). However, we believe that cowbird parasitism may have played a role in at least some local flycatcher declines and probably reduced the capability of flycatcher populations to recover after habitat was lost.

Several lines of evidence support this conclusion. First, flycatcher population declines occurred concurrently with increasing parasitism. Unitt (1987) summarizes the historical status of the Southwestern Willow Flycatcher, and found it to be widespread and abundant until the early 1900s. Historical data sources (Table 9) and Rothstein (1994) show that Brown-headed Cowbirds were uncommon in the Southwest prior to the 1860s, but had become fairly common by 1925.

Historical flycatcher nest data reflect an association between increasing size of regional cowbird populations and increasing rates of flycatcher parasitism; cowbird parasitism was very rare prior to the turn of the century, but increased thereafter. It is possible that nest collectors were biased towards or against parasitized nests; however, most modern (i.e., twentieth century) egg collectors and collections were not biased, and data from these sources probably present an accurate overview of the frequency of host parasitism at the time they were collected (L. Kiff, pers. comm.).

Thus, regional cowbird abundance increased as sympatric Southwestern Willow Flycatcher

TABLE 9. HISTORICAL ACCOUNTS OF COWBIRD PRESENCE IN THE SOUTHWEST (1858 TO 1945)

Author(s)	Year	States	Comments
Baird	1858	NV, UT, CA, CO, NM, and AZ	Compilation of zoological collection records from over a dozen survey parties exploring the West. Fewer than a dozen cowbird specimens were collected in the Southwest through the mid-1850's.
Linsdale	1936	NV	Information about Ridgeway collecting a male and female cowbird in 1867 in the Humboldt Valley at Oreana, Pershing Co., NV. The only other individual seen by him was an adult male collected by him in 1868 at Truckee Reservation, Wahoe, Co., NV.
Henshaw	1875	NV, UT, CA, CO, NM, and AZ	Report on the ornithological collections for Nevada, Utah, California, Colorado, New Mexico, and Arizona. He found that in Utah and Colorado, the cowbird was in "about the same abundance as in the eastern states" (meaning common, given data presented by Mayfield 1965). He also found that the cowbird did not appear to occur in great numbers in portions of Arizona.
Ridgeway	1880	UT	Found only two adult and one juvenile cowbirds during an expedition that covered major portions of three years and included a wide geographic region including the Great Basin/central Utah.
Fisher	1893	UT and CA	Report on the biological survey for The Death Valley Expedition. The author only mentions finding several cowbirds in the Lower Santa Clara Valley, Utah, a few in Pahranagat Valley, Utah, and shooting one male at Furnace Creek, Death Valley, California.
Bailey	1923	AZ	Author notes that in 1903, Swarth found cowbirds to be fairly abundant in the Santa Rita Mountains in southern Arizona but not as common as in the lowlands.
Swarth	1914	AZ	Author found that cowbirds were common and widespread along the Colorado and Gila Rivers and associated tributaries.
Woodbury and Russell	1945	AZ, NM, CO and UT (four corners area)	The authors state: "This cowbird nowhere appears to be common, but seems to be well distributed in small numbers in the lower altitudes."

populations decreased. This correlation, however, does not address how heavy the impact of parasitism has been on the flycatcher. As noted above, cowbird parasitism negatively impacts flycatcher reproductive success at many current breeding sites. It is reasonable to assume that, historically, parasitism had the same negative influence on the flycatcher's reproductive success as it does today. By the late 1920s, Willow Flycatchers in some areas in southern California suffered from heavy parasitism. Hanna (1928: 162) referring to an area in San Bernardino Co., writes, "The Traill Flycatcher, California Least Vireo and California Yellow Warbler suffer even more than this report would indicate. They not only have the most parasitized nests and the most Cowbird eggs per nest, but a large number of nests of these species were absolutely destroyed by the Cowbirds (at least I blame the destruction to them), and such nests were not considered in making the survey." In 1937, M.C. Badger commented on an identification card for an egg set collected at the Santa Clara

River mouth (Ventura Co., CA), that cowbird eggs were "nearly always found in the nests of this species" (Unitt 1987). Cowbird parasitism almost certainly reduced flycatcher populations such as those described above.

Unfortunately, quantitative data do not exist to document the degree to which cowbird parasitism contributed to and/or prolonged the historical decline of the Southwestern Willow Flycatcher. However, increased cowbird parasitism coincided with decreasing flycatcher populations, some local populations were heavily parasitized, and parasitism probably affected flycatcher productivity then as it does now. Given this, we believe that cowbird parasitism, at the very least, played a role in the reduction of some local flycatcher populations and reduced the capacity for some flycatcher populations to recover once they were reduced due to habitat destruction or degradation.

MANAGEMENT OF PARASITISM

Cowbird control programs have reduced parasitism rates and stabilized or increased populations of several endangered species and can be an important tool in Willow Flycatcher management and recovery (Kepler et al. 1996, Rothstein and Cook in press, Whitfield et al. *this volume*). However, it is important to keep in mind that habitat destruction and modification are the primary causes of the decline of the Willow Flycatcher, and that high cowbird parasitism is a symptom of this problem (Unitt 1987; Robinson et al. 1993; Rothstein 1994; USFWS 1993b, 1995; Whitfield in press). Therefore, habitat acquisition, improvement and restoration must be given high priority and, wherever possible, be implemented along with cowbird control measures. Also, given the high variability of parasitism rates, it is important to evaluate each site separately before initiating a cowbird control program. Furthermore, because parasitism rates vary geographically and temporally, the degree of cowbird parasitism at one site cannot be predicted based on only a single year's data, or by extrapolating from other sites.

ACKNOWLEDGMENTS

Investigating cowbird parasitism impacts at this large geographic scale required that we draw upon the data, assistance, and knowledge of many others. This manuscript owes much to the many agencies and nongovernmental organizations who have funded recent Willow Flycatcher surveys and research throughout the Southwest, and to the biologists undertaking these efforts. In particular, we are grateful to the staff of the Arizona Game and Fish Department Nongame Branch, the New Mexico Department of Game and Fish, the US Fish and Wildlife Service, and the US Bureau of Reclamation. We also thank the numerous natural history museums that shared nest record data, and W. Haas, R. B. McKernan, and S. H. Stoleson, who provided us with valuable unpublished information. J. Grahame assisted greatly with data acquisition and management. B. Kus and D. Deutschman helped us with some of our statistical analyses. J. Uyehara, J. Sedgwick, B. Kus, and C. Hahn provided excellent reviews of this manuscript.

Studies in Avian Biology No. 18:191–199, 1999.

IMPORTANCE OF PREDATION AND BROOD PARASITISM ON NEST SUCCESS IN FOUR SPARROW SPECIES IN SOUTHERN CALIFORNIAN COASTAL SAGE SCRUB

KEVIN ELLISON

Abstract. Current knowledge of Brown-headed Cowbird (*Molothrus ater*) parasitism rates in nests of resident southern Californian Coastal Sage Scrub (CSS) birds has been limited to studies of the California Gnatcatcher (*Polioptila californica*), a frequent cowbird host. Therefore, I located nests of the four most abundant potential host species to determine the occurrence and impact of parasitism on CSS species other than the gnatcatcher. I then explored the potential impact of parasitism on CSS hosts using a seasonal-fecundity model that accounts for both predation and parasitism. The effects of parasitism were minimal; only 3 of 217 nests were parasitized. However, host breeding phenology was shown to differ significantly from cowbird breeding activity, suggesting that the potential for parasitism in CSS birds is often low. In addition, high nest predation rates appear to minimize the effects of what parasitism does occur. Thus management activities for CSS species may be better focused at processes other than cowbird control.

Key Words: Aimophila ruficeps, Amphispiza bellii, California Towhee, coastal sage scrub, *Molothrus ater,* nest predation, phenology, *Pipilo crissalis, Pipilo maculatus,* Rufous-crowned Sparrow, Sage Sparrow, Spotted Towhee.

Nest predation and brood parasitism are two principal determinants of reproductive success in many passerine birds (Ricklefs 1969, Martin 1987). Both processes have been shown to affect host reproductive success and population dynamics (Martin 1987, Trail and Baptista 1993), and population declines in many North American songbirds have been attributed to these processes (Terborgh 1989). However, rates of nest predation and parasitism are frequently intercorrelated, and the identification of their relative effects on nesting success is important both in an evolutionary context, to identify principal selection pressures, and in practical application, to appropriately direct management activities aimed at conserving avian populations that may be adversely impacted by these processes.

Coastal Sage Scrub (CSS) is a vegetation type dominated by drought deciduous shrubs that occurs along the California coast from the San Francisco Bay area, south to Baja California, Mexico (Westman 1983). CSS in southern California is bordered inland by the Coast and Peninsular ranges. Historically CSS occurred in large contiguous patches. Today, however, CSS is highly fragmented by agriculture and urbanization, with few intact patches greater than 500 ha remaining (Westman 1981, 1983; O'Leary 1990). Such fragmentation may alter predator population dynamics (Soulé et al. 1992) as well as facilitate access by the brood parasitic Brown-headed Cowbird (*Molothrus ater*) (Rothstein et al. 1980).

Fragmentation is thought to result in heightened nest predation rates by increasing edge-to-area ratios. A majority of studies (14 of 21 reviewed) have shown positive associations between edge and higher nest predation rates (Paton 1994). Because fragmentation may provide less area of adequate habitat for large-bodied predators (Soulé et al. 1992), a reduction in the abundance of large predators may result in the proliferation of medium-sized nest predators, thereby resulting in elevated nest predation (Wilcove 1985, Soulé et al. 1988).

Brown-headed Cowbirds first began breeding in southern California sometime in the 1900s (Laymon 1987), and cowbird populations have since steadily increased within portions of this region as indicated by 1966–1996 Breeding Bird Survey data (Sauer et al. 1997). In addition, cowbird parasitism has been shown to have reduced some host populations within the region (Laymon 1987). Brood parasitism, therefore, represents a novel source of reproductive loss for the host species in this region.

I conducted a two-year study on the relative effects of brood parasitism and nest predation in four resident sparrow species in southern California CSS. Moderate cowbird parasitism has been documented in nests of the California Gnatcatcher (*Polioptila californica*), a resident of CSS. Therefore, to determine the impact of cowbird parasitism on other resident CSS species, I studied nests of the four most abundant potential host species in southern Californian CSS. A study of cowbird host-use in CSS was desirable as cowbirds are known to acquire and frequently parasitize new host species, and because parasitism levels on common species are known to vary geographically (Friedmann and Kiff 1985). Recent records of parasitism in sagebrush vegetation have been attributed to fragmentation and thus, increased cowbird access to an environment previously rarely used (Friedmann and Kiff 1985). Specifically, I wished to determine whether Brown-headed Cowbirds impact host nest success in this vegetation type beyond the effects of nest predation on hosts. In addition to comparing the relative impact of each process to nest success, I also explore the potential effect of each process on population dynamics, under measured and hypothetical conditions, using a model of seasonal fecundity (Pease and Grzybowski 1995).

METHODS

My study was conducted during the breeding seasons of 1996–1997 at the University of California Motte Rimrock Reserve, a typical remnant 250-ha CSS patch located near Perris, Riverside County, California. The areas surrounding the reserve consisted largely of small ranchette homesteads, lightly grazed grassland, and agricultural fields. To assess nest predation and parasitism I followed nest fates of the four most abundant species on the site known to be parasitized by cowbirds.

I conducted 7-min, 50-m fixed-radius point counts during both years to determine the relative abundance of cowbirds and potential host species. Counts were conducted at 15 points located along two transects at 140-m intervals. In addition, I recorded observations of any cowbirds detected outside of point count periods. Female cowbird detections in CSS were assumed to be correlated with breeding activity as all detections occurred prior to noon, females were observed to be actively searching for nests, and because of the absence of cowbird feeding areas within the CSS at my site.

The site had a known history of cowbird parasitism on the California Gnatcatcher, and trapping efforts in 1994 resulted in the capture and removal of 42 cowbirds (19 of which were female) (Braden et al. 1997b; R. L. McKernan, pers. comm.). No trapping was conducted in any other year at the Motte Reserve (Braden et al. 1997b).

I studied the California Towhee (*Pipilo crissalis*), Spotted Towhee (*Pipilo maculatus*), Sage Sparrow (*Amphispiza bellii*), and Rufous-crowned Sparrow (*Aimophila ruficeps*). The four host species were found to be the four most abundant species detected during 34 point counts at my site. These species are also among the most common potential hosts in CSS regionally; California Towhee, Spotted Towhee, Rufous-crowned Sparrow, and Sage Sparrow were detected at 94%, 90%, 57%, and 24% of 155 CSS point counts throughout Southern Califor-

nia (M. K. Chase et al., unpubl. data). All four species are known cowbird hosts (Friedmann and Kiff 1985). However, there are few recent nest records for these species in southern Californian CSS, where current studies have documented fairly frequent parasitism in nests of other species (Braden et al. 1997b).

I located nests of the four potential host species through repeated visits to territories, following individuals, and opportunistic discovery. Emphasis was placed on locating nests while under construction to ensure the detection of any cowbird eggs before host abandonment occurred. Nest contents were checked every 1 to 5 days. To minimize observer-impact on nest predation, nest contents were checked using a 1.5-m pole with a mirror attached. The condition of each depredated nest was recorded in an attempt to identify broad categories of nest predators. Depredated nest categories included tilted or disturbed nest, undisturbed and empty nest and nestcup, and damaged eggs, which may represent predation by medium-sized mammals, snakes, and birds or small mammals, respectively (Bergin et al. 1997).

Each species' seasonal onset and duration of breeding was compared between years using a Wilcoxon rank sum test. Similarly, I compared the dates of female cowbird detection and host breeding dates.

SEASONAL FECUNDITY MODEL

The Pease and Grzybowski (1995) model estimates seasonal fecundity based on rates of nest predation, parasitism, host response to parasitism, period of susceptibility to both predation and parasitism, and number of young fledged. Nest fate probabilities are fit into time windows of the nesting cycle during which they may occur. The cumulative probability is then further modified by renesting parameters, which are limited by the time remaining for nesting prior to the end of the breeding season. Renesting is accounted for by mathematically tracking the number of females at different stages of the breeding season and nesting cycle. This is accomplished through continuous-time equations, which are used to compute a daily fraction of females that are at a given day of the nesting cycle, and the daily probabilistic fates of each nest. The rate at which females fledge young from nests of both fates (parasitized and unparasitized) is combined with fate-dependent productivity parameters for all nests. This information is then incorporated with the onset and length of the breeding season to produce an estimate of seasonal fecundity. To assess their relative effects on host productivity, I entered observed brood parasitism and predation rates, and the observed duration of each nest stage for each species into the model.

To measure the impact of parasitism on seasonal fecundity, I generated seasonal fecundity estimates for both species I found to be parasitized at my site (California Towhee and Sage Sparrow) under observed conditions and compared them to estimates generated without parasitism. To determine the hypothetical effects of significantly higher parasitism levels than observed, I estimated seasonal fecundity assuming a 50% rate of nests parasitized.

PARAMETER ESTIMATION

Predation

Active nests are continuously exposed to nest predation throughout a nest cycle; therefore, the susceptible period to predation is equivalent to the length of each species nest cycle. Since intervals between nest checks were often as much as 4 and 5 days, I obtained daily nest predation rates using the maximum-likelihood estimation program developed by Pease and Grzybowski (1995). The maximum-likelihood method avoids potential biases associated with the assumption that nest fate changes occur at the midpoint of nest-check intervals. Daily predation rates obtained were then used to calculate overall probability of nest survival.

Parasitism

Since many resident birds typically breed earlier than Brown-headed Cowbirds in southern California (Bent 1968, Finch 1983, Lowther 1993, Braden et al. 1997b), it was necessary to calculate parasitism rates based on host nest availability coincident with cowbird presence. Thus, brood parasitism rates were obtained by dividing the number of parasitized nests by the total number of observed nest-days available to laying cowbirds. To define this period, I used the criteria that cowbirds in CSS do not lay until mid-April (Braden et al. 1997b), and that normally parasitism occurs within the first 6 days of the host nesting cycle (Pease and Grzybowski 1995). The six-day window of opportunity for brood parasitism was thus set to encompass the day before a first egg was laid and the following five days. Therefore, nest-days available to cowbirds represent the sum of days during the six-day window of susceptibility to parasitism for each nest initiated after 15 April.

Time windows

Each species' breeding season length was measured as the difference between the earliest and latest first egg dates. Nest stage durations were estimated from nest check observations,

back-dating based on clutch size (assuming one egg was laid per day), and age estimation of young (based on multiple observations of young of different known ages). Limited data on renesting after successfully fledging young suggested a refractory period of 7–21 days; therefore I used the 10-day period suggested by Pease and Grzybowski (1995).

The model also requires an estimate of number of young fledged per nest; this was problematic for 1996 data due to the small number of successful nests. Therefore, to estimate the 1996 productivity per nest values, 1996 clutch sizes were compared with 1997 clutches and any significant differences were adjusted by reducing 1997 productivity estimates by the ratio of eggs laid. Productivity of parasitized nests was set at one young, based on the value used in Pease and Grzybowski (1995), as I have no information on the number of host young fledged in parasitized nests of these species.

RESULTS

EMPIRICAL RESULTS

Breeding phenology

Annual rainfall in inland CSS is highly seasonal, with virtually all precipitation occurring from September through April. Although total precipitation was essentially the same in both seasons of the study, the cumulative precipitation curve for 1996–1997 was shifted about one month earlier compared to that for 1995–1996 (Fig. 1). Onset and duration of host breeding season were likewise shifted and differed significantly between years (Table 1). The 1996 season was shortened by intense heat and drought, resulting in season lengths ranging from 30 to 61 days across the species studied. In contrast, 1997 temperatures were milder and periods of rainfall were more evenly dispersed (E. Konno, unpubl. data), and thus individual species season lengths were prolonged to 46–81 days (Figs. 1, 2). The 1997 breeding season was initiated an average of 36 days earlier than in 1996; 1996 nesting began in late March, whereas 1997 nesting started in mid-February (Table 1). 1997 breeding duration was an average of 26 days longer per species than the 1996 season.

Nest predation

Nest predation rates were relatively high in CSS. Nest predation accounted for 91% of 140 failed nests across all species. In 1996 (the shorter season), nest success rates ranged from 17% to 36% across the four species studied; in 1997 (the longer season), nest success was between 28% and 44% (Table 2).

Depredated nest conditions ranged from

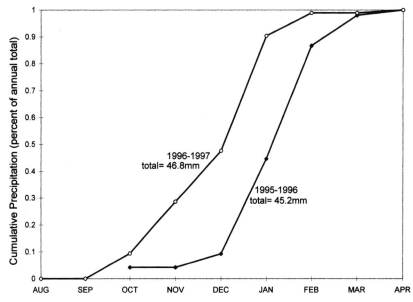

FIGURE 1. Proportional monthly cumulative rainfall at the University of California Motte Rimrock Reserve (1995–1997).

clutch reduction of one egg to complete nest destruction. A total of 84 nests was empty with cup intact, 33 were empty and disturbed, four had damaged eggs, three were directly observed to be depredated by snakes, and three exhibited a loss of one egg.

Nests were initiated throughout the duration of each breeding season (Fig. 2). Multiple nests (associated with banded birds or birds whose territory was known) were found each season. Two California Towhees were observed constructing subsequent nests while still feeding young at prior nests. Several Rufous-crowned Sparrows were observed to attempt three nests and some pairs successfully fledged two broods. In two cases, Sage Sparrows attempted second nests after fledging young. Multiple nest attempts by Spotted Towhees were detected in response to predation; however, no nest attempts were observed after a successful nest (although they are known to raise multiple broods; Greenlaw 1996).

Cowbird detection

Female cowbird detection rates varied from 0.24 females/day in 1996 to 0.88 females/day in 1997. Female cowbirds were detected early to mid-mornings throughout each breeding season. Cowbird breeding activity dates were similar between years, although median activity dates differed significantly (Wilcoxon's $Z = 2.23$, $P = 0.026$). However, the cumulative cowbird detec-

TABLE 1. 1996 AND 1997 BREEDING SEASON INITIATION DATES (AND DURATION IN DAYS) BASED ON FIRST EGG DATES OF NESTS LOCATED FOR FOUR SPECIES OF COASTAL SAGE SCRUB SPARROWS IN WESTERN RIVERSIDE COUNTY, CALIFORNIA

	First egg dates		Season length difference (1997–1996)	Initiation date difference (1997–1996)	Wilcoxon 2-sample Z $P > |Z|$
	1996	1997			
California Towhee	16 April to 17 May (32)	19 Feb to 27 Apr (68)	36	57	<0.001
Rufous-crowned Sparrow	25 Mar to 25 May (61)	24 Feb to 4 May (81)	20	30	0.018
Sage Sparrow	14 Apr to 18 May (34)	10 Mar to 18 May (68)	34	34	<0.001
Spotted Towhee	17 Apr to 16 May (30)	24 Mar to 10 May (46)	16	21	<0.001
Average duration	39	66	27	36	—

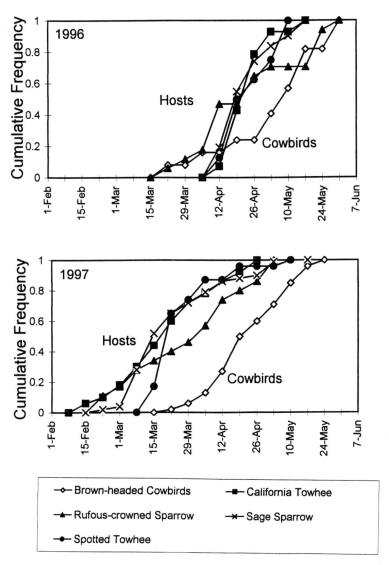

FIGURE 2.   1996 (top) and 1997 (bottom) sparrow species breeding phenology by first egg dates and female cowbird detections in coastal sage scrub in western Riverside County, California. The mid-point in cumulative frequency represents the peak in sparrow breeding/female cowbird detections.

tion frequency differed from host laying seasons in duration and onset (Fig. 2) and median female cowbird detection dates differed significantly from the median first egg date of all hosts combined in each year (1996: Wilcoxon's $Z = 2.71$, $P = 0.007$; 1997: Wilcoxon's $Z = 7.99$, $P < 0.001$).

Parasitism

Of nests located in 1996, 374 nest-days distributed among 62 nests were susceptible to cowbird parasitization (i.e., their vulnerable stage overlapped the presence of cowbirds at the

site). Since two parasite eggs were found in two host nests, the parasitism rate for nests of that period was 3.2%. In 1997, host nest availability after 15 April was 188 nest-days (31 nests); with one nest parasitized, the 1997 parasitism rate was also 3.2% of available nests.

Three of the total of 217 nests discovered were parasitized; one of 14 California Towhee nests and one of 30 Sage Sparrow nests were parasitized in 1996, and one of 50 California Towhee nests was parasitized in 1997. Of the three nests parasitized, the two California Towhee nests were subsequently depredated, and

TABLE 2. LIFE-HISTORY PARAMETERS (N = 217 NESTS) USED IN SEASONAL FECUNDITY ESTIMATION FOR SPARROWS IN COASTAL SAGE SCRUB IN WESTERN RIVERSIDE CO., CALIFORNIA (1996–1997)

	California Towhee		Rufous-crowned Sparrow		Sage Sparrow		Spotted Towhee	
	1996	1997	1996	1997	1996	1997	1996	1997
Season length (days)	32	68	61	81	34	68	30	46
Fledglings/successful nest	—[a]	2.65	—[a]	3	—[a]	2.7	2.6[b]	3.4
Daily parasitism	0.012	0.003	0	0	0.005	0	0	0
Maximum likelihood estimated daily predation	0.068	0.032	0.040	0.044	0.053	0.048	0.048	0.046
Nest success (%)	16.9	44.0	36.3	34.0	23.1	27.8	30.6	32.3
Average clutch size (N)	3.00 (14)	3.12 (49)	3.18 (17)	3.18 (16)	3.07 (14)	3.22 (23)	2.88 (8)	3.74 (23)
Estimated seasonal fecundity # of young/pair/season	1.35	4.05	3.98	4.86	1.60	3.22	2.28	3.23

[a] Sample too small; 1997 estimates used as no significant difference was found between 1996–97 clutch sizes (two-tailed t-test: California Towhee $P > 0.55$; Rufous-crowned Sparrow $P > 0.97$; Sage Sparrow $P > 0.42$).
[b] Estimate generated by reducing 1997 value by ratio of 1996: 1997 clutch size.

the Sage Sparrow nest was abandoned (0.7% of all nest failure). No clutch reduction by cowbirds was detected. Additionally, no cowbird fledglings were detected in either year.

SEASONAL FECUNDITY ESTIMATES

I used the season length, productivity per nest, and clutch size data obtained on each species (Table 2) to estimate seasonal fecundity. The time window for susceptibility to predation ranged from 24 to 27 days. Abandonment was detected in 13 nests, and accounted for 9.3% of nest failure. Abandoned unparasitized nests were treated as depredated, as nests abandoned represent a similar detriment to productivity and result in renesting. Only the one aforementioned parasitized Sage Sparrow nest appeared to have been abandoned in response to cowbird activity. Spotted Towhee 1996 clutch sizes were significantly smaller than those in 1997 (one-tailed t-test, $P < 0.02$). As a result, the 1996 productivity estimate was calculated by reducing 1997 productivity per nest by the ratio of clutch sizes (Table 2).

All 1997 seasonal fecundity estimates were greater than those based on 1996 rates (Table 2). In 1996, California Towhee and Sage Sparrow estimates were below the productivity levels required to maintain replacement level reproduction (≥ 2.0 young/pair/season). In contrast, all species seasonal fecundity estimates were above 2.0 young/pair/season in 1997.

Varying only the parasitism rate, with all other 1996 California Towhee parameters held constant, seasonal fecundities were 1.46 young/pair/season with no parasitism, 1.35 young/pair/season at the observed parasitism rate, and 1.02 young/pair/season with a 50% parasitism rate. Therefore, observed reproductive loss to parasitism was a 7.5% decrease in seasonal fecundity. If 50% of nests had been parasitized, a 24.4% decrease in seasonal fecundity would have resulted. Repeating the process with 1997 California Towhee parameter values resulted in estimates of 4.22 young/pair/season with no parasitism, a 4.0% decrease at observed parasitism rates, and a 27.4% reduction at 50% parasitism.

Sage Sparrow fecundity modeled at the predation levels measured in 1996 resulted in seasonal fecundity estimates of 1.85 young/pair/season with no parasitism, 1.60 young/pair/season at observed level of parasitism (−13.5%), and 1.29 young/pair/season at 50% parasitism (−19.4%). At 1997 predation levels, seasonal fecundity in the absence of parasitism was 3.22 young/pair/season, and if 50% of nests were parasitized, 2.25 young/pair/season (−30.1%). For both towhees and sparrows, observed levels of parasitism did not result in fecundity estimate

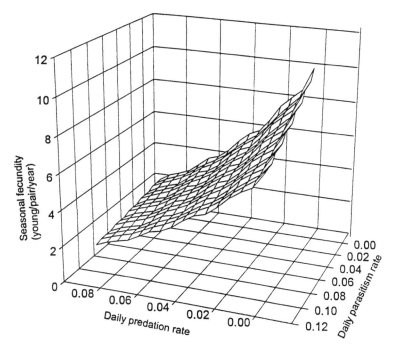

FIGURE 3.   Sensitivity of seasonal fecundity estimates to variation in parasitism and predation rates. A 50% parasitism rate is comparable to a daily rate of 0.11.

differences in excess of −0.25 young/pair/season.

The sensitivity analysis revealed daily predation rate is the dominant and more sensitive parameter in the calculation of seasonal fecundity values (Fig. 3). The predation axis slope is greatest and the effect is across the resultant surface generated by the matrix of parameters.

DISCUSSION

SEASONAL FECUNDITY ESTIMATION

Comparison of estimates of seasonal fecundity based on observed parasitization rates for California Towhee and Sage Sparrow to estimates generated with parasitism set to zero demonstrated a minimal loss of seasonal fecundity due to parasitism. It appears that parasitism did not occur at levels of biological significance. The potential impact of parasitism on seasonal fecundity was minimized by high nest predation and extended season length. Seasonal fecundity was more sensitive to predation over the range of parasitism levels I observed (Table 2, Fig. 3), yet this relationship was most likely a factor of the amount of breeding season overlap with cowbirds, season length, and, to a lesser degree, the level of brood reduction associated with rearing parasite young.

Increased season length raises average seasonal fecundity by improving an individual's likelihood of successfully nesting. As season length increases, the interaction between parasitism and predation weakens (Grzybowski and Pease, in press). This occurs due to the increased number of nesting attempts, which reduce the chance nests will be both parasitized and depredated. Therefore, season length directly affects seasonal fecundity as it effects the number of renesting attempts possible.

Between-year fecundity varied greatest in the California Towhee, ranging from 1.49 to 4.05 young/pair. This variation was associated with varied season length and quite different levels of predation. Clearly, seasonal fecundity is lowest when season length is short, yet factors of food abundance and quality of vegetation for cover must also play a role in this system. Such variation in avian productivity appears to be common in arid environments as suggested by several studies (Grant and Boag 1980, Rotenberry and Wiens 1980, Carter 1986, Newton and Newton 1997).

CLIMATE AND PHENOLOGY

CSS plants are drought-adapted and sensitive to climatic variation (Minnich 1985), with a corresponding variation in avian breeding season initiation and length. During my study, both peak rainfall and sparrow breeding exhibited a corresponding five-week shift between 1996 and 1997 (Figs. 1, 2). A similar relationship has been found in the California Gnatcatcher (which also nests on the site), in which males began pre-nuptial molt six to seven weeks after the first significant winter rain (K. Preston, pers. comm.). In addition to variation in the time available for nesting, the variation in nest initiation dates most likely induces variation in both nest pre-dation and parasitism levels. For instance, snakes, a major nest predator, were not as active in February 1997 when many birds were initi-ating nests (K. Ellison, pers. obs.). Whatever the mechanism, nest predation was 22% higher on nests initiated during the first month of the 1996 breeding period than on nests of the first month of 1997 (the early season).

Although the consequences of a 21–57 day shift in breeding season initiation date may in-clude subtle differences in predation, one can easily envision changes in predator impact dur-ing more dramatic changes. Five weeks follow-ing Hurricane Nora, which passed through northern Baja California, Mexico, in September 1997, several CSS passerine bird species nest were observed in breeding condition (with brood patches and enlarged testes) and an active Cal-ifornia Towhee was discovered outside of nor-mal reported nest season dates (P. Unitt, pers. comm.). Although such events are likely infre-quent, these observations support the hypothesis that CSS birds will breed opportunistically. Such variation presumably results in exposure to quite different predator abundances and/or predation levels.

Predation rates measured in CSS (Braden et al. 1997a,b; K. Preston and S. Morrison, pers. comm.; this study) are relatively high compared to those commonly reported for passerine birds in other habitat types (Ricklefs 1969, Martin 1992). The levels of predation and variation in depredated nest appearance likely reflect the high diversity of potential nest predators present in CSS.

PARASITE-HOST ASYNCHRONY

The parasitism rates I recorded ranged be-tween 1.8% and 6.9% of susceptible nests dur-ing the six-day window to parasitism among nests of the four most abundant potential host species at the site. There are several reasons for the apparent low levels of parasitism detected at the Motte Reserve. Foremost is the seasonal variation in dates of host breeding initiation and duration. As cowbirds do not appear in CSS un-til mid-March, and as the first cowbird eggs do not appear until mid-April, host species often are free from exposure to parasitism for at least one complete nesting cycle. It is apparent that cow-birds lag behind the peak in host nest availability on my site (Fig. 2). This lag was especially ap-parent in 1997, presumably due to the earlier season initiation by sparrows and towhees in that year (Fig. 2). The midpoint of female cow-bird detection lagged 3 to 4 weeks after the peak in host nesting, and nest availability after 15 April was 188 nest-days. In 1996, cowbird de-tections more closely tracked host nest avail-ability and of the nests located in 1996, 374 nest-days were available during cowbird laying. Despite greater nest availability in 1996, at the midpoint of cowbird breeding, as measured by cumulative number of detections, cowbirds were left with around two weeks to deposit their eggs (Fig. 2).

My data suggest that cowbirds are not able to track the initiation of host nesting in CSS. The lack of synchrony in host and cowbird breeding seasons appears to be due to the variation in host breeding dates (presumably in response to vari-ation in rainfall), combined with apparently less flexible cowbird breeding dates. In this case, cowbirds may simply not be able to synchronize their breeding season with a majority of hosts in CSS.

In southern California resident cowbird flocks spend the non-breeding season in agricultural ar-eas largely associated with dairy cattle and feed-lots, which may lie at considerable distance from breeding areas. Presumably cowbirds utilize a mixture of cues, such as day length, host song, and/or migration of hosts or congeners to initiate breeding season movements. Several such cues may be advantageous throughout historic cow-bird breeding range, yet not as adaptive in south-ern California, where cowbirds may be relative-ly isolated from hosts, which, in turn, respond to different cues that may vary in timing be-tween years. However, resident bird breeding seasons tend to be extended in this region, thus reducing selection on cowbirds to initiate breed-ing coincident with the onset of host nesting.

Nest success in the resident sparrows studied was largely determined by nest predation levels; parasitism rates were relatively low, around 3.2%. However, a higher incidence of parasitism (48.1% of 27 nests) has been observed for Cal-ifornia Gnatcatchers breeding at this site (Bra-den et al. 1997b). This is likely due to several factors: (1) gnatcatchers are small-bodied hosts, as preferred by Brown-headed Cowbirds (King 1979, Peck and James 1987); (2) their nests are easily located; and (3) they have a prolonged breeding season (February–July) (Braden et al. 1997b).

CONCLUSIONS

Whether the observed predation levels reflect impacts of fragmentation is unknown due to the lack of nest predation data from larger, more contiguous areas of CSS. Further questions have been raised as fragmentation studies in the West have found parasitism and predation rates to be higher in unfragmented habitat (Langen et al. 1991, Tewksbury et al. 1998), whereas many studies primarily in the Mid-West have demonstrated both processes to increase in habitat fragments (Robinson 1992; reviewed by Paton 1994). Nonetheless, several studies have found that fragmentation of southern Californian chaparral is associated with a rapid disappearance of bird and rodent species (Soulé et al. 1988), suggesting that processes associated with the negative effect of fragmentation cannot be generalized across broad geographic areas.

Cowbird trapping is not nearly as complex as attempting to restore predator populations to more natural levels. However, I think it is apparent that cowbird control at my site would have had a minimal impact on host seasonal fecundity. Before initiating a cowbird trapping program, my recommendation to CSS land managers would be to monitor host nesting initiation dates and cowbird numbers. This could be achieved simply through point counts, for a fraction of cowbird trap maintenance costs. If sparrow nesting seasons were retarded due to weather conditions, cowbird trapping might then be deemed necessary. Thus, knowledge of winter rainfall patterns (a predictor of avian breeding initiation dates) and its associated potential for a temporal refuge from reproductive loss to parasitism could enable managers to appropriately focus trapping funds and efforts to better conserve avian populations on a year-to-year basis.

ACKNOWLEDGMENTS

I thank G. T. Braden, R. L. McKernan, and K. Preston for the cowbird trapping and California Gnatcatcher information. Thanks also to D. T. Bolger, E. Konno, M. D. Misenhelter, S. Morrison, M. K. Stapleton, Y. Thomson, P. Unitt, and A. Whitesides for help in obtaining field data; and B. Kristan and J. T. Rotenberry for suggestions, assistance, and reviews. J. A. Grzybowski and C. M. Pease provided programs, instruction, and comments. Support for this work was provided by the Los Angeles Audubon Society Ralph Schreiber Award, the University of California, Riverside Irwin A. Newell Award, the University of California Natural Reserve System Mildred E. Mathias Research Award, and a Sigma-Xi Grant-in-aid of research.

Studies in Avian Biology No. 18:200–203, 1999.

INFLUENCE OF LANDSCAPE AND COWBIRD PARASITISM ON THE REPRODUCTIVE SUCCESS OF PLUMBEOUS VIREOS BREEDING IN COLORADO

JAMESON F. CHACE AND ALEXANDER CRUZ

Abstract. We studied the impact of Brown-headed Cowbird (*Molothrus ater*) parasitism on the reproductive success of Plumbeous Vireos (*Vireo plumbeus*) nesting in the foothills of the Rocky Mountains west of Boulder, Colorado, between 1984 and 1997. Cowbirds parasitized 51.9% of 185 vireo nests monitored, with a range of 37.5% in 1992 (N = 8) to 65.7% in 1994 (N = 35). Parasitized nests had significantly smaller clutch sizes (3.3 ± 0.10 vs. 3.8 ± 0.06), lower hatching success (43.9% vs. 73.5%), and lower fledging success (14.6% vs. 54.4%) than unparasitized nests. Significantly fewer vireos fledged from parasitized nests (mean 0.5 young/nest) than unparasitized nests (mean 2.1 young/nest). Of eleven variables measured around 81 vireo nests, parasitized nests were significantly closer to openings in the canopy (> 400 sq. m) and had significantly less canopy cover than unparasitized nests. A stepwise logistic regression correctly classified 61.9% of 68 nests based on canopy cover, which was the best predictor of whether a vireo nest was parasitized in 1993–1994. Cowbirds are probably better able to observe host nest building activity from open canopies. Nests found in sites with lower tree density and canopy cover tended to have a higher likelihood of being parasitized, although the differences were not significant. While the ponderosa pine (*Pinus ponderosa*) forest has many natural canopy openings, openings created by roads also tended to increase the local frequency of parasitism. Managers concerned about the reproductive success of birds nesting in ponderosa pine forests should seek to reduce anthropogenic sources of canopy openings, which may not only increase the likelihood of parasitism, but nest predation as well.

Key Words: Brown-headed Cowbird, canopy openings, landscape ecology, *Molothrus ater*, Plumbeous Vireo, reproductive success, *Vireo plumbeus*.

Local features of the landscape can influence the distribution and abundance of Brown-headed Cowbirds (*Molothrus ater*) and the frequency of parasitism on host populations. Higher levels of cowbird parasitism have been reported along forest-field edges than in forest interiors (Gates and Gysel 1978, Brittingham and Temple 1983, Johnson and Temple 1990, but see Hahn and Hatfield 1995). Likewise, the frequency of cowbird parasitism has been reported as high on host nests along powerline corridors (Chasko and Gates 1982), in small forest tracts (Robinson et al. *in press*), and near livestock (Verner and Ritter 1983). Cowbirds tend to travel along streams (Gates and Giffen 1991) and are more abundant near clearcuts (Thompson et al. 1992). Frequency of parasitism is high across fragmented Midwestern landscapes where cowbird densities are high (Robinson and Wilcove 1994, Thompson 1994).

Most landscape level studies of cowbird distribution and frequency of parasitism have been conducted in eastern and midwestern deciduous forests where forest-field edges are sharp, and usually caused by anthropogenic disturbance (Gates and Gysel 1978, Johnson and Temple 1990, Gates and Giffen 1991, Robinson et al. 1995a). Coniferous forests of the West are often naturally fragmented, with open meadows and canopy openings occurring because of the patch-

iness of mature forests, especially of ponderosa pine (*Pinus ponderosa*).

Along the Front Range of the Rocky Mountains in Colorado, lower elevation ponderosa pine forests have been under increasing pressure of urban development. Furthermore, in Boulder County, a large portion of ponderosa pine forest has been set aside as Open Space, which has been an exceedingly popular program and receives over 3 million visitors annually (City of Boulder Open Space statistics, 1997). Thus, the canopy of the ponderosa pine forest is disrupted both naturally, with mature low density forest stands, successional stands, open meadows, and riparian vegetation, and anthropogenically, with trails, roads, homes, and at the edge of the city of Boulder, Colorado. In this study we examined the influence of both natural and anthropogenic sources of canopy disruption on cowbird parasitism of the Plumbeous Vireo (*Vireo plumbeus*). We hypothesize that openings, both natural and anthropogenic, facilitate cowbird observations of vireo nests, and that parasitism should be higher on nests closer to openings in the canopy.

METHODS

Plumbeous Vireo nest data were collected during the summers of 1984–1986, 1992–1994, and 1997 in the foothills of the Rocky Mountain Front Range west of the city of Boulder, Colorado (40° 00'N, 105° 20'W). Study sites range from 1,800 m to 2,400 m in elevation and had a park-like appearance of open canopy ponderosa pine. Sites contained scattered Douglas fir (*Psuedotsuga menziesii*) and an understory dominated by chokecherry (*Prunus virginiana*), wax currant (*Ribes cereum*), skunkbrush (*Rhus aromatica*), small ninebark (*Physocarpus monogynus*), Oregon grape (*Mahonia repens*), kinnikinnick (*Arctostaphylos uva-ursi*), and various grasses (*Bromus, Achillia,* and *Stipa*).

Plumbeous Vireos were chosen for this study because their low nests were relatively easy to locate and monitor. Additionally, Plumbeous Vireos are relatively abundant on the study sites, and in various parts of their range are known acceptors of cowbird eggs (Friedmann et al. 1977, Curson 1996, this study)

Vireo nests were found during all stages of the nesting cycle and subsequently visited once every 2–4 days. Care was taken to minimize disturbance and attraction of nest predators to the nest site (Major 1990, Ralph et al. 1993). Outcome of each clutch (i.e., parasitism, predation, abandonment, or fledging) was determined. Nest appearance and mode of disturbance were used to determine whether nests were disturbed by predators. Nests that were found empty before young could potentially fledge, i.e., oldest vireo nestling was < 12 days or cowbird < 9 days old, were determined to have been preyed upon. Nests found empty on or after that point were determined to have been preyed upon if adults gave no alarm calls and no juveniles could be found in the nest area after a careful search. Only nests in which the final outcomes were known were used in the analysis. Nesting success was calculated using the Mayfield (1975) method to reduce the error introduced when nests observed for different lengths of time are treated equally.

Following the termination of nest site activity in 1993–1994, eleven landscape measurements were taken around each nest site. Distances to the nearest road (ROAD), trail (TRAIL), natural forest canopy opening (OPEN: an opening was > 400 m², with at least 10 m on one side and had < 15% canopy cover from the points of measurement), riparian vegetation (RIPAR), town (TOWN: Boulder or Lyons, Colorado), and year-round occupied residence (RESID) were measured from each nest. Using a 5-m and 50-m measuring tape, we measured these distances to the nearest 0.1 m within 50 m, 1 m between 51 m and 200 m, and to the nearest 50 m when distances were > 200 m. Canopy cover (CANOPY) of the site was estimated from 20 forest densiometer (concave) readings taken at uniform points within a 11.3 m radius circular plot centered on the nest. Ground cover

(GROUND) was estimated from 20 ocular tube readings taken within the circular plot from the same points as canopy cover (James and Shugart 1970, Noon 1981). The number of trees (woody plants with a dbh ≥ 8 cm) were counted per 11.3 m radius circle around the nest and extrapolated to density per ha (TREES). Slope (SLOPE) of the nest site was measured with a clinometer. All variables were continuous.

Data were pooled across years for analysis after testing for significant differences in site characteristics revealed no differences between years. Since variables were not normally distributed all nest site variables were log-transformed. Comparisons of unparasitized and parasitized nest sites were made with equal sample size Student's t-tests. Because data were not normally distributed, median tests (Wilcoxon two-sample test) were employed to compare shapes of frequency distributions of mean clutch size and mean number of fledglings per nest. Goodness-of-fit tests (G-tests with William's correction; Sokal and Rohlf 1981) were used to compare hatching and fledging success between unparasitized and parasitized nests. Means ± SE are reported for descriptive statistics. Results are reported as significant when $P < 0.05$.

A stepwise logistic regression was used to test for landscape differences between parasitized and unparasitized nests. Variables were log-transformed. Because of the high amount of variability in analyses of many factors, and to reduce the possibility of type II statistical errors, the values with $P < 0.2$ were allowed to enter the regression model, but allowed to remain only when $P < 0.1$.

RESULTS

Brown-headed Cowbirds parasitized 51.9% of 185 Plumbeous Vireo nests (Table 1). Parasitized nests (N = 81) had significantly smaller mean clutch sizes (3.3 ± 0.10) than unparasitized nests (N = 80, mean = 3.8 ± 0.06, z = 3.4284, $P < 0.001$). Parasitized nests also had significantly lower hatching success ($P < 0.001$), fledging success ($P < 0.001$), and mean number of young to fledge ($P < 0.001$) than unparasitized nests (Table 2). Nest predation was monitored in 1993–1994, and 49.4% of Plumbeous Vireo nests (N = 81) were preyed upon with predation independent of parasitism (G = 0.1056, df = 1, $P > 0.75$). Of forty nests that were preyed upon, three were only partially depredated, and two of those fledged at least one vireo.

Nest success was not significantly different between 1993 and 1994, and therefore the data were combined (G = 0.1128, df = 1, $P > 0.05$). The probability of a Plumbeous Vireo clutch

TABLE 1.   FREQUENCY OF PARASITISM OF PLUMBEOUS VIREO NESTS IN BOULDER COUNTY, COLORADO[a]

| | Year | | | | | | | |
	1984	1985	1986	1992	1993	1994	1997	Total
Unparasitized	11	12	17	5	25	12	7	89
Parasitized	9	12	17	3	21	23	11	96
% Parasitism	45.0%	50.0%	50.0%	37.5%	45.6%	65.7%	61.1%	51.9%

[a] Frequency of parasitism is independent of year (G_{ADJ} = 3.5658, df = 6, P > 0.05).

surviving 30 days to fledge at least one young was 0.27, with egg success greater than nestling success. Furthermore, parasitized nests had a significantly lower probability of success than unparasitized nests (Table 3).

The majority of vireo nests were in ponderosa pine. In 1993–1994, 92.6% (N = 81) of vireo nests were built in ponderosa pine trees, while 5 nests in 1993 (10.9%) and 1 nest in 1994 (2.8%) were built in shrubs. Parasitized nests were significantly closer to openings in the forest canopy (OPEN) and nests with lower canopy cover (CANOPY) (Table 4). Distance to opening was the best predictor of whether a Plumbeous Vireo nest was parasitized in 1993–1994, and a stepwise logistic regression correctly classified 61.9% of 68 nests based on that criteria alone (criteria for model fit, χ^2 = 5.483, df = 1, P = 0.019).

DISCUSSION

Brown-headed Cowbirds typically parasitized 50% of Plumbeous Vireo nests we observed in each of the seven years of the study (Marvil and Cruz 1989, Chace et al. *in press*, Table 1). Cowbirds had a significant, negative impact on the Plumbeous Vireo nests they parasitized (Table 2). In the Colorado Front Range, Plumbeous Vireos nested in mature park-like stands of ponderosa pine, with low canopy cover and well spaced trees lacking any significant shrub or

sapling layer. Cowbirds used canopy openings as small as 0.04 ha, and reduced canopy cover to search for nests to parasitize. Plumbeous Vireos nesting near such openings were significantly more likely to be parasitized (Table 4). Roads, trails, and residential areas also created openings in the canopy, but only natural openings showed any trend towards increased parasitism.

In an exploratory analysis based on the 1992 and 1993 data we lumped 55 vireo nests into one discrete landscape group (e.g., near road, near residence, in lower foothills, etc.), and found that parasitized vireo nests were strongly associated with roads and residential areas (Chace et al. *in press*). In that initial analysis we documented that anthropogenic factors of the landscape have an influence on Plumbeous Vireos reproductive success. However, here we illustrate the importance of finer scale canopy openings and the impacts they may have on the parasitism probability of vireo nests. The earlier analysis did not separate openings created by natural processes from anthropogenic openings, and while the few vireos that nest near roads and residential areas are very likely to fail due to both parasitism and predation, the majority of vireos nesting in more natural conditions are greatly affected by small changes in canopy density and distances to openings. This analysis is also more robust with larger, equal, sample sizes

TABLE 2.   REPRODUCTIVE SUCCESS IN UNPARASITIZED AND PARASITIZED NESTS OF PLUMBEOUS VIREOS, BOULDER COUNTY, COLORADO, 1984–1986, 1992–1994, AND 1997

| | Vireo nests[a] | | | Cowbird |
	Unparasitized	Parasitized	All	
No. active nests	80	81	162	—
Total eggs	309	246	555	111
Total hatched	227	108	355	67
Total fledged	168	36	204	41
Hatching success (%)	73.5[b]	43.9	60.4	60.4
Fledgling success (%)	54.4[b]	14.6	36.8	36.9
Fledge/egg hatch (%)	74.0[b]	33.3	61.0	61.2
Mean fledge/active nest	2.1[c]	0.5	1.3	0.5

[a] Includes only nests found during incubation and followed to fledging or failure.
[b] Differences in fledgling success between unparasitized and parasitized nests are significant for hatching success (G_{ADJ} = 12.8689, df = 1, P < 0.001), fledgling success (G_{ADJ} = 49.0334, df = 1, P < 0.001), and fledgling/egg hatched (G_{ADJ} = 14.2999, df = 1, P < 0.001).
[c] Differences between unparasitized and parasitized nests are significant (Wilcoxon two-sample test, Z = 6.24, P < 0.001).

TABLE 3.   MAYFIELD'S NESTING SUCCESS[a] CALCULATED FOR PARASITIZED AND UNPARASITIZED PLUMBEOUS VIREO NESTS, 1993–1994

	Probability of survival		
	Egg stage	Nestling stage	Overall
Parasitized	0.48	0.21	0.17
Unparasitized	0.66	0.59	0.40
Overall	0.55	0.43	0.27

[a] Probabilities based on survival of at least one offspring for duration of 16 day incubation period and 14 day nestling period.

and univariate parametric and multivariate statistics.

Cowbird abundance and parasitism have been shown to decrease with distance from the edge to the forest interior (Gates and Gysel 1978, Brittingham and Temple 1983, Temple and Cary 1988, Yahner and DeLong 1991, O'Conner and Faaborg 1992). Furthermore, cowbird abundance and parasitism increase when openings are created in an otherwise contiguous forest canopy (Brittingham and Temple 1983, Evans and Gates 1997). In the ponderosa pine forests of Boulder County, Plumbeous Vireos nested in a naturally discontinuous forest landscape with large openings and consequent edge effects. When observed in the ponderosa pine, female cowbirds have been found perched on the tops of trees. Plumbeous Vireo nests that are closer to openings and under lower canopy cover would be easier for cowbirds to locate, and parasitism reduces the reproductive success of vireos placing their nest in such locations.

Many of the bird species that breed in the ponderosa pine forests of the Colorado Front Range are sensitive across their southwestern range. In Arizona, Colorado, and New Mexico, the Plumbeous Vireo is designated as a high priority species, and it is of special concern in Arizona and Colorado (Winternitz and Crumpacker 1985, Hall et al. 1997). However, Breeding Bird Survey results (1966–1994) show that Plumbeous Vireo populations are increasing or are stable across their range. Plumbeous Vireos are an ideal species to study the impacts of cowbird parasitism, compare the frequency of parasitism across the Southwest, and determine habitat features that influence cowbird parasitism because they have low nests that are relatively easy to find, and they are a principal host of cowbirds in ponderosa pine and pinyon-juniper forests (Curson 1996). Land managers interested in evaluating the effects of landscape or habitat changes on a sensitive local migratory songbird in ponderosa pine or pinyon-juniper forests could get a reasonable estimation from examining Plumbeous Vireo reproductive success.

ACKNOWLEDGMENTS

We greatly appreciate R. E. Marvil for sharing her field notes and data (1984–1986) with us. D. Bennet, S. Severs, C. Bechtoldt, D. Evans, and J. Walsh provided invaluable field assistance. This manuscript greatly benefited from the comments of two anonymous reviewers. Funding for this study has been provided by the Boulder County Nature Association, City of Boulder Open Space, and the University of Colorado Graduate School and Department of E.P.O. Biology.

TABLE 4.   MEAN VALUES ($\pm$ SE) OF LANDSCAPE VARIABLES AT UNPARASITIZED AND PARASITIZED PLUMBEOUS VIREO NEST SITES, 1993–1994

Variables	Unparasitized	Parasitized	n	P[a]
SLOPE (°)	15.5 (1.25)	16.7 (1.51)	74	0.949
TREES (#/ha)	321.3 (33.84)	296.3 (47.62)	78	0.387
GROUND (%)	37.0 (3.40)	41.3 (34.10)	78	0.339
CANOPY (%)	69.0 (2.47)	61.1 (3.18)	78	*0.045*
ROAD (m)	904 (90.59)	752 (91.11)	78	0.269
TRAIL (m)	251 (81.03)	282 (100.04)	72	0.562
OPEN (m)	60.6 (14.21)	25.8 (4.67)	62	*0.007*
RIPAR (m)	363 (66.42)	247 (59.23)	78	0.123
RESID (m)	1119 (116.62)	1108 (148.67)	78	0.506
TOWN (m)	2094 (231.37)	1706 (245.79)	78	0.136
NRHUMAN (m)	169 (38.70)	166 (40.77)	72	0.591

[a] Result of Student t-test conducted on log-transformed variables.

Studies in Avian Biology No. 18:204–217, 1999.

A SPATIAL AND GENETIC ANALYSIS OF COWBIRD HOST SELECTION

D. CALDWELL HAHN, JAMES A. SEDGWICK, IAN S. PAINTER, AND NANCY J. CASNA

Abstract. Molecular genetics makes it possible to measure basic but long elusive parameters of the breeding biology of the Brown-headed Cowbird (*Molothrus ater*). We examined cowbird fecundity and host selection behavior using a combination of molecular genetic techniques to link female cowbirds to the eggs they lay, radio-telemetry techniques to track female cowbirds' daily movements, and geographic information systems (GIS) to integrate these genetic and spatial data. Our study site lay within a forested 1300-ha landscape in New York composed primarily of mature forest with adjacent old fields. We found that female cowbirds used their home ranges as principal egg-laying areas. Individual females used characteristic individual home ranges throughout the breeding season, and they returned to the same home range every breeding season. Over one-half (54%) of females laid all their eggs in host nests inside or close to their home range. Proximity to a female's home range was the only significant ecological or biological feature affecting a cowbird's host selection. Neither host species identity, nest height, adult mass, egg size, incubation period, nor host taxonomic classification predicted which nests would be parasitized. Eggs laid outside the home range were frequently found in multiply-parasitized nests located along common flyways or in conspicuous sites that a cowbird could discover opportunistically. We also found that female cowbirds avoided laying more than one egg in a particular host nest, even though multiple parasitism characterized over one-third of parasitized nests in the study. Finally, we estimated that effective cowbird fecundity lies between a minimum of 1.72 eggs per female and an upper bound of 8.16 eggs per female. Effective cowbird fecundity is defined as the actual number of cowbird eggs laid in appropriate host nests and not ejected; it is lower than raw fecundity or the physiological egg production capacity of cowbirds. We suggest that the female cowbird's use of home range is a critical element in its breeding behavior, enabling cowbirds to use a known-host selection strategy. Experienced female cowbirds selectively parasitize the host pairs that nested in their home ranges in previous breeding seasons and were most successful. The three elements of cowbird breeding behavior reported here challenge the stereotype of the Brown-headed Cowbird as an *r*-selected species that produces a large number of young and invests no parental care. Instead, these results suggest that cowbirds lay fewer eggs in host nests than has been speculated and that they do invest parental care. Two examples of parental care we discuss are observing a host's parental behavior and nest success before parasitizing it, and laying each egg in a different host nest, even though that requires females to search longer and to find a larger number of host nests. Current cowbird trapping programs should be evaluated for their effect on age structure of cowbird populations and resulting parasitism patterns. Yearling females may be associated with higher rates of multiple parasitism and higher rates of parasitism on more conspicuous hosts. Conspicuous hosts such as the Black-capped *(Vireo atricapillus)* and Least Bell's (*Vireo bellii pusillus*) vireos are probably most at risk from cowbird populations with disproportionately high numbers of immigrant yearling female cowbirds such as those created by trapping programs.

Key Words: Brown-headed Cowbird, DNA fingerprinting, fecundity, GIS, home range, management, *Molothrus ater,* telemetry.

To evaluate whether Brown-headed Cowbirds (*Molothrus ater*) pose a threat to particular species or communities, conservation biologists need to measure basic parameters that have long been invisible. Fundamental reproductive traits such as the average laying rate per female, percentage of breeding females in a population, use of a breeding territory, and the number of eggs laid per nest are readily determined in non-parasitic birds, but are still not well established for the Brown-headed Cowbird. These reproductive traits require measurement at the individual level, and in brood parasites this is a feat that was not possible until the recent advent of molecular genetic techniques.

Without genetic information, previous investigators have been limited to analyzing parasit-ism patterns at the population level rather than at the individual level, focusing on features that generally make host nests more conspicuous to cowbirds, such as proximity to forest edge (e.g., Brittingham and Temple 1983); nest height above the ground, with low nests being more exposed in some sites (Hahn and Hatfield in press) and more camouflaged in other sites (Martin 1993); differences in host density (e.g., Clark and Robertson 1979); and breeding behavior that makes a host's nest more susceptible to parasitism, such as the nest singing of the endangered Least Bell's Vireo (*Vireo bellii pusillus*; Kus *this volume*) and Black-capped Vireo (*Vireo atricapillus*; e.g. Graber 1961).

Examining habitat features or host behavior has been of limited value in deciphering cowbirds' host selection patterns. Determining cowbird fecundity has become increasingly urgent to conservation biologists, since physiological and laboratory data suggested that cowbirds were unusually fecund, potentially laying 20–40 eggs per female each season (Payne 1976, Scott and Ankney 1980, Holford and Roby 1993). However, fecundity under field conditions, the critical parameter, required genetic techniques to be measured.

Our goal in this study was to obtain accurate estimates of cowbird reproductive rate and host selection patterns that could be used to speed recognition of host populations in trouble. We designed this study to estimate the proportion of female cowbirds actively breeding in a local population, the fecundity of individual cowbirds, and the biological or ecological features that guide an individual female's host selection. Previous studies had established that cowbirds use territories or home ranges (Dufty 1982a, Darley 1983, Rothstein et al. 1984, Teather and Robertson, 1985, Smith and Arcese 1994), but no one had looked quantitatively at the relationship between female home range and the locations of parasite eggs throughout an entire host community. This approach required documentation both of the individual female cowbird's movements and of the specific nests where she laid her eggs. We designed a study to locate as many parasitized nests as possible in the study area, then to use molecular genetic techniques to match the cowbird eggs to the individual cowbird females that had laid them. Our strategy was to combine parentage information from cowbird young with radiotelemetry data from females' movements in order to explain their breeding behavior.

METHODS

STUDY AREA

We conducted a study of cowbird parasitism during 1991–1993 near Millbrook, Dutchess County, NY (51° 50 N, 73° 45 W), in a 1300-ha oak-maple-hemlock forest and in old fields adjacent to the forest and within cowbird commuting distance (Fig. 1; Hahn and Hatfield 1995). The study occurred on lands belonging to Rockefeller University and for the portion of the study reported here, we searched for nests within a 226-ha block. The study area is located within the township of Washington, a 38,000-ha area of which 55% is forested and the remaining area is a mosaic of equal parts pasture, livestock, and suburban development (Glitzenstein et al. 1990). The forest contains stands ranging in age from 70–150 years, experiences little disturbance, and is bisected by a seldom-used one-lane dirt road.

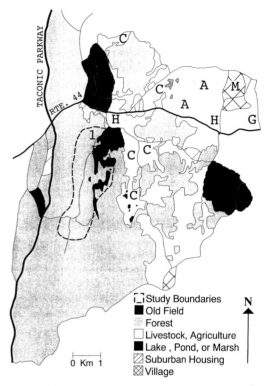

FIGURE 1. The study area in Millbrook, NY, 1991–1993, and surrounding landscape. The study area is numbered "1" and enclosed in dashed lines. A = agricultural fields; C = cattle and dairy farms; G = golf course; H = horse farms; M = village of Millbrook; R = Rockefeller University Field Research Center.

The stands are dominated by chestnut oak (*Quercus prinus*) and northern red oak (*Q. rubra*) on rocky slopes, and by white oak (*Q. alba*), black oak (*Q. velutina*), and pignut hickory (*Carya glabra*) on valley bottoms and mesic uplands. Hemlock (*Tsuga canadensis*), beech (*Fagus grandifolia*), and sugar maple (*Acer saccharum*) are confined to moist habitats such as ravines and streamsides. Understory tree species are flowering dogwood (*Cornus florida*), ironwood (*Ostrya virginiana*), shadbush (*Amelanchier* spp.), and striped maple (*Acer pensylvanicum*). Maple-leaved viburnum (*Viburnum acerifolium*) and blackberry (*Rubus* spp.) are the dominant shrubs. The swamps are vegetated with cinnamon fern (*Osmunda cinnamomea*), skunk cabbage (*Symplocarpus foetidus*), spicebush (*Lindera bezoin*), and tussock sedge (*Carex stricta*).

The old fields are dominated by blackberry (*Rubus* spp.), rose (*Rosa* spp.), alder (*Alnus* spp.), and haw (*Viburnum* spp.). The old field study areas include a 1-ha lawn with ornamental trees and shrubs on the north side of Tyrrell Lake.

TRAPPING ADULT COWBIRDS

Brown-headed Cowbirds were caught at the Rockefeller University Field Research Center (RUFRC) in Millbrook, Dutchess County, New York. A local population of cowbirds has been observed and studied there intermittently during two decades (Dufty 1983; P. Marler, pers. comm., J. Wingfield, pers. comm). There is a large local cowbird population, readily seen at the dairy, beef, and horse farms in the local countryside, as well as at numerous residential bird feeders. Cowbirds are attracted in feeding flocks to the field station lawns and to the nearby trash disposal area, where discarded seed associated with maintenance of captive canaries and finches is available year round.

We trapped cowbirds in funnel (or confusion) traps, which were constructed of 14-gauge wire (2.54 × 5.1 cm mesh) and measured 76.2 × 50.8 × 25.4 cm. Cowbirds walk into the traps through one of two openings in the trap wall and are led via wire tunnels (10.2 cm in length) into the center of the trap. Birds are reluctant to exit because the tunnel (funnel) narrows at the exit end. We set eight traps daily on a 0.25 ha lawn at RUFRC; the field station and trapping area were adjacent to the study site where we searched for parasitized nests and followed radiotagged females. We ran a trapping and banding program here throughout the field season (15 May–25 July) on weekdays from 1600 to 1900 hours, checking traps every 30 minutes. Cowbirds were banded with USFWS aluminum bands and individually unique color bands. Animals were handled and treated in accord with the guidelines and principles of the American Ornithologists' Union animal use practices guidelines (Oring et al. 1988).

NEST SEARCHING FOR COWBIRD YOUNG

A team of six searched for nests over approximately 1500 hours between 15 May–15 July. In the forest, the principal cowbird host species (N ≥ 20 nests) were Wood Thrush, American Redstart, Veery, and Ovenbird (scientific names in Table 3). Eastern Phoebes were a frequent species in the forest, on the ubiquitous rock faces, and also on sheds in old fields. In the old field community, Song Sparrow and Chipping Sparrow were common species.

POINT-COUNT SURVEY

To obtain an estimate of host density independent of the estimate obtained from nest searching, we conducted six point-count surveys across the breeding season, three in the forest and three in the old fields. Two observers conducted early morning surveys in late May and early June at points spaced 100 m apart on two different transects. We used the program DISTANCE (Burnham et al. 1980, Laake et al. 1993, Buckland et al. 1996) to analyze the survey data.

RADIOTELEMETRY, HOME RANGE MAPPING, AND TERRITORIAL BEHAVIOR

Each year we attached radio transmitters to female cowbirds that we trapped that weighed over 35 g (1991: N = 7; 1992: N = 26; 1993: N = 22). Transmitters, manufactured by Holohil, Inc., Ontario, Canada, weighed 1 g and were equipped with 30-day batteries. We attached the transmitters to the birds' backs between the scapulae using Superglue™. We prepared the transmitters by gluing silk or cotton fabric to one side of the transmitter and allowing it to dry at least one day before putting them on the birds. We selected birds > 35g and prepared the bird for the transmitter by pushing aside feather coverts, then clipping underfeathers to a stubble on the back. We applied glue to the fabric side of the transmitter, then pressed the radio against the feather stubble. We held each bird quietly in our hands for 5 min after affixing the transmitter, gently pressing the radio against the bird's back and allowing the bond to set. We next placed the birds in a large 4 m × 4 m holding cage to let the bond cure for an additional 30 min before releasing them.

We tracked all radiotagged birds daily 0500 to 1200 Monday through Saturday throughout the breeding season. One full-time biologist, assisted by two others part-time, searched for each female daily, tracking both on foot with a handheld antenna and also with a vehicle carrying a mounted antenna. Our objective was to obtain a daily morning location for each female while she was engaged in non-feeding activities, for the life of the battery.

In addition to mapping daily points on individual topographic maps for each female, we entered the daily telemetry points for all females on an enlarged (2.25 m × 1 m) master map where we also noted all nest locations, so that the study team had an integrated picture of the data being collected and an overview of parasitism on the study site. Subsequently all radiotelemetry points were translated into UTM locations and entered into home range coverages in ARC/INFO.

We designated as the principal group those females that we had followed 10 days and for which we had collected at least 10 location points, although we also analyzed the home range size and location of other radio tagged females for which we had fewer points. We gathered limited baseline data on cowbird territorial behavior during Year 1 of the study to use in the design of the larger radio tracking program in Year 2. We counted boundary disputes between females with adjacent home ranges while following radio tagged individuals. We also studied the responsiveness of female cowbird home range holders to intruder female cowbirds by audiotape playback experiments, using the calls of cowbird females. To conduct the playback experiment, we first established by radiotelemetry that a radiotagged female was in the vicinity of her home range, although not in sight. Along what we identified as the home range boundary, we placed two portable speakers in a canvas field case under shielding shrubs. We then stood nearby, also shielded by shrubs, holding a small portable tape recorder. We played the audiotaped female cowbird vocalizations for 10 s, then waited 30 s, then played another 10 s of tape; 30 s later, we played another 10 s. We then waited 3 min and noted if a marked home range holder female appeared during that period, either checking visually and/or calling. We conducted 6 separate tests with 6 different female cowbirds on their home ranges.

GIS: Integrating Spatial and Genetic Information

To obtain an overview of cowbird parasitism on the study area, we integrated the three datasets using ARC/INFO, namely: (1) spatial information (nest locations and daily location points of radio tagged females); (2) ecological and biological information (for all nests: nest height, host species, parasitized or not, number of cowbird eggs or nestlings); and (3) genetic data (band sharing coefficients showing genetic relationships between pairs of individual cowbirds). To provide accurate land cover information, we scanned aerial photographs of the study area into ARC/INFO; to provide information on elevation and slope, we imported the appropriate U.S. Geological Survey topographic maps.

Individual home ranges were depicted and calculated using the minimum convex polygon function of ARC/INFO, joining the outermost points of each individual's cluster. Maps displayed each female's home range and the location of parasitized nests of cowbird young with known degrees of genetic relatedness. We used three classifications for the spatial relationship between a female's home range boundary and her parasitized nests: "inside," "close to" (within a 50-m buffer zone of the boundary), and "distant from" (beyond a 50-m boundary).

Genetic Analyses

We conducted genetic analyses using multilocus DNA probes on 104 cowbirds trapped or collected from the study site in Year 2 of the study (43 females and 61 eggs or nestlings). The 43 adult females were selected on the basis of weight (> 35 g), the best indicator available to distinguish older, reproductive females; the 61 young cowbirds or eggs represented those we found that yielded viable genetic material.

We collected 10–40 microliters of blood by venipuncture of the brachial vein, added lysis buffer, and stored it in a freezer until analysis. DNA profiles were performed at Therion Corporation, Troy, NY. DNA was isolated, digested with restriction endonuclease *Hae*III, electrophoresed, and transferred to a nylon membrane following standard methods (Haig et al. 1994, 1995). Molecular weight sizing standards (MWSS) were loaded in up to three lanes so that they bracketed samples and facilitated objective identification of bands. Ten samples were run on each gel. The set of standard DNA fragments of known molecular size was composed of 48 bands ranging from 0.504 to 34.679 kilobase pairs. The transferred DNA was probed sequentially with two ^{32}P-labeled proprietary probes, Opt-03 ™ and Opt-05™, washed, and exposed to x-ray film following the protocols of Haig et al. (1994, 1995). The two probes had been selected on the basis of a pilot study that showed that they gave highly variable DNA profile patterns among unrelated cowbirds collected from widely separated sites. To estimate relatedness we calculated band sharing coefficients (BSCs) for all pairs of individuals in the study. Similarity (S) was calculated as the ratio of number of bands shared divided by the total number of bands scored for a pair of individuals (Lynch 1988), and it yielded just over N = 5,000 pairwise comparisons. Because we consider that each probe detected a different set of minisatellites (Georges et al. 1988), we treated these BSC data as independent assessments of relatedness.

DNA fragment scoring and data analyses

We scored fragments within and among gels as described in Haig et al. (1994, 1995). Each DNA fragment (band) was independently scored by two investigators. We eliminated any band that was lighter than the lightest bands in the molecular weight sizing standards. To calculate band-sharing among individuals on all gels, band sizes were hand-digitized and resulting data entered into computer programs designed by Therion Corporation. Prior to making comparisons among cowbirds, MWSS lanes were compared within gels and then among gels to determine the accuracy and precision of our band matching methodology. The program matched identical MWSS bands within and among gels.

Band sizes for each individual were then determined by comparison to the MWSS within the range of 13.823–2.532 kb. Using this method the sizing error within and between gels was estimated to be ± 0.6% of band size (i.e., the total range was equal to 2 SD or 1.2% of band size; Balazs et al. 1989, 1990; Risch and Devlin 1992). Therefore, when determining band-sharing between individuals, bands were considered to be a match when their respective sizes overlapped within a range of ± 0.9% of each band size (i.e., the total range is equal to 3 SD or 1.8% of band size). These values were consistent with those reported by Galbraith et al. (1991) who suggested that the distance between bands be at least 2.8 SD before they are declared different at the 0.05 level.

DATA ANALYSES: INVESTIGATING HOST SELECTION PATTERNS USING GENETIC DATA

Comparing band-sharing coefficients among groups

We examined several factors that might influence cowbird laying behavior: (1) location of female's home range; (2) host nest height (low, medium, high); (3) host adult mass; (4) host egg volume; (5) host body length; (6) host clutch size; and (7) host taxonomic identity (by subfamily). We tested the influence of each factor by comparing average relatedness (BSCs) between groups of cowbirds. Comparison of groups of BSCs maximizes the information that can be gleaned from a large sample of BSCs without assigning maternity. Each factor was tested by comparing the average relatedness of pairs of individuals with a similar value (for that factor) with the average relatedness of individuals with dissimilar values. Standard errors were calculated separately for each group following Lynch (1988, 1990) by taking a random sample of pairs, where no pair shared an individual with any other pair, and treating each pair as uncorrelated. Standard errors for the mean pairwise bandsharing coefficients were then calculated using a conservative estimate of the correlation between pairs with one individual in common. A correlation of 0.5 was used, which was approximately the upper 95% point of a bootstrap distribution of the correlation calculated from uncorrelated pairs of pairs with one individual in common (Lynch 1988). The standard error calculated for the difference was used in the power calculations.

Estimating most likely mother-offspring pairs

We assigned probable maternity of cowbird young on the basis of BSCs using as a cut-off value the upper 95% confidence interval. BSCs have been repeatedly shown to be a robust estimate of relatedness (Lynch 1988, 1990; Webster and Westneat 1998). For most typical outbred avian taxa using the Jeffreys' probe, the band-sharing or similarity index (S of Lynch 1988, 1990) varies between about 0.1 and 0.4 among unrelated individuals and between 0.5 and 0.8 for first-order relatives (Burke et al. 1989, Meng et al. 1989, Morton et al. 1990, Westneat 1990, Oring et al. 1992, Stutchbury et al. 1994). Thus, pairs of individuals in populations with S-values greater than 0.5 are very likely to be siblings or parents and offspring (Lynch 1988). We confirmed this finding in Year 1 of the study when we did multilocus analyses of cowbird DNA using Jeffreys' probe (Hahn and Fleischer 1995); we found a significant difference between the mean BSCs for unrelated individuals (mean = 0.31 ± 0.08) vs. mothers and offspring (mean = 0.45 ± 0.13). We had confirmed this finding by also calculating a cut-off value to define first-order relatives using the upper 95% confidence limit.

For Year 2, we generated cut-off values to define first-order relatives using the upper 95% confidence limit (probe Opt-03: 0.30 ± 2(0.10) = 0.50; Opt-05: 0.24 ± 2(0.12) = 0.48) as in Haig et al. (1994, 1995) and Hahn and Fleischer (1995). We assigned putative mothers to young when a mother-young pair had a BSC ≥ cut-off value on at least one probe.

RESULTS

CHARACTERISTICS OF FEMALE COWBIRD HOME RANGES

Cowbird females followed at least 10 days and which had at least 10 point locations (N = 12), consistently used an identifiable home range throughout the breeding season. Their point locations created a characteristic cluster of points within a defined spatial area (Fig. 2). The average home range size for these principal females was 9.38 ha ± 7.9 SD, range = 2.6–32.2 ha, median = 7.6 ha.

Cowbirds were commonly seen in feeding flocks in the afternoon and early evening. Flocks congregated at a variety of sites in the Millbrook township including the lawn of the field station at RUFRC as well as at barns and fields associated with local dairies, horse, and cattle farms, and at residential bird feeders (Fig. 1). We did not find a communal evening roost of the cowbirds in this study area. We conducted several searches for individual radio tagged females at

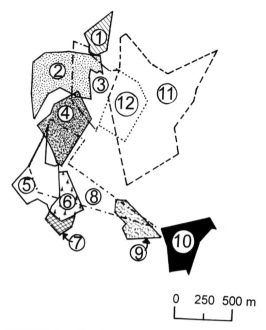

FIGURE 2. The home ranges, showing zones of overlap, of the 12 principal female cowbirds followed by radiotelemetry in Millbrook, NY, 1992.

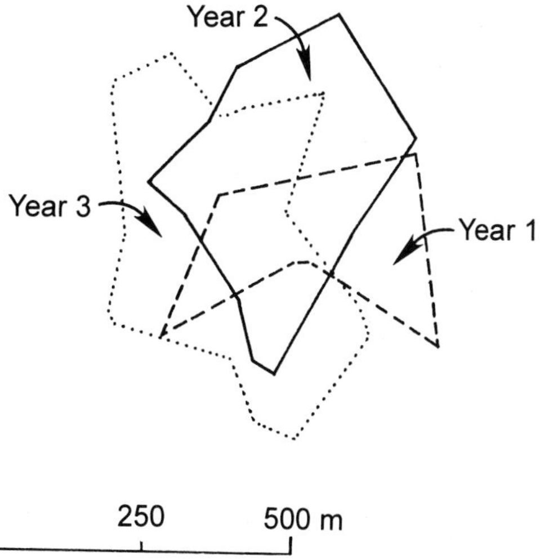

FIGURE 3. The home range fidelity of a female cowbird (F91337) followed by radiotelemetry over three successive breeding seasons in Millbrook, NY, 1991–1993.

dusk and after nightfall, but on each occasion located only a single female on her home range.

HOME RANGE FIDELITY ACROSS SUCCESSIVE BREEDING SEASONS

The characteristic home ranges of females within the host community were re-established from one breeding season to the next. For example, one female (F91337) used a Year 2 home range that overlapped with 53% of her Year 1 home range; in Year 3, she used a home range that consisted of 89% of the area she used as home ranges in Years 1 and 2 (Fig. 3).

We have multi-year data on six females radioed in Year 2 of the study, and each returned to nearly the same spatial area as its previous home range. The mean size of the 13 home ranges established over three years by the six females was 8.0 ha ± 5.3. The mean home range size in Year 2 was 9.38 ± 7.9 when looking at the 12 principal females, and it was 7.0 ha ± 3.2 (Year 2) when looking only at the subset of six females with multi-year data. Home range size did not differ among years (one-way ANOVA: $F_{2,10}$ = 2.31, P > 0.14).

A multi-year map of home ranges of six of the seven females for which we have telemetry data in more than one year displays how consistently each individual returned to the same distinct home range (Fig. 4). While there was some

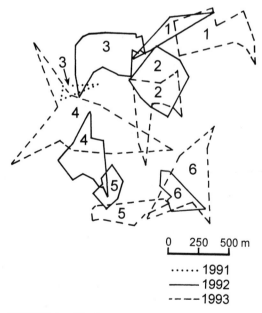

FIGURE 4. The home range fidelity of six female cowbirds that were followed for more than one year via radiotelemetry at Millbrook, NY, 1991–1993. The home range outlined in a dotted line was observed in 1991. Six home ranges outlined in black solid lines were observed in 1992. The five home ranges outlined in dashed lines were observed in 1993.

TABLE 1. SIZE OF THE STUDY POPULATION OF COWBIRDS AT MILLBROOK, NY, 1991–1993, BASED ON INDIVIDUALS TRAPPED ON THE FEEDING GROUND, 15 MAY–25 JULY

| | Females | | Males | | Hatch Year Birds (HY) | | | |
| | | | | | Eggs and nestlings[a] | Fledglings | Total | HY/ |
	N	%	N	%	N	N	N	females
1991	53		92		16	109	125	2.36
1992	111		127		72	36	108	0.97
1991 adult returns	23	21%	20	15.7%				
1991 HY returns	7		11					
1993	43		64		61	90	151	3.5

[a] Found in host nests on the study site.

year to year variability, each female returned to a characteristic area within the landscape. Trapping records showed that 21% of the females were returnees and thus were familiar with the study area and the avian host community (Table 1).

Home range overlap zone between neighbors

Neighboring home ranges overlapped in their use of space (Fig. 2). Because it was extremely rare to actually sight the female being radiotracked, disputes between neighbors were observed infrequently. We noted only eight boundary disputes in the form of physical chases or aggressive calling during 3 weeks (approximately 120 hours) of following six radio tagged females during Year 1. However, resident females were highly responsive to unknown "intruders," as indicated by our playback experiments; during Year 1, resident females responded every time to experimental playbacks of cowbird audiotapes, approaching, and making visual or auditory contact in the vicinity of the playback speaker (binomial exact interval 0.607, 1.000; N = 6, P < 0.05). This suggested that female cowbirds responded to intruders and defended a home range.

We explored the possibility that overlapping home ranges were characteristic of neighboring females that were close relatives; however, we found that the average BSCs of female cowbirds who shared overlapping home ranges was not different from the average BSCs of female cowbirds who did not share overlapping home ranges (Table 2, last hypothesis; P > 0.1).

HOME RANGE-BASED HOST SELECTION

Female cowbirds laid their eggs within their home range (Table 2, first hypothesis; P < 0.001). We found that female cowbirds were more closely related to the young cowbirds in nests inside their home ranges than to young in nests outside their home ranges, based on the difference between average bandsharing coefficients of the two groups. No other relationship

was found between groups of young cowbirds based on other ecological and biological parameters that could have affected females' host selection patterns (e.g., nest height or host species; Table 2). The same pairwise comparisons of the average bandsharing coefficients between two groups were conducted for each hypothesis, but no significant differences were found between any groups.

ESTIMATING MOST LIKELY MOTHER-OFFSPRING PAIRS

Effective cowbird fecundity

We found 298 nests in the study area, belonging to 26 species that are known cowbird hosts, and 31% were parasitized (Table 3). We collected samples from 72 cowbird eggs and nestlings, and 61 yielded successful genetic analyses. Over three-quarters of these 61 young cowbirds (N = 50, including one egg laid in the lab by a female held overnight) were assigned to probable mothers (N = 29) on the basis that all pairs had BSCs on one or both probes that fell outside the 95% confidence interval. Eleven young cowbirds (11 / 61 = 18%) could not be assigned to a probable mother, because they did not share a high enough BSC with any adult female in our sample. We estimated cowbird fecundity by calculating the ratio of cowbird eggs detected to the number of females to which they were assigned, and at this study site we found it to be 1.7 ± 1.2 eggs per female (i.e., 50 eggs/29 assigned females). The 14 females to whom no young were assigned may have been inactive breeders, or they may have laid eggs that did not yield genetic material (N = 11) or that we did not find. Seventeen of the 29 actively breeding females (58.6%) were assigned one egg, and over three-quarters of the known breeding cowbird females (23/29 = 79.3%) were assigned only one or two eggs (Fig. 5). Only one female in our sample (1/29 = 3.4%) was assigned more than three eggs.

This estimate of fecundity (1.7 eggs per fe-

TABLE 2. COMPARISONS OF AVERAGE BAND SHARING COEFFICIENTS BETWEEN GROUPS OF INDIVIDUALS[a]

Hypothesis tested	Groups compared	Observed difference: d	SE_d	95% confidence interval	P-value	$q_{.95}$	$q_{.50}$
Young within the range of an adult female are more closely related to that female than are young outside the range of the female	Female–young relatedness: (1) young inside or close to HR vs (2) young outside HR	0.1	0.032	0.036 to 0.165	<0.001	0.110	0.050
Young found in nests at one height range are more closely related than young found in nests at different heights	Host nest height: (1) <1 m vs (2) 1–3 m vs (3) >3 m	0.006	0.028	−0.049 to 0.061	>0.1	0.093	0.046
Young found in nests of hosts with similar mean body mass are more closely related than young in nests of hosts having dissimilar mean body mass	Host mass (adult): (1) <27 gm vs (2) >27 gm	0.002	0.018	−0.033 to 0.038	>0.1	0.059	0.030
Young in nests of host species with similar mean egg volume are more closely related than young in nests of host species having dissimilar mean egg volume	Host egg volume: (1) <175 cm^3 vs (2) >1+75 cm^3	0.002	0.015	−0.028 to 0.032	>0.1	0.051	0.025
Young in nests of host species with similar mean body length are more closely related than young in nests of host species with dissimilar mean body length	Host body length (adult): (1) <6.4 cm vs (2) >6.4 cm	−0.006	0.019	−0.042 to 0.030	>0.1	0.061	0.030
Young in nests of host species with similar mean clutch size are more closely related than young in nests of host species having dissimilar mean clutch size	Host clutch size: (1) <4.25 eggs vs (2) >4.25 eggs	0.002	0.017	−0.031 to 0.035	>0.1	0.056	0.028
Young in nests of hosts within the same taxonomic family are more closely related than young in nests of hosts from different taxonomic families	Host taxonomic relationship: (1) same family vs (2) different family	−0.002	0.016	−0.034 to 0.029	>0.1	0.053	0.027
Females with overlapping home ranges are more closely related than females without overlapping home ranges	Female neighbors: (1) overlapping home ranges vs (2) non-overlapping home ranges	0.025	0.271	−0.519 to 0.570	>0.1	0.909	0.454

[a] d is the estimated mean difference in relatedness, se_d is the estimated standard error of this difference, $q_{.95}$ and $q_{.50}$ are estimates of the actual mean difference in the population that would be required to observe a statistically significant difference (at the 0.05 level) with a probability of 95% and 50%, respectively.

TABLE 3.　THE COWBIRD HOST COMMUNITY AT MILLBROOK, NY, 1992

	Nests		
Host species	Total N	Parasitized N	%
Eastern Wood-Pewee	4	0	0
(*Contopus virens*)			
Eastern Phoebe	21	6	28.6
(*Sayornis phoebe*)			
Least Flycatcher	4	1	25.0
(*Empidonax minimus*)			
Blue-headed Vireo	2	0	0
(*Vireo solitarius*)			
Red-eyed Vireo	11	6	54.5
(*Vireo olivaceus*)			
Carolina Wren	3	1	33.3
(*Thryothorus ludovicianus*)			
Blue-gray Gnatcatcher	2	0	0
(*Poliptila caerulea*)			
Wood Thrush	60	5	8.3
(*Hylocichla mustelina*)			
Veery	31	7	22.6
(*Catharus fuscescens*)			
Hermit Thrush	13	7	53.8
(*Catharus guttatus*)			
Blue-winged Warbler	5	1	20.0
(*Vermivora pinus*)			
Black-and-white Warbler	2	1	50.0
(*Mniotilta varia*)			
Yellow-rumped Warbler	1	0	0
(*Dendroica coronata*)			
Worm-eating Warbler	5	0	0
(*Helmitheros vermivorus*)			
Ovenbird	20	10	50.0
(*Seiurus aurocapillus*)			
Louisiana Waterthrush	8	2	25.0
(*Seiurus motacilla*)			
Common Yellowthroat	4	1	25.0
(*Geothlypis trichas*)			
American Redstart	37	13	35.1
(*Setophaga ruticilla*)			
Northern Cardinal	6	1	16.5
(*Cardinalis cardinalis*)			
Eastern Towhee	6	2	33.3
(*Pipilo erythrophthalmus*)			
Song Sparrow	14	1	7.1
(*Melospiza melodia*)			
Field Sparrow	4	0	0
(*Spizella pusilla*)			
Chipping Sparrow	18	0	0
(*Spizella passerina*)			
Rose-breasted Grosbeak	10	1	10.0
(*Pheucticus ludovicianus*)			
Scarlet Tanager	4	2	50.0
(*Piranga olivacea*)			
Red-winged Blackbird	3	0	0
(*Agelaius phoeniceus*)			
Total	298	68	30.56

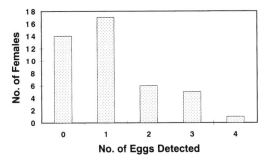

FIGURE 5.   Estimate of effective cowbird fecundity at Millbrook, NY, 1992, based on the number of eggs detected in the study area and assigned to probable mothers on the basis of DNA analyses.

male) constitutes a minimum estimate of cowbird fecundity that reflects only the parasitized nests that we found. In effect, the number of nests found gives us an estimate of host density, which in conjunction with genetic analyses defines cowbird fecundity. However, we also calculated an upper estimate of cowbird fecundity to take into account any parasitized nests in the study area that we did not find. We calculated this upper estimate of host fecundity using data on host density from point-count surveys (Table 4). Point-count survey data suggested an upward

correction of host density estimates for 10 of 13 parasitized species with correction factors ranging from 1.13 (Wood Thrush) to 13.33 (Red-eyed Vireo). The resulting estimate of effective cowbird fecundity was 8.16 eggs per female.

Home range-based host selection

We used ARC/INFO to display each female's home range and the parasitized nest(s) holding her assigned young. An overview of the study area (Fig. 6) shows the home ranges of nine of the females for which we had radiotelemetry data, genetic data, and assigned young. Seven of the 13 (54%) females in our sample laid their assigned eggs either inside or close (< 50 m) to their home range boundary (Table 5); six laid eggs in nests more distant than 50 m beyond their home range boundaries (mean = 401 ± 331, range = 105–1070 m). Three females had assigned young only in distant nests, but eggs that did not yield genetic material were also found in nests inside their home ranges (Table 5). All but one of the parasitized nests > 50 m from the home range boundary were multiply parasitized and were typically found in conspicuous locations.

MULTIPLY PARASITIZED NESTS

Female cowbirds avoided laying more than one of their own eggs in a single host nest.

TABLE 4.   ESTIMATES OF EFFECTIVE COWBIRD FECUNDITY AT MILLBROOK, NY, 1992, BASED ON TWO DIFFERENT MEASURES OF HOST DENSITY

Species	Fecundity estimates					
	Nest density—based			Point-count density—based		
	Host[a] density per 100 ha	No. cowbird eggs found	Female[b] laying rate	Host[c] density per 100 ha	Point[d] count correction factor	Point[e] count adjusted number of eggs	Point[f] count adjusted laying rate
Wood Thrush	27	2	0.07	30.6	1.13	2.3	0.08
Eastern Phoebe	10.2	8	0.28	5.8	1	8	0.28
Ovenbird	8.8	7	0.24	38.7	4.4	30.8	1.06
American Redstart	16.4	8	0.28	147.2	8.98	71.8	2.48
Veery	13.7	5	0.17	96.7	7.06	35.3	1.22
Red-eyed Vireo	4.9	4	0.14	65.3	13.33	53.3	1.84
Blue-winged Warbler	3.1	1	0.03	15.7	5.06	5.1	0.18
Hermit Thrush	5.8	6	0.21	4.5	1	6	0.21
Song Sparrow	10.2	2	0.07	4.8	1	2	0.07
Scarlet Tanager	1.8	1	0.03	12.1	6.72	6.7	0.23
Eastern Towhee	2.7	4	0.14	4.2	1.56	6.2	0.22
Louisiana Waterthrush	3.5	1	0.03	22.7	6.48	6.5	0.22
Rose-breasted Grosbeak	4.9	1	0.03	10.1	2.06	2.1	0.07
Total eggs		50				236.1	
Fecundity estimates			1.72[g]				8.16

[a] Host density based on actual number of nests found.
[b] Laying rate per 29 females with assigned young.
[c] Host density based on point count surveys.
[d] Ratio of point count to nest density.
[e] Number of eggs found × correction factor.
[f] Nest density laying rate × correction factor.
[g] Based on actual number of nests found and cowbird eggs assigned using genetic analyses.

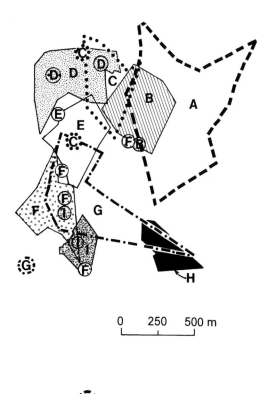

0   250   500 m

⟨Ā⟩

FIGURE 6. Results of integrated radiotelemetry and genetics studies of cowbirds in Millbrook, NY, 1992. The map depicts the spatial relationship between nine female's home ranges and the 16 parasitized nests containing eggs assigned to these females. Nests (small circles) are lettered to match the letter of the home range of the female that parasitized them.

TABLE 5. SUMMARY OF THE LAYING PATTERNS OF COWBIRDS IN RELATION TO THEIR HOME RANGES

Location of parasitized nests	No. females
At least one egg laid inside mother's home range	6
1. All eggs inside	3
2. Some eggs inside and some close	2
3. Some eggs inside, some close, and some distant	1
All eggs laid close[a] to mother's home range	1
All eggs laid distant[b] from mother's home range	3
Some eggs laid distant from mother's home range and some laid inside but with no genetic results	3
Total	13

[a] Close eggs were laid outside of the home range but within a 50-m buffer zone of the boundary.
[b] Eggs laid > 50 m from the home range boundary.

duces a large number of young and invests no parental care. They substitute the picture of a brood parasite that produces limited numbers of young and does invest parental care, both by selection of known-host parents and by placing each parasitic egg in a separate host nest without a competitive cowbird sibling. The home range is the foundation of the known-host selection strategy, making it possible for female cowbirds to preferentially parasitize successful host pairs observed in previous breeding seasons.

The first result, home range fidelity of female cowbirds, enables breeding cowbirds to learn the physical territory and thus detect more nests as well as observe the relative success of resident songbirds. This information can be used in host selection. The well known site fidelity of songbirds (e.g., Brown 1975, Krebs and Davies 1993) makes it likely that experienced cowbird females return to their previous home range and encounter many of the same host pairs that nested there during the preceding breeding season. Long-term studies of parasitism are rare, but two notable studies of host species reported seemingly strategic parasitism patterns that are explained by home range-based host selection and preferential selection of known hosts by cowbirds. In Song Sparrows, cowbirds preferentially parasitized older females (Smith 1981, Smith and Arcese 1994), and in Willow Flycatchers (*Empidonax traillii*) cowbirds appeared to parasitize superior host parents (Sedgwick and Iko *this volume*). Fidelity to home range has further benefit for cowbirds, allowing females to monitor the progress of their young in host nests. Such monitoring has already been reported for the parasitic Great Spotted Cuckoo (*Clamator glandarius*; Soler et al. 1995), and it would ex-

While multiple parasitism characterized nearly one-third of the nests in the study area, we noted multiple parasitism of one nest by the same female in only one case. Nearly three-quarters of the multiply parasitized nests for which we had genetic results (11/15 = 73%) lay in locations within overlap zones covered by more than one known home range.

DISCUSSION

The results presented here, combining genetic and telemetry data, suggest the importance of the home range in cowbird breeding behavior. The three principal results we report are female cowbirds' use of a characteristic home range year after year, lower cowbird fecundity than expected, and avoidance of multiple laying in a single nest by female cowbirds. These three elements of cowbird breeding behavior challenge the stereotype of cowbirds as a species that pro-

plain how female cowbirds were found associating with their own offspring after fledging (Hahn and Fleischer 1995).

Several previous investigators have shown that cowbirds use a home range (Dufty 1982a, Darley 1983, Teather and Robertson 1985, Yokel 1989, Smith and Arcese 1994, Raim in press), but this is the first report of genetic evidence linking a female cowbird's use of a home range to her egg-laying pattern. In this diverse avian community spanning forest, edge, and old field habitats, female home range was the only predictor of which nests would be parasitized. No other biological or ecological factor predicted where an individual cowbird would lay an egg, including host species identity, body size, clutch size, egg size, incubation period, or nest height. Rather than targeting a particular host species, as some investigators have suggested (e.g., Walkinshaw 1983), each individual female cowbird used a mixture of host species. Such lack of host specialization is, of course, the expected pattern if female cowbirds use their home range as an egg-laying range. Host territorial behavior creates species-specific spacing patterns that effectively limit the number of nests of any one host that occur within a single cowbird's home range.

We observed few instances of aggressive behavior at territorial boundaries, which is consistent with other observations that female cowbirds have non-exclusive home ranges (e.g. Payne 1977, Fleischer 1985). Krebs and Davies (1993) review the concept of territories with renewing resources, using those with flowers for nectar-feeding birds as the classic example of a system in which the owner's knowledge of the pattern of resource renewal and location of recently depleted patches may be so superior to an intruder's that the need for defensive behavior is reduced. Brood parasites similarly depend on renewing resources, a series of host nests that are available for receiving a parasitic egg only at brief, precise time intervals. Since it was not our objective in this study to obtain a thorough description of home range acquisition and maintenance, we did not follow individuals for long periods each day and thus we cannot evaluate how territorial defense may be used. However, future studies of cowbirds may examine whether female cowbirds display more aggressive behavior early in the breeding season when home ranges are being established, as is characteristic in many species (Stamps 1994).

The second principal result of this study is that effective cowbird fecundity is lower than previous studies of fecundity have suggested. We use the term "effective cowbird fecundity" (S.I. Rothstein, pers. comm.) to describe only those eggs that cowbirds succeed in laying in appropriate host nests and that are not subsequently ejected by hosts. Based on ovarian dissections of wild breeding birds, several investigators have independently estimated a high cowbird laying rate of 0.7–0.8 eggs per day with an extrapolation to 20–40 eggs per season (Payne 1976, Scott and Ankney 1983, Rothstein et al. 1986b). However, the physiological egg-laying capacity, or raw fecundity, of cowbirds is likely to be higher than their effective fecundity, because when a cowbird does not find a host nest in which to lay, she may dump the egg in an inappropriate nest (e.g., Mourning Dove, *Zenaida macroura*; D.C. Hahn, pers. obs.) or other site, she may reabsorb the egg in the oviduct (Payne 1998), or she may eat it after laying to regain nutrients (R.C. Fleischer, pers. comm.; D.C. Hahn, pers. obs.). In addition, a number of cowbird eggs are successfully ejected by some hosts (Rothstein 1975a). Effective fecundity is the measurement of interest to conservation biologists and resource managers, since it reflects the true impact cowbirds potentially have on host species' reproductive success.

The average number of eggs that we detected and assigned to individual cowbird females using genetics techniques was 1.7 ± 1.2 eggs per female (range = 1–4). This estimate is a lower bound on effective fecundity, because it does not include cowbird eggs in nests we did not find or eggs that did not yield genetic results. We calculated 8.16 eggs per female as the upper bound of effective cowbird fecundity using host density estimates from point count surveys in the study area (Table 4). Our subjective assessment of the study area based on field experience did not suggest that there were nearly five times more nests present than we found, but many factors hamper a field study in locating all parasitized nests and cowbird eggs in a large study area. Nests located in the forest canopy are particularly difficult to locate, and predation of parasitized nests or removal of a cowbird egg by rival cowbirds can occur before an observer finds the nest. Once a host abandons a parasitized nest, observers are less likely to find it without the cues associated with active nests.

Trapping data offer a third perspective on effective cowbird fecundity. We ran traps until late in the breeding season on lawns adjacent to the study area, and we captured a number of recently fledged cowbirds (with short tails) that appeared to have emerged from nests that we had not found (Hahn and Fleischer 1995). We calculated the ratio of total cowbird young found (including eggs and nestlings found in host nests plus cowbird fledglings trapped) to total adult females trapped during the breeding season (Table 1). For 1992 this yielded a fecundity estimate of 0.97 young per female, a lower estimate than the one we first calculated using only the young found in host nests that could be assigned to adult females using genetic analyses (Table 4). We used our radiotelemetry data to evaluate this ratio of 0.97 and to determine whether it was skewed by females that came to the feeding site but were not breeding in the local area. Specifically, since we had attached radio transmitters to 26 females and subsequently located only 19 (73%) of these females within the study area, we reduced the estimate of trapped females by 27%. This increased the ratio of effective fecundity from 0.97 to 1.33 young per female, still lower than the 1.72 eggs per female estimated from nest searching data alone. It is important to note that this estimate of cowbird fecundity using fledglings and trapping data is both more robust and more limited than the estimate using only nest data, since the number of fledgling cowbirds trapped reflects the number of cowbird eggs laid minus any egg and nestling mortality; at the same time it may include additional cowbird eggs that hatched and fledged from nests that were not detected.

The range of estimates of cowbird fecundity considered here and the proposed difference between effective fecundity and raw fecundity emphasize the difficulty of measuring accurately the pressure of parasitism on a host community. Given this difficulty, the most reliable approach of measuring cowbird impact on host species appears to be the long-term studies that track the cost that parasitism imposes on lifetime reproductive success of individual birds. Such studies have shown that parasitism exerts severe pressure in some communities (e.g., Wood Thrush in southern Illinois; Robinson 1992, Trine in press) and limited pressure in others (Song Sparrow in British Columbia, Smith and Arcese 1994; Indigo Bunting in Michigan, Payne 1998; Willow Flycatcher in eastern Oregon, Sedgwick and Iko *this volume*).

We suggest that the third finding of this study, that individual female cowbirds avoided laying more than one of their own eggs in a host nest, is an indicator of cowbird parental investment. Laying more than one egg in a nest makes breeding easier for the cowbird female because it reduces the number of nests she must find. However, multiple parasitism of single nests probably reduces her reproductive success because it puts her aggressive offspring in competition with one another (Nice 1937, Klaas 1975, Nolan 1978, Walkinshaw 1983). Trine (in press) found that each additional cowbird egg in a Wood Thrush nest reduced cowbird hatching success by 8–10%. Home range-based breeding

behavior increases the home range holder's chances of being the first to parasitize a given host nest and to parasitize it at the optimum time because the owner knows her territory and its resources better than any intruder female.

The explanation for the multiply-parasitized nests in our study area may be other pressures that conflict with the strategy of single parasitism to optimize an individual cowbird chick's survival. For example, a cowbird might lay her second egg in a previously parasitized nest if the host nest that she had targeted were unexpectedly lost to predation, weather damage, or other accidents (e.g., Morse 1988, Wiens 1992). As the breeding season progresses, the costs of laying twice in a host nest decline relative to the risk of not finding a better, future laying opportunity.

Finally, multiple parasitism is probably often the result of opportunistic laying by a yearling female cowbird. While experienced female cowbirds may lay most eggs inside their home range, younger females probably lay more eggs outside a home range. Our data do not permit testing this hypothesis, because we lack information on cowbird females' ages. However, two of Darley's (1983) findings suggest that yearling cowbird females may not be mature enough to hold a home range. Darley observed that younger cowbirds were less consistent in their use of home range and that for both male and female cowbirds dominance hierarchies dictate behavior among birds of the same gender. Unable to hold a home range, yearling cowbird females may employ a callow host selection strategy, searching widely throughout the host community and parasitizing any conspicuous nest. The challenges of the brood parasitic breeding strategy probably force yearling females to lay many eggs that have a low probability of success, either in previously parasitized nests or in nests that are not at the optimal stage in the host's breeding cycle. As a female cowbird acquires experience over successive seasons, we suggest that she would master the known host selection strategy: establish a home range, study the host birds within the range, and synchronize her parasitic laying schedule with that of the best pairs.

The frequency of multiple parasitism among communities varies widely according to published reports (e.g., Wiens 1963, Brittingham and Temple 1983, Collins et al. 1988, Robinson 1992, Hahn and Hatfield 1995, Payne 1998, Trine in press). Cowbird density or host density are the factors typically assumed to determine frequency of multiple parasitism. However, our conclusions support Holford and Roby's (1993) suggestion that age structure of the cowbird population may also be a factor, with higher rates of multiple parasitism occurring in cowbird populations that have a larger proportion of yearling and young females. If experienced cowbird females rely on home range-based breeding behavior and on a known-host selection strategy, then a host community parasitized by a stable cowbird population with a diverse age mix would experience lower levels of multiple parasitism and less negative impact from brood parasitism. In contrast, a host community parasitized by a disproportionately high number of yearling cowbirds or new immigrants would experience more multiple parasitism and more negative impact.

MANAGEMENT IMPLICATIONS

The patterns reported here characterize the cowbirds we studied in the northeastern U.S. where cowbird populations are not expanding (Robbins et al. 1989, Peterjohn et al. in press). Comparative studies are required in the West and Southwest to see if the home range-based breeding behavior that we observed also characterizes cowbirds in regions where parasitism exerts severe pressure on host communities and cowbird management programs are underway.

The known-host selection strategy proposed here suggests that knowledge of cowbird population demographics can assist wildlife managers in managing cowbird parasitism and determining whether to initiate cowbird trapping programs. For example, in a stable cowbird population composed of mixed-age birds, a large proportion of females would be experienced breeders that will primarily parasitize a mix of host species within their individual home ranges. However, in communities where cowbird trapping programs are in place, a high proportion of the cowbird population each year will be immigrant, yearling females, which may disproportionately parasitize conspicuous hosts. Endangered species such as the Least Bell's and Black-capped vireos that advertise the nest site by song would be more at risk from a population of younger cowbirds that lay a large proportion of their eggs opportunistically in the nests of conspicuous hosts. Continuous trapping probably prevents the cowbird population from stabilizing and developing a predominance of older, experienced females that would exert a lower parasitism rate on vireos. Managers of endangered species populations should beware of intermittent or inconsistent trapping programs. These may expose conspicuous host species to unexpectedly high parasitism rates by the high numbers of yearling females that characterize a local cowbird population in off years when trapping is not underway.

Host-parasite population dynamics also suggest that host communities that experience steady levels of cowbird parasitism across long time periods may evolve better defenses against parasitism than host communities that experience intermittent parasitism. For example, secretive behavior and camouflaged nest building may be effective against younger, inexperienced cowbirds that search opportunistically, but not against the majority of experienced females that maintain a home range and search it thoroughly for all nests. More aggressive host defense, such as physically preventing a cowbird's access to lay her egg or physically ejecting the parasite egg, may evolve sooner in host communities where cowbird populations are stable and where experienced home range-based females exert steady selection pressure on all hosts. This suggests that resource managers be alert to the negative effect of cowbirds on host communities that are experiencing intermittent parasitism, whether due to natural population cycles or to trapping programs that are inconsistent or short term. In these communities, population stability should be monitored most carefully in species that lack secretive behavior and camouflaged nest building and thus may serve as indicator species.

ACKNOWLEDGMENTS

We thank Rockefeller University Field Research Center, the Institute of Ecosystem Studies, and Mr. Bruce Kovner for permission to use their land. DCH appreciates long term support from R. Jachowski (USGS) and helpful discussion and maps provided by F. Nottebohm (RUFRC) and R. Winchcombe (IES). We are grateful to our skilled and dedicated team of nest searchers, including J. Boone, K. Corey, S. Plentovich, G. Oines, and J. Cherry, and to D. Clugston, J. Koloszar, J. Wisniewski, K. Corey, and G. Oines, who very ably collected home range information on radio tagged cowbirds in difficult terrain. We thank L. Williams for managing the incubator; I. Thomas and H. Bourne for skillful GIS work; L. Loges and P. Osenton for assistance with database management; and K. Boone and D. Crawford for preparing figures. W. Gergits provided invaluable help in presentation of genetic data; J. S. Hatfield provided helpful advice on statistical analysis of genetic data and, with G. A. Gough, carried out preliminary DISTANCE analyses. We appreciate helpful reviews by M. Morrison, J. Rotenberry, M. P. Scott, J. Longmire, J. Rhymer, J. S. Hatfield, and an anonymous reviewer that greatly improved the manuscript. We thank S. I. Rothstein for proposing the term "effective fecundity" to distinguish cowbird eggs that are actually laid in appropriate host nests and not ejected from the total number of cowbird eggs produced by in a population.

Studies in Avian Biology No. 18:218–228, 1999.

COMMON YELLOWTHROAT BROOD PARASITISM AND NEST SUCCESS VARY WITH HOST DENSITY AND SITE CHARACTERISTICS

HILDIE SPAUTZ

Abstract. I found significant differences in the level of Brown-headed Cowbird (*Molothrus ater*) brood parasitism and nest success of Common Yellowthroats (*Geothlypis trichas*) nesting at different densities and in different habitats on the South Fork Kern River, CA. Of 149 active nests, 16% were parasitized in 1995 and 36% in 1996. Yellowthroats responded to parasitism with an increased rate of nest desertion. Parasitized clutches were significantly smaller and produced significantly fewer fledglings, but the decrease in Mayfield nest success rate was not statistically significant. There were significant differences among sites in terms of parasitism rates, predation and Mayfield nest success. Nests in an extensive cattail marsh were rarely parasitized (4–5% of nests), experienced the lowest predation rates, and had the highest nest success. Common Yellowthroat density was significantly negatively correlated with parasitism. A forward step-wise logistic regression model developed without the marsh nests included four habitat variables. A higher level of parasitism was associated with nests built near smaller trees, and with three habitat measures in a 0.008 ha circle centered on the nest: fewer vegetation hits between 2 and 2.5 m and higher percent cover of cattails and willows.

Key Words: brood parasitism, Brown-headed Cowbird, Common Yellowthroat, *Geothlypis trichas, Moluthrus ater,* riparian habitat, riparian restoration.

The Common Yellowthroat (*Geothlypis trichas*) is one of the most widely distributed and locally abundant neotropical migrant passerines (Dunn and Garrett 1997). It is also a common host of the Brown-Headed Cowbird (*Molothrus ater*) across its range (Hofslund 1957, Brown 1994). Many other small-bodied open-cup nesters are experiencing population reductions that may be due in part to a significant reduction in nesting success associated with increases in brood parasitism by the cowbird (Laymon 1987, Marvil and Cruz 1989, Böhning-Gaese et al. 1993). Some species are particularly vulnerable and rarely fledge their own young from parasitized nests (Marvil and Cruz 1989, Harris 1991). The effects of parasitism on the Common Yellowthroat are largely unknown. One subspecies, *G. t. sinuosa,* of northern California, is experiencing a decline in population size in large part due to habitat destruction, but possibly also due to brood parasitism (Hobson et al. 1985).

One objective of this study was to describe the impact of brood parasitism on the nesting success of the Common Yellowthroat. Parasitism may trigger several responses in a host, including nest desertion, burial of eggs in nest material, egg ejection, or acceptance (Clark and Robertson 1981). If an egg is accepted, there may be a reduction in the number of host young fledging due to a reduction in clutch size (Sealy 1992), further partial predation of host eggs or of young (Arcese et al. 1996), or loss of nestlings due to starvation (Marvil and Cruz 1989). I compared the occurrence of these effects in parasitized nests with that in unparasitized nests.

A second objective concerns the examination of patterns of parasitism in yellowthroats at the landscape level. Yellowthroats breed in a wide range of marsh, riparian, and adjacent upland habitats. In this study, I compared parasitism rates and nesting success of a population found in a natural riparian area, two nearby riparian restoration sites, and a marsh.

Several hypotheses have been proposed to explain the differences in brood parasitism among habitat types or sites. I will test whether parasitism rates vary among sites due to (1) differences in cowbird density, (2) differences in host density, and (3) differences in habitat structural characteristics at the scale of the nest or of the site (Clark and Robertson 1979, Larison 1996; Barber and Martin 1997; Larison et al. 1998; G. Guepel and N. Nur, unpubl. data; S. Rothstein, unpubl. data).

STUDY SITE

The study site is located within the South Fork Kern River Preserve, in Kern Co., California, at an elevation of approximately 800 m. The preserve was purchased and restored by The Nature Conservancy and is now being managed by the Audubon Society.

Five adjacent but distinct natural forest and restoration sites were studied (Fig. 1). Riverbottom site was a mature, natural cottonwood-willow riparian forest (dominants *Populus fremontii* and *Salix laevigata*), with many trees over 100 years old. Grazing occurred here historically, but is no longer permitted. Understory dominants included mulefat (*Baccharis salicifolia*), sting-

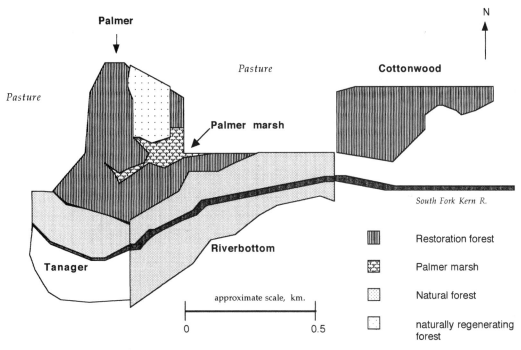

FIGURE 1.   South Fork Kern River Preserve study sites, 1995–1996.

ing nettle (*Urtica dioica holosericea*), goldenrod (*Solidago spectabilis*), and patches of cattails (*Typha angustifolia*) and tules (*Scirpus acutus*). Approximately 4 ha of the site were surveyed in 1995 and 20 ha in 1996. Yellowthroats were found in cattail marsh, near the forest edge, in open areas, and in mulefat patches, but were uncommon overall in the mature forest. Other potential cowbird hosts on Riverbottom included Song Sparrow (*Melospiza melodia*), Red-winged Blackbird (*Agelaius phoeniceus*), Yellow Warbler (*Dendroica petechia*), Willow Flycatcher (*Empidonax traillii*), Lazuli Bunting (*Passerina amoena*), Blue Grosbeak (*Guiraca caerulea*), and Yellow-breasted Chat (*Icteria virens*). The most abundant host species on Riverbottom was Song Sparrow. During the study the average density of all potential cowbird hosts was 9.3 pairs per ha.

In 1996, approximately 7 ha of Tanager natural forest site were surveyed. The habitat consisted of mature cottonwood-willow forest interspersed with small patches of cattail and tule marsh. The vegetation was similar to Riverbottom, but with a wider strip of young trees on the forest edge and a more open understory due to winter cattle grazing. Yellowthroats nested in cattail marsh, near the forest edge, in open areas, and in mulefat patches, but were uncommon overall in the mature forest, as on Riverbottom.

Other potential cowbird hosts included Song Sparrow, Red-winged Blackbird, Yellow Warbler, Willow Flycatcher, Lazuli Bunting, Blue Grosbeak, and Yellow-breasted Chat. The most abundant host species on Tanager was Song Sparrow. During the study the average density of all potential cowbird hosts was 11.5 pairs per ha.

Palmer restoration site, previously an irrigated pasture, was planted with Fremont cottonwoods and red willows in 1990. Fourteen hectares were surveyed in both years of the study. Habitat consisted of young trees with an understory of alkali rye (*Leymus triticoides*) and various non-native forbs. A narrow, mature riparian strip remained along a seasonal irrigation channel. Other potential cowbird hosts included Song Sparrow, Red-winged Blackbird, Yellow Warbler, Lazuli Bunting, Blue Grosbeak and Yellow-breasted Chat. Common Yellowthroat, Red-winged Blackbird, and Song Sparrow were all common on Palmer. During the study, the average density of all potential cowbird hosts was 5.2 pairs per ha.

Palmer marsh is surrounded on two sides by the Palmer restoration site and is fed by an adjacent irrigated pasture drainage. The entire 2 ha area was surveyed both years, with the exception of the center of the marsh, which was inaccessible due to high cattail density. The vegetation consisted primarily of cattails interspersed with rush (*Juncus* spp), sedge (*Carex* spp., *Eleocharis* spp.), and alkali rye in the drier patches. This marsh had the highest density of yellowthroats in both years of the study. The Red-winged Blackbird was the most common species in the marsh, while the yellowthroat was the next most abundant. The Song Sparrow was the only other potential cowbird host in the marsh, but was uncommon. During the study, the average density of all potential cowbird hosts (including red-wings) was 40 pairs per ha.

Cottonwood restoration site consisted of an overstory of cottonwood and willow planted in 1991. Prior to restoration it was irrigated pasture, and a thick understory of non-native forbs (e.g., *Lactuca* and *Cirsium* spp.) and grass (e.g., *Hordeum* spp.) remained in areas where canopy closure was not yet complete. There was no open water or marsh on the site. Approximately 12 hectares were surveyed both years. Here the Common Yellowthroat was the second most common species following the Song Sparrow. Other potential cowbird hosts included Red-winged Blackbird, Yellow Warbler, Lazuli Bunting, Blue Grosbeak and Yellow-breasted Chat. During the study the average density of all potential cowbird hosts was 5.9 pairs per ha.

METHODS

Common Yellowthroats were mist-netted and banded with USFWS numbered bands and a unique combination of three color-bands. Standard morphological measurements were taken (Ralph et al. 1993, Pyle et al. 1987). Locations of all yellowthroats seen or heard within the study sites were recorded in order to locate and track territories. Densities were based on independent spot-mapping efforts in May and June (IBCC 1970, Laymon et al. 1996, 1997). Locations were estimated with the aid of a permanent grid of 3-m tall white posts spaced 50 m apart.

An index of cowbird abundance was made using spot-mapping data (Laymon et al. 1997). Any data on cowbird population size taken over an extended time period would be imprecise because the population was always in flux due to trapping. However, here the spot-mapping data were treated as an index of habitat suitability and habitat use, although only for singing males.

Nests were located by observing pair behavior. Once a nest was located, its contents were monitored every 1–3 days. Nestlings were given USFWS numbered bands and a single color-band, and measured at approximately day 6. After the seventh day, we avoided approaching nests to minimize premature fledging (Hofslund 1959, Martin and Geupel 1993). We assumed a nest was successful if it contained at least one yellowthroat nestling at the last visit on or after day 7. If we visited the nest again between day 10 and day 14, and it was empty and damaged and we could not detect adults or young within 20 m of the nest, we assumed the nest had failed.

We manipulated some parasitized broods and did not include them in most analyses. Cowbird eggs in approximately half of the parasitized broods found during incubation were shaken or pierced to prevent hatching. These nests were included in prehatch calculations but were not included in any post-hatch calculations of nest success, fledglings per nest, brood size reduction, or predation. Cowbird eggs were allowed to hatch only in nests selected for a study of nestling growth rates (H. Spautz, unpubl. data). If a brood was parasitized, we usually removed the cowbird chick on the day the yellowthroat young were banded (approximately day 7). Because we did not observe parasitized broods for the entire nestling period, my success estimates of parasitized broods may be biased upward.

HABITAT MEASUREMENTS

Fifty-one habitat measurements were made at each nest. Each vegetation plot encompassed a 0.008 ha circle (radius 5 m) centered on the nest. Two 10-m long ropes were laid perpendicularly across the circle. To avoid bias on restoration plots, which were planted systematically in north-south rows, the direction in which the ropes were laid was varied by +5° for each subsequent plot measured. Most plots were measured in July or August, after yellowthroats had left their territories, to avoid disturbing a second nesting attempt. Nests were often built within 10 m of a previous attempt.

Nest measurements

The following measurements were made at each nest: (1) NESTHT: nest height; (2) PLSP: nest substrate species; (3) COVSP: nest cover species; (4) PLHT: height of nest plant; (5) percent concealment of a white disk placed in the nest, (a) CONAB: as viewed from directly above, at standing height, (b) CONST: as viewed 1 m away from a standing position, from each of the four directions (these figures were averaged), (c) CONLO: as viewed 0.5 m away from the ground, and from each of the four directions (these figures were averaged); (6) EDMIC: distance of the nest from the edge of the micropatch (the micropatch is the smallest area in the understory where a discontinuity between the nest plant and surrounding vegetation could be detected. If the nest was in a patch with structure distinctly different from the surrounding vegetation, the dimensions of that clump were used. If the nest plant was indistinguishable from the surrounding vegetation, as with most cattail marsh nests, the dimensions of the micropatch and macropatch were identical); (7) HTMIC: average height of the micropatch; (8) AREAMIC: area of the micropatch; (9) EDMAC: distance of the nest from the edge of the macropatch (the macropatch is the next larger area of structural discontinuity in which the micropatch was found); (10) HTMAC: average height of the macropatch; (11) AREAMAC: area of the macropatch.

Vegetation measurements

The following measurements were made within each nest-centered plot: (12) CANCLOS: percent canopy cover above the nest and 5 m from the center in each cardinal direction, using a monocular viewer engraved with a 10-square grid (Laymon 1988; these five values were averaged); (13) lateral foliage volume: the percentage of 50 squares at least one-half concealed on a 3 m high vertical cloth held 5 m from the nest, in each of the four cardinal directions, as viewed from the nest, (a) FOL1: between 0 and 1 m from the ground, (b) FOL2: between 1–2 m from ground, (c) FOL3: between 2–3 m from the ground (Noon 1981); (14) DNWV: distance from nest to the nearest tree or shrub; (15) SPNWV: species of nearest tree/shrub; (16) FOLNWV: foliage radius of nearest tree/shrub; (17) HTNWV: height of nearest tree/shrub; (18) DBHNWV: diameter at breast height of nearest tree/shrub estimated with a measure stick; (19) the percent cover of each of the following plant species or growth forms was estimated visually to the nearest 10%, and later categorized to one of 4 levels (0%, $0 \leq 10\%$, $10 < 50\%$, $\geq 50\%$); the species and percent cover of the two most common species of grass, annual forb and brush was also recorded: (a) TREE, (b) WILL: willow, (c) COTT: cottonwood, (d) GRASS, (e) FORB, (f) BRUSH: shrub (e.g., mulefat), (g) BARE: bare ground, (h) DEAD: dead forb, (i) CAT: cattail, (j) TULE; (20) HP0 to HP7: height profile, measured as the number of hits of vegetation (0 or 1) within 5 cm of a marked vertical pole, in each 0.5 m height category up to 3 m from the ground, each 1 m from 3 to 7 m, and 7 m and up; measured at the nest, and at 1 m intervals out from the nest in each of the four directions for a maximum number of hits of 21 per plot per unit height above the ground.

Other habitat measurements recorded for each plot included: (21) FORED: distance to closest forest edge (restoration or natural) or ecotone; (22) DISTWAT: distance to closest water when nest was active; (23) DISPAST: distance to closest pasture. When distances could not be measured in the field, estimates were made later using maps.

In addition, nests were classified as being in marsh habitat if they were built in marsh vegetation (e.g., cattails or tules) or above water. All others were considered upland nests.

DATA ANALYSIS

Nest success was calculated using a number of estimates including proportion of successful nests, number of fledglings per nest, and the Mayfield daily success rate (Mayfield 1961, 1975; Hensler and Nichols 1981). Mayfield values were compared with the Z test in Hensler (1985) on Excel 3.0.

Other tests included Pearson's χ^2, Fisher's exact P test, Spearman's rank correlation and Kruskal-Wallis one-way analysis of variance χ^2 (using H as an estimate of χ^2). Percentage data were arcsine transformed to approximate normality (Zar 1984). Distance data (e.g., distance to pasture) were log-transformed. Except where noted otherwise, analyses included data from only one randomly chosen nesting attempt per pair per year.

Univariate logistic regressions were performed using each habitat variable as the independent variable and presence or absence of parasitism as the dependent variable. No interaction variables were tested. A multivariate logistic regression model was then developed using a forward stepwise method. All variables with significant Wald's Z statistics (at the level of $P < 0.20$) in the univariate models were added sequentially beginning with the variable with the highest significance. A variable was then removed if its addition decreased the fit of the model (i.e., log-likelihood ratio and Pearson's χ^2 goodness of fit statistics), and if its Wald's Z statistic was not significant at $P < 0.05$ (Hosmer and Lemshow 1989). To verify the validity of the model, the process was repeated using a backward stepwise method, beginning with a model containing all variables with significant Wald's Z statistics (at $P < 0.20$) in the univariate models. Variables with the largest P-values were sequentially removed until those that remained were significant at $P < 0.05$ and the fit of the model was significant.

Analyses were performed with STATA release 5 (Stata Corporation 1997) or MINITAB release 8 (Minitab, Inc. 1991) for Macintosh.

RESULTS

EFFECTS OF PARASITISM

In 1995, 16% of all yellowthroat nests were parasitized. In 1996, in spite of increasing cowbird trapping efforts, the parasitism rate increased significantly to 36% ($\chi^2 = 7.42$, df = 1; $P = 0.006$). Although the parasitism rate was higher in 1996, the effects of parasitism were

TABLE 1. EFFECTS OF PARASITISM ON THE COMMON YELLOWTHROAT AT THE SOUTH FORK KERN RIVER STUDY SITE, 1995–1996

	Proportion unparasitized nests	N	Proportion parasitized nests	N	χ^2 (df = 1)	P
Behavioral response						
Nest deserted	0.03	102	0.12	42		0.041[a]
Eggs buried in bottom of nest	0	102	0	42	0	1.000
Reduction in clutch/brood size						
Eggs removed/partial predation clutch[b]	0.08	37	0.47	23	12.51	0.000
Host egg(s) remain unhatched	0.20	50	0.50	20	6.30	0.012
Nestlings lost/partial predation[c]	0.30	50	0.19	15	0.773	0.379
Loss of entire brood to predation	0.32	94	0.50	42	3.37	0.066

[a] Fisher's exact test.
[b] Nests found on or before 6th day of incubation.
[c] Nests found before day hatched; parasitized broods considered are only those in which a cowbird hatched.

generally not significantly different between years, so the years were pooled for all analyses, except where noted.

Yellowthroats deserted 12% of parasitized nests but only 3% of unparasitized nests, a significantly lower rate (Table 1). However, there was no evidence that this population of the species reacts to parasitism by burying cowbird eggs in the bottom of the nest as Yellow Warblers do (Clark and Robertson 1981).

Parasitism had a variety of other significant effects that contributed to an overall decrease in brood size (Table 1). Yellowthroat eggs vanished due to partial predation or removal by parents significantly more often from parasitized than unparasitized nests. The rate for parasitized nests is probably an underestimate, since it includes nests that were found up to the sixth day of incubation and some earlier removals may have been missed. Other studies indicate that cowbirds often remove a host egg for each egg laid (Sealy 1992). Significantly more yellowthroat eggs did not hatch in parasitized nests than in unparasitized nests (Table 1). Unhatched eggs were rarely removed during the nestling stage.

In only four nests (11% of parasitized nests) were cowbird eggs laid after incubation of the yellowthroat eggs had begun. None of these cowbird eggs hatched. Multiple parasitism was uncommon; only four nests were found with more than one cowbird egg or nestling.

The average size of unparasitized clutches was significantly larger in 1995 (4.0 eggs) than in 1996 (3.47; Wilcoxon rank-sum Z = 2.19. df = 33, P = 0.03). The average size of parasitized clutches was smaller in 1995 (2.8 eggs) than in 1996 (3.08), but the difference was not statistically significant (Z = 0.00, df = 18, P = 1.0). There was a large clutch reduction due to parasitism when years were considered separately, but the reduction was not statistically significant

(1995: Z = 1.75, df = 20, P = 0.08; 1996: Z = 1.11, df = 30, P = 0.27). However, when years were pooled to increase the sample size, the reduction in clutch size from an average of 3.71 to 3.00 eggs per nest was significant (Z = 2.17, df = 57, P = 0.03).

After hatching, parasitized broods were no more likely to experience a reduction in size due to partial predation or nestling starvation than were unparasitized broods; in fact, fewer young disappeared from parasitized nests than from unparasitized nests (Table 1). This was unexpected. However, 50% of parasitized broods were entirely lost to predators, whereas only 32% of unparasitized broods were depredated, although the difference was marginally significant (Table 1).

All of these factors had the effect of reducing the average number of host young fledging from nests of parasitized broods. There were significantly fewer fledglings on average from successful unparasitized nests in 1996 (3.06 young) than in 1995 (3.59 young; Z = 2.285, df = 56, P = 0.022). However, there was no statistically significant difference between years for successful parasitized nests (1995: 1.67; 1996: 1.91; Z = 0.326, df = 12, P = 0.744). In 1995 an average of two fewer young fledged from parasitized broods than unparasitized broods, while in 1996 the average was only one fewer host young. In both years the reduction in the number of young fledging per successful nest due to parasitism was significant (1995: Z = 2.45, df = 20; P = 0.014; 1996: Z = 2.50, df = 40, P = 0.009).

In 1995, parasitized nests had a lower Mayfield nest success rate than unparasitized nests, but the difference was not statistically significant (Z = 1.764, df = 60, P = 0.083; Table 2). The difference in 1996 was less pronounced (Z = 1.090, df = 77, P = 0.278). The difference in success between years was low enough for un-

TABLE 2. SUCCESS OF PARASITIZED AND UNPARASITIZED COMMON YELLOWTHROAT NESTS AT THE SOUTH FORK KERN RIVER STUDY SITE, 1995–1996

		Pre-hatch daily nest survival rate[a]	N	Post-hatch daily nest survival rate[a]	N	Full nesting period success rate (SD)	N	Proportion of nests successful[c]	N
Unparasitized	1995	0.974	34	0.944	45	0.435 (0.087)	51	0.62	
	1996	0.963	36	0.960	39	0.422 (0.087)	49	0.69	
	pooled	0.968	70	0.949	84	0.423 (0.060)	100	0.65	106
Parasitized[b]	1995	0.939	9	0.875	5	0.143 (0.141)	11	0.40	
	1996	0.952	24	0.931	17	0.283 (0.094)	30	0.42	
	pooled	0.949	33	0.922	22	0.253 (0.079)	41	0.43	42

[a] Mayfield (1961, 1975); pre-hatch period: 14 days = laying (2 days) + incubation (12 days); post-hatch period: 8 days.
[b] Post-hatch includes only nests in which the cowbird hatched.
[c] Number of successful nests per all nests.

parasitized and for parasitized nests to warrant pooling across years (parasitized: $Z = 0.015$, df $= 38$, $P = 0.988$; unparasitized: $Z = 0.103$, df $= 98$, $P = 0.917$). However, when years were pooled, the difference was large but still not quite statistically significant ($Z = 1.710$, df $= 139$, $P = 0.089$).

Overall, failures of unparasitized nests were attributable to predation (81% of losses), abandonment (5%), and unknown factors (14%). Failures of parasitized nests were due to predation (65% of losses), loss of all host young (21%), and abandonment (13%).

HABITAT EFFECTS

In every measure of nest success, and in terms of predation and parasitism, Palmer marsh nests were always the most successful, while Cottonwood or natural forest nests were the least successful. The sites could be grouped and habitat compared in several different ways. For most analyses, sites were not grouped.

Palmer marsh had the highest Mayfield nest success rate for 1995 and 1996 pooled (Table 3). This was significantly higher than the success of restoration upland nests, including those on adjacent Palmer field ($Z = 3.708$, df $= 110$, $P <$

0.00). Palmer upland nests were more successful than Cottonwood nests although the difference was not statistically significant ($Z = 1.022$, df $= 64$, $P = 0.311$). Palmer marsh nests were also significantly more successful than those in the natural forest marsh areas ($Z = 3.197$, df $= 41$, $P = 0.003$). Although natural forest upland nests were slightly more successful than restoration upland nests, the difference was not significant ($Z = 0.572$, df $= 81$, $P = 0.569$). In the natural forest sites, upland nests were slightly more successful than marsh nests, although sample sizes were small and the difference was not significant ($Z = 0.523$, df $= 26$, $P = 0.605$). The difference in success between the two natural forest sites, Tanager and Riverbottom, was not statistically significant ($Z = 0.752$, df $= 28$, $P = 0.458$).

The differences in nest success measures between sites were due primarily to variations in parasitism and predation rates (Table 4). Parasitism rates in 1995 did not differ significantly between sites although there was a large difference between Palmer marsh and Riverbottom. In 1996, the contrast between sites was statistically significant, with Riverbottom's parasitism rate increasing to 69%. The difference in the para-

TABLE 3. COMMON YELLOWTHROAT NEST SUCCESS AT THE SOUTH FORK KERN RIVER STUDY SITE, 1995–1996

	Pre-hatch daily nest survival rate[a]	N	Post-hatch daily nest survival rate[a]	N	Mayfield full nesting period success rate (SD)	N	Proportion of nests successful[b]	N
Palmer Marsh	0.980	33	0.982	40	0.652 (0.095)	42	0.82	45
Restoration Upland-pooled	0.953	46	0.909	47	0.240 (0.059)	63	0.45	69
Palmer	0.961	19	0.929	22	0.317 (0.108)	28	0.55	19
Cottonwood	0.949	29	0.891	27	0.189 (0.064)	38	0.38	20
Natural Forest Marsh	0.952	10	0.906	8	0.229 (0.135)	12	0.50	14
Natural Forest Upland	0.950	11	0.956	13	0.339 (0.161)	16	0.60	20
Riverbottom	0.962	14	0.899	17	0.249 (0.114)	20	0.50	20
Tanager	0.938	8	1.00	6	0.411 (0.183)	10	0.60	13

[a] Mayfield (1961, 1975); pre-hatch period: 14 days = laying (2 days) + incubation (12 days); post-hatch period: 8 days.
[b] Number of successful nests per all nests.

TABLE 4. PARASITISM AND PREDATION OF COMMON YELLOWTHROAT NESTS ON THE SOUTH FORK KERN RIVER SITE, 1995–1996

	Parasitism rate[a] (N)		Predation rate[a] (N)		Predation rate of parasitized nests[a] (N)	
	1995	1996	1995	1996	Unparasitized	Parasitized
Palmer Marsh	0.05 (21)	0.04 (24)	0.14 (21)	0.08 (24)	0.12 (42)	0 (3)
Restoration Upland— Palmer	0.29 (14)	0.53 (15)	0.36 (14)	0.35 (15)	0.35 (17)	0.50 (12)
Restoration Upland— Cottonwood	0.15 (20)	0.40 (20)	0.47 (15)	0.60 (20)	0.48 (29)	0.45 (11)
Natural Forest— Riverbottom	0.25 (7)	0.69 (13)	0.43 (7)	0.46 (13)	0.33 (9)	0.54 (11)
Natural Forest— Tanager		0.38 (13)		0.15 (13)	0.25 (8)	0 (5)
Site Comparison	$\chi^2 = 2.52$ df = 3 P = 0.47	$\chi^2 = 19.46$ df = 4 P = 0.001	$\chi^2 = 3.51$ df = 3 P = 0.32	$\chi^2 = 16.98$ df = 4 P = 0.002	$\chi^2 = 9.2$ df = 4 P = 0.055	$\chi^2 = 5.43$ df = 3 P = 0.143
All sites pooled	0.16 (63)	0.36 (85)	0.29 (63)	0.33 (85)	0.32 (94)	0.50 (42)

[a] Based on proportion of all nests depredated or parasitized.

sitism rates between years was significant only for Riverbottom.

In 1995, the difference between sites in predation rates was not statistically significant (Table 4). In 1996, however, predation rates were lower in Palmer marsh and higher in Cottonwood and the difference between sites was statistically significant. Predation rates did not differ significantly between years for any site (Pearson's χ^2, df = 1, P > 0.05).

The predation rate of parasitized and unparasitized nests was compared on a site-by-site basis. For no site was there a consistent trend in the relationship between predation and parasitism (Table 4). When years were pooled there was no statistically significant difference between sites in terms of predation rate of parasitized nests ($\chi^2 = 5.43$, df = 3, P = 0.143). For unparasitized nests, the difference in predation rates across sites was almost statistically significant ($\chi^2 = 9.2$, df = 4, P = 0.055).

There was no statistically significant difference among sites in terms of fledglings per successful nest, either for parasitized or unparasiti-

zed nests (unparasitized: Kruskal-Wallis one-way ANOVA $\chi^2 = 2.03$, df = 4, P = 0.73; parasitized: Kruskal-Wallis one-way ANOVA $\chi^2 = 3.07$, df = 3, P = 0.38; there were no independent parasitized Palmer marsh nests in the sample).

TESTS OF HYPOTHESES EXPLAINING DIFFERENCES IN PARASITISM RATES

Brown-headed Cowbird density

This hypothesis predicts that there should be a higher rate of brood parasitism in areas where cowbirds are most abundant. In 1996 there were 5 datapoints while in 1995 there were only 4. Only 1996 data were used in a correlation of parasitism with cowbird density (and for the host density analysis below).

Cowbirds were most common on Tanager, which was approximately 1 km from the nearest trap (Table 5). The second highest cowbird density was in Palmer marsh, which is less than 1 km from a trap, but is adjacent to pasture. This is also the site with the lowest incidence of par-

TABLE 5. COMMON YELLOWTHROAT AND BROWN-HEADED COWBIRD DENSITY AT THE SOUTH FORK KERN RIVER SITE, 1995–1996

	Area 1996 (1995) (ha)	Common Yellowthroat density (pairs/ha)		Brown-headed Cowbird density (pairs/ha)		Ratio Yellowthroat : Cowbird	
		1995	1996	1995	1996	1995	1996
Palmer Marsh	2 (2)	10	10	0	0.25	very large	40.0
Restoration Upland—Palmer	14 (14)	1.7	1.7	0.14	0.21	12.1	8.1
Restoration Upland—Cottonwood	12 (12)	2.1	1.7	0.16	0.17	13.1	10.0
Natural Forest—Riverbottom	20 (4)	1.25	1	0.25	0.15	5.0	4.0
Natural Forest—Tanager	7	—	3	—	0.43	—	7.0

TABLE 6. LOGISTIC REGRESSION OF PROBABILITY OF PARASITISM ON NEST-SITE SCALE VEGETATION CHARACTERISTICS, COMMON YELLOWTHROAT, SOUTH FORK KERN RIVER, 1995–1996[a]

Habitat variable	Regression coefficient	Odds ratio	Wald's Z	P
Constant	0.743		1.153	0.249
Height of nearest tree or shrub	−0.232	0.792	−2.183	0.029
Measurements in 0.008 ha nest-centered plot				
number of vegetation hits 2 to 2.5 m. from ground	−0.230	0.794	−2.635	0.008
percent cover category—willows	0.751	2.120	2.750	0.006
percent cover category—cattails	1.085	2.96	2.604	0.009

Notes: Log-likelihood ratio χ^2 = 24.84, df = 4, P < 0.001 (difference between model with and without vegetation variables). Fit: Pearsons χ^2 = 96.44, df = 77, P = 0.066.
[a] Palmer marsh nests omitted

asitism. The correlation was negative, but not statistically significant (Spearman's rank correlation rho = −0.08, P = 0.10). G. Geupel and N. Nur (unpubl. data) also observed a significant negative relationship between the mean number of cowbirds detected from point counts and the incidence of parasitism in the Common Yellowthroat.

Host density

Host density was significantly negatively associated with parasitism rate (Spearman's rank correlation rho = − 0.97, P = 0.005; Table 5). Palmer marsh, which had the highest yellowthroat density, had the lowest parasitism rate. Riverbottom, which had the lowest yellowthroat density, had the highest parasitism rate.

Habitat characteristics

Habitat characteristics of parasitized nests were compared with those of unparasitized nests using univariate logistic regression. Because there were so few parasitized nests in Palmer marsh, the site "Palmer marsh" predicted the absence of parasitism perfectly. Variables with significant Wald's Z statistics (P < 0.05) in models including Palmer marsh nests included plant height (PLHT), species of nearest woody vegetation (SPNWV), distance to nearest woody vegetation (DNWV), height of nearest woody vegetation (HTNWV), foliage radius on nearest woody vegetation (FOLNWV), foliage density between 1–2 m (FOL2), height profile between 1–1.5 m (HP10), 1.5–2 m (HP15), and 2–2.5 m (HP20), percent cover of willows (WILL), percent cover *Juncus* (JUNC), percent cover annual forb (FORB), percent cover *Melilotus* spp. (MELO), percent cover mulefat (MULE), percent cover *Hordeum* (HOR), percent cover goldenrod (GOLD) and percent cover cattails (CAT). The analyses were then performed without Palmer marsh nest data. Significant univariate models then included the variables HTNWV, HP20, and MULE.

A final multivariate logistic model to predict parasitism based on habitat variables was developed without Palmer marsh nests (Table 6). The best fitting model contained four significant habitat variables. Coefficients associated with the height of the nearest tree or shrub (HTNWV) and the number of hits of vegetation from 2 to 2.5 m from the ground (HP20) were negative. Coefficients associated with the percent cover of willow (WILL) and cattails (CAT) were positive. This means that outside Palmer marsh, a higher rate of parasitism is associated with shorter trees close to the nest, sparser vegetation in the area around the nest between 2 and 2.5 m above the ground and a higher percent cover of cattails and willows.

DISCUSSION

It is important to note that Brown-headed Cowbirds are being trapped along the South Fork Kern River in an effort to encourage the recovery of a small population of the endangered Southwestern Willow Flycatcher (*Empidonax traillii extimus*; Whitfield and Enos 1996, Whitfield et al. *this volume*). Thus the brood parasitism patterns in this study may differ from patterns found in regions without artificial cowbird population regulation.

Hofslund (1957) found that 8% of parasitized Common Yellowthroat nests were deserted, but the rate for unparasitized nests was not given. Stewart's (1953) desertion rate was 18% overall. My data indicate that parasitism is associated with increased nest desertion rates, a common reaction to parasitism across species (e.g., Graham 1988). Sample sizes are small, however, and I have no data to indicate whether the trigger for desertion was the removal of a yellowthroat egg, the appearance of a foreign egg, a clutch size change, or disturbance by a cowbird at the nest (Hill and Sealy 1994). Most desertions were either early in the season, or involved experienced females (which I knew had bred the previous year). I found no evidence of cowbird egg burial in the 149 nests examined. Acceptance of cowbird eggs seems to be the most common reaction for the South Fork Kern River population

Clutch sizes were smaller in parasitized nests. In 1995, the reduction was approximately 1.2 eggs per nest. In 1996 however, the loss was less than 0.5 egg per nest when clutch sizes were smaller overall. This confirms that cowbirds do not always remove a host egg when they parasitize a brood (Hofslund 1957, Marvil and Cruz 1989, Sealy 1992).

In about half the parasitized nests studied, a yellowthroat egg disappeared during incubation, in addition to the egg often initially removed by a cowbird during laying. It is unknown whether these losses were due to further removal by cowbirds, by some other predator, or by the parent because they were damaged. Arcese et al. (1996) found a positive correlation between parasitism rates and rates of nest failures due to partial predation, but the success of parasitized broods was higher due to defense of laying areas by female cowbirds. On the Kern River, cowbirds are removed beginning in May (Whitfield et al. *this volume*), and this may cause a disruption in cowbird territorial defense. Thus rates of partial predation by cowbirds should theoretically be high in prime cowbird laying habitat as new females move into the area to replace those removed by trapping.

The significant reduction in the number of host young fledging from parasitized nests was expected. In both 1995 and 1996, there were approximately 1.5 fewer fledglings from successful parasitized broods than from unparasitized broods. In all cases in which a cowbird hatched, it hatched one day before the host young. In 12% of parasitized nests only a cowbird egg (3 nests) or young (2 nests) remained, due to removal of host eggs or young. The sample size is small, in part because I addled approximately half of the cowbird eggs I found, and these nests were not included in any post-hatch measures.

In terms of reduction in host productivity, brood parasitism appears to have a lower impact on Common Yellowthroats than it does on some other small hosts, e.g., vireos and flycatchers (Marvil and Cruz 1989, Briskie et al. 1990), but similar to the impact on some other warblers (Weatherhead 1989, Petit 1991). However, the average reduction in the number of fledglings by 1.5 probably has a significant impact on the population growth rate in areas with high parasitism rates (Trail and Baptista 1993). More information is needed on yellowthroat adult and juvenile mortality before the impact of parasitism on the population dynamics of the species can be fully understood.

The effect of parasitism on host fledging rates is not entirely conclusive due to the removal of cowbird nestlings by the seventh day. It is possible that a cowbird's impact on a yellowthroat nestmate is highest during the final days of the nestling period and that fewer host young fledge from parasitized nests than I have estimated. Cowbirds were allowed to fledge from only 2 nests studied, and all host young were assumed to have also fledged successfully from both.

Another factor that may contribute to the yellowthroat's ability to fledge its own young along with a cowbird is that the cowbird nestling period is longer than that of the yellowthroat. Cowbirds fledge at 10–11 days (Scott 1979) whereas yellowthroats fledge between 8–10 days (H. Spautz, pers. obs.). Assuming the cowbird hatches one day before the yellowthroats, the yellowthroat young may commonly fledge one day before the cowbird. In one nest that contained one cowbird and one yellowthroat, the yellowthroat did in fact fledge first. No other nests were observed often enough to witness this phenomenon. If yellowthroats are commonly able to fledge first, this opportunity to receive exclusive parental care from one parent may make a significant difference in their survivorship, and may lessen the impact of parasitism.

The effects of parasitism did not vary significantly across sites. The number of young fledging from parasitized nests was not significantly different among sites. Palmer marsh, which had the lowest rates of parasitism and predation, had no successful parasitized nests, and so was not included in the analysis.

I have offered several possible explanations for the large differences in parasitism rates between sites, in particular for the very low rate in Palmer marsh. In the marsh, the density of yellowthroats was highest, and nest-site characteristics were significantly different from other sites. I have shown that there was a strong negative correlation between yellowthroat density and parasitism. Two habitat factors associated with marsh nests (i.e., taller trees and more vegetation hits between 2 and 2.5 m) were associated with low rates of parasitism outside Palmer marsh. A high percent cover of cattails was also characteristic of Palmer marsh nests but was associated with higher parasitism rates outside the marsh. This latter point may indicate that cowbirds actually use this habitat characteristic as a cue, but that in a large contiguous marsh like Palmer, other factors may prevent or discourage parasitism.

If cowbirds parasitize yellowthroats less often in the marsh due to the higher population density, several explanations are possible. At high host densities, there may be a swamping effect

(S. Rothstein, unpubl. data; Freeman et al. 1990). In some other systems, parasitism rates are highest where densities of all potential hosts are highest (Barber and Martin 1997). Most first nesting attempts in Palmer marsh occurred within a two-week time span in 1996 (April 23 to May 5), and during a later three-week span on Cottonwood and Riverbottom (May 1 and May 21; H. Spautz, unpubl. data). The earliest first egg dates were in Palmer marsh because most of the first territories to be occupied when the first birds arrive in spring are there. The early nesting in Palmer marsh coincided with the start of Red-winged Blackbird nesting in 1995 and 1996. However, marsh pairs usually had two successful broods, and the second usually began after the red-wings had finished breeding. Second nests were not parasitized any more often than first attempts.

At higher densities, yellowthroats may be more likely to hear neighbors' warning calls when cowbirds are present, and they may be less likely to reveal nest locations. Notoriously well-concealed yellowthroat nests are difficult for humans to find in dense homogeneous cattail stands, although there is no evidence that cowbirds are deterred. This may also be an explanation for the reduced predation rate in the marsh. Red-winged Blackbirds densities are also higher in Palmer marsh than in any of the other sites. Clark and Robertson (1979) showed that Yellow Warbler parasitism rates are lowest in high density red-wing habitat. It is likely that the red-wings in the South Fork Kern River area offer the same benefits to yellowthroats. Although elsewhere red-wings are common cowbird hosts, no parasitized red-wing nests have been discovered in the study area either in marsh or sparsely populated upland habitat (S. Laymon, pers. comm.). Red-wing nests have not yet been systematically studied in the area but others in the Southwest have found that they are often not preferred hosts (S. Rothstein, pers. comm.). Thus cowbirds may be deterred from entering the marsh by blackbirds more than in other regions where blackbirds are preferred hosts.

The Song Sparrow is the most abundant species in most parts of the riparian forest along the river, and in restoration sites, and it is probably the most common and preferred cowbird host. Sparrow densities are lowest in Palmer marsh (Laymon et al. 1996, 1997). In 1996, 16% of Song Sparrow nests in Cottonwood and 15% in Riverbottom were parasitized (sparrows were not studied in Tanager or in Palmer marsh or upland areas; C. Strong, unpubl. data). These rates were lower than the rates I report here for yellowthroats during 1996. The highest parasitism rates I found were in Riverbottom and Cottonwood. The highest density of all potential cowbird host species combined (primarily the Song Sparrow) was 11.5 pairs per ha on Tanager and 9.3 pairs per ha on Riverbottom in 1996 (Laymon et al. 1996). Cottonwood's density was 5.9 pairs per ha. The densities were similar both years. A positive relationship between Song Sparrow density and parasitism rates for all hosts would be expected. Further study is needed to determine the relationship between parasitism and host density at the community level on the South Fork Kern River.

Another alternative explanation for differences in parasitism rates among sites is the habitat hypothesis. Some structural aspect(s) of dense cattail marshes may discourage parasitism. Nest height (Hahn and Hatfield 1995, Briskie et al. 1990), nest concealment, canopy cover, vegetation density (Larison 1996, 1997), and distance to forest edge (Gates and Gysel 1978) have been found (or predicted) to be related to high parasitism rates. Other studies have found no significant differences in habitat variables between parasitized and unparasitized nests (Barber and Martin 1997).

In this study, Palmer marsh nests, which were almost exclusively built in cattails, were parasitized so seldom that the dummy variable associated with the site predicted the absence of parasitism perfectly in a univariate logistic regression analysis. The multivariate logistic regression model developed without these marsh nests contains several non-intuitive relationships. The negative relationship between parasitism and vegetation hits in the 2 to 2.5 m height range is expected and echoes Larison's (1996, 1997) results. Since yellowthroat nests are usually built no higher than 0.5 m above the ground and are usually well-concealed, the cowbird search strategy probably works best in areas which are relatively open around the nest.

There was also a negative relationship between the height of the tree or shrub closest to the nest and the probability of parasitism. Smaller trees may provide more optimum perches for cowbirds. Nest plots with a higher percent cover of willows also had a higher predicted parasitism rate. The absence of willows or any other tree may make nest observation by cowbirds difficult (Freeman et al. 1990). The positive relationship between percent cover of cattails and the probability of parasitism was unexpected. This calls into question the hypothesis that cowbirds are deterred from parasitizing yellowthroat nests in the cattail marsh due to the structure of cattails alone. There were few very dense cattails stands in the natural forest, however. Most of the stands are small, sparse, and surrounded by or completely under the canopy of ancient trees. The nests found in most of these stands were often poorly concealed. That factor, combined with the abundance of other potential hosts and the fact that red-wing densities are very low in the natural forest, may combine to make yellow-throats in the smaller, natural marsh areas prime hosts.

The explanation for the low parasitism and predation rates on Palmer marsh nests is probably a combination of several factors. Habitat structural characteristics and high densities of both yellowthroats and Red-winged Blackbirds may deter cowbirds (and predators) from searching for yellowthroat nests. An ideal extension of this study would include samples of nests from other extensive cattail marshes in the area. It is unknown if the low parasitism rate found in Palmer marsh is characteristic of other marsh sites along the South Fork Kern River or in other parts of the Common Yellowthroat's range. If it is, my recommendations for cowbird management would include maintenance of larger tracts of marsh rather than small fragmented stands. The optimum habitat for Common Yellowthroats on the South Fork Kern River appears to be extensive freshwater marsh, rather than the natural mosaic of marsh and upland that is found now in the narrow riparian zone. Of the sites studied, Palmer marsh probably contains a source subpopulation. Free from brood parasites and predation, recruitment in Palmer marsh is very high. Most of the birds banded as nestlings in 1995 and 1996 and seen the following year were hatched in the Palmer marsh.

One goal of this study was to compare the breeding success of Common Yellowthroats nesting in riparian restoration areas with those using natural habitat. Densities in the natural forest were generally very low, and sample sizes small. I cannot generalize that yellowthroats nesting in restoration sites have a different rate of nest success than those in natural sites. The Mayfield success rate of nests in natural upland sites was higher than in restoration upland sites, but not significantly so. Natural forest nests were significantly less successful than Palmer marsh, which is not a natural site. It is surrounded by pasture and the small restoration trees of Palmer upland on three sides, and a naturally regenerating forest on the fourth. The highest parasitism rate for any of the sites I studied was in Riverbottom, a natural site. Thus, I cannot make a definitive statement at this time as to the relative quality of restoration sites vs. natural forest as Common Yellowthroat habitat.

A more complete understanding of any cowbird-host relationship requires a community-level perspective (Clark and Robertson 1979, Barber and Martin 1997). Common Yellowthroats and Song Sparrows are the most abundant cowbird hosts along the South Fork Kern River. Efforts to decrease parasitism pressure on the rarer and more vulnerable host, the Southwestern Willow Flycatcher (Whitfield et al. *this volume*), may become even more effective when the community level dynamics are more completely understood.

ACKNOWLEDGMENTS

Special thanks to S. Laymon and P. Williams for their guidance throughout the study. R. Tollefson, South Fork Kern River Preserve manager, gave me access to the site. Kern River Research Center staff provided logistic support, research advice, and equipment. Thanks to C. Hahn and two anonymous reviewers for helpful comments on the manuscript. B. Larison and J. Uyehara gave valuable advice on methods and the manuscript. Many people helped in the field, especially M. Tarre, N. Kogut, D. LaBerteau, M. Thomey, S. Hubbard, B. McAlexander, C. Strong and S. Rowe. R. Tollefson, M. Whitfield, and M. Halterman provided housing. Funding was provided by a GAANN fellowship from the US Department of Education through San Francisco State University.

Studies in Avian Biology No. 18:229–234, 1999.

COWBIRD REMOVAL PROGRAMS AS ECOLOGICAL EXPERIMENTS: MEASURING COMMUNITY-WIDE IMPACTS OF NEST PARASITISM AND PREDATION

KRISTA L. DE GROOT, JAMES N. M. SMITH, AND MARY J. TAITT

Abstract. Removal of Brown-headed Cowbirds (*Molothrus ater*) has been increasingly employed as a management tool for the protection of songbirds. Removal programs are ecological experiments that can yield information on the population and community impacts of cowbird parasitism. We illustrate this point with two examples. First, we used an existing cowbird removal program in Michigan to test the hypothesis that cowbirds alter the composition of host communities through their parasitic activities. We compared songbird abundance and species composition in areas where cowbirds had been removed for 5–11 years to carefully matched habitats where there had been no recent cowbird removal. As expected, communities at cowbird removal sites had a higher percentage of suitable hosts in the community relative to control sites >5 km from cowbird traps. Second, we used cowbird removal to test the hypothesis that cowbirds behave as nest predators. We removed cowbirds over two years from a site in British Columbia where Song Sparrows (*Melospiza melodia*) had experienced intense cowbird parasitism and frequent nest failure. Failure rates of sparrow nests declined sharply after cowbird removal, but remained high at nearby reference sites without removals. Both approaches suggest that cowbirds have more profound effects on songbirds at the community and population levels than is currently recognized. Removal programs are a relatively untapped source for improving our understanding of cowbird biology.

Key Words: brood parasitism, cowbird removal, *Melospiza melodia*, *Molothrus ater*, nest predation, removal experiments, suitable hosts.

There has been considerable recent concern that the brood-parasitic activities of Brown-headed Cowbirds (*Molothrus ater*) are contributing to declines of endangered or threatened songbird populations (e.g., Robinson et al 1995a,b) and to poor health of songbird populations and communities in general (Terborgh 1989). Because cowbirds are abundant host generalists (Lowther 1993, 1995, Robinson et al. 1995a), they have the potential to generate strong impacts on preferred hosts and to threaten particular populations with extinction (Robinson et al. 1995a). Although the range expansion of the Brown-headed Cowbird has slowed (Lowther 1993, Rothstein 1994), and its numbers are actually declining in many areas (Peterjohn et al. in press, Wiedenfeld in press), Shiny (*M. bonariensis*) and Bronzed cowbirds (*M. aeneus*) are still extending their ranges and threatening new host populations and communities (Post et al. 1993, Lowther 1995). Finally, even constant or declining numbers of cowbirds might have strong ecological effects when combined with increasing habitat loss and degradation.

To make strong inferences about how cowbirds affect host populations and communities, it is desirable to do controlled experiments that are replicated across several geographical locations. Constraints on budgets and personnel have so far precluded research of this type. The two largest costs involved in such research are: (1) the removal of cowbirds so that large areas with fewer cowbirds may be compared with similar,

but unmanipulated areas; and (2) the costs of monitoring the numbers and breeding success of songbirds on experimental and control areas.

There is, however, a potential solution to the high costs of experimental manipulation of cowbird abundance. Cowbird removal on a landscape scale is already in progress in the form of cowbird control programs. Cowbird control figures prominently in the management of four endangered taxa: the Kirtland's Warbler (*Dendroica kirtlandii*), the Least Bell's Vireo (*Vireo bellii pusillus*), the Southwestern Willow Flycatcher (*Empidonax traillii extimus*), and the Black-capped Vireo (*V. atricapillus*) (Robinson et al. 1995a).

As a result of concerns about impacts of cowbirds on other songbird populations, extensive cowbird removal programs are becoming an increasingly common management practice in the U.S. (Robinson et al. 1995a, Kepler et al. 1996). There is general agreement that cowbird removal has been an appropriate tool for protecting populations of endangered species (but see Robinson et al. 1995a). However, Rothstein and Cook (in press), have noted that some recent cowbird control operations are founded on the tenuous idea that, if cowbird removal works in specific cases, it is generally an appropriate management tool. It is far from clear that cowbird parasitism has been a major contributor to population declines in songbirds (Peterjohn et al. in press, Wiedenfeld in press), despite the publicity accorded such claims (Terborgh 1989,

Holmes 1993). It is therefore important to test the assumption that cowbirds are a significant general conservation concern, as well as a potentially serious local concern.

Over one million dollars of federal and state funds is spent annually on cowbird control programs in California alone (S. I. Rothstein pers. comm.). Therefore, it is likely that several million dollars are spent annually on cowbird control across the U.S. With such a significant allotment of conservation dollars to cowbird control, we believe that managers and researchers have a duty to collaborate to gain as much information as possible from a management action that can absorb much of a regional conservation budget.

Viewing cowbird removal programs as ecological experiments permits fruitful investigation into several areas of cowbird biology. Our aim in this paper is to illustrate the use of removal programs through two examples that explore (1) the effects of cowbirds on host communities, and (2) the mechanisms of parasite/host interactions. Although these two studies were conducted at different spatial and temporal scales, they both employed cowbird removal as an experimental tool. Hereafter, we refer to cowbird trapping as "cowbird removal" and restrict use of the term "control" to the experimental sense, i.e., reference sites that do not receive the experimental treatment (cowbird removal).

I. EFFECTS OF LONG-TERM COWBIRD REMOVAL ON HOST COMMUNITY COMPOSITION

Cowbird pressure on suitable host species may reduce abundance of suitable host populations relative to the abundance of host species with which the cowbird does not interact strongly, e.g., species that have evolved egg ejection (Rothstein 1975a). As cowbirds are host generalists, they can have strong effects on a number of preferred hosts without negative feedback on their own numbers (Robinson et al. 1995a). If several host species are affected, cowbird pressure may eventually change the composition of entire songbird communities. One prediction of the hypothesis that cowbirds have significant effects on host communities is that suitable hosts will make up a larger percentage of songbird individuals in areas where cowbirds have been removed on a long-term basis compared to areas in similar habitat where cowbird densities are unmanipulated. Few studies of cowbird biology to date have examined the host community as a whole (but see Peck and James 1987, Strausberger and Ashley 1997) and none, to our knowledge, have conducted a search for such patterns. We now use a cowbird removal program as a

treatment in a community-wide experiment to test this prediction.

EFFECTS OF COWBIRD REMOVAL ON SONGBIRD COMMUNITIES IN JACK-PINE HABITAT

One of us (KD) conducted a study in the jack-pine (*Pinus banksiana*) ecosystem of northern lower Michigan, where cowbirds have been removed since 1972 in an effort to protect the Kirtland's Warbler. Cowbird traps are patchily distributed across a 19,200 km² region near breeding sites used by the warblers. Since the distribution of the warblers is dynamic, the location of traps shifts over periods of a few years. However, many local areas have been trapped consistently for 5–11 years. Details of cowbird removal procedures on the breeding grounds of the Kirtland's Warbler are given in DeCapita (in press) and Kelly and DeCapita (1982).

Unlimited radius point counts of 8 min duration were performed in 1996 at ten cowbird removal sites where cowbird trapping had been conducted for 5–11 years, and at ten control sites in similar-aged jack pine habitat that were >5 km from cowbird traps (total number of sites censused = 20). Control sites were in areas that had not experienced cowbird removal for at least five years. All control areas were chosen according to detailed survey maps followed by extensive ground-truthing to match the early successional jack pine forests of removal sites. Further detailed habitat measurements confirmed that density and composition of vegetation were similar at removal and control sites (K. De Groot, unpubl. data).

Point counts and habitat measurements were performed similarly in 1997 with the following changes. (1) Eight removal sites and eight control sites between 5 and 10 km from cowbird traps were used. (2) An additional eight control sites >10 km from cowbird traps were censused (total number of sites censused = 24). (3) Point counts were extended to ten min. (4) Five min of playback of cowbird female chatter call was added after each point count. Thus, counts of cowbirds and other songbirds are not directly comparable from 1996 to 1997. Cowbird playback was implemented to improve the likelihood of detecting cowbirds, following very low cowbird detection rates in 1996. Counts were performed twice in 1996 and three times in 1997 between mid-May and early July.

Songbirds (excluding cowbirds) detected during counts were placed into two categories: suitable hosts, i.e., species that accept cowbird eggs and feed their young a largely animal diet, and unsuitable hosts, such as cavity nesters, species that feed a mainly plant diet to their young, corvids, and species that reject cowbird eggs

TABLE 1. THE NUMBER OF COWBIRDS DETECTED IN THE SONGBIRD COMMUNITIES OF REMOVAL SITES, CONTROL SITES 5–10 KM FROM COWBIRD TRAPS AND >10 KM FROM COWBIRD TRAPS IN JACK-PINE FORESTS OF NORTHERN LOWER MICHIGAN

		Number of cowbirds detected per count station					
		1996		1997			
		8-min point counts		10-min point counts		5-min playback	
		females	males	females	males	females	males
Removal sites	Mean	0	0.025	0	0.063	0.021	0.028
	SE	0	0.018	0	0.034	0.015	0.015
Control sites	Mean	0	0.167	0.069	0.326	0.056	0.257
5–10 km	SE	0	0.069	0.025	0.062	0.021	0.035
Control sites	Mean	n/a	n/a	0.174	0.583	0.222	0.576
>10 km	SE	n/a	n/a	0.062	0.081	0.047	0.103

from their nests (Rothstein 1975a). The proportion of suitable cowbird hosts in the songbird communities was then analyzed using repeated measures analysis of variance (Kuehl 1994). Differences in cowbird numbers among removal sites, control sites 5–10 km from traps and control sites >10 km from traps were tested using Mann-Whitney U (1996) or Kruskall-Wallis (1997) non-parametric analyses, followed by Dunnett T3 multiple comparison tests (1997).

COWBIRD DENSITIES AS A FUNCTION OF DISTANCE FROM COWBIRD TRAPS

Cowbird removals were highly effective at reducing cowbird abundance at removal sites. In 1996, 0.025 male cowbirds were detected per count station at removal sites and no female cowbirds were counted on removal or control sites (Table 1). Male cowbird numbers increased over six-fold at control sites >5 km from cowbird traps compared to cowbird removal sites (Table 1; $Z = 2.171$, $P = 0.03$).

In 1997, the mean number of female cowbirds detected on removal sites ranged from zero during the 10-min point count to 0.021 per count station during the 5-min cowbird playback (Table 1). Mean numbers of male cowbirds ranged from 0.063–0.028 per count station on removal sites (Table 1). Both female and male cowbird abundances differed significantly among removal and all control sites (females $\chi_{0.05} = 11.015$, df = 2, $P = 0.004$; males $\chi_{0.05} = 18.795$, df = 2, $P < 0.001$). Mean number of female cowbird detections more than doubled when distance from removal sites increased to 5–10 km. However multiple comparison tests reveal that this difference is not statistically significant ($P > 0.05$). Female cowbird numbers at control sites >10 km from cowbird trap were more than three times higher than at sites 5–10 km from cowbird traps ($P = 0.025$) and more than ten-fold higher than at removal sites ($P = 0.01$). Male cowbirds

were five times more abundant when distance from traps increased from removal sites (0 km) to control sites 5–10 km from cowbird traps ($P = 0.001$). Nine times more male cowbirds were counted at sites >10 km from traps compared to removal sites ($P = 0.003$). Male cowbird numbers were also significantly higher at sites >10 km from cowbird traps compared to sites 5–10 km from traps ($P = 0.046$).

IMPACTS ON SONGBIRD COMMUNITY COMPOSITION

The percentage of suitable host individuals in cowbird removal areas was 4–9% higher than in control sites (Fig. 1). This difference was significant at the 5% level in 1996 ($F_{1,18} = 11.762$, $P = 0.003$) but not in 1997, where it was significant at the 10% level only ($F_{2,21} = 2.859$, $P = 0.08$). No individual species accounted for a large part of the difference in proportions of suitable hosts. Rather, the shift in community composition was a result of small positive shifts in the abundance of suitable host individuals in cowbird removal sites, compared to control sites.

II. COWBIRDS ACT AS PREDATORS TO INDUCE NEST FAILURE IN SONG SPARROWS

It is widely agreed that nest predation (total nest failure) is one of the principal limiting factors in songbird populations (e.g., Martin 1993, Robinson et al. 1995b). Cowbirds can cause total nest failure in several ways. (1) Hosts may desert clutches when harassed by laying cowbirds or when a parasitic egg appears in the nest (Burhans in press). (2) Egg removal may reduce host clutches below a desertion threshold (Rothstein 1982). (3) Cowbirds may damage or puncture eggs and induce hatching failure (Post and Wiley 1977, Smith and Arcese 1994). (4) Cowbirds may prey on clutches or broods of host young (Arcese et al. 1992, 1996).

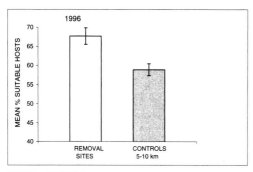

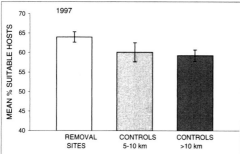

FIGURE 1. Mean percentages of suitable hosts detected during point counts in the songbird communities of jack-pine forests of northern lower Michigan at ten removal sites and ten control sites >5 km from cowbird traps in 1996 and eight removal sites, eight control sites 5–10 km from traps and control sites >10 km from cowbird traps in 1997. Bars represent one SE.

If cowbirds commonly exhibit such "predatory" activity, their effects on their hosts will be underestimated simply by monitoring their parasitic effects on hosts. Experimental removal of cowbirds is one way to estimate the extent to which cowbirds act as nest predators. If cowbirds commonly cause host nest failure, there should be a reduction in failure rates when cowbirds are removed from an area where they were abundant.

LOCAL COWBIRD REMOVALS TO TEST THE STRENGTH OF "PREDATORY" BEHAVIOR BY COWBIRDS

Cowbirds were removed from a study site on Westham Island in southwestern British Columbia, Canada. Cowbirds are abundant on Westham (5–10 % of the local songbird community), and parasitism of the Song Sparrow (*Melospiza melodia*) was frequent there during four years of previous work (Rogers et al. 1997). Two additional study sites in similar riparian habitat were established as experimental controls (i.e., no cowbird removal) in 1995. These sites were 8 km (Deas Island Regional Park) and 20 km (Delta Nature Reserve) from the removal site.

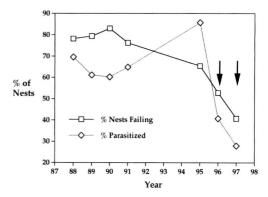

FIGURE 2. Annual percentages of nests parasitized by Brown-headed Cowbirds and daily nest failure rates in Song Sparrow nests on Westham Island, British Columbia, in relation to cowbird removals in 1996 and 1997. Arrows indicate cowbird removal.

Cowbirds were removed using modified portable Swedish Crow Traps supplied with three female and two male decoys (Griffith and Griffith in press), and by trapping at a feeding station on the study site. Removals began in mid-May 1996 and in mid-April 1997. Male cowbirds were released immediately, and females were held in captivity until the end of the cowbird breeding season (mid-July), when they too were released. Nests of Song Sparrows were monitored at the removal site from 1988 to 1991, and at removal and control sites from 1995 to 1997. Nests were found mainly by following incubating females back to their nests after foraging trips. Percentages of nests parasitized and failing at the three sites were compared using Chi-square tests of homogeneity.

We conducted longitudinal comparisons within one site (Westham) and horizontal comparisons across sites within each year. In each case, we predicted lower nest failure where cowbirds were removed. In longitudinal comparisons at the removal site across seven years, cowbird removals were associated with a sharp decline in rates of Song Sparrow nest failure and lower parasitism levels (Fig. 2). This occurred despite incomplete cowbird removal in both 1996 and 1997 (parasitism was never reduced below 29%). Proportions of nests failing at the two control sites were 18–58 % higher than at the removal site in 1996 and 1997 (Table 2). Daily nest failure rates were also higher at control sites than at the removal site in both 1996 and 1997 (Table 2).

Failures at Westham varied significantly across years ($\chi^2 = 6.22$, df = 2, P < 0.05), with lower values in the two removal years. Within years and across sites, failure rates were similar

TABLE 2. FREQUENCIES OF PARASITISM BY BROWN-HEADED COWBIRDS AND NEST FAILURE IN SONG SPARROWS AT THREE SITES IN SOUTHWESTERN BRITISH COLUMBIA, CANADA

Year/site	Number of nests	% parasitized	Proportion failing	Daily failure rate[a] (SE)
1995 Westham	55	76.4	0.654	0.037 (0.011)
1995 Delta	10	70.0	0.750	0.042 (0.036)
1995 Deas	5	100.0	0.600	0.036 (0.055)
1996 Westham[b]	85	40.7	0.528	0.037 (0.005)
1996 Delta	38	60.5	0.622	0.061 (0.022)
1996 Deas	19	70.6	0.684	0.050 (0.029)
1997 Westham[b]	132	29.4	0.454	0.030 (0.005)
1997 Delta	67	44.4	0.716	0.066 (0.012)
1997 Deas	44	64.6	0.574	0.041 (0.014)

[a] Daily failure rates (Hensler and Nichols 1981) were calculated from a slightly different sample of nests than those used to calculated the percentages of nests parasitized and the proportions of nests failing.
[b] Female Brown-headed Cowbirds were removed at this year and site.

in 1995 before the onset of cowbird removals ($\chi^2 = 0.15$, df = 2, P > 0.10). In 1996, when cowbird removals began in mid-May, there was again no significant difference in failure rates across sites ($\chi^2 = 2.55$, df = 2, P > 0.10). In 1997, when removals began a month earlier, there was a clear difference across sites ($\chi^2 = 12.40$, df = 2, P = 0.002), with much lower failure rates at Westham (Table 2).

There were few data from the control sites in the pre-removal year (1995), precluding a strong test of the hypothesis that the three sites were not inherently different in their nest failure rates. Failure rates at the removal site in 1995, however, did not differ significantly from those at the control sites in 1996 and 1997 (χ^2 tests, P > 0.10). This result makes it unlikely that site effects, rather than cowbird removal, caused apparent temporal differences in failure rates at the removal site.

Parasitism levels did not differ significantly across sites in the pre-removal year (1995: $\chi^2 = 1.790$, df = 2, P > 0.10), but were significantly lower at the removal site than at control sites in both 1996 ($\chi^2 = 7.63$, df = 2, P < 0.025) and 1997 ($\chi^2 = 16.902$, df = 2, P = < 0.001). Thus, cowbird removals were associated with lower nest failure rates and sharply reduced parasitism levels both among sites within years and within one site across years.

DISCUSSION

COMMUNITY PATTERNS OF HOSTS IN RELATION TO COWBIRD ABUNDANCE

In the jack-pine forests of Michigan, cowbird removals greatly reduced the local density of cowbirds and were associated with a quantitative shift in the host community. Removal sites supported a higher percentage of suitable cowbird hosts compared to control sites at least 5 km

from cowbird traps. While the magnitudes of these shifts were small, this region is heavily forested, and supports few cowbirds compared to other regions of the continent (Peterjohn et al. in press, Robinson et al. in press, Wiedenfeld in press, Whitfield in press). A marked shift in community composition would be much more likely in areas that support higher cowbird densities, and where cowbird removal is continuous at the same location over a longer period.

Similar comparisons at removal sites where cowbirds are much more abundant regionally would provide better tests of the idea that cowbirds have strong effects on host communities. Indeed, Griffith and Griffith (in press) have made precisely this claim for southern coastal California, but it has not yet been supported by survey data from a systematic study.

COWBIRDS AS CAUSES OF NEST FAILURE IN HOSTS

In the local cowbird removal study we conducted in British Columbia, cowbird removal reduced rates of nest failure in a common host, the Song Sparrow. Nest failure rates at the removal site in 1996 and 1997 were lower than in all five previous years of study at this site, although failure rates did vary somewhat from year to year, being lower for an unknown reason in 1995 (Fig. 2). Nest failure rates at the control sites were higher in 1996, and significantly higher in 1997, compared to failure rates at the removal site. Parasitism levels also varied among years, being high in 1995 and significantly lower after cowbird removal was initiated in 1996. Parasitism rates at control sites remained high in 1996 and 1997.

The two principal nest finders had 20 and 7 years experience in locating Song Sparrow nests and attempted to find and monitor all nests of

10 to 45 breeding pairs at each site. It is therefore unlikely that differences in nest failure and parasitism rates among years were due to differential sampling of well-concealed and poorly-concealed nests across years.

Cowbird abundance and local nest failure rates in Song Sparrows were also correlated on Mandarte Island, British Columbia, where cowbird abundance is moderate to low (Smith and Arcese 1994, Arcese et al. 1996). These data suggest that cowbird parasitism and predation may influence the metapopulation dynamics of Song Sparrows in coastal British Columbia (Arcese et al. 1992, Smith et al. 1996, Arcese et al. 1996, Rogers et al. 1997).

Song Sparrows in coastal British Columbia reproduce poorly at sites with high cowbird abundance (Smith et al. 1996, Rogers et al. 1997). These sites, however, are probably not representative of regions where cowbird abundance is declining (Peterjohn et al. in press, Wiedenfeld in press), and where most Song Sparrows and other host species may live in healthy metapopulations. Neither Whitfield (in press) nor Stutchbury (1997) found strong effects of cowbird removal on nest failure rates of Southwestern Willow Flycatchers (*Empidonax traillii extimus*) and Hooded Warblers (*Wilsonia citrina*), respectively.

COWBIRD REMOVALS AS ECOLOGICAL EXPERIMENTS—RECOMMENDATIONS

The removal studies discussed here suggest that cowbirds may have strong effects on host populations and communities. However, this conclusion is tentative and our results should not be used to justify cowbird removal programs in general. We advocate further investigation and present recommendations for ways managers and researchers can learn from cowbird control programs.

Researchers and managers should obtain pre-trapping baseline data on cowbird and host abundance and host reproductive success and, after the onset of trapping, they should monitor changes in host demographics and cowbird abundance across time and space (i.e., compare songbird populations and communities in cowbird removal areas to reference populations in similar habitat). It is important to note that temporal comparisons alone are not sufficient (see above), as year to year variation in host breeding success can mimic the effects of cowbird removal.

Managers who follow these guidelines will learn whether cowbird removal will be useful, before the initiation of a costly removal program. Pre- and post-trapping demographic data on host numbers and nesting success will allow managers to evaluate the effectiveness of the removal program in achieving its goals, and whether cowbird removal is still necessary.

When it is not feasible to design an experimental cowbird removal program from the outset, the next best approach for researchers is to use an existing cowbird removal program, and to add a monitoring program at both removal sites and non-removal sites, as illustrated in our northern Michigan study. Following these guidelines for data collection will allow powerful tests of the effects of cowbirds on host population and community dynamics. Finally, information from cowbird removal programs may illuminate other aspects of cowbird biology. For example, behavioral tests of the responses of hosts to cowbirds (e.g., Neudorf and Sealy 1992) in removal and control areas might reveal how quickly hosts alter anti-parasite behaviors. Removal programs represent an almost untapped resource for improving our understanding of the ecological impacts of parasitic cowbirds.

ACKNOWLEDGMENTS

Financial support for these projects was provided by the Natural Sciences and Engineering Research Council of Canada, the U.S. Fish and Wildlife Service, and Sigma Xi, The Scientific Research Society. We thank many field personnel for helping to collect field data, particularly A. Goulet, A. Hillaby, M. Kleitch, T. Martinovic, R. Porte, M. Romich, K. Sander, J. Shapiro, and C. Wright. We are indebted to the Kirtland's Warbler Recovery Team, especially M. E. DeCapita of the U.S. Fish and Wildlife Service, P. Huber of the U.S. Forest Service, and J. Weinrich of the Michigan Department of Natural Resources for encouragement, advice and survey maps of the Michigan study areas. J. Griffith kindly provided plans for building cowbird traps.

Studies in Avian Biology No. 18:235–240, 1999.

PARASITISM AND EGG PUNCTURE BEHAVIOR BY BRONZED AND BROWN-HEADED COWBIRDS IN SYMPATRY

BRIAN D. PEER AND SPENCER G. SEALY

Abstract. We monitored parasitism by the sympatric Bronzed (*Molothrus aeneus*) and Brown-headed (*M. ater*) cowbirds in south Texas to determine whether the two cowbird species avoid overlap in host use. We also investigated egg puncture behavior by Bronzed Cowbirds. Nests of 11 potential host species were found and 5.1% of 1256 nests were parasitized. Brown-headed Cowbirds parasitized seven host species, whereas Bronzed Cowbirds parasitized three species. The two cowbirds demonstrated overlap in host use. Punctured eggs were found in the nests of three host species. Nearly 81% of nests where egg puncture was observed were subsequently deserted. Egg puncture may force hosts that have escaped parasitism to renest, thereby creating additional opportunities for parasitism.

Key Words: Bronzed Cowbird, brood parasitism, Brown-headed Cowbird, egg puncture, *Molothrus aeneus, Molothrus ater.*

The Brown-headed Cowbird (scientific names given in Appendix) is the only obligate brood parasite that occurs throughout most of North America. Its range overlaps that of the Bronzed Cowbird in the southwestern United States and northern Mexico (see Lowther 1993, 1995). Scant information exists on host use by Brown-headed and Bronzed cowbirds in areas of sympatry (but see Carter 1986). Other species of brood parasites that are sympatric, particularly the cuckoos (*Cuculus, Chrysococcyx, Clamator, Eudynamis, Oxylophus, Scythrops*), reduce competition by partitioning their primary hosts (Friedmann 1928, 1967a; Payne and Payne 1967; Brooker and Brooker 1989a, b, 1992).

Little is known concerning the parasitic behavior of Bronzed Cowbirds in general. Bronzed Cowbirds puncture host eggs (Friedmann 1929, Carter 1986), behavior that differs from egg removal by Brown-headed Cowbirds. Brown-headed Cowbirds often pierce eggs in their open beaks and remove them from nests (Blincoe 1935, Sealy 1992), whereas Bronzed Cowbirds puncture holes in eggs but leave them in the nests (Friedmann 1929, Carter 1986, this study). Egg removal by Brown-headed Cowbirds appears to enhance incubation of the parasite's eggs (Sealy 1992, McMaster and Sealy 1997; Peer and Bollinger 1997, in press; see also Davies and Brooke 1988). The function of egg puncture by Bronzed Cowbirds, however, is unclear. Carter (1986) hypothesized that Bronzed Cowbirds puncture eggs to decrease competition with host nestlings or other cowbird nestlings. Shiny Cowbirds also puncture eggs (Friedmann 1929), and Mason (1986) suggested this behavior serves the same function in Shiny Cowbirds. Other researchers have suggested egg puncture by Shiny Cowbirds is spiteful behavior (Post and Wiley 1977), or that it is a general habit that is unrelated to brood parasitism (Hoy and Ottow

1964). Recent evidence, however, indicates Shiny Cowbirds puncture eggs to force hosts to desert and renest, thus providing the cowbirds with future opportunities for parasitism (Nakamura and Cruz in press). In the present study we tested two hypotheses. First, that sympatric Bronzed and Brown-headed cowbirds parasitize different host species to reduce competition, and second, that Bronzed Cowbirds puncture eggs to force hosts to desert and renest in order to obtain additional opportunities for parasitism.

METHODS

We conducted this study at the Welder Wildlife Refuge in San Patricio County, Texas (28°0'N, 97°5'W), from 1994–1996. The refuge is 3156 ha and is characterized by a mesquite-mixed grass community interspersed with chaparral (Drawe et al. 1978). Cattle were present and grazed throughout most of the refuge. Brown-headed and Bronzed cowbirds occur at the refuge in approximately equal numbers during the breeding season (B. Peer, pers. obs.). To the south of this region of Texas, Bronzed Cowbirds predominate with very few Brown-headed Cowbirds present during the breeding season, and in areas of Texas to the north, the Brown-headed Cowbird predominates with very few Bronzed Cowbirds present (Oberholser 1974, Carter 1986, Price et al. 1995).

One of us (B. Peer) searched for nests throughout most of the refuge almost daily in all three years, and one assistant also searched in 1996. The only vegetation type not searched was grassland where Eastern Meadowlarks nested in all years and Dickcissels in 1994. This area was not searched due to the low densities of these hosts and time constraints. We did not census birds, but the number of nests found were generally reflective of overall passerine densities. The exceptions, in addition to the two afore-

FIGURE 1.   Northern Cardinal nest containing one punctured host egg and one Brown-headed Cowbird egg.

mentioned grassland species, were the Painted Bunting and White-eyed Vireo, both of which were more common than the number of nests found.

Only suitable hosts in terms of body mass, diet, and nest accessibility were included in the analyses. Unsuitable hosts (e.g., Killdeer, Mourning Dove, Common Ground-Dove, Yellow-billed Cuckoo, Greater Roadrunner, and Ash-throated Flycatcher) were excluded because such species are typically avoided by cowbirds (Friedmann 1963, Friedmann and Kiff 1985; but see Rothstein 1976, Clotfelter and Brush 1995), and indeed we found no parasitism on these species. The Great-tailed Grackle is too large to be a suitable host for the Brown-headed Cowbird, but it is suitable for the Bronzed Cowbird (Peer 1998), which is the largest of the molothrine cowbirds (males = 67 g, females = 57 g; Dunning 1993). We included species that reject cowbird eggs (e.g., Scissor-tailed Flycatcher, Northern Mockingbird, Great-tailed Grackle, and Bullock's Oriole [Rothstein 1977, Carter 1986, Regosin 1994; Peer 1998, unpubl. data]), because rejecters are sometimes parasitized (Scott 1977; see below).

Nests were marked with flagging tape and subsequently inspected every one to three days for evidence of parasitism and egg puncture. Our estimates of egg puncture are conservative because some punctured eggs may have been removed by hosts before nests were inspected. Only eggs that had holes poked through the eggshells (see Fig. 1) were considered as punctured by Bronzed Cowbirds. We used this criterion to reduce the risk of including damage that was caused by other predators (see also Nakamura and Cruz in press and below).

RESULTS

BRONZED AND BROWN-HEADED COWBIRD PARASITISM

There was no apparent partitioning of hosts by Bronzed and Brown-headed cowbirds. Bronzed Cowbirds parasitized three host species, and Brown-headed Cowbirds parasitized seven species, including all three parasitized by Bronzed Cowbirds (Table 1). The Northern Cardinal was the most frequently parasitized host overall (59 of 115 nests parasitized vs. 7 of 1151 for all other hosts; $G = 272.7$, $P < 0.001$), and individually by both Bronzed (31 of 115 vs. 2 of 1139; $G = 141.9$, $P < 0.001$) and Brown-

TABLE 1. FREQUENCY OF BRONZED AND BROWN-HEADED COWBIRD PARASITISM ON HOSTS AT THE WELDER WILD-LIFE REFUGE, TEXAS FROM 1994–1996

| | Total nests | | Nests parasitized | | | |
| | | | Bronzed Cowbird | | Brown-headed Cowbird | |
Host species	N (%)		N (%)		N (%)	
Parasitized by both cowbirds						
Northern Cardinal	115	(9.2)	31 (27.0)		32 (27.8)	
Painted Bunting	2	(0.2)	1 (50.0)		1 (50.0)	
Olive Sparrow	3	(0.2)	1 (33.3)		1 (33.3)	
Subtotal	120	(9.6)	33 (27.5)		34 (28.3)	
Parasitized by Bronzed Cowbird only						
None	—		—		—	
Parasitized by Brown-headed Cow-bird only						
Verdin	4	(0.3)	—		1 (25.0)	
White-eyed Vireo	2	(0.2)	—		2 (100)	
Red-winged Blackbird	8	(0.6)	—		1 (12.5)	
Bullock's Oriole	4	(0.3)	—		1 (25.0)	
Subtotal	18	(1.4)	—		5 (12.8)	
Not parasitized						
Scissor-tailed Flycatcher	279[a,b]	(22.2)	—		—	
Northern Mockingbird	40	(3.2)	—		—	
Lark Sparrow	2	(0.2)	—		—	
Great-tailed Grackle	797	(63.4)	—		—	
Subtotal	1118	(89.0)	—		—	
Total	1256	(100)	33 (2.6)		39 (3.1)	

[a] Includes unpublished data from F. Guerrero.
[b] One nest containing a Mourning Dove egg.

headed (32 of 115 vs. 7 of 337; $G = 62.5$; $P < 0.001$) cowbirds (Table 1). Four cardinal nests, one Painted Bunting nest, and one Olive Sparrow nest were parasitized simultaneously by both cowbird species. There was no evidence that Bronzed and Brown-headed cowbirds partition the nests of cardinals as four of 31 nests parasitized by Bronzed Cowbirds were also parasitized by Brown-headed Cowbirds, and four of 32 nests parasitized by Brown-headed Cowbirds were parasitized by Bronzed Cowbirds (Fisher's exact test, $P > 0.99$). The 66 parasitized nests we found contained an average of 1.4 cowbird eggs per nest. Forty-five Bronzed Cowbird eggs were found in 33 nests, and 49 Brown-headed Cowbird eggs were found in 39 nests.

EGG PUNCTURE BEHAVIOR

Punctured eggs were found in nests or on the ground below nests of three species (Table 2), with cardinals having the most number of nests with punctured eggs (N = 24 nests). Nests that had eggs punctured were more likely to be deserted (80.8% of 26 nests) than nests that did not have eggs punctured for these three species (10.7% of 103 nests; Fisher exact test, $P <$

TABLE 2. FREQUENCY OF EGG PUNCTURE ON HOSTS NESTING AT THE WELDER WILDLIFE REFUGE, TEXAS FROM 1994–1996

| Host species | Total no. nests | No. unparasitized nests with punctured eggs | Nests parasitized by Bronzed Cowbird | | Nests parasitized by Brown-headed Cowbird | |
			N (%)	No. with punctured eggs	N (%)	No. with punctured eggs
Northern Cardinal	115	10	27 (27)	8[a]	32 (28)	6[b]
Olive Sparrow	3	0	1 (33)	1	1 (33)	1
Yellow-billed Cuckoo	11	1	0 (0)	0	0 (0)	0

[a] One Bronzed Cowbird egg was removed prior to puncture.
[b] Two Brown-headed Cowbird eggs were removed prior to puncture.

0.001). The stage of the nesting cycle at which eggs were punctured was known for 10 nests: six nests that had eggs punctured during incubation were deserted, whereas only one of four nests that had eggs punctured during laying was deserted (Fisher's exact test, $P = 0.03$). Four nests that had eggs punctured during the laying stage were also parasitized, and puncture occurred the same day as parasitism or later.

Parasitized nests contained punctured eggs more frequently than unparasitized nests (15 of 66 parasitized nests vs. 11 of 1190 unparasitized nests; $G = 57.4$, $P < 0.001$; Table 2). Single cowbird eggs were removed from four of these nests for other experiments, three of which were removed before puncture occurred (two brown-headed eggs and one bronzed egg) (Peer 1998). Taking these three nests into account, parasitized nests still had eggs punctured more frequently (12 of 63 vs. 11 of 1193; $G = 43.2$, $P < 0.001$). Nests parasitized by Bronzed Cowbirds were no more likely to have eggs punctured than were those parasitized by Brown-headed Cowbirds (9 of 33 nests vs. 7 of 39, respectively; $G = 0.90$, $P = 0.34$).

Host eggs were punctured more frequently (37 punctured vs. 14 not punctured) than cowbird eggs (6 vs. 10; $G = 6.3$, $P = 0.01$) in all nests that had eggs punctured. However, host eggs were punctured at the same frequency as cowbird eggs of both species combined in parasitized nests (9 of 13 vs. 6 of 14, respectively; Fisher exact test, $P = 0.25$). Bronzed Cowbird eggs were also punctured at the same frequncy as host eggs in parasitized nests (7 of 8 vs. 5 of 8; Fisher's exact test, $P = 0.57$). However, Brown-headed Cowbird eggs were punctured less often than host eggs (0 of 7 vs. 6 of 6, respectively; Fisher exact test, $P < 0.001$), and Bronzed Cowbird eggs in parasitized nests (0 of 7 vs. 7 of 8, respectively; Fisher's exact test, $P = 0.001$).

DISCUSSION

BRONZED AND BROWN-HEADED COWBIRD PARASITISM

Friedmann (1967b) coined the terms "homoxenia" to designate the situation where two or more brood parasitic species use the same hosts in areas of sympatry, and "alloxenia" where parasites use different hosts in areas of sympatry. It should be to the advantage of sympatric parasites to avoid using the same hosts to reduce competition. Indeed African and Australian cuckoos avoid overlap of their primary hosts (Friedmann 1928, Brooker and Brooker 1989b). In southern Texas, however, Bronzed and Brown-headed cowbirds are seemingly homoxenic. All three species parasitized by Bronzed Cowbirds were also parasitized by Brown-headed Cowbirds. The fact that Brown-headed Cowbirds used a wider variety of host species reflects the host use by these two cowbirds in general. Brown-headed Cowbirds have parasitized about 220 host species (Friedmann and Kiff 1985), whereas Bronzed Cowbirds are known to have parasitized only 87 species (Lowther 1995, Sealy et al. 1997). Possibly, some of the hosts we observed parasitized only by Brown-headed Cowbirds were also parasitized by Bronzed Cowbirds, but escaped our detection because our samples were small for those four species. However, only two of these species, the Red-winged Blackbird and Bullock's Oriole, are known hosts of the Bronzed Cowbird (Friedmann and Kiff 1985). We also have no data on parasitism of Eastern Meadowlarks or Dickcissels. Both are hosts of the Brown-headed Cowbird, but neither has been observed to be parasitized by Bronzed Cowbirds (Friedmann and Kiff 1985, Lowther 1995, Sealy et al. 1997).

Our small samples for some hosts limit our conclusions somewhat. However, our findings are similar to those of Carter (1986) at the Santa Ana refuge, a semi-arid forest-brushland area of southernmost Texas. Carter found that all nests parasitized by Brown-headed Cowbirds ($N = 6$) were also parasitized by the more common Bronzed Cowbirds. Perhaps the best explanation for the overlap in host use is that the two cowbird species have just recently come into contact in this area of Texas. The Bronzed Cowbird was not known to occur in Texas until the late 19th century (Merrill 1876), thus there may not have been sufficient time for competition between the two species to force differences in host utilization.

EGG PUNCTURE BEHAVIOR

Our data support the hypothesis that egg puncture forces hosts that have escaped parasitism to desert and renest, thereby creating additional opportunities for parasitism (Nakamura and Cruz in press; see also Arcese et al. 1996). Female cowbirds may not be ready to lay, or they may find nests during the incubation stage or later. Such nests are too advanced to be successfully parasitized because the parasite's eggs must often hatch before or at the same time as host nestlings if they are to fledge (Carter 1986, Peer and Bollinger 1997). Although we were often unaware of what stage of the nesting cycle at which egg puncture occurred, 81% of nests that had eggs punctured were deserted. Nests that had eggs punctured during the laying stage were less likely to be deserted than those that had eggs punctured during incubation. Eggs that were punctured during the laying stage may have been punctured by females who were not ready to lay, but were unsuccessful at forcing desertion. These results concur with studies of the Shiny Cowbird in which nests that had eggs punctured were also frequently deserted (Post and Wiley 1977, Fraga 1985, Nakamura and Cruz in press). Similarly, Arcese et al. (1996) found that nest failure in Song Sparrows increased when Brown-headed Cowbirds were present and they suggested Brown-headed Cowbirds depredate nests to create additional opportunities for parasitism.

Nakamura and Cruz (in press) further suggested that egg puncture by Shiny Cowbirds may reflect competitive interactions between cowbirds for parasitism opportunities because punctured eggs were more common in areas with higher cowbird densities. We have no data on cowbird densities at the Welder Wildlife Refuge. Parasitized nests were, however, more likely to have eggs punctured than nonparasitized nests, which may indicate that cowbirds puncture eggs in nests that have already been parasitized. This would require that cowbirds recognize cowbird eggs in the nests of their hosts. Presumably, Bronzed Cowbirds should be able to recognize the immaculate eggs of other Bronzed Cowbirds in the nests of the most frequently parasitized host, the cardinal, which has spotted eggs (Baicich and Harrison 1997). However, it seems unlikely that they can recognize Brown-headed Cowbird eggs in cardinal nests because cowbird eggs closely resemble cardinal eggs (see Baicich and Harrison 1997). Inexperienced researchers frequently mistake Brown-headed Cowbird eggs for cardinal eggs (B. Peer, pers. obs.); thus, it is possible that cowbirds cannot distinguish between the two egg types. If so, we would expect that nests parasitized by Bronzed Cowbirds would be more likely to have eggs punctured than those nests parasitized by Brown-headed Cowbirds, but there was no difference. The fact that parasitized nests were more likely to contain punctured eggs may be a result of cowbirds keying in on the nests of these frequently parasitized hosts, particularly the cardinal.

Similar to Nakamura and Cruz (in press), we found no evidence that egg puncture helps cowbirds fledge from nests by reducing competition with host nestlings or other cowbird nestlings (e.g., Carter 1986, Mason 1986). Hosts clearly deserted their nests in association with puncture behavior in our study and this would make the elimination of host or other cowbird nestlings superfluous. Moreover, the contents of punctured eggs often leaked into nests and caused the remaining eggs to stick to the bottom of the nest,

and this also attracted ants (B. Peer, pers. obs.; see also Nakamura and Cruz in press). This would prevent the remaining eggs including the cowbird eggs from being turned, which would result in the death of the embryos (Gill 1990). Thus, this behavior would actually decrease the likelihood of a cowbird fledging.

Great Spotted Cuckoos damage host eggs indirectly as a result of their eggs hitting host eggs during laying (Soler 1990, Soler et al. 1997). Soler et al. (1997) suggested that damage to host eggs decreases competition from host nestlings and increases the chances of late-laid eggs hatching. Indeed, one of us witnessed an incident where a Bronzed Cowbird laid her egg in a cardinal nest and, upon inspection, we found that one of the cardinal eggs had been cracked (see Peer and Sealy 1999). The egg was subsequently removed, presumably by the adult, and the nest was later depredated. Soler et al. (1997) state that this sort of damage is beneficial because it makes host eggs inviable and decreases the risk of attracting insects and bacteria. However, if as they suggest this change in the egg is so subtle that the host does not notice it, the host may not remove the egg. Eggs that are cracked or dented often hatch; the inner membrane must be damaged for the egg to become inviable (Røskaft et al. 1993; S. Sealy, pers. obs.). Therefore, this would not reduce competition. Soler et al. (1997) also incorrectly state that when brood parasites damage eggs they do so without breaking them. The references they list (Hoy and Ottow 1964, Post and Wiley 1977, Carter 1986) refer to Bronzed and Shiny cowbirds and these parasites puncture holes in the eggs making them inviable (see above and Nakamura and Cruz in press).

Egg puncture also does not appear to be of a generalist nature in Bronzed Cowbirds, nor does it appear to be spiteful (e.g., Hoy and Ottow 1964, Post and Wiley 1977). Egg puncture was clearly associated with Bronzed Cowbird parasitism. Punctured eggs were found only in the nests of species that were parasitized by Bronzed Cowbirds, or are known hosts of this cowbird (Table 1; Clotfelter and Brush 1996). In addition to being the most frequently parasitized host, the cardinal also suffered the highest frequency of egg puncture, which indicates that this behavior is associated with parasitism (see also Nakamura and Cruz in press). Thus, despite the fact that we did not witness Bronzed Cowbirds puncture eggs, we are confident the eggs were indeed punctured by Bronzed Cowbirds rather than other predators. Furthermore, egg predators typically consume eggs, i.e., they do not puncture eggs and leave them in the nests. Eastern Meadowlarks puncture eggs (Picman 1992) and they nested at the refuge; however, meadowlarks were not present in the habitats where egg puncture was observed. Red-winged Blackbirds puncture eggs (Sealy 1994) and they also nested at the refuge, but they were relatively rare and we did not observe punctured eggs at the lake where they nested.

We are also confident that Brown-headed Cowbirds were not responsible for egg puncture in our study. Instead of puncturing eggs, Brown-headed Cowbirds may depredate host nests (Arcese et al. 1996), but it is unclear how widespread this behavior is in Brown-headed Cowbirds. It is possible that Brown-headed Cowbirds depredated some nests in our study. However, only hosts that were parasitized or are known hosts of the Bronzed Cowbird suffered egg puncture (see Clotfelter and Brush 1995 and below), and none of the hosts that were parasitized by only Brown-headed Cowbirds suffered egg puncture.

Egg puncture also differs from the "mafia" behavior described in Great Spotted Cuckoos. Mafia cuckoos (Zahavi 1979, Soler et al. 1995) purportedly depredate some or all the eggs or nestlings of their Black-billed Magpie hosts to punish them for rejecting cuckoo eggs. The three hosts that experienced egg puncture in our study are not known to reject cowbird eggs, although the cardinal is the only one that has been tested experimentally (Rothstein 1975a; see also Carter 1986). Furthermore, we found no evidence of egg puncture in the nests of the four rejecter species that nested at the refuge. Thus, it appears that egg puncture by Bronzed Cowbirds, similar to Shiny Cowbirds, functions to force hosts to renest to provide the cowbirds with future opportunities for parasitism.

ACKNOWLEDGMENTS

We thank J. Teer and the staff of the Welder Wildlife Refuge for allowing us to conduct this study at the refuge and for logistical assistance. F. Guerrero, L. Nelson, M. L. Peer, and K. Stewart provided valuable assistance during the study. F. Guerrero also provided unpublished data on Scissor-tailed Flycatcher nests. D. C. Hahn, J. Wiley, and an anonymous reviewer provided comments that improved the manuscript. This study was funded by an NSERC research grant to SGS and a G. A. Lubinsky scholarship from the University of Manitoba Department of Zoology to BDP.

APPENDIX. SCIENTIFIC NAMES OF BIRDS MENTIONED IN TEXT OR TABLES.

Killdeer	*Charadrius vociferus*
Mourning Dove	*Zenaida macroura*
Common Ground-Dove	*Columbina passerina*
Great-spotted Cuckoo	*Clamator glandarius*
Yellow-billed Cuckoo	*Coccyzus americanus*
Greater Roadrunner	*Geococcyx californianus*
Scissor-tailed Flycatcher	*Tyrannus forficatus*
Ash-throated Flycatcher	*Myiarchus cinerascens*
Black-billed Magpie	*Pica pica*
Verdin	*Auriparus flaviceps*
Northern Mockingbird	*Mimus polyglottos*
White-eyed Vireo	*Vireo griseus*
Northern Cardinal	*Cardinalis cardinalis*
Painted Bunting	*Passerina ciris*
Olive Sparrow	*Arremonops rufivirgatus*
Song Sparrow	*Melospiza melodia*
Lark Sparrow	*Chondestes grammacus*
Dickcissel	*Spiza americana*
Eastern Meadowlark	*Sturnella magna*
Red-winged Blackbird	*Agelaius phoeniceus*
Brown-headed Cowbird	*Molothrus ater*
Bronzed Cowbird	*Molothrus aeneus*
Shiny Cowbird	*Molothrus bonariensis*
Great-tailed Grackle	*Quiscalus mexicanus*
Bullock's Oriole	*Icterus bullockii*

Studies in Avian Biology No. 18:241–253, 1999.

A META-ANALYSIS OF THE IMPACT OF PARASITISM BY THE BROWN-HEADED COWBIRD ON ITS HOSTS

Janice C. Lorenzana and Spencer G. Sealy

Abstract. We used a meta-analytical technique to synthesize the results of studies that have quantified the effect of parasitism by Brown-headed Cowbirds *(Molothrus ater)* on host productivity. The cost of parasitism was defined as the difference in the number of young fledged in parasitized and unparasitized nests because 95% of the empirical studies used this method for calculating the cost of parasitism. We conducted two meta-analyses: one using productivity data based on nests that fledged at least one chick and the other using productivity data based on all nests. The meta-analysis based on successful nests included 40 studies and 19 species, and the meta- analysis based on all nests included 44 studies and 25 species. Across all studies, the number of young fledged per nest was significantly decreased by cowbird parasitism. Larger hosts incurred a smaller cost of parasitism that approached significance when all nests were used in the calculation of parasitism costs. Three granivorous species included in the analyses incurred a significant cost of parasitism. The inclusion of failed nests decreased the overall cost of parasitism, which indicates that predation dilutes the effect of parasitism on a population level. Our analysis is only as good as the studies on which it was based, and we point out several short-comings of many empirical studies that have estimated the cost of parasitism. A better estimate of the cost of parasitism is the difference between the number of young produced by parasitized and unparasitized females during the entire breeding season. Researchers should be aware of the biases that exist when cost is calculated on a per-nest basis.

Key Words: Avian brood parasitism, Brown-headed Cowbird, cost of parasitism, host species, meta-analysis, *Molothrus ater.*

Many studies have quantified the effect of parasitism by the Brown-headed Cowbird *(Molothrus ater)* on host productivity. The question of how cowbird parasitism affects host productivity is particularly interesting because the cowbird has been recorded parasitizing at least 220 species (Friedmann and Kiff 1985) and, therefore, likely affects the reproductive success of different hosts to varying degrees. In this paper, we compiled the results of many of these studies and performed a meta-analysis to confirm whether cowbirds decrease host productivity and, if so, to what extent.

Although meta-analytical techniques were developed in the mid-1970s, only since the early 1990s have these techniques been used in ecology. Since then, several papers have promoted the use of these techniques (Mann 1990, Fernandez-Duque and Valeggia 1994, Arnqvist and Wooster 1995). Meta-analysis is a scientific review in which data are quantitatively synthesized and, as such, provides a better alternative to traditional narrative reviews. Meta-analytical techniques are used to summarize the results of studies in terms of an effect size, calculate a mean effect size for groups of similar studies (referred to as classes), and calculate the overall effect size for all studies. The overall effect size is useful in determining the overall trend in the data, and whether it is significantly different from zero (Gurevitch and Hedges 1993, Arnqvist and Wooster 1995). Often in the past, reviewers combined the results of studies conducted on

a subject by comparing the number of studies that rejected the null hypothesis with those that did not reject the null hypothesis. The problem with the latter approach is that studies based on small sample sizes are more likely to result in a Type II error, which is failing to reject the null hypothesis when it is actually false. This is not a problem when meta-analytical techniques are used because the calculated effect size is weighted according to sample size (Gurevitch and Hedges 1993).

Cowbird parasitism lowers the productivity of species that accept cowbird eggs in the following ways: host egg removal by the female cowbird (Sealy 1992), egg breakage during or after parasitism (Marvil and Cruz 1989, Weatherhead 1989, Smith and Arcese 1994), lowered hatching success of host eggs due to inefficient incubation and/or earlier hatching of parasite eggs (Petit 1991, McMaster and Sealy 1997), and lower nestling survival due to crowding and competition for parental care (Marvil and Cruz 1989). Undeniably, cowbirds greatly affect the productivity of some of their hosts. Some small hosts seldom fledge any of their own young when they are parasitized (e.g., Goldwasser et al. 1980), and many reviews have recorded the production of fewer host offspring in parasitized nests versus unparasitized nests (e.g., Payne 1977, May and Robinson 1985). Weatherhead (1989) and Trine (in press) provide data on the productivity of nests of Red-winged Blackbirds (*Agelaius phoeniceus*) and Wood Thrushes (*Hylocichla mustelina*), respectively, that contain more than one cowbird egg. Herein, we test the hypothesis that multiply parasitized hosts incur a greater cost of parasitism than singly parasitized hosts.

As a generalist brood parasite, Brown-headed Cowbirds parasitize many inappropriate hosts, such as large species, seed-eating species, species that reject parasitic eggs, and even non-passerines. For our study, we predict that inappropriate hosts do not incur as great a cost of parasitism. Large host young should be able to compete with or even outcompete a cowbird chick during the nestling stage (e.g., Common Grackle, *Quiscalus quiscula*; Peer and Bollinger 1997). Hosts that feed seeds to their young should incur little cost associated with parasitism, except possibly for host egg removal and egg damage, because cowbird nestlings are insectivorous and die when fed only seeds (e.g., Middleton 1991, Kozlovic et al. 1996). Species that eject cowbird eggs and desert or bury the contents of parasitized nests should experience less cost than species that raise the cowbird young.

Performing a meta-analysis allowed us to determine how the cost of raising a cowbird differs among host species. We sought answers to the following questions: (1) Do nests fledge fewer young when they are parasitized by the Brown-headed Cowbird? (2) Do small bodied hosts incur a greater cost of parasitism than large bodied hosts? (3) Is brood parasitism less costly for granivorous species that do not usually raise cowbirds than for primarily insectivorous species? (4) Is the calculated cost of parasitism different when fledging success is calculated for all nests or only for successful nests?

METHODS

We reviewed the literature back to 1945 and included studies that presented data on host productivity in parasitized and unparasitized nests. To be included in the meta-analysis, the following data were required for both parasitized and unparasitized nests: (1) some measure of reproductive success for each, (2) an estimate of the variability of these measures (standard deviation or standard error), and (3) sample sizes. Most researchers quantified productivity in terms of the number of host young that fledged from nests, with four exceptions, namely studies by Klaas (1975), Smith (1981), Clark and Robertson (1981), and Roth et al. (1996) (Tables 1, 2).

Some studies that reported the productivity of parasitized and unparasitized nests could not be included in the meta-analysis because standard deviations were not provided. Several authors were contacted for additional information (e.g., standard deviations) not given in their papers.

We urge authors to provide a measure of the variance for all estimated parameters reported because this not only allows others to re-analyze their data, but this is necessary for readers to have an idea of the extent of variation.

Overall, 36 papers and unpublished sources presented information on 29 host species that could be used in our analyses (Tables 1, 2). Some of the papers included more than one host species or broke up the information for the same species by year, time of year, habitat, or number of cowbird eggs in nest. We conducted two meta-analyses, one using productivity data based on nests that fledged at least one host or cowbird chick, and the other using productivity data based on all nests. We conducted the analyses separately because some studies provided productivity data based on both methods and the data were not independent. Studies that presented data on the total number of young produced per female over the entire breeding season were analyzed in the meta-analysis based on all nests. G.T. Braden (pers. comm.) provided raw data for banded California Gnatcatchers (*Polioptila californica*) that allowed us to calculate the cost of parasitism based on all nests, successful nests only, and on a per-female basis. This was the only data-set for which the cost of parasitism was calculated in all three ways.

We only briefly summarize the methods here (see Gurevitch and Hedges [1993] for a detailed account of the equations and steps used to perform the meta-analysis). First, we transformed the outcome of each study to an "effect size," which is the difference in the mean number of young fledged in parasitized and unparasitized nests divided by the pooled standard deviation. The effect size for each study was then weighted by the number of parasitized and unparasitized nests. Similar studies were grouped into "classes." In our meta-analyses, studies conducted on the same species were analyzed as one class. Because each class must contain more than one study, species that were studied only once were grouped as insectivorous or granivorous (in the case of the meta-analysis involving successful nests only) or in terms of adult mass (in the case of the meta-analysis involving all nests). Effect sizes for studies that belong to the same class were then combined by taking a weighted average to see whether the class effect size differed from zero. A one-tailed test was used to calculate the 95% confidence limits for class effect size. We used a mixed model that, unlike the fixed model, did not make the stringent assumption that a class of studies shared a common true effect size. In a mixed model, it is assumed that the studies within a class share a common mean effect, but that there is random variation among studies in a class, in addition to sampling variation. An overall effect size was then found by calculating a weighted average of the class effect sizes (Gurevitch and Hedges 1993). The overall effect size was converted to a Z-score using a standard normal distribution table (as in Tonhasca and Byrne 1994). A test for heterogeneity among the effect sizes of all classes was performed using the between-class heterogeneity statistic, Q_B, which has approximately a chi-square distribution with degrees of freedom equal to the total number of classes minus one. The greater the value of Q_B, the greater the heterogeneity in effect sizes among the classes (Gurevitch and Hedges 1993). For significance, we used $\alpha = 0.05$ in all statistical tests.

The meta-analysis based on successful nests included 40 studies, 19 species and 10 classes. The following eight species were the subject of more than one study and were treated as separate classes: Willow Flycatcher (*Empidonax traillii*), Wood Thrush, Red-eyed Vireo (*Vireo olivaceus*), Prothonotary Warbler (*Protonotaria citrea*), Yellow Warbler (*Dendroica petechia*), Dickcissel (*Spiza americana*), Song Sparrow (*Melospiza melodia*), and Red-winged Blackbird. The remaining 11 species were separated into two classes: granivorous and other insectivorous hosts. The two granivorous hosts were American Goldfinch (*Carduelis tristis*) and House Finch (*Carpodacus mexicanus*). The nine insectivorous hosts included: California Gnatcatcher, Ovenbird (*Seiurus aurocapillus*), Louisiana Waterthrush (*S. motacilla*), Indigo Bunting (*Passerina cyanea*), Lark Sparrow (*Chondestes grammacus*), Grasshopper Sparrow (*Ammodramus savannarum*), Dark-eyed Junco (*Junco hyemalis*), Chestnut-collared Longspur (*Calcarius ornatus*), and Western Meadowlark (*Sturnella neglecta*) (Tables 1, 3). These nine insectivorous hosts were not divided into classes according to mass, as in the meta-analysis involving all nests (see below), because natural breaks in the mass data did not exist such that each class would have more than one study. Meta-analytical techniques require more than one study to be included in each class so that the error associated with the class effect size may be estimated.

The meta-analysis based on all nests included 44 studies, 25 species, and 13 classes. The following species were studied more than once and treated as separate classes: Willow Flycatcher, California Gnatcatcher, Wood Thrush, Plumbeous Vireo (*V. plumbeous*), Red-eyed Vireo, Yellow Warbler, Indigo Bunting, Song Sparrow, and Red-winged Blackbird. The remaining 16 species were grouped into four additional classes according to adult mass. The following four classes were formed using natural breaks in the

mass data with the restriction that each class had to contain more than one study: (1) Blue-gray Gnatcatcher (*Polioptila caerulea*, 6.0 g), Clay-colored Sparrow (*Spizella pallida*, 12.0 g), Western Wood-Pewee (*Contopus sordidulus*, 12.8 g), Warbling Vireo (*Vireo gilvus*, 14.8 g); (2) Grasshopper Sparrow (17.0 g), Baird's Sparrow (17.5 g), Chestnut-collared Longspur (18.9 g), Eastern Phoebe (*Sayornis phoebe*, 19.8 g), Savannah Sparrow (20.0 g), Louisiana Waterthrush (20.3 g); (3) Purple Finch (*Carpodacus purpureus*, 24.9 g), Sprague's Pipit (*Anthus spragueii*, 25.3 g), Western Tanager (*Piranga ludoviciana*, 28.1 g), Lark Sparrow (29.0 g); and (4) Bobolink (*Dolichonyx oryzivorus*, 42.0 g), Western Meadowlark (100.7 g) (Tables 2, 4). Mean adult masses were obtained from Dunning (1993). We used the average mass of both sexes combined for dimorphic species. Note that the Purple Finch was the only granivorous species included in this meta-analysis and, therefore, could not be analyzed in a separate class.

Trine (in press) provided data on fledging success for Wood Thrush nests containing up to six cowbird eggs. Simple linear regression was used to determine whether the number of cowbird eggs in Wood Thrush nests affected the effect size of parasitism. Linear regression was also used to determine whether host mass affected the effect size of parasitism. When more than one study was conducted on a species, a pooled effect size for the species was used as a single observation in the regression analysis to avoid pseudoreplication.

Although our analysis included species that often desert or bury parasitized nests (e.g., Yellow Warbler, Clark and Roberston 1981; Willow Flycatcher, Sedgwick and Knopf 1988; Red-eyed Vireo and Song Sparrow, Graham 1988), the effect of nest desertion or burial on the cost of parasitism could not be determined accurately because most studies provided productivity data on a per-nest basis rather than on a per-female basis. Our meta-analysis does not include ejector species because no one has compared the productivity of naturally parasitized and unparasitized nests of ejector species. It is difficult to study naturally parasitized nests of ejector species because a cowbird egg may be ejected before the foreign egg can be detected (Scott 1977, Sealy and Bazin 1995).

A criticism of meta-analytical studies is that the results may be affected by a publication bias because papers that demonstrate no effect are less likely to be published than those with statistically significant effects. Referred to as the "file-drawer" problem, there is a possibility that the number of unpublished statistically insignificant results is high enough to invalidate the re-

TABLE 1. MEAN NUMBER OF HOST YOUNG FLEDGED SUCCESSFUL FROM PARASITIZED AND UNPARASITIZED NESTS IN 40 STUDIES OF 19 HOST SPECIES

Host	Unparasitized mean ± SD (N)	Parasitized mean ± SD (N)	Effect size	Reference
Willow flycatcher	2.20 ± 0.3 (9)	2.00 ± 0.0 (2)	-0.65	Sedgwick and Knopf 1985
	2.00 ± 1.00 (3)	0.80 ± 1.30 (5)	-0.86	Harris 1991[a]
California Gnatcatcher	2.75 ± 0.93 (102)	2.16 ± 0.96 (19)	-0.63	M.J. Whitfield, pers. comm.
	2.90 ± 1.13 (80)	0.00 ± 0.00 (9)	-2.67	G.T. Braden, pers. comm.[a]
Wood Thrush	2.94 ± 1.03 (47)	2.07 ± 0.73 (14)	-0.88	Donovan et al. 1995[b]
	2.70 ± 1.03 (6)	1.90 ± 1.29 (10)	-0.63	Trine, in press (nests with 1 cowbird egg)[b]
	2.70 ± 1.03 (6)	1.00 ± 0.71 (9)	-1.89	Trine, in press (2 cowbird eggs)[b]
	2.70 ± 1.03 (6)	1.10 ± 0.90 (13)	-1.63	Trine, in press (3 cowbird eggs)[b]
	2.70 ± 1.03 (6)	1.40 ± 1.52 (6)	-0.92	Trine, in press (4 cowbird eggs)[b]
	2.70 ± 1.03 (6)	0.83 ± 0.75 (8)	-1.99	Trine, in press (5 cowbird eggs)[b]
	2.70 ± 1.03 (6)	0.33 ± 0.58 (5)	-2.52	Trine, in press (6 cowbird eggs)[b]
Red-eyed Vireo	2.94 ± 0.87 (18)	0.90 ± 1.05 (29)	-2.04	Southern 1958[a]
	3.00 ± 1.00 (19)	2.40 ± 1.34 (5)	-0.54	Donovan et al. 1995[b]
Prothonotary Warbler	4.50 ± 0.90 (42)	3.50 ± 1.40 (14)	-0.95	Petit 1991 (early nests)
	3.90 ± 1.00 (42)	2.90 ± 1.20 (7)	-0.96	Petit 1991 (late nests)
Yellow Warbler	0.80 ± 0.16 (35)	0.44 ± 0.33 (31)	-1.4	Clark and Robertson 1981[c]
	3.23 ± 1.12 (125)	2.50 ± 1.38 (30)	-0.62	Goossen and Sealy 1982[d]
	3.76 ± 0.77 (21)	2.67 ± 1.12 (9)	-1.2	Burgham and Picman 1989
	3.56 ± 1.11 (48)	1.90 ± 0.91 (20)	-1.55	Weatherhead 1989
	2.56 ± 1.26 (25)	2.31 ± 1.44 (13)	-0.19	J.C. Ortega, C.P. Ortega, S. Allerton, S.A. Backensto, C.A. Rapp, and S. Vorisek, unpubl. abstract
Ovenbird	4.16 ± 0.94 (63)	2.00 ± 0.95 (8)	-2.27	Donovan et al. 1995[b]
Louisiana Waterthrush	5.20 ± 1.30 (5)	2.29 ± 1.60 (7)	-1.8	Eaton 1958
Indigo Bunting	3.44 ± 0.88 (9)	1.46 ± 1.20 (13)	-1.76	Twomey 1945[a]
Dickcissel	3.70 ± 0.72 (9)	1.80 ± 1.22 (41)	-1.63	Zimmerman 1983 (prairie habitat)[e]
	3.20 ± 1.03 (54)	2.00 ± 1.28 (57)	-1.02	Zimmerman 1983 (old field habitat)[e]
Lark Sparrow	3.20 ± 0.79 (10)	2.25 ± 0.96 (4)	-1.07	Newman 1970[a]
Grasshopper Sparrow	3.72 ± 0.24 (18)	2.40 ± 0.60 (5)	-3.75	Davis and Sealy, in press
Song Sparrow	4.13 ± 0.88 (16)	2.64 ± 1.57 (11)	-1.2	Cavalcanti 1981 (early season)
	3.60 ± 1.30 (15)	2.71 ± 1.38 (7)	-0.65	Cavalcanti 1981 (late season)
Dark-eyed Junco	2.70 ± 1.10 (12)	1.50 ± 1.10 (8)	-1.04	Wolf 1987
Chestnut-collared Longspur	3.61 ± 0.22 (23)	3.50 ± 0.50 (4)	-0.4	Davis and Sealy, in press
Red-winged Blackbird	2.40 ± 0.97 (39)	1.30 ± 0.50 (4)	-1.14	Ortega and Cruz 1988 (1984 data)
	2.90 ± 0.93 (60)	2.40 ± 0.90 (19)	-0.54	Ortega and Cruz 1988 (1985 data)
	2.90 ± 0.99 (111)	1.40 ± 0.54 (7)	-1.53	Ortega and Cruz 1988 (1986 data)
	3.15 ± 1.01 (46)	2.92 ± 1.06 (24)	-0.22	Weatherhead 1989 (singly parasitized)
	3.15 ± 1.01 (46)	2.28 ± 1.11 (7)	-0.84	Weatherhead 1989 (multiply parasitized)
	2.72 ± 1.00 (654)	1.78 ± 1.50 (55)	-0.9	Røskaft et al. 1990

TABLE 1. CONTINUED

Host	Unparasitized mean ± SD (N)	Parasitized mean ± SD (N)	Effect size	Reference
Western Meadowlark	3.00 ± 0.38 (14)	2.25 ± 0.49 (8)	−1.71	Davis and Sealy, in press
American Goldfinch	2.90 ± 2.37 (77)	2.30 ± 2.12 (18)	−0.26	Middleton 1977, pers. comm.[c]
House Finch	3.80 ± 0.79 (10)	2.64 ± 1.21 (11)	−1.08	Kozlovic, in press

[a] The mean number of young fledged in parasitized and unparasitized nests, standard deviations, and sample sizes were calculated from raw data.
[b] Donovan et al. (1995) and Trine (in press) were contacted for exact values of the means and standard deviations that were presented in graphical form in their papers.
[c] Productivity is in terms of number of host young fledged per egg laid, including buried eggs.
[d] Goossen and Sealy's (1982) data were re-analyzed to obtain standard deviations.
[e] Standard errors were converted to standard deviations.

sults of the meta-analysis by bringing the significance level up to P ≥ 0.05 (Fernandez-Duque and Valeggia 1994, Arnqvist and Wooster 1995). We used the formula provided in Fernandez-Duque and Valeggia (1994) to calculate the number of unpublished studies with insignificant results that would be required to invalidate the results of our meta-analysis. We set the minimum meaningful value for the mean effect size at 0.2. To evaluate effect size, Cohen (1988:25) suggested that d = 0.2 is small, d = 0.5 is medium, and d = 0.8 is large. Presumably an effect size greater than 1.0 is "very large" (Gurevitch and Hedges 1993).

RESULTS

OVERALL EFFECT SIZE

Regardless of whether the calculation of fledging success was based on all nests or on successful nests only, brood parasitism by the Brown-headed Cowbird significantly decreased host productivity across all studies. The overall effect size across all of the classes was −1.09 (± 0.01) when the meta-analysis was based on successful nests, and −0.81 (± 0.01) when the analysis was based on all nests. Therefore, in our analyses, the mean effect size of parasitism on the productivity of its hosts was "large" when productivity was based on all nests and "very large" when productivity was based on successful nests only, according to Cohen's (1988) and Gurevitch and Hedge's (1993) guidelines. Calculating fledging success based on successful nests resulted in a greater cost of parasitism compared with calculating fledging success using all nests. For example, 15 of the 17 studies for which productivity data were calculated using both methods had a smaller effect size when fledging success was based on all nests (Table 5).

Another way of interpreting the value of effect sizes is in terms of the difference in standard deviation units between the experimental and control groups (Gurevitch and Hedges 1993). Cowbird parasitism caused a mean decrease of 0.79 standard deviations in the number of young that fledged from a nest, and a mean decrease of 1.09 standard deviations when based on successful nests only. Converting the effect size to a Z-score revealed that an average parasitized nest fledged fewer young than 79% of the unparasitized nests, and an average parasitized successful nest fledged fewer young than 86% of the unparasitized successful nests.

Using the formula provided in Fernandez-Duque and Valeggia (1994), 134 unpublished studies that estimated productivity based on all nests with statistically insignificant results and 178

TABLE 2. MEAN NUMBER OF HOST YOUNG FLEDGED FROM ALL PARASITIZED AND UNPARASITIZED NESTS IN 44 STUDIES OF 25 HOST SPECIES

Host	Unparasitized mean ± SD (N)	Parasitized mean ± SD (N)	Effect size	Reference
Western Wood-Pewee	1.69 ± 1.41 (111)	0.29 ± 0.85 (17)	-1.02	D.R. Curson, pers. comm.
Willow Flycatcher	1.50 ± 1.29 (4)	0.31 ± 0.85 (13)	-1.18	Harris 1991[a]
	1.51 ± 1.54 (186)	0.31 ± 0.84 (133)	-0.92	M.J. Whitfield, pers. comm.
Eastern Phoebe	4.39 ± 3.62 (97)	1.97 ± 2.48 (79)	-0.76	E.E. Klaas, pers. comm.[b]
California Gnatcatcher	3.30 ± 2.85 (23)	0.63 ± 1.18 (27)	-1.24	G.T. Braden, pers. comm. (1992–1993 data)[a,b]
	2.11 ± 2.39 (64)	0.50 ± 1.07 (8)	-0.69	G.T. Braden, pers. comm. (1994–1995 data)[a,b]
Blue-grey Gnatcatcher	1.44 ± 1.68 (36)	0.11 ± 0.58 (129)	-1.43	D.R. Curson, pers. comm.
Wood Thrush	4.00 ± 0.00 (3)	2.00 ± 1.73 (3)	-1.31	Twomey 1945[a]
	3.10 ± 2.00 (128)	3.10 ± 2.20 (90)	0.00	Roth et al. 1996[b]
Sprague's Pipit	1.36 ± 0.43 (14)	0.00 ± 0.00 (3)	-3.22	Davis and Sealy, in press
Warbling Vireo	0.40 ± 0.54 (5)	0.06 ± 0.25 (16)	-0.98	C.P. Ortega, pers. comm.[c]
Plumbeous Vireo	2.09 ± 1.66 (80)	0.49 ± 1.04 (81)	-1.15	Chace et al., this volume
	1.39 ± 1.69 (18)	0.25 ± 0.80 (76)	-1.1	D.R. Curson, pers. comm.
Red-eyed Vireo	2.00 ± 2.83 (2)	1.60 ± 1.07 (10)	-0.27	Twomey 1945[a]
	2.41 ± 1.40 (22)	0.46 ± 0.87 (56)	-1.84	Southern 1958[a]
Yellow Warbler	1.89 ± 1.82 (227)	0.96 ± 1.49 (78)	-0.53	Goossen and Sealy 1982[d]
	2.00 ± 1.94 (15)	0.32 ± 1.10 (25)	-1.12	DellaSala 1985[e]
	2.28 ± 1.94 (75)	0.88 ± 1.14 (43)	-0.82	Weatherhead 1989
Louisiana Waterthrush	3.71 ± 2.75 (7)	2.00 ± 1.69 (8)	-0.72	Eaton 1958
Western Tanager	2.00 ± 1.65 (26)	1.00 ± 1.06 (42)	-0.75	D.R. Curson, pers. comm.
Indigo Bunting	1.24 ± 1.76 (25)	1.19 ± 1.22 (16)	-0.03	Twomey 1945[a]
	2.25 ± 1.75 (8)	0.00 ± 0.00 (5)	-1.5	Phillips 1951[a]
	1.54 ± 1.46 (763)	0.37 ± 0.81 (277)	-0.89	Payne and Payne 1998 (Niles)
	1.62 ± 1.51 (556)	0.40 ± 0.90 (140)	-0.86	Payne and Payne 1998 (George Reserve)
Clay-colored Sparrow	1.49 ± 0.74 (148)	0.04 ± 0.20 (26)	-2.10	Knapton 1978, pers. comm.
Lark Sparrow	1.88 ± 1.73 (17)	0.64 ± 1.15 (14)	-0.81	Newman 1970[a]
Savannah Sparrow	1.09 ± 0.33 (21)	0.11 ± 0.11 (9)	-3.35	Davis and Sealy, in press
Baird's Sparrow	1.55 ± 0.29 (42)	1.21 ± 0.31 (24)	-1.13	Davis and Sealy, in press
Grasshopper Sparrow	2.03 ± 0.35 (33)	0.92 ± 0.39 (13)	-3.02	Davis and Sealy, in press
Song Sparrow	3.27 ± 1.73 (26)	3.28 ± 2.01 (45)	0.01	Smith 1981 (adult)[e,f]
	2.06 ± 2.21 (32)	2.13 ± 2.01 (24)	0.03	Smith 1981 (juvenile)[e,f]
	1.77 ± 1.13 (30)	0.63 ± 0.83 (19)	-1.09	Smith and Arcese 1994 (1983 data)[e,g]
	1.92 ± 1.40 (37)	0.92 ± 1.02 (24)	-0.78	Smith and Arcese 1994 (1984 data)[e,g]
	1.05 ± 1.25 (94)	0.58 ± 0.76 (31)	-0.41	Smith and Arcese 1994 (1986 data)[e,g]
	1.04 ± 1.25 (51)	0.49 ± 0.86 (43)	-0.50	Smith and Arcese 1994 (1987 data)[e,g]
Chestnut-collared Longspur	1.73 ± 0.28 (48)	1.75 ± 0.70 (8)	0.05	Davis and Sealy, in press
Bobolink	1.33 ± 1.33 (3)	1.33 ± 1.33 (3)	0.00	Davis and Sealy, in press
Red-winged Blackbird	0.80 ± 1.26 (121)	0.60 ± 0.73 (9)	-0.16	Ortega and Cruz 1988 (1984 data)

TABLE 2. CONTINUED

Host	Unparasitized mean ± SD (N)	Parasitized mean ± SD (N)	Effect size	Reference
Red-winged Blackbird (continued)	1.00 ± 1.48 (176)	1.50 ± 1.36 (30)	0.34	Ortega and Cruz 1988 (1985 data)
	1.10 ± 1.51 (299)	0.70 ± 0.82 (15)	-0.27	Ortega and Cruz 1988 (1986 data)
	1.24 ± 1.68 (118)	1.33 ± 1.63 (57)	0.05	Weatherhead 1989 (singly parasitized)
	1.24 ± 1.68 (118)	1.23 ± 1.42 (13)	-0.01	Weatherhead 1989 (multiply parasitized)
Western Meadowlark	1.13 ± 0.28 (37)	0.64 ± 0.64 (28)	-1.03	Davis and Sealy, in press
Purple Finch	1.88 ± 1.87 (186)	1.00 ± 1.85 (8)	-0.47	Wootton 1996

[a] The mean number of young fledged in parasitized and unparasitized nests, standard deviations, and sample sizes were calculated from raw data.
[b] Productivity is in terms of number of young fledged per female or pair per breeding season.
[c] C. P. Ortega (pers. comm.) recorded the number of young that fledged per nest, but she remarked that this value was probably not any different from the number of young fledged per female because at her study site in southwestern Colorado, the nesting season is short and second nesting attempts are rare.
[d] Goossen and Sealy's (1982) data were re-analyzed to obtain standard deviations.
[e] Standard errors were converted to standard deviations.
[f] Productivity is in terms of number of young that reached independence per female (i.e., number of young that survived to four weeks after hatching).
[g] Data from 1985 and 1988 were not included in meta-analysis because food experimentally added to territories in these years decreased the cost of parasitism.

unpublished studies that estimated productivity based on successful nests with statistically insignificant results would be required to conclude that cowbird parasitism had no effect on the hosts.

META-ANALYSIS BASED ON SUCCESSFUL NESTS

There was a significant difference in the effect of cowbird parasitism among all classes in the meta-analysis based on successful nests ($Q_B = 63.7$, df = 9, P < 0.001). Fledging success was reduced by cowbird parasitism in all species, as indicated by uniformly negative effect sizes (Table 3). Furthermore, the 95% confidence limits for effect sizes did not overlap zero in any of the classes in the meta-analysis based on successful nests, which indicated that the effect sizes for all species were significantly less than zero. Thus, cowbird parasitism significantly decreased the productivity of successful nests in Willow Flycatchers, Wood Thrushes, Red-eyed Vireos, Prothonotary Warblers, Yellow Warblers, Dickcissels, and Red-winged Blackbirds (Table 3). Cowbird parasitism also significantly decreased the productivity of successful nests of the nine species in the "other insectivorous hosts" class and the two species in the "granivorous hosts" class. This finding was confirmed because all individual effect sizes for the studies in the two latter classes were negative.

META-ANALYSIS BASED ON ALL NESTS

There was a significant difference in the effect of cowbird parasitism among all of the species ($Q_B = 36.2$, df = 12, P < 0.001; Table 4). The 95% confidence interval for effect sizes overlapped zero for Wood Thrushes and Red-winged Blackbirds, indicating that the effect sizes for these two species were not significantly different from zero, and that cowbird parasitism did not significantly affect the productivity of these species. The class effect sizes for all other species were significantly less than zero, indicating that cowbird parasitism significantly decreased the productivity of these species.

COMPARISON OF THE COST OF PARASITISM WHEN CALCULATED USING DIFFERENT METHODS

G.T. Braden's (pers. comm.) data on California Gnatcatchers were the only data for which the cost of parasitism could be calculated in all three ways. The effect size of parasitism based on the productivity of females was -0.81 (Table 6). The use of successful nests only grossly overestimated the cost of parasitism (effect size = -2.27), whereas the use of all nests underestimated the cost of parasitism (effect size = -0.54).

TABLE 3. THE MASS AND EFFECT SIZES FOR EIGHT SPECIES STUDIED MORE THAN ONCE, AND FOR THE NINE INSECTIVOROUS AND TWO GRANIVOROUS SPECIES STUDIED ONCE; PRODUCTIVITY IS BASED ON SUCCESSFUL NESTS

| | Mean adult mass (g) | Effect size (no. studies in class) | 95% confidence limits | |
			Lower	Upper
≥2 studies per species:				
Willow Flycatcher	13.4	−0.67 (3)	−0.87	−0.47
Wood Thrush	47.4	−1.32 (7)	−1.42	−1.22
Red-eyed Vireo	16.7	−1.44 (2)	−1.69	−1.19
Prothonotary Warbler	14.3	−0.95 (2)	−1.16	−0.74
Yellow Warbler	9.5	−0.95 (5)	−1.03	−0.88
Dickcissel	27	−1.24 (2)	−1.41	−1.07
Song Sparrow	20	−0.94 (2)	−1.2	−0.68
Red-winged Blackbird	52.6	−0.79 (6)	−0.85	−0.73
1 study per insectivorous host:				
California Gnatcatcher	6	−2.67		
Ovenbird	19.4	−2.27		
Louisiana Waterthrush	20.3	−1.8		
Indigo Bunting	14.1	−1.76		
Lark Sparrow	29	−1.07		
Grasshopper Sparrow	17	−3.75		
Dark-eyed Junco	20	−1.04		
Chestnut-collared Longspur	18.9	−0.4		
Western Meadowlark	100.7	−1.71		
		−1.81 (9)	−1.88	−1.74
1 study per granivorous host:				
American Goldfinch	12.9	−0.26		
House Finch	21.4	−1.08		
		−0.55 (2)	−0.75	−0.35

EFFECT OF MULTIPLE PARASITISM ON COST OF PARASITISM

The effect size of parasitism tended to increase as the number of cowbird eggs laid in Wood Thrush nests increased; however, this trend was not significant (effect size = − 0.258 [number of cowbird eggs] − 0.693; $t = -1.88$, $P = 0.13$, $r^2 = 0.25$). Successful multiply parasitized Red-winged Blackbird nests had a greater effect size of parasitism than successful singly parasitized nests (-0.84 and −0.22, respectively).

EFFECT OF HOST MASS ON COST OF PARASITISM

When the meta-analysis was based on all nests, the cost of parasitism decreased as host mass increased for species that were studied more than once (effect size = −1.21–0.022 [mass]; $F = 8.8$, df = 1, 7; $P = 0.02$, $r^2 = 0.49$) (Fig. 1). The relationship only approached significance ($F = 4.44$, df = 1, 11; $P = 0.06$, $r^2 = 0.22$) when the four classes grouped by mass were included in the regression analysis. When all 25 species were included in the regression analysis, the trend was still apparent but the relationship was no longer statistically significant ($F = 1.16$, df = 1, 23; $P = 0.29$, $r^2 = 0.007$). When the meta-analysis was based on successful nests only, no association was found between the cost of parasitism and host mass, regardless of whether all species were included or when only species studied more than once were included ($F < 0.005$, df = 1, 17; $P = 0.95$, $r^2 = 0$; and $F = 0.08$, df = 1, 6; $P = 0.78$, $r^2 = 0$, respectively).

DISCUSSION

Overall, brood parasitism significantly affected host productivity. The results of our meta-analyses were resistant to the file-drawer problem (see Fernandez-Duque and Valeggia 1994, Arnqvist and Wooster 1995) because a sufficiently high number of unpublished studies with statistically insignificant results would have been required for us to conclude that cowbird parasitism had no effect on the hosts: 134 studies that estimated productivity based on all nests and 178 studies that estimated productivity only on successful nests.

Calculation of the cost of parasitism based on all nests resulted in a more moderate estimate of the cost of parasitism than using successful nests only (Table 5). Whether to calculate the cost of parasitism using all nests or only successful nests is debatable. The difference in fledging success of successful parasitized and unparasitized nests reflects the combination of both

TABLE 4.   MASS AND EFFECT SIZES FOR NINE SPECIES STUDIED MORE THAN ONCE, AND FOR THE 16 SPECIES STUDIED ONLY ONCE; PRODUCTIVITY IS BASED ON ALL NESTS

	Mean adult mass (g)	Effect size (no. studies in class)	95% confidence limits	
			Lower	Upper
≥2 studies per species:				
Willow Flycatcher	13.4	−1.00 (2)	−1.33	−0.68
California Gnatcatcher	6	−0.99 (2)	−1.31	−0.67
Wood Thrush	47.4	−0.17 (2)	−0.37	0.03
Plumbeous Vireo	16.6	−1.13 (2)	−1.27	−0.99
Red-eyed Vireo	16.7	−1.50 (2)	−1.76	−1.23
Yellow Warbler	9.5	−0.84 (3)	−0.99	−0.69
Indigo bunting	14.1	−0.55 (2)	−0.95	−0.15
Song Sparrow	20	−0.35 (6)	−0.42	−0.28
Red-winged Blackbird	52.6	0.004 (5)	−0.11	0.11
1 study per species:				
Blue-grey Gnatcatcher	6	−1.43		
Clay-colored Sparrow	12	−2.1		
Western Wood-Pewee	12.8	−1.02		
Warbling Vireo	14.8	−0.98		
		−1.47 (4)	−1.56	−1.38
Grasshopper Sparrow	17	−3.02		
Baird's Sparrow	17.5	−1.13		
Chestnut-collared Longspur	18.9	0.05		
Eastern Phoebe	19.8	−0.76		
Savannah Sparrow	20	−3.35		
Louisiana Waterthrush	20.3	−0.72		
		−1.21 (6)	−1.29	−1.13
Purple Finch	24.9	−0.47		
Sprague's Pipit	25.3	−3.22		
Western Tanager	28.1	−0.75		
Lark Sparrow	29	−0.81		
		−0.87 (4)	−0.99	−0.76
Bobolink	42	0		
Western Meadowlark	100.7	−1.03		
		−0.78 (2)	−1.13	−0.42

clutch and brood reduction caused by cowbirds, whereas the overall difference in fledging success of parasitized and unparasitized nests includes differences in nest-survival frequencies in the two groups (Weatherhead 1989). If the intention is to isolate the effect of brood parasitism, then it is most appropriate to consider successful nests only. If one is interested in determining the effect of parasitism on the entire population, then it is necessary to consider all nests. Roth et al. (1996) remarked that only studies that consider both parasitism and predation truly evaluate the effect of parasitism on host productivity. When predation frequencies are high, the effects of parasitism will be swamped (Stutchbury 1997). A criticism, however, of using all nests is that failed nests are less likely to be found than successful ones (Mayfield 1961). Below, we suggest a method of calculating the cost of parasitism that is better than using nest productivity data.

EFFECT OF HOST MASS ON COST OF PARASITISM

We predicted that host mass would have a significant effect on the cost of parasitism when cost was based on successful nests because the cost of parasitism would not be confounded by predation. Interestingly, we found the opposite. Host mass significantly affected the cost of parasitism when cost was based on all nests; larger species experienced a lower cost of parasitism (Fig. 1). Scott and Lemon (1996) suggested that a cowbird nestling is less able to compete with nestlings of large host species, therefore, hosts larger than a certain mass experience negligible costs due to nestling competition. Much of the cost of parasitism for species larger than 20 g (Song Sparrow, Dark-eyed Junco, Dickcissel, Wood Thrush, and Red-winged Blackbird) is manifested through egg removal by the female cowbird (Smith 1981, Zimmerman 1983, Wolf 1987, Røskaft et al. 1990, Trine in press). The

TABLE 5. EFFECT SIZE OF PARASITISM FOR STUDIES THAT CALCULATED PRODUCTIVITY OF HOSTS IN PARASITIZED AND UNPARASITIZED NESTS BASED ON SUCCESSFUL NESTS AND ALL NEST

| Species | Effect size | | Reference |
	Successful nests	All nests	
Willow Flycatcher	−0.86	−1.18	Harris 1991
Willow Flycatcher	−0.63	−0.92	M.J. Whitfield, unpubl. data
California Gnatcatcher	−2.67	−0.98	G.T. Braden, pers. comm.[a]
Red-eyed Vireo	−2.04	−1.84	Southern 1958
Yellow Warbler	−0.62	−0.53	Goossen and Sealy 1982[b]
Yellow Warbler	−1.55	−0.82	Weatherhead 1989
Louisiana Waterthrush	−1.8	−0.72	Eaton 1958
Indigo Bunting	−1.76	−0.03	Twomey 1945
Lark Sparrow	−1.07	−0.81	Newman 1970
Grasshopper Sparrow	−3.75	−3.02	Davis and Sealy, in press
Chestnut-collared Longspur	−0.40	0.05	Davis and Sealy, in press
Red-winged Blackbird	−1.14	−0.16	Ortega and Cruz 1988 (1984 data)
Red-winged Blackbird	−0.54	0.34	Ortega and Cruz 1988 (1985 data)
Red-winged Blackbird	−1.53	−0.27	Ortega and Cruz 1988 (1986 data)
Red-winged Blackbird	−0.22	0.05	Weatherhead 1989 (singly parasitized)
Red-winged Blackbird	−0.84	−0.01	Weatherhead 1989 (multiply parasitized)
Western Meadowlark	−1.71	−1.03	Davis and Sealy, in press

Note: A negative sign indicates a cost of parasitism, and an effect size of 0.2 is small, 0.5 is medium, and ≥0.8 is large (see text for details).
[a] Pooled effect size for 1992–1995. Productivity is in terms of number of young fledged per female.
[b] Goossen and Sealy's (1982) data were re-analyzed to obtain standard deviations.

next logical question is how does host mass affect the number of host eggs that are removed?

Preliminary results based on 21 studies on 18 species suggest that the size of the host does not affect the average number of host eggs that are removed from parasitized nests (y = 0.991–0.005 [host mass]; t = −0.46, P = 0.65, r^2 = 0). The mean number of host eggs removed at parasitized nests by female cowbirds was 0.88 ± 0.51 (N = 18 species; Lorenzana and Sealy, unpubl. data). Therefore, the significant relationship between host mass and cost of parasitism apparently exists because fewer host young are outcompeted by cowbird nestling(s) as hosts increase in size, rather than an increased number of host eggs removed by cowbirds.

There was no significant relationship between host mass and the cost of parasitism when cost was based on successful nests only. This is puzzling; we cannot adequately explain these results. Other factors besides host mass probably affect the difference in the number of young that fledge from parasitized and unparasitized nests.

For example, the relative availability of food in different habitats affects the cost of parasitism. Smith and Arcese (1994) found that the cost of parasitism was less in years when food supplies were artificially supplemented. Consideration of species characteristics may also help explain the lack of effect of host mass on cost of parasitism when cost was calculated on the basis of successful nests only. Yellow Warblers (9.5 g) probably incurred a smaller cost of parasitism than expected for their size because they often bury cowbird eggs; Clark and Roberston (1991) demonstrated that buried and unparasitized Yellow Warbler nests fledged the same number of young. Wood Thrushes (47.4 g) probably incurred a larger cost of parasitism than expected for their size because their nests received up to 6 cowbird eggs (Trine in press).

Parasitized nests of Red-winged Blackbirds and Wood Thrushes did not fledge significantly fewer young than their unparasitized counterparts when cost was calculated using all nests. However, for successful nests only, Ortega and

TABLE 6. THE EFFECT SIZE OF THE COST OF PARASITISM FOR CALIFORNIA GNATCATCHERS (G.T. BRADEN, PERS. COMM.)

| Method used to calculate effect size | Unparasitized | | | Parasitized | | | Effect size |
	N	Mean no. fledged young	SD	N	Mean no. fledged young	SD	
All nests	346	0.67	1.34	58	0	0	−0.54
Successful nests	80	2.9	1.13	9	0	0	−2.27
Females only	87	2.43	2.56	35	0.6	1.14	−0.81

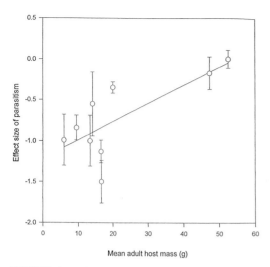

FIGURE 1. The effect of host mass on the cost of raising a Brown-headed Cowbird chick when host productivity is calculated based on all nests, including only species on which more than one study was conducted. Each data point represents the mean effect size for one host species, and error bars are 95% confidence intervals. Negative scale on y-axis indicates a cost of parasitism.

Cruz (1988) and Weatherhead (1989) demonstrated that parasitized individuals suffered reproductive loss due to cowbird parasitism, but that ejection behavior for the population as a whole was not selected because of the relatively low parasitism frequency. This may explain why Red-winged Blackbirds accept cowbird eggs despite being able to eject objects as large as cowbird eggs (Ortega and Cruz 1988).

GRANIVOROUS HOSTS

We hypothesized that granivorous hosts should incur fewer costs associated with parasitism because the insectivorous cowbird nestlings are unable to survive on a diet of seeds (Middleton 1991, Kozlovic et al. 1996, Wootton 1996). Our hypothesis was supported because the granivorous hosts class had the lowest effect size among all classes. Nonetheless, parasitized nests of American Goldfinches and House Finches fledged significantly fewer young than unparasitized nests because of host egg removal by the cowbird. Hatchability of the remaining host eggs was not affected by the cowbird eggs (Middleton 1977, Kozlovic in press).

LIMITATIONS OF USING NEST PRODUCTIVITY TO CALCULATE THE COST OF PARASITISM

A meta-analysis is only as good as the studies on which it is based. A limitation of our analysis is that 95% of the studies calculated the cost of parasitism on a per-nest basis. It is important to note that nest productivity does not accurately reflect seasonal fecundity because birds may renest after successfully fledging a brood or after nest failure due to parasitism, predation, severe weather or nest desertion (May and Robinson 1985, Pease and Grzybowski 1995). Therefore, females that renest after nesting failure due to cowbird parasitism may still successfully fledge young in the same breeding season (e.g., Roth et al. 1996). For this reason, a better method of calculating the cost of parasitism is to determine the effect of parasitism on the productivity of parasitized individuals over the entire breeding season rather than on an individual's nesting success (Pease and Grzybowski 1995). Calculation of the costs based on seasonal fecundity more accurately reflects the selective pressure of cowbird parasitism on a host population.

To our knowledge, only four studies have attempted to follow parasitized and unparasitized females over the course of the entire nesting season. Considering only nesting attempts during the time that cowbirds actively lay may overestimate the cost of parasitism. Smith (1981) found that parasitism depressed the breeding success of female Song Sparrows in a given breeding attempt, but females raised the same total number of young to independence in a breeding season, regardless of whether they were parasitized because they made more breeding attempts per year. Similarly, in a 16-year study Roth et al. (1996) found that parasitized and unparasitized Wood Thrush females fledged the same number of young per year because females renested when the frequency of cowbird parasitism was lower. On the other hand, Klaas (1975) and G.T. Braden (pers. comm.) found that Eastern Phoebes and California Gnatcatchers, respectively, incurred a significant cost of parasitism when breeding success was based on the entire nesting season. However, Klaas (1975) did not work with a marked population and he assumed that pairs renested in their original territories.

The analysis of G.T. Braden's (pers. comm.) data on the fledging success of California Gnatcatchers indicated that the use of successful nests only in the calculation of cost of parasitism grossly overestimated the cost. The use of all nests, however, underestimated the cost relative to cost calculated on the basis of female productivity over the entire breeding season (Table 6). The difference in the calculated costs of parasitism is likely due to the high frequency of nest failure of gnatcatcher nests. Indeed, 74% of unparasitized gnatcatcher nests failed due to predation, nest desertion, weather, or infertility (Braden et al. 1997b). Because a high proportion of gnatcatcher nests failed for reasons other than cowbird parasitism, the calculated cost of parasitism was quite low when all nests were considered in the cost of parasitism. Although these data may be extreme because of frequent failure, a comparison of the results obtained when the cost of parasitism is calculated in different ways confirms that the way in which the cost of parasitism is calculated influences strongly the value for the cost. Researchers should be cautious when interpreting costs of parasitism calculated using nest productivity data.

Pease and Grzybowski (1995) developed a model that may be used to estimate the seasonal fecundity of a population based on several life history parameters that are more easily measured in the field. They tested their model using Prairie Warbler (*Dendroica discolor*) and Black-capped Vireo (*Vireo atricapillus*) data and found that their theoretical estimates of seasonal fecundity matched closely values measured directly (empirical observation = 2.2 and prediction from model = 2.2 Prairie Warblers raised per female; empirical observation = 0.9 or 1.0 and prediction from model = 1.0 Black-capped Vireos raised per female). Researchers who cannot measure the seasonal fecundity of their host population in question should consider using the Pease and Grzybowski (1995) model. Furthermore, studies that measure the seasonal fecundity of a host population directly may be used to test the validity of the model.

A second problem with most studies that quantified the cost of parasitism is that young produced in a season were monitored only until they fledged. Much more effort is required to monitor fledged young because it requires color-marked individuals that generally are very difficult to relocate once they have left the nest. To our knowledge, only Smith's (1981) study determined the survivorship of host young to independence (four weeks after hatching). Basing host productivity on the number of young that fledge from a nest underestimates the cost of parasitism if disproportionately fewer host young survive to independence because their parents are also caring for fledgling cowbirds. Robinson (1992) found that hosts often cared only for cowbird fledglings. Clearly, studies of the productivity of cowbird hosts should look beyond the nestling stage.

Further studies are also needed to determine whether there is a difference in the number of young fledged by parasitized and unparasitized hosts and recruited into a breeding population. Even when the number of young fledged by parasitized and unparasitized females does not differ (see Smith 1981, Roth et al. 1996), the number of young recruited to future breeding seasons may be different. Payne and Payne (1998) found that Indigo Buntings that fledged from nests that also fledged a cowbird were only 18% as likely to return the next year compared to buntings from nests that did not fledge cowbirds. Whitfield and Sogge (*this volume*) also found that young fledged by parasitized pairs were less likely to return than young fledged from unparasitized pairs. This was due to the fact that parasitized pairs were forced to renest before successfully fledging young, and young that fledged later had lower return rates than earlier-fledged young (see also Perrins 1970, Hochachka 1990).

Another possible cost of parasitism that was not addressed by our study is the reduction in a host's future reproductive success. Caring for an additional chick may reduce a host's future productivity by reducing adult survival (May and Robinson 1985). Parasitized adults may work harder to feed additional cowbird young (Furrer in Friedmann et al. 1977). This cost is likely to be more important for small hosts. Only one study has attempted to assess the long-term cost of parasitism. Payne and Payne (1998) did not find that survival or reproductive success of Indigo Buntings was affected by parasitism in the previous year, and concluded that nearly all costs of parasitism are manifested in the parasitized brood. However, results from Gustafsson and Sutherland's (1988) study, in which a conspecific egg was added to Collared Flycatcher (*Ficedula albicollis*) nests, demonstrated that raising additional young may decrease an adult's future fecundity. Gustafsson and Sutherland (1988) reported that more chicks fledged from nests with enlarged clutches, but juveniles survived less well and those that did survive had reduced fecundity as measured by the number of their offspring that survived to breed. Furthermore, females with experimentally enlarged clutches laid fewer eggs the following year. The difference between Gustafsson and Sutherland's (1988) experiment and cases involving cowbird parasitism is that female cowbirds often remove one host egg from nests they parasitize (e.g., Sealy 1992). Host egg removal may reduce some of the negative effects of brood parasitism on future fecundity (McMaster and Sealy 1997); however, one cowbird egg may represent the equivalent of more than one small host egg. It is conceivable, therefore, that some of the effects of enlarged Collared Flycatchers clutches are analogous to the effect of cowbird parasitism on the future fecundity of hosts. A limitation of the studies of Payne and Payne (1998) and Gustafsson and Sutherland (1998) is that they assessed long-term costs by considering the survivorship and fecundity of females in the next year; they did not consider the lifetime cumulative effects of parasitism. Assessing the lifetime cumulative effects of parasitism is difficult because breeding individuals must be tracked over their lifetime with an accounting of all of their breeding attempts.

RECOMMENDATIONS FOR FUTURE STUDIES OF PRODUCTIVITY

Our meta-analysis summarized empirical studies that quantified the cost of cowbird parasitism. Across all studies, the number of young fledged per nest was significantly decreased by cowbird parasitism, and larger species incurred a smaller cost of parasitism that approached significance when all nests were used in the calculation of parasitism costs. It is important to assess the costs of parasitism accurately to understand better host responses to cowbird parasitism. If the cost of parasitism is not as great as the cost of evolving anti-parasite strategies such as egg ejection behavior, then it makes sense that some species raise cowbird young. For example, our meta-analysis revealed that Red-winged Blackbirds and Wood Thrushes did not incur a significant cost when the cost of parasitism was calculated on the basis of all nests (Table 4). It is also necessary to understand the impact of cowbird parasitism because of its conservation implications. If cowbird parasitism is not as costly as traditionally believed, there will be less support for the control of female cowbirds. Calculating the cost of parasitism based on successful nests only overestimated the cost of parasitism relative to the cost of parasitism based on all nests (Table 5) or on female seasonal fecundity (Table 6).

Ninety-five percent of the studies defined the cost of parasitism in terms of the difference in the number of young fledged from parasitized and unparasitized nests. This estimation does not necessarily reflect the selection pressure that parasitized individuals face because some parasitized individuals that renest raise the same number of young as unparasitized individuals (Smith 1981, Roth et al. 1996). Fledglings of parasitized pairs may have a lower probability of surviving to the next year than young of unparasitized pairs (e.g., Whitfield and Sogge *this volume*). We strongly encourage researchers to quantify the productivity of females over the entire breeding season. If this is not possible, the Pease-Grzybowski model may be used to estimate the seasonal fecundity of the host in question. Following young beyond the nestling stage and determining how parasitism affects the lifetime reproductive success of hosts are necessary to obtain a more accurate representation of the cost of parasitism. These questions are difficult to assess through empirical studies; hence, mathematical models may be required to determine the cost of parasitism.

ACKNOWLEDGMENTS

M. V. Abrahams was instrumental in this study because he introduced JCL to meta-analysis in his quantitative and theoretical ecology course. He provided useful comments on an early draft of the manuscript. We thank G. T. Braden, T. M. Donovan, E. E. Klaas, R. W. Knapton, A. L. A. Middleton, C. L. Trine, and M. J. Whitfield for providing additional information not contained in their original papers. J. F. Chace, D. R. Curson, C. P. Ortega, and J. C. Ortega kindly provided us with unpublished data. D. R. Kozlovic allowed us to read an unpublished manuscript that contained data pertinent to our study. We are thankful for comments made by L. S. Hall, B. E. Kus, and M. J. Whitfield that improved the manuscript. Financial support was provided by a NSERC research grant to SGS and NSERC postgraduate scholarship to JCL.

Studies in Avian Biology No. 18:254–259, 1999.

SECTION III: COWBIRD CONTROL: THE EFFICACY OF LONG-TERM CONTROL AND PROPOSED ALTERNATIVES TO STANDARD CONTROL PRACTICES

LINNEA S. HALL AND STEPHEN I. ROTHSTEIN

THE PROBLEM

Relatively little research has been conducted on the types of measures that can be employed to control Brown-headed Cowbird (*Molothrus ater*) numbers or to reduce levels of parasitism of sensitive host species without limiting cowbird numbers. The predominant control technique has consisted of intensive trapping and removal (Rothstein and Cook in press), and few other options have been discussed. This session of the 1997 conference was initially designed to provide a forum for evaluating other measures for controlling the impacts of cowbirds on hosts; however, the forum resulted primarily in papers that evaluated the long-term impacts of traditional controls (i.e., trapping and shooting) on cowbirds. Thus, the majority of the papers in this section provide illustrations of the outcomes of intensive control programs; only one paper speaks to the possible effects of an alternative control measure on cowbirds and hosts. We hope that the dearth of papers on this topic will stimulate researchers and managers to explore it more in the future.

EVALUATING THE EFFECTS OF LONG-TERM COWBIRD CONTROL

Whitfield et al. describe a control program implemented from 1993 through 1997, during which the authors trapped cowbirds, addled their eggs, and removed their chicks from nests of endangered Southwestern Willow Flycatchers (*Empidonax traillii extimus*) on the Kern River, Kern County, California. They found that parasitism rates decreased substantially over the time period, from an average of 65% in four years preceding trapping to 22% since cowbird control began. Concordant with the change in parasitism rates, the number of flycatcher fledglings per female per season increased from 1.4 to 1.72.

However, there was no marked increase in the number of breeding pairs occupying the study site, which apparently had room for population expansion. There were 34 pairs at the start of trapping in 1993, and 38 in 1997. Trapping may have stopped a decline in the size of the breeding population, which numbered 44 pairs in 1989 and declined to 24 in 1992 before cowbird control began. But the most recent data show yet another decline, even with cowbird trapping, to

26 pairs in 1998 (M. Whitfield, pers. comm.). Assessing effects of cowbird control on the size of the breeding population is complicated further by an apparent increase in the Kern River flycatcher population from 26 pairs in 1982 to 44 in 1989, even though no cowbird trapping was done in those years (Harris and Sanders 1987; Whitfield et al.). Whitfield et al. point out that surveys done in the 1980s may not have been comparable because they used varying methodologies and covered different-sized areas; however, they suggest that flycatcher numbers were probably at least stable then despite the lack of cowbird control. They further suggest that this stability may have occurred because of lower rates of parasitism in the 1980s, but we note that Harris (1991) reported a parasitism rate of approximately 68% (of 19 nests) in 1987, comparable to the mean pre-control rate of 65% for 1989–91 reported by Whitfield et al.

It seems clear that the Kern River flycatcher population has low productivity, because Whitfield et al.'s demographic analysis indicates that the number of fledglings produced annually seems too small to result in population growth in most years. Increasing the effectiveness of cowbird control so that parasitism rates fall below 22% could help, but Whitfield et al.'s data further suggest to us that high rates of nest predation and possibly other factors may indicate that the Kern River population would not be self-sustaining even with a parasitism rate of zero. Assuming all cases of parasitism result in an irreversible and complete loss of annual reproductive output for flycatchers (which actually exaggerates the effect of parasitism because flycatchers at the Kern River desert 54% of parasitized nests and subsequently renest [Harris 1991]), the average parasitism rate of 22% since 1993 means that the population has realized only 78% of the potential output it would realize with no parasitism. If this population were to realize all of its potential without parasitism, it would produce 1.28 times as many young per female (or 2.23 young per female; 1.28 x the mean of 1.74 young since 1993 reported by Whitfield et al.). An annual output of 2.23 young per female is just barely within the range that is needed to keep most populations of passerines stable, using available estimates for annual survival rates of juveniles and adults (Robinson et al. 1993, 1995). Thus, it is difficult to determine if continued cowbird removal will result in increased population sizes of Willow Flycatchers at the site. Nevertheless, we agree with Whitfield et al. that continued cowbird control, as conducted via trapping and/or addling eggs and removing cowbird chicks, is prudent, but we also think that some effort should be directed towards decreasing nest predation. One unique aspect of Whitfield et al.'s study is that it indicates that cowbird trapping suppresses cowbird numbers from one year to the next in the Kern River area. This year-to-year effect has not been found in other trapping programs (Rothstein and Cook in press), probably because cowbirds have very high dispersal rates (Fleischer and Rothstein 1988, Fleischer et al. 1991).

Winter and McKelvey discuss another long-term cowbird trapping program (1992–1997) that was designed to aid in the conservation of Least Bell's Vireos (*Vireo bellii pusillus*) and Willow Flycatchers on the Cleveland National Forest, San Diego County, California. The authors report that numbers of pairs and fledging success were high for flycatchers during the study, whereas numbers of pairs and fledging success were low for two of three vireo populations. In fact, two of the vireo populations were either extirpated or reduced to a single male by 1997. They conclude that their cowbird trapping efforts, for the most part, were ineffective in lowering parasitism rates on Least Bell's Vireos because of a limited number of traps that could be placed in the remote and rugged breeding locations on the National Forest. For remote sites, the authors suggest that nest monitoring and cowbird egg removal may be more effective, and less costly, than cowbird trapping. In addition to the flexible cowbird management approach advocated by Winter and McKelvey, it is worthwhile considering whether any cowbird management at all should be pursued with such small vireo populations, which ranged in size from only 4 to 6 pairs. There are now over 1000 pairs of vireos elsewhere in San Diego County (U.S. Fish and Wildlife Service 1998), and so it is questionable if these small populations will ever make a major contribution to the vireo's recovery if the local riparian habitat they use is limited. Unless small populations have the potential to become very large or occur in regions where an endangered species is still rare, the scarce resources available for conservation might be put to better use than that of aiding small populations that may be marginal under any circumstances.

Unlike the vireos, the Willow Flycatcher population studied by Winter and McKelvey was

near an existing road, which allowed for effective cowbird trapping, and only 2 of 82 nests were parasitized over four years. This flycatcher population was stable over the course of the study and ranged from 18–24 pairs. However, as the authors point out, it is unclear whether this stability could be attributed to cowbird control or whether control was even needed because no data were collected on pre-trapping rates of parasitism. This lack of pre-trapping data is unfortunate and conflicts with suggested cowbird control program guidelines that urge the collection of such data due to the considerable spatial variation in cowbird parasitism rates that can occur even within a single host species (Robinson et al. 1993). Without pre-trapping baseline data on rates of parasitism, managers run the risk of initiating control activities that will continue for many years without evidence that cowbird control is needed or is more cost-effective than other management approaches.

Eckrich et al. discuss a program that used trapping and shooting of Brown-headed Cowbirds on Ft. Hood, in Bell and Coryell counties, Texas, to aid the recovery of Black-capped Vireos (*Vireo atricapillus*). Cowbird control from 1987 to 1997 emphasized four measures: trapping in pastures with high concentrations of cattle, rather than in host breeding habitat; manipulating trap numbers; using several different trap designs to increase capture efficiency; and conducting both systematic and opportunistic shooting of cowbirds. Control was relatively ineffective until 1991 when trapping efforts were concentrated in cowbird feeding areas. The authors suggest that host breeding habitat is so extensive on Fort Hood that trapping in breeding habitat is not cost-effective, but they do show that a regular shooting program in which female cowbirds are attracted by playbacks in breeding habitat is an effective supplement to trapping at feeding sites.

Before any cowbird control began, vireos at Fort Hood experienced a parasitism rate of 90.9%. When trapping was not focused on cowbird feeding sites from 1988–1990, parasitism rates were still above 50%. But the rate has generally been below 20% since then, and was only 8.6% in 1997. The cowbird control program at Fort Hood is the second control program, after the program for the Least Bell's Vireo in southern California (Griffith and Griffith in press), for which there is good evidence that control has led to an increase in an endangered host species. Territorial male Black-capped Vireos at Fort Hood have increased from 85 in 1987 to 357 in 1997. However, this is a much slower rise than for the Least Bell's Vireo at Camp Pendleton in southern California (Griffith and Griffith in press), and may be due to relatively ineffective control efforts prior to 1991. Thus, in the future there should be an accelerated rate of vireo increase at Fort Hood if cowbird parasitism has been limiting vireo population growth. As with most cowbird control programs, the numbers of cowbirds killed at Fort Hood has not decreased since the program began.

EFFECTS OF COWBIRD TRAPS ON HOSTS

Terpening, in the fourth paper, reports on an incident in Travis County, Texas, in which an endangered host, a Golden-cheeked Warbler (*Dendroica chrysoparia*), was seen feeding, from outside a trap, a juvenile Brown-headed Cowbird caught in the trap. After several days, an adult warbler was found dead inside the same trap. To minimize chances of host mortality from cowbird trapping, the author recommends that traps be checked every day and that attempts be made to place traps in cowbird foraging areas rather than in host breeding areas. The former suggestion is well taken and should be followed even when there is little or no chance of capturing host species. The federal guidelines for animal welfare that apply to universities and other entities that receive federal funding cover all vertebrates (cowbirds too!) and require daily checks for captive animals.

Although placing cowbird traps at feeding sites may be the best strategy in some landscapes, as Eckrich et al. argue, we are not sure that risks to endangered host species should be a major factor in trap placement. Terpening's review of other trapping programs indicates that captures of endangered species are extremely rare. Because they are insectivores, none of the endangered North American species for which cowbird trapping might be beneficial are likely to be attracted to cowbird traps for food, although many non-endangered non-target species are attracted. However, if host birds are attracted into traps to feed their "offspring" more often than is currently reported in the literature, then this could be a more serious problem. Of more importance perhaps is that placement of traps at feeding sites could compromise the efficacy of cowbird trapping in landscapes where trapping is more effective in breeding habitat (see Griffith and Griffith in press). And, trapping at feeding sites can result in the capture of numerous cowbirds that are not threatening endangered species, so the killing of such birds conflicts with animal welfare guidelines, and is ethically suspect.

THE EFFECT OF FIRE ON PARASITISM RATES

In the final paper in this section, Clotfelter et al. report the effects of prescribed burning on

cowbird parasitism of Red-winged Blackbirds (*Agelaius phoeniceus*) at a prairie reserve in Wisconsin. The likelihood of a nest being parasitized decreased with increasing distance from the nearest habitat edge or road, but increased with increasing distance from the perimeter of a burn. Parasitism was not related, however, to the quality or timing (spring versus fall) of a burn, nor to the time elapsed since a burn. There was a trend for blackbird nests in burned areas to have fewer cowbird eggs, and the success of nests increased with increasing distance from the perimeter of the burn. The authors suggest that if future research demonstrates results similar to theirs, wildlife managers might consider using burns to lessen rates of parasitism on particular host species.

SYNTHESIS

The first three contributions in this section on cowbird control provide two important lessons. First, even extreme reductions in the level of parasitism and increases in host productivity do not guarantee population increases in endangered species impacted by cowbirds. Only trapping programs to aid the Least Bell's and Black-capped vireos have resulted in large increases in endangered hosts (Eckrich et al. *this volume*, Griffith and Griffith in press, Rothstein and Cook in press). By contrast, the Kirtland's Warbler (*Dendroica kirtlandii*) did not increase for over 15 years after trapping reduced parasitism to negligible levels (DeCapita in press). The Southwestern Willow Flycatcher story may prove to be similar to that of the Kirtland's Warbler, as Whitfield et al. show for the Kern River population. Fifteen years of cowbird trapping for Least Bell's Vireos at Camp Pendleton also has not resulted in any major changes in Southwestern Willow Flycatcher numbers occurring on the base. Thus, the effects of cowbird control for this species are questionable, and although there appears to be much unoccupied breeding habitat in many parts of the flycatcher's range, it is also questionable whether we are able to accurately assess habitat suitability or not. This difficulty in assessing habitat suitability is shown by the recent history of Kirtland's Warbler. Rothstein and Cook (in press) summarized literature that suggested that neither breeding nor wintering habitat were limiting for this species in the 1970s and early 1980s, yet the warbler began to increase only after the creation of new breeding areas (Kepler et al. 1996, DeCapita in press) and wintering areas (Haney et al. 1998; see also Sykes and Clench 1998). Thus, although cowbird control has brought-about decreases in parasitism rates and increases in host reproductive output in many cases, it has a mixed track record as regards the ultimate measure of "success" for rare hosts, namely increases in host population size. However, even though cowbird control has not resulted in increases in two of the four endangered species that have prompted its use, it may have kept these species, Kirtland's Warbler and Southwestern Willow Flycatcher, from declining. Nevertheless, the evidence that trapping forestalled declines is somewhat equivocal (Rothstein and Cook in press) and the 50% success rate of cowbird control programs should motivate managers to seek additional solutions to the problems of endangered hosts.

The second lesson demonstrated by the papers on cowbird control is that there is no single formula for maximizing the efficacy of control programs. As we have discussed, different strategies, such as trapping in breeding versus feeding habitat, and using trapping versus shooting or nest monitoring, seem to work well in different situations. The message here is that managers need to be flexible and innovative in designing control programs for their own local areas.

Another important point to keep in mind is that even when control programs seem to have resulted in rapid and large increases in endangered hosts, they typically have little effect on year-to-year numbers of cowbirds and so must be carried out each year (Eckrich et al. *this volume*; Griffith and Griffith in press). Thus, even when cowbird control measures are appropriate and effective management tools, they are short-term fixes such that control must be repeated year after year or until some other management option is adopted. More appropriate tools for long-term management might be measures such as the restoration of breeding habitat, and the development of land use practices that minimize cowbird numbers. These types of long-term measures will be key in recovering the population viability of declining hosts. As with other aspects of cowbird parasitism, effective long-term measures are likely to be landscape-specific. An example of such a measure is T. L. Cook et al.'s (unpubl. data) demonstration of the effects of removing cattle from a portion of Fort Hood. In this situation, Cook et al. found that removal of cattle, and, hence, removal of cowbird feeding sites, led to a steep decline in parasitism rates of Black-capped Vireos (from 34.8% in 1996 to 0% in 1997) on their study site. Their results therefore suggest that in some instances, moving the primary foraging areas of cowbirds may affect parasitism as strongly as cowbird trapping can.

Another point to consider about cowbird impacts on endangered hosts is the possibility that no management is needed once local populations

of such species become large. Based on evidence collected from several studies of cowbird and host laying strategies, S. I. Rothstein (unpubl. data) proposed that the impact of parasitism will be reduced naturally as host population sizes increase, due to differences between cowbird and host egg-laying rates. Thus, in effect, large host populations may "swamp" the impact of cowbirds so that a population that experienced a high rate of parasitism when it was small may experience a much lower rate, from a similar number of cowbirds, when it is large. This extrapolation assumes that cowbirds do not increase in direct proportion to the endangered host, which is likely if the host is just one of a number of local species that are parasitized. Because the rates of parasitism on enlarged populations of an endangered host may be low enough to allow the population to continue to grow, it is possible that cowbird removal could be discontinued in areas where host populations have shown significant increases in size. An important consequence of discontinuing trapping in these situations would be that the money could be directed to other projects that are essential for recovering host species. In addition, other downsides of cowbird control, such as impacts on non-target species (Rothstein and Cook in press), could be avoided. But most importantly, if cowbird control does not have to be continued once local populations become large, then it is a much better management tool than we have realized up to now, because it may only need to be carried out until local populations have increased.

Despite considerable evidence showing the need for a flexible approach to cowbird management, the government agencies that fund and mandate management actions are likely to suffer from considerable inertia, as do most bureaucracies. If this inertia results in inflexibility once cowbird control programs are initiated, then recovery efforts may be retarded in regards to the long-term goal of the Endangered Species Act, namely, to restore endangered species to the point where they no longer need management intervention. It is unclear to us if a species can be removed from the Endangered Species List if it is the subject of perpetual management efforts. Another aspect of this situation is that of funding for cowbird control: cowbird trapping has become a large business in some regions. For example, in tabulating data on trapping programs, D. C. Hahn (unpubl. data) estimated that at least $1,000,000 is spent annually for cowbird trapping in California alone, and the work is completed primarily by consulting firms. Thus, there is a potential profit incentive for individuals and firms to lobby for cowbird control and this incentive may add further inflexibility to cowbird control programs.

From a completely different angle, Griffith and Griffith (in press, and unpubl. data) have argued for regional trapping, rather than just localized trapping where impacted hosts occur, to reduce cowbird numbers over large areas. They suggest that regional control could be more cost-effective than local control, could increase the productivity of a number of host species in addition to a few endangered ones, and would be longer lasting than local control, which usually has no effect from one year to the next. It is not clear how regional control would be achieved, but one cost-effective approach they suggest could be to kill cowbirds by the millions in large winter roosts. Rothstein and Robinson (1994) have pointed out several significant drawbacks to such suggested approaches, including that local trapping may still be required because cowbirds breeding in the southwestern U.S. may not join large wintering flocks. As for benefiting hosts in addition to endangered ones, recent analyses have found little or no evidence that cowbirds limit the populations of any passerines other than the several species formally recognized as endangered (Peterjohn et al. in press, Wiedenfeld in press). Even if cowbirds do affect the distribution and abundance of other species, it is worth keeping in mind that ecologists have found that numerous species affect other species in nature, and that some, such as "keystone species", may even shape entire communities or faunas. Thus, because the Brown-headed Cowbird is an ancient inhabitant of North America (e.g., DNA evidence indicates that it split from its sister species, the Shiny Cowbird [*Molothrus bonariensis*] about a million years ago [S. I. Rothstein, unpubl. data], and fossils dating to a 0.5 million years ago have been found at sites across North America from California to Florida [Lowther 1993]), some of the effects of cowbirds on other species are natural.

MANAGEMENT QUESTIONS

The studies presented in this section seem to indicate that localized cowbird removal programs are only one way among several for combating brood parasitism. Before any method of controlling brood parasitism is chosen, however, there are at least four items to consider:

1. The nature of the problem. Is cowbird control, of any kind, clearly warranted? For instance, have host populations been shown to be declining, and is parasitism a major reason for the decline? Or, is habitat loss the primary reason, which would warrant habitat restoration rather than, or in combination with, cowbird control? Would a cowbird control program only

be addressing the proximate, rather than the ultimate, reasons for declines (Rothstein and Cook in press)? It is clear that some cowbird control programs are dealing only with proximate issues because they involve hosts that have long been sympatric with cowbirds and presumably have become endangered because of anthropogenic effects. For example, the ranges of the Black-capped Vireo and Golden-cheeked Warbler are completely within the cowbird's ancestral center of abundance in the center of North America (Mayfield 1965), and most of the extant population of a third endangered species, the Southwestern Willow Flycatcher, is within a region where cowbirds have long occurred (Rothstein 1994).

2. Long term monitoring. Unfortunately there are instances in California in which there have been funds available for trapping cowbirds, but none available for assessing the numbers of the host species the trapping is targeted to aid. Thus, we suggest that managers need to consider if monitoring, both of the cowbird and its host, will be carried out during the management program. If it will, how frequently will it occur? How will "success" be measured in the program? Will there be any experimental evaluations of the program, for example, as in an adaptive management framework (e.g., Morrison and Marcot 1995)?

3. The nature of the funding. Cowbird trapping programs for declining host species usually need to be long-lived, and so funding must similarly be long-term. If a cowbird control program is to be started, will the money be there to see it through? Or, could the money perhaps be put to a better use, for example, for studying reproductive success and population sizes, or for conducting focused trapping at wintertime roost locations used by local cowbird populations that impact endangered hosts? The former use of funds may be especially appropriate for the Southwestern Willow Flycatcher, some of whose populations appear to have limited reproductive output even in the absence of cowbird parasitism.

4. The ethics of cowbird control. If the situation indicates that removal of cowbirds from a locale or a region is a necessity, then we need to ask if we have the right to kill large numbers of cowbirds, which are a native species, and which are successful primarily because we paved the way for them to become so. The ethical questions surrounding cowbird control are difficult to answer, but must be addressed because the public will want to see that we have considered these issues. Indeed, the use of vertebrate species in research at universities and other entities that receive federal funds must be fully justified according to federal animal welfare guidelines. These guidelines dictate that researchers use no more than the minimum number of subjects needed to meet objectives, and that all subjects be treated humanely. Thus, it would be ironic, at best, to fail to set high scientific standards for justifying cowbird control actions taken in response to another federal mandate, the Endangered Species Act.

Future research on cowbird control, and management of cowbird and host populations will need to consider the above issues so that sound programs can be designed for recovering host species. We hope that the papers in this section provide managers and researchers with food-for-thought in regards to how such programs can be developed.

ACKNOWLEDGMENTS

We thank J. Rotenberry, M. L. Morrison, and the other co-editors of this proceedings for their diligence in bringing this publication to fruition in such a timely manner, and for their comments and insights both at the 1997 Conference and on earlier drafts of this paper.

Studies in Avian Biology No. 18:260–266, 1999.

IS BROWN-HEADED COWBIRD TRAPPING EFFECTIVE FOR MANAGING POPULATIONS OF THE ENDANGERED SOUTHWESTERN WILLOW FLYCATCHER?

Mary J. Whitfield, Kristen M. Enos, and Sean P. Rowe

Abstract. We examined the effectiveness of cowbird trapping as a management tool for the recovery of a central California population of the endangered Southwestern Willow Flycatcher (*Empidonax traillii extimus*). After trapping Brown-headed Cowbirds (*Molothrus ater*), the parasitism rate on Willow Flycatchers decreased from an average of 65% (4 years prior to cowbird trapping) to 22% (during 5 years of cowbird trapping). As a result, flycatcher nest success increased from an average of 23% prior to cowbird control to an average of 39% after cowbird trapping. More importantly, the number of young fledged per female increased from an average of 1.04 prior to cowbird control efforts to 1.72 with cowbird control. The number of Willow Flycatcher pairs declined from 44 in 1989 to 27 in 1992. After trapping began in 1993, the decline stopped and the population stabilized at an average of 34 pairs, peaking in 1997 at 38 pairs. Despite increased flycatcher reproductive success, there has been little increase in the number of breeding Willow Flycatchers in the study area. A demographic analysis indicates that in all but one of the 9 years of this study, Willow Flycatchers have not produced enough young for the population to grow. Despite the significant increase in reproductive success due to cowbird trapping, it appears that parasitism rates may still be high enough to suppress the growth of this Willow Flycatcher population. In addition, other factors besides cowbird parasitism are likely affecting reproductive success and consequent population growth. Nevertheless, continued cowbird control efforts seem prudent as these efforts may eventually result in a large increase in flycatchers.

Key Words: brood parasitism, Brown-headed Cowbird, cowbird trapping, *Empidonax traillii, Molothrus ater,* reproductive success, Willow Flycatcher

Brood parasitism by Brown-headed Cowbirds (*Molothrus ater*) has been suggested as an important factor in the decline of many species of songbirds throughout the United States (Mayfield 1965, Gaines 1974, Rothstein et al. 1980, Brittingham and Temple 1983, Terborgh 1989, Robinson 1992). It has been implicated in the decline of a number of endangered species and subspecies: Kirtland's Warbler (*Dendroica kirtlandii*) (Mayfield 1965), Black-capped Vireo (*Vireo atricapillus*) (Gryzbowski et al. 1986), Golden-cheeked Warbler (*Dendroica chrysoparia*)(Ehrlich et al. 1988), Least Bell's Vireo (*Vireo bellii pusillus*)(Goldwasser et al. 1980), and Southwestern Willow Flycatcher (*Empidonax traillii extimus*) (Unitt 1987, Whitfield and Sogge *this volume*). As a result, cowbird trapping and removal has become a popular management tool for increasing populations of small, endangered hosts.

Currently, there are several cowbird trapping programs throughout the United States for managing populations of endangered songbirds such as the Kirtland's Warbler (Mayfield 1977), Least Bell's Vireo (Beezley and Rieger 1987), Black-capped Vireo (Hayden et al. in press), Golden-cheeked Warbler (K. Terpening, pers. comm.), and Southwestern Willow Flycatcher (Rothstein 1994, Whitfield in press). Despite the increasing use of cowbird trapping, relatively little has been published on the effectiveness of trapping for target host populations (but see Kepler et al.

1996, DeCapita in press, Griffith and Griffith in press, Hayden et al. in press, Rothstein and Cook in press, Whitfield in press).

In this paper, we examine the effectiveness of cowbird trapping on a population of the endangered Southwestern Willow Flycatcher in central California. The goals of our cowbird trapping control program were to reduce the cowbird population and cowbird parasitism of the flycatchers, which should lead to increased reproductive success and ultimately increase the Willow Flycatcher population size. In addition to comparing Willow Flycatcher numbers and population trends at our study site from 1989 to 1992 before the initiation of cowbird control with numbers from 1993 to 1997 after control, we also assess data on flycatcher population trends collected by other workers (Serena 1982, Harris et al. 1987) in the same area from 1982 to 1986, before our study began.

METHODS

STUDY AREA

The study area is located on The Nature Conservancy's (now managed by Audubon California) Kern River Preserve (KRP) and the adjoining USDA Forest Service's South Fork Wildlife Area (SFWA), Kern County, California (Fig. 1). The KRP was established in 1981 to protect and enhance existing riparian habitat. Since then, portions of the land have been reforested and habitat has been improved by the elimination of

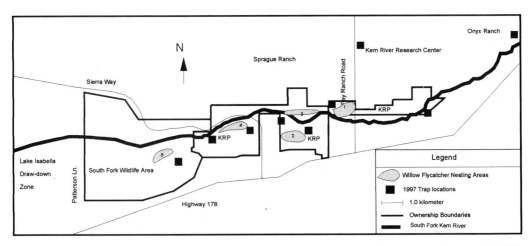

FIGURE 1. Study area and location of the main Willow Flycatcher nesting areas and cowbird traps in 1997, South Fork Kern River, California. Two traps not shown are located 5 km and 14 km east of the study area.

grazing. The SFWA was established in 1977 as a result of concern over the loss of 1300 ha of habitat due to the construction of Isabella Dam (Fleshman and Kaufman 1984). The SFWA is periodically flooded when the reservoir level rises. Large portions (60% or greater) of the SFWA have been flooded, on average, from approximately May to September in 4 of the 9 years of this study (1993,1995, 1996 and 1997). At elevations between 762 and 805 m, the study area encompasses approximately 500 ha of cottonwood-willow forest. The riparian woodland is dominated by three tree species: red willow (*Salix laevigata*), Goodding's black willow (*Salix gooddingii*), and Fremont cottonwood (*Populus fremontii*). The forest is interspersed with open areas that are often dominated by mulefat (*Baccharis salicifolia*) and hoary nettle (*Urtica dioica holosericea*), and flooded areas that support freshwater marshes dominated by cattails (*Typha* spp.) and tules (*Scirpus* spp.). Hoary nettle and mulefat are also common understory plants in the forest. Pastures for cattle grazing and cultivated fields border the riparian forest.

COWBIRD MONITORING AND CONTROL

Starting in 1991, we surveyed Brown-headed Cowbirds using 10-min point-count surveys at 60 stations throughout the study area. In 1994, we added 15 stations. The stations were located 200 m apart, along the forest edge. We counted male and female cowbirds seen or heard at each station and visited each station three times between late April and mid-July. The April/May survey was completed before the cowbird traps were opened. The last surveys were completed by mid-July because cowbirds in the Sierra Ne-

vada and along the South Fork Kern River show a noticeable decline in detectability by late July (Rothstein et al. 1980; M. Whitfield, pers. obs.). To reduce observer bias in the data, an average of 86% (range 72% to 93%) of the counts were conducted by M. Whitfield each year. With the exception of two to six of the stations per year, each station was visited at least twice in a given year by this observer. There were a total of six other observers and no more than three were used in a given year. We tested whether there was a correlation between the number of cowbirds counted in the first surveys and the year the count was made in order to see whether trapping cowbirds reduced the cowbird population from one year to the next.

There were no cowbird control efforts from 1989 through 1991. In 1992, we addled cowbird eggs by shaking them and removed cowbird nestlings found in Willow Flycatcher nests. During that same year, between 10 June and 10 July, we shot approximately 30 female cowbirds found near Willow Flycatcher nesting areas but did not trap cowbirds. Therefore, this was an intermediate year between no cowbird control in 1989–1991 and intensive cowbird control from 1993–1997. As a result, 1992 was not included in the analysis of the effects of cowbird control on the reproductive success of Willow Flycatchers.

In 1993, we set up four cowbird traps ($2 \times 2 \times 2.5$ m, modified Australian Crow traps). Three traps were located near Willow Flycatcher nesting areas at KRP and one was located at a Brown-headed Cowbird feeding area at the Kern River Research Center. The SFWA was a "nontrap" area until 1996 when we added one trap into the area. We baited each trap with wild bird-

TABLE 1. SUMMARY OF BROWN-HEADED COWBIRDS TRAPPED ALONG THE SOUTH FORK KERN RIVER, KERN CO., CALIFORNIA, 1993–1997

Year	Number of Traps	Females	Males	Males released[a]	Juveniles	Total
1993	4	343	193	227	287	1050
1994	7	152	104	132	62	450
1995	8	141	136	28	71	376
1996	9	87	98	22	131	338
1997	11	225	164	17	115	521
Totals		948	695	426	666	2735[b]

Note: These numbers do not accurately reflect the local cowbird sex ratio because males and females were treated differently in 1993 and 1994, see text for details. In addition, the sex ratio determined by point counts is two males per female.
[a] Some males were temporarily marked (1993) or banded (1994) and released; from 1995–1997, the banded males were recaptured and released.
[b] When the recaptured banded birds (1995–1997) are not counted, the total number of individuals captured is 2668.

seed (made up of millet, milo, wheat hearts, and sunflower seed), water, and live cowbirds (three females and two males). We checked the traps daily to release non-target birds and to euthanize cowbirds. In 1993, we cut small pieces off the two outer tail feathers and released 227 male cowbirds. We banded and released 132 male cowbirds in 1994. However, from 1995–1997, we did not band any new cowbirds and we euthanized all unbanded cowbirds.

Each year since 1993, we increased our trapping effort (Table 1). In 1997, we expanded our trapping effort to 11 traps including three additional traps east of the KRP (Fig. 1). In all trap years, we addled cowbird eggs and removed cowbird nestlings found in Willow Flycatcher nests throughout the study area.

WILLOW FLYCATCHER MONITORING

We monitored Willow Flycatchers from 1989 to 1997 to determine population trends, reproductive success, and cowbird parasitism rates. Each year, we started surveying for the flycatchers and searching for their nests during the last week in May when their breeding season begins. We surveyed all portions of the study area that contained suitable nesting habitat using a playback recording of a singing male Willow Flycatcher. We checked nests daily during the egg-laying stage and then every 2 or 3 days during incubation and nestling stages. A nest was categorized as depredated when it was found empty before the young could have fledged from it, when the number of eggs in the nest were reduced or damaged (and no cowbird egg was subsequently laid in the nest), or a nestling (or nestlings) disappeared from the nest, thus causing abandonment. We estimated nest success using the Mayfield method, which calculates the probability of survival at each nesting stage (Mayfield 1975). A successful nest was defined as one that fledged at least one Willow Flycatcher young and an active nest was a nest in which at

least one egg (flycatcher or cowbird) had been laid.

We used Chi-square tests of homogeneity to compare the parasitism and predation rates between years with and without cowbird control. A t-test was used to compare differences between number of young fledged per female in years with and without cowbird control. We used the method devised by Hensler and Nichols (1981) and Hensler (1985) to test for differences in Mayfield nest success between years with and without cowbird control.

RESULTS

COWBIRD CONTROL AND MONITORING

From 1993 to 1997, we caught 2,735 individual cowbirds: 948 females, 1121 males, and 666 juveniles (Table 1). Only 12 females were caught in the trap in the SFWA (6 in 1996, 6 in 1997). In contrast, the two new easternmost traps outside the study area (5 and 14 km from the study area) captured 61% (138) of the females caught in 1997. These traps were not located in the original trap area (KRP) and when cowbirds caught only in the original trap area are considered, the number of female cowbirds trapped decreased each year (Fig. 2).

Since trapping began, the female cowbird population has decreased in the trap area each year between May and July (Table 2). In addition, the number of females trapped and the number of females detected during the first survey on the KRP has significantly decreased from one year to the next ($r^2 = 0.943$, N = 5, P = 0.001). However, the number of cowbirds detected in the SFWA (prior to 1996, the nontrap area) remained fairly stable until 1995 (Table 2).

WILLOW FLYCATCHER MONITORING

During times of high cowbird parasitism and low nest success, the number of nesting Willow Flycatcher pairs declined from 1989 to 1992 (Table 3). The number of flycatchers has in-

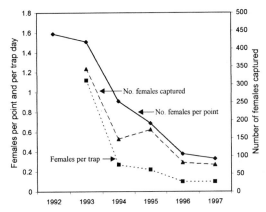

FIGURE 2.   Comparison of Brown-headed Cowbird trap rates (number of females caught per year 1993–1997), capture rates (number of females caught per trap day 1993–1997), and detections per 10-min point count (females per point, 1992–1997) on the Kern River Preserve, Kern Co., California. The number of traps increased from four traps in 1993 to 11 in 1997.

creased since 1992, but is still below the population levels of 1989 and 1990. We compared five parameters (parasitism and predation rates, nest success, total number of young fledged, and number of young fledged per female) before and after cowbird control to directly test the effect of cowbird control on the flycatcher's reproductive success. Since 1992, cowbird parasitism rates have declined from an average of 64% (prior to cowbird trapping), to 22% after cowbird trapping. These rates were significantly lower during the four years of cowbird control than the three years without cowbird control (Table 3) (χ^2 = 62.5, df = 1, P < 0.001). However, there were no significant differences in the predation rate between the years before and after cowbird control (χ^2 = 0.24, df = 1, P = 0.63). Nest success

increased from an average of 23% (1989–1991) to 32% in 1992, when there were low-level cowbird control efforts. During the period of intense cowbird control (1993 to 1997), nest success averaged 39%. Furthermore, the number of young fledged per nest and the number fledged per female over the whole season were significantly higher in the cowbird control years (1.24 and 1.72) than the years prior to cowbird control (0.63 and 1.04) (number of young fledged per nest: t = −3.67, df = 287, P < 0.001; young fledged per female: t = 2.86, df = 192, P = 0.005) (Table 3).

In addition, the overall Mayfield nest success rate was significantly higher in years with cowbird control (0.3894) than without cowbird control (0.2284) (Table 4). However, when Mayfield nest success was broken into three different stages, only the nestling stage had significantly higher success in the cowbird control years (0.7356) than in the years prior to control (0.5422). Nonetheless, the laying stage was close to being significantly higher in the years with (0.8715) than without cowbird control (0.7745), and all three stages showed a trend of being higher in years with control than years without control.

DISCUSSION

All indices of cowbird abundance significantly declined since we started trapping cowbirds on the KRP portion of our study area. In contrast, other cowbird trapping programs have shown relatively constant trapping rates each year due to immigration of cowbirds each breeding season (DeCapita in press, Griffith and Griffith in press, Hayden et al. in press, Rothstein and Cook in press). However, the immigration rate into our study site is probably low because the site is surrounded by arid mountain habitats

TABLE 2.   BROWN-HEADED COWBIRD POINT COUNT RESULTS (MEAN NUMBER OF FEMALES PER POINT ± SE), FOR THE PRE-TRAP (MAY) AND POST-TRAP (JULY) COUNTS 1992–1997 (SAMPLE SIZES IN PARENTHESES)

Year	Month	Kern River Preserve	Number of traps	SF Wildlife Area	Number of traps
1992[a]	May	1.59 ± 0.14 (41)	0	1.58 ± 0.17 (19)	0
	July	1.37 ± 0.17 (41)		1.74 ± 0.18 (19)	
1993	May	1.51 ± 0.16 (41)	4	2.00 ± 0.22 (19)	0
	July	0.71 ± 0.13 (14)		2.22 ± 0.18 (18)	
1994	May	0.91 ± 0.13 (45)	7	1.93 ± 0.21 (30)	0
	July	0.40 ± 0.09 (45)		1.60 ± 0.19 (30)	
1995	May	0.69 ± 0.11 (45)	8	1.33 ± 0.15 (30)	0
	July	0.24 ± 0.08 (45)		1.20 ± 0.11 (30)	
1996	May	0.38 ± 0.09 (45)	9	0.90 ± 0.16 (30)	1
	July	0.27 ± 0.07 (45)		0.57 ± 0.12 (30)	
1997	May	0.33 ± 0.09 (45)	11	0.40 ± 0.09 (30)	1
	July	0.18 ± 0.07 (45)		0.37 ± 0.11 (30)	

[a] Thirty female cowbirds shot from 10 June to 10 July.

TABLE 3.   BREEDING AND DEMOGRAPHIC PARAMETERS FOR WILLOW FLYCATCHERS ALONG THE SOUTH FORK KERN RIVER, CALIFORNIA (1989–1997)

Year	Number of pairs	Number of nests[a]	Predation Rate	Parasitism Rate	Mayfield nest Success	Total number of young fledged	Number of young fledged per female
			No cowbird trapping				
1989	44	34	33%	50%	24%	25	1.04
1990	41	38	42%	61%	24%	21	0.88
1991	31	45	35%	78%	17%	25	1.14
Means	39	116[b]	37%	63%	23%	24	1.04
			No cowbird trapping, 30 female cowbirds removed				
1992	27	36	14%	69%	32%[c]	33	1.83
			Cowbird trapping				
1993	34	33	37%	38%	33%[c]	37	1.76
1994	34	32	47%	16%	39%[c]	42	2.10
1995	34	32	34%	19%	43%[c]	40	1.90
1996	29	29	28%	11%	61%[c]	58	2.42
1997	38	51	57%	20%	30%[c]	37	1.09
Means	34	178[b]	40%	22%	39%	43	1.74

[a] In all years, we did not find nests for all pairs of Willow Flycatchers in the study area.
[b] Total instead of mean.
[c] This rate reflects investigator intervention by removing Brown-headed Cowbird eggs and nestlings from Willow Flycatcher nests.

with few cowbirds (Rothstein and Cook in press).

We have also seen a decrease in the number of cowbirds on the SFWA, but this decline has been more recent, smaller, and more complex than the one at KRP. We believe that the lower number of cowbirds on the SFWA was mostly due to the inundation of habitat rather than the effects of cowbird trapping. The inundation coincided with declines in the densities and numbers of all host species, with the exception of the Yellow Warbler (*Dendroica petechia*), in most of the SFWA (M. Whitfield, unpubl. data). As a result, we believe the cowbirds moved to other areas to find enough nests to parasitize.

Our data indicated that the reduction in cowbird numbers led to a reduction in cowbird parasitism of Willow Flycatchers. Consequently, nest success significantly increased. It is interesting to note that most of the difference in nest success occurred from the nestling stage and laying stage rather than from the incubation stage. These are the two stages that are affected the most from cowbird parasitism. The laying stage is affected by increased abandonment rates due to parasitism, and the nestling stage is affected by the competition of cowbird young (Whitfield 1990, Hill and Sealy 1994, Goguen and Matthews 1996, Rogers et al. 1997, Payne and Payne 1998, Whitfield and Sogge *this volume*). In contrast, cowbird parasitism rarely causes total failure of the nest during the incubation stage (M. Whitfield, unpubl. data).

Willow Flycatcher females have produced an average of 1.72 young per female with trapping compared to an average of 1.04 young prior to trapping. This increase in production could be due to manipulation of parasitized nests (i.e., addling cowbird eggs and removing cowbird chicks) rather than trapping alone or, most likely, a combination of the two. However, data in Whitfield and Sogge (*this volume*) indicate that the egg-to-fledging ratio for manipulated parasitized nests (23%) is not significantly higher than unmanipulated parasitized nests (18%). Therefore, most of the increased production can be attributed to trapping cowbirds rather than manipulating parasitized nests.

TABLE 4.   MAYFIELD NEST SUCCESS FOR SOUTHWESTERN WILLOW FLYCATCHERS BEFORE COWBIRD TRAPPING (1989–1991) AND AFTER COWBIRD TRAPPING (1993–1997) ON THE SOUTH FORK KERN RIVER, CALIFORNIA

	Laying		Incubation		Nestling		Overall	
	Success	SD	Success	SD	Success	SD	Success	SD
No Trapping	0.7745	0.053	0.5648	0.052	0.5422	0.074	0.2284	0.039
Trapping	0.8715	0.036	0.6177	0.040	0.7356	0.044	0.3894	0.039
Z	1.51		0.80		2.24		2.93	
P	<0.15		>0.42		<0.025		<0.003	

The cowbird control program was successful in achieving the immediate goals of reducing cowbird numbers, reducing cowbird parasitism, and increasing Willow Flycatcher reproductive success. Unfortunately, the proximate success of the control program has not translated into an ultimate success of a larger population of Willow Flycatchers in the study area. It is likely that other factors besides cowbird parasitism are preventing this population of Willow Flycatchers from increasing and/or we have not reduced the parasitism rate enough.

Possible limiting factors may be habitat loss and/or pesticide use on the Willow Flycatcher's wintering grounds and/or migratory stopover sites. Yet, the return rates of both the adult (males: 53%, females: 35.5%) and juvenile (34%) Willow Flycatchers are average to above average for this species (Stoleson et al. in press), suggesting that over-winter survival is not a limiting factor for this population. Alternatively, the Willow Flycatchers on the South Fork Kern River may not have declined but may have moved out of the study area onto adjacent private lands where we are not allowed to survey. To investigate this possibility, we examined aerial photos of riparian habitat upstream of the study area to get an estimate of the amount of suitable habitat outside our study area. With the exception of the Canebrake Ecological Reserve (CER), located on the easternmost end of the valley, there appeared to be no more than 20 ha of suitable Willow Flycatcher habitat. Furthermore, we have surveyed for Willow Flycatchers on the CER the past 3 years, but have never found more than two pairs on the property. Thus, we doubt that there has been an increased number of Willow Flycatchers breeding outside of our study area along the South Fork Kern River.

Habitat quality and quantity in the study area does not appear to be a limiting factor for this population. Each year, many areas that appear to be suitable habitat are not used. Willow Flycatchers have bred successfully in many of these areas, abandoned them for a year or two, and then returned to the area in subsequent years. Furthermore, there are no apparent changes in the habitat on the KRP, but there have been some changes in the SFWA due to flooding. However, the number of Willow Flycatchers in the SFWA has never been high (average of five pairs for seven years), and an average of two pairs have used the area in the past two years when most of it was flooded.

A recent demographic analysis for this population by Uyehara et al. (in press) indicates that, for all but 1 of the 9 years of this study, Willow Flycatchers have not produced enough young for the population to grow. Furthermore,

data from Stoleson et al. (in press) indicate that the nest success for this population is low compared to other populations of Willow Flycatchers. Predation was the largest cause of nest failure during the 9 years of the study (M. Whitfield, unpubl. data). In addition, unparasitized, nondepredated nests produced 3.02 offspring on average (M. Whitfield, unpubl. data), indicating that the flycatchers can produce enough young for the population to grow in the absence of parasitism and predation. It should be noted, however, that prior to cowbird control, egg losses due to parasitism sometimes exceeded those lost to predators. In addition, the demographic analysis by Uyehara et al. (in press) indicated that this population of Willow Flycatchers can increase only if the parasitism rate remains below or at approximately 10%. The parasitism rate has approached that figure only once (11% in 1996), and in that year, Willow Flycatcher reproductive success was the highest ever documented for this population. We suspect that this resulted in the population growth from 29 pairs in 1996 to 38 pairs in 1997. At least 12 of the 38 nestlings (32%) that were banded in 1996 came back to breed in 1997. If the nestlings that we were not able to band returned at similar rates, then as many as 18 young from 1996 were recruited to the 1997 population. In addition, Uyehara et al. (in press) calculated a population growth rate of 1.25 for 1996, which indicated a growing population.

An assessment of Willow Flycatcher population estimates for our study area in the 1980s complicates the demographic picture and interpretations regarding the extent to which cowbird trapping has influenced the number of the locally breeding flycatchers in the 1990s. Serena (1982) found 26 singing males in 1982, using tape playback. The population appeared to be stable in 1984 and 1985 when other surveyors found 23 and 29 males, respectively (Harris et al. 1987), without using tape playback. When Harris et al. (1987) surveyed the area in 1986 using tape playback and some sightings from local researchers, they found 39 singing males, an apparent increase in the population from 1982. However, both tape playback surveys (1982 and 1986) involved only one site visit, and none of the surveys from 1982 to 1986 covered the entire area that we have surveyed since 1989. The 1982 to 1986 surveys also had small differences among themselves in the amount of area they covered. Thus, these early surveys did not have consistent efforts or methods and it is difficult to tell whether there was an actual increase in the Willow Flycatcher population.

However, it appears that the Willow Flycatcher population was at least stable in the 1980s even without cowbird control. This apparent paradox might be explained due to changes in land management in the early 1980s and the regeneration of over 150 ha of riparian forest in the SFWA due to floods in 1983 and 1986. Spring and summer cattle grazing was eliminated from the KRP and the SFWA in the early 1980s. Thus, throughout the 1980s, approximately 100 ha of willow forest grew along the river corridor and in low-lying areas on the KRP. This increased the available nesting areas for the Willow Flycatchers and possibly decreased cowbird parasitism pressure.

None of the surveys in the 1980s were comparable to our more intensive survey efforts from 1989–1997 that involved multiple site visits and tape playback. However, using consistent and intensive survey efforts throughout the riparian habitat bordering 7 miles of the South Fork Kern River, we found a population decline prior to trapping and a relatively stable post-trapping population size. The population stability during the trapping years is likely in response to lowered parasitism rates and increased reproductive success, although one cannot exclude the possibility that stability would have occurred without cowbird trapping. In addition, it is unlikely that the parasitism rates would have sig-

nificantly decreased without trapping; therefore trapping cowbird control probably kept this population from declining in the 1990s.

In summary, Willow Flycatcher reproductive success has increased significantly as a result of cowbird trapping. It appears, however, that parasitism rates are still high enough to suppress population growth. Besides cowbird parasitism, other factors such as predation are likely affecting reproductive success and consequent population growth. Nevertheless, continued cowbird control efforts seem prudent for the foreseeable future as it is possible that these efforts will eventually result in a large increase in flycatchers.

ACKNOWLEDGMENTS

The California Department of Fish and Game and Army Corps of Engineers provided funding for this study. The North Kern Water Interests provided funding in past years and continues to provide logistical support. J. Uyehara provided advice and reviewed an earlier draft of this manuscript. T. Pearson and T. Benson were a great help in the field. We are also grateful to H. Green for volunteering for a week of fieldwork every year for the past 7 years. R. Tollefson of The Nature Conservancy's Kern River Preserve provided invaluable support, assistance in the field, housing for field assistants, and reviews of the manuscript. This manuscript greatly benefited from reviews by S. Rothstein, J. Sedgwick, and J. Verner.

Studies in Avian Biology No. 18:267–274, 1999.

EFFECTIVE LANDSCAPE MANAGEMENT OF BROWN-HEADED COWBIRDS AT FORT HOOD, TEXAS

G. H. Eckrich, T. E. Koloszar, and M. D. Goering

Abstract. Fort Hood is an 87,890 ha military installation in central Texas that contains the largest known breeding populations of the endangered Black-capped Vireo (*Vireo atricapillus*) and the Golden-cheeked Warbler (*Dendroica chrysoparia*) under any single management authority. Habitat loss and brood parasitism by the Brown-headed Cowbird (*Molothrus ater*) have been cited as critical factors associated with the decline of both species. In 1987, prior to initiation of cowbird control efforts, 90.9% of vireo nests on Fort Hood were parasitized. Due to the large size of Fort Hood and the wide distribution of endangered bird habitat, it is not feasible to trap and/or shoot cowbirds in every block of habitat. We implemented a cowbird control program that emphasized trapping in pastures with high cattle concentrations, manipulation of trap numbers, and innovations in trap designs. Trapping, in conjunction with a rigorous, methodical shooting program, reduced parasitism to 8.6% by 1997.

Key Words: Black-capped Vireo, brood parasitism, cowbird control, Golden-cheeked Warbler, *Molothrus ater.*

Managers of Brown-headed Cowbird (*Molothrus ater*) populations have to consider landscape-level mosaics of habitat in deciding how to control cowbird abundance and parasitism (Robinson et al. 1993). Robinson et al. (1995a) state that in areas with locally endangered hosts, intensive cowbird trapping and removal may be the best immediate protection strategy. Fort Hood, a large military base in central Texas, has the largest known breeding populations of the endangered Black-capped Vireo (*Vireo atricapillus*) (vireo hereafter) (Grzybowski 1995) and Golden-cheeked Warbler (*Dendroica chrysoparia*) (warbler hereafter) (USFWS 1992) under a single management authority. Here, we update Hayden et al.'s (in press) report on cowbird management and vireos at Fort Hood from 1987 to 1994 with data collected in 1994–1997. These additional data present new insight into methods and recommendations for control of parasitism on a landscape scale. Our paper also addresses a research need identified by Robinson et al. (1995a) to measure the effect of cowbirds on host populations using trapping and shooting to manipulate parasitism rates. Barber and Martin (1997) recently reported on other factors besides cowbird removal, such as abundance of alternate hosts, that appears to influence rates of cowbird parasitism of vireos at Fort Hood.

Before presenting our new data, we first briefly review the status of the warbler and vireo and the cowbird impacts these hosts experience. The Golden-cheeked Warbler was listed as endangered in May 1990 because of habitat loss, degradation, and increasing fragmentation (USFWS 1992). Pulich (1976) estimated the total breeding population of the warbler throughout its range to be approximately 15,000 birds. However, Ehrlich et al. (1992) indicate a breeding

population of only 2,200–4,600 warblers in 1990. Although the number of warblers on Fort Hood is unknown, 915 male warblers were reported on the installation in 1996 (Jette et al. 1998). The precise number of warblers is probably higher because of the large size of the installation and restrictions on entering the areas the Army uses for live-fire activities. In 1963, Pulich (1976) found a parasitism rate as high as 84.2% in Kendall County, Texas. Parasitism by cowbirds appears to be an increasing threat in much of the warbler range due to habitat fragmentation (Collar et al. 1992). Parasitization of warbler nests on Fort Hood, 1991–97, was not substantial with 8.7% (4 of 46) nests parasitized (R. Craft pers. comm., Jette et al. 1998). Because the initiation of warbler studies coincided with increased cowbird control effectiveness in 1991, there are no estimates of warbler parasitization prior to effective cowbird management.

The Black-capped Vireo was listed as an endangered species in 1987 (USFWS 1991). Brood parasitism undoubtedly contributed to the decline of the vireo (Robinson et al. 1995a). The estimated global population of the vireo is controversial, ranging from less than 2,000 pairs (Collar et al. 1994) to between 3,139 and 9,463 pairs based on a breeding population in Coahuila (Benson and Benson 1990). The number of territorial male vireos on Fort Hood has risen from 85 in 1987 (Tazik and Cornelius 1993) to 357 in 1997 (Koloszar 1998). Initial data from the 1998 breeding season indicate a continuing increase in the vireo population, in both numbers and newly occupied habitat (J. Koloszar pers. comm.). As in the case of the warbler, the actual number is unknown due to size of the installation and restrictions on entry into live-fire areas.

The primary reasons stated in the U.S. Fish

and Wildlife Service Recovery Plan (USFWS 1991) for listing the vireo are (1) documented population decline, (2) loss of suitable habitat, and (3) brood parasitism by the Brown-headed Cowbird (cowbird hereafter). Of these, parasitism previously had the greatest effect on Fort Hood. In addition to the Brown-headed Cowbird, the Bronzed Cowbird (*M. aeneus*) is found on Fort Hood (approximately 12 are trapped per breeding season). Also, two Shiny Cowbirds (*M. bonariensis*) have been trapped on Fort Hood (Hunt 1991, G. Eckrich pers. obs. 1993). Initial studies on the installation in 1987 and 1988 reported a cowbird parasitism rate of vireo nests at 90.8% and vireo nest success rate at 4.7% (Tazik and Cornelius 1993). Based on 60% adult annual survival and juvenile survival of 30%, Tazik and Cornelius (1993) determined a critical parasitism rate (the highest parasitism rate the population can withstand without decline) of approximately 35%.

The vireo recovery plan (USFWS 1991) states that cowbird removal is needed in vireo breeding sites where parasitism is a threat to reproductive success, and that removal should begin about two weeks prior to arrival of vireos. Fort Hood Natural Resources Branch initiated cowbird control measures in 1988, but with little effect. Subsequent experimentation with trap placement, numbers, and styles, combined with shooting has successfully reduced cowbird parasitism of vireo nests and increased cowbird capture rates. Our research has emphasized studies of vireos because vireo nests are easier to locate than warbler nests, thus providing larger sample sizes. However, warblers should benefit from cowbird reduction and lower parasitism rates since warbler habitat lies within the areas influenced by the cowbird control program.

STUDY AREA

Fort Hood is an active Army installation that occupies 87,890 ha within Bell and Coryell counties, and is adjacent to the city of Killeen. The installation has a mixture of perennial grassland (65%) and woodland (31%). The remainder of the installation is a build-up cantonment area. Ashe juniper (*Juniperus ashei*) and various oak species (*Quercus* spp.) dominate the woodland (Tazik et al. 1993). Most of the installation has free-ranging cattle, with the exception of the cantonment area and one non-live fire training area. Fort Hood has two basic types of training areas (Fig. 1). In maneuver (non-live fire) training areas two armored divisions with other corps support units conduct year round training. There is no direct firing of weapons; however, artillery units fire indirectly at targets in the impact area in the center of the installation. The maneuver

training areas constitute 53,300 ha or 61 % of the entire installation and are divided into East Range, West Range, and West Fort Hood (WFH). Researchers and cowbird control personnel usually have access to these areas. The live-fire (LF) training areas and the artillery impact area (classified a permanent "dudded" zone due to presence of duds, unexploded, but still live munitions) cover about 24,000 ha. Researchers and cowbird control personnel have sporadic access to the areas in which units fire, and have no access to the artillery impact area. Housing areas, motor pools, and barracks make up the Fort Hood cantonment area. Although the cantonment area is not grazed, extensive mowed fields, lawns, parade grounds, a horse stable, golf courses, and airfields provide suitable foraging areas for cowbirds. Cowbird control measures at Fort Hood have been applied to the entire installation since endangered birds and cowbird feeding areas are present installation-wide. The wide distribution of the warblers and vireos across the installation (Fig. 1) necessitated a cowbird control strategy combining trapping and shooting since some cowbirds are trap-shy while others ignore traps in favor of feeding areas (cattle concentrations and bird feeders) off post.

Warbler habitat is dominated by Ashe juniper (needed for nesting material) and various oak species, especially Texas oak, along with other hardwood species (Pulich 1976). There are approximately 16,000 ha of warbler habitat on Fort Hood. Vireo habitat is described as low scrubby growth, mostly deciduous and of irregular height and distribution, but with spaces between small thickets and clumps and with hardwood foliage to ground level (Graber 1961). Vireos are often found in areas that have recently been burned, with the highest concentrations in areas subjected to hot fires (Grzybowski 1995). Burned areas on Fort Hood have been occupied by vireos as early as two years after a burn. Fort Hood has approximately 4,300 ha of available vireo habitat in all stages of occupancy and successional growth.

METHODS

TRAPPING

Beginning in 1991, trapping efforts focused on pastures frequently grazed by cattle since cowbirds prefer foraging on ground with short grass and in proximity to grazing mammals (Friedmann 1929, Mayfield 1965). Cowbird trapping had been initiated in 1988 following the standards of the cowbird control program to save the Kirtland's Warbler (*Dendroica kirklandii*) (Shake and Mattson 1975). In 1988 three traps were placed in one vireo breeding colony

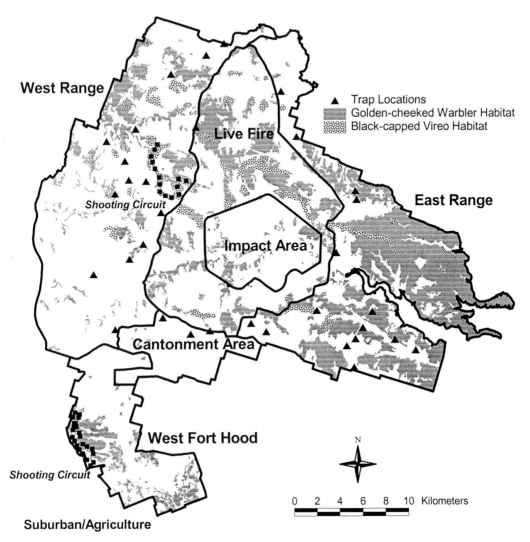

FIGURE 1. Brown-headed Cowbird trap distribution and shooting circuits in relation to designated Black-capped Vireo and Golden-cheeked Warbler habitat across the Fort Hood military installation, 1997, Fort Hood, Texas.

and operated during the breeding season, 1 March–30 June (Tazik and Cornelius 1993). The number of traps was increased to 8 in 1988 and 25 in 1990 (Hayden et al. in press). The trapping strategy was changed in 1991 by placing 40 traps in cattle grazing areas, and leaving 12 in vireo habitat. The number of traps varied in subsequent years due to vandalism, new construction, flooding, or military activity. After reaching a high of 52 in 1991, 30 traps were in operation in 1997 along a 115 km circuit (Fig. 1).

Control efforts varied according to area. The area with the most cowbird control effort was the West Range where both trapping and shooting were used. Very limited trapping and shoot-

ing were conducted in the Live-fire Area because of limited access. West Fort Hood (WFH) presented a unique problem in cowbird control because it is a 6,628 ha peninsula-shaped area surrounded by civilian suburban and agricultural lands (Fig. 1). No cattle were grazed on WFH from 1992 until reintroduction in December 1996. Prior to the 1992 breeding season, all cowbird control measures were suspended on WFH to determine the effect of cowbird removal. Trapping was resumed in 1993. When cowbirds were repeatedly observed flying from vireo breeding habitat past traps to civilian homes to feed (G. Eckrich pers. obs.), we changed the cowbird control strategy for West Fort Hood. In

TABLE 1. TRAP CAPTURE RATE (# FEMALES/TRAP DAY) BY TRAP TYPE FOR BROWN-HEADED COWBIRDS TRAPPED DURING 1997 BREEDING SEASON ON FORT HOOD, TEXAS

Trap type (N)	Trap capture rate				
	March	April	May	June	All
Australian (3)	0.142	0.958	1.242	0.051	0.606
Hybrid (5)	2.354	1.900	1.045	0.147	1.294
Mega (10)	2.108	2.471	3.226	0.248	2.024
USFWS (12)	0.519	0.587	0.524	0.087	0.430
Total	1.158	1.296	1.365	0.131	0.990

1994 we removed all traps from WFH due to their low 1993 capture rate of 0.11 females/trap day versus 0.46 installation-wide and instituted a rigid, methodical shooting program.

The other area with variation in cowbird control was the East Range, containing a 10,800 ha cowbird telemetry research area (Fig. 1) for a 5-year (1994–1998) study (Cook et al. 1998) of spatial and temporal movements of female cowbirds. The number of traps in that area was reduced from 14 in 1993 to 5 in 1994–95, and 3 in 1996–97 to prevent interference with radio-tracking operations. Additionally, all shooting in that area was stopped in 1994.

In accordance with the USFWS Biological Opinion (1993a), trapping has occurred year round. Individual traps were closed when the capture of non-target species exceeded cowbirds, military training interfered, or the trap was repeatedly vandalized. Since one person carried out all cowbird control measures (trapping and shooting) in 1996 and 1997, trap placement had to allow for coverage of as much of the installation as possible in a single day. All traps were placed near paved or improved roads and on terrain that was accessible throughout the year. Four cowbird trap designs were used on Fort Hood in 1996–97. There were three Washington starling traps (1.8 m × 2.4 m × 1.8 m) (USFWS 1984), 12 standard USFWS traps (1.8 m × 2.4 m × 1.8 m) (USFWS 1973), five Hybrid traps (1.8 m × 2.4 m × 2.1 m), and ten Mega traps (4.88 m × 4.88 m × 2.44 m). John Cornelius of the Fort Hood Natural Resources Branch designed the Hybrid and Mega traps based on cowbird control personnel observations and lessons learned. The respective trap capture rates are in Table 1. The apparent advantage of Mega traps is somewhat misleading. While that style trap can catch and hold more birds, Mega traps are placed only at sites that have had high capture rates in preceding seasons. We left 10–15 cowbirds in the Washington starling, USFWS, and Hybrid traps to act as decoys. Approximately 50 decoys were left in the Mega traps, the premise being that more decoys attract more birds since

breeding season social aggregations occur during the afternoon at feeding sites (Robinson et al. 1995a, Rothstein et al. 1987). We have found the sex ratio of decoy birds to be irrelevant to capture rates, in contrast to the 2 males to 3 female ratio of Griffith and Griffith (in press). Traps with few or no females were as effective in catching females as those with a more even sex ratio. The number of females in each trap was intentionally kept low to minimize the number of potentially escaping birds if a trap was vandalized or damaged by storms, cattle, predators, or armored vehicles.

Vegetation in and within 50 cm of the traps was maintained at approximately 5 cm or less so that field personnel could better detect snakes which periodically enter traps to eat cowbirds. Captured female cowbirds were killed by cervical dislocation, while males were banded with USFWS bands and released. Cowbirds were removed as needed to relieve overcrowding or reduce the number of females. The number of birds removed per trap was recorded each visit.

SHOOTING

Shooting female cowbirds in vireo breeding habitat and wherever else found throughout the year augmented the trapping program. A methodical shooting program was conducted along two shooting circuits covering three previously existing vireo study areas on base (Fig. 1). There was no shooting in the telemetry study area, which contains a fourth vireo study area. Additionally, there was no shooting in human occupied areas.

One person, in conjunction with running the trap circuit, patrolled the two circuits on alternating days. Each circuit was covered between 0700–1130 hours from 1 March–30 June. Periodic stops along the circuits were made at sites with dead snags or potential cowbird foraging areas. There was no specific distance between shooting points since suitable shooting sites occurred at irregular intervals along both circuits. Taped playback of the female chatter (rattle) call was played at each stop to attract cowbirds within shooting range (Dufty 1982b). Some females were specifically targeted when field technicians with the Fort Hood endangered species program reported specific time and location of cowbird sightings in vireo habitat. Opportunistic shooting such as in grazing areas (Rothstein et al. 1987) was conducted throughout the year as time and circumstances (safety and presence of personnel) permitted.

RESULTS AND DISCUSSION

TRAPPING

A total of 3,413 female cowbirds were removed by trapping in 3449 trap days (TD) (trap

TABLE 2.   BROWN-HEADED COWBIRD PARASITISM RATE (PERCENT PARASITIZED, TOTAL NUMBER OF NESTS) OF
BLACK-CAPPED VIREO NESTS BY YEAR AND REGION ON FORT HOOD, TEXAS

	East Range	West Range	West Fort Hood	Live Fire	Total
1987[a]	90.3 (31)	—	100 (1)	100 (1)	90.9 (33)
1988[a]	84.4 (32)	83.3 (12)	100 (19)	95.8 (24)	90.8 (87)
1989[a]	51.8 (56)	70.8 (24)	58.6 (29)	83.7 (43)	65.1 (152)
1990[b]	66.7 (15)	25.0 (4)	100 (5)	53.3 (15)	63.0 (39)
1991[c]	13.6 (22)	50.0 (2)	25.0 (8)	57.1 (35)	38.8 (69)
1992[c]	4.2 (24)	14.3 (7)	42.9 (21)	61.5 (13)	29.2 (68)
1993[c]	14.8 (27)	13.3 (15)	60.0 (15)	22.2 (9)	25.8 (67)
1994[c]	11.1 (45)	3.8 (26)	11.8 (34)	25.0 (28)	12.8 (133)
1995[c]	18.5 (65)	0.0 (22)	6.9 (29)	21.0 (62)	15.2 (178)
1996[c]	34.8 (23)	18.2 (33)	14.8 (27)	29.6 (27)	22.9 (118)
1997[d]	1.6 (62)	9.1 (22)	11.3 (53)	16.2 (37)	8.6 (174)

[a] Taken from Table 6 in Hayden et al. 1998.
[b] Taken from Table 3 in Hunt 1991.
[c] Taken from Table 7 in Weinberg et al. 1998.
[d] Taken from Table 2.7 in Koloszar 1998.

capture rate = 0.989 females/TD) during the period 1 March–30 June 1997. Vireo parasitization was reduced to 8.6% in the 1997 breeding season (Koloszar 1998). The initial vireo studies on Fort Hood in 1987 found a cowbird parasitism rate of 90.9% (Table 2) and only a 4.7% nest success rate (Tazik and Cornelius 1993). Cowbird control efforts were initiated in 1988 by placing traps in vireo breeding habitat, and 10 females were removed from 3 traps in 230 trap days, yielding 0.04 females per trap day (TD). Six traps were operated in vireo habitat during 1989 and 120 females removed (0.05 females/TD), and in 1990, 25 traps in vireo habitat yielded 162 females (0.12 females/TD)(Hayden et al. in press). Trapping in breeding habitat has been successful in protecting birds such as Least Bell's Vireo (*Vireo bellii pusillus*) in southern California (Griffith and Griffith in press). However, this strategy, combined with random shooting of females, proved ineffective on Fort Hood (Table 2) in reducing parasitism to the 35% level, below which estimates indicate the vireo population can sustain itself (Tazik and Cornelius 1993).

Changing the trapping focus from vireo habitat to cattle grazing concentrations caused a dramatic increase in the number of female cowbirds captured, from 162 in 1990 to 1284 in 1991 (0.24 females/TD)(Hayden et al. 1998). A concurrent decrease in parasitism rates was detected, from 63% (N = 39) (Hunt 1991) in 1990 to 38.8% (N = 67) in 1991 (Hayden and Tazik 1991). As of 1993, all traps were placed in open cattle grazing areas.

The Spearman correlation between the number of female cowbirds removed per year and the parasitism rate of vireo nests from 1987–1997 was highly significant ($r_s = -0.952$, P < 0.01; Fig. 2). Barber and Martin (1997) also re-ported a relation between the level of cowbird parasitism of vireos at Fort Hood and the number of female cowbirds removed; however, their analysis involved comparison among different sites, not among different years. It is important to note that these statistical relationships indicate that if trapping were suspended or reduced, the frequency of parasitism would probably increase. When trapping effort within the aforementioned East Range cowbird telemetry study area was reduced, and all shooting stopped, parasitism rose to 34.8% in 1996 (Table 2). The 1997 drop to 1.6% parasitism in the East Range was potentially due to two factors: the reduction of cattle from 752 animal units (animal unit = 1 bull or 1 cow plus calf) to 103 and higher capture rates of four specific Mega traps (Table 3). These four traps had been placed into operation for the 1996 breeding season with 2.9 cm (1⅛ inches) entry slots to exclude non-target species. After cowbird control personnel observed female cowbirds being reluctant to enter through such a narrow slot, we concluded that cowbirds, not just non-target species, were also being excluded. Widening the slots to 3.2 cm (1¼ inches) did increase non-target captures while greatly increasing the number of cowbirds caught (Table 3). The effect of cattle removal/reduction may also explain that while three of the four Mega traps with widened slots saw significant increases in their capture rates, one trap (3OAK) declined (Table 3). This trap was the only one of the four with no cattle present in 1997. Since the increasing parasitism rates on the east range from 1994 to 1996 were based on reduced trapping effort and cessation of shooting, the results may not meet the criteria of a scientific experimental removal program in which all cowbird control measures are stopped

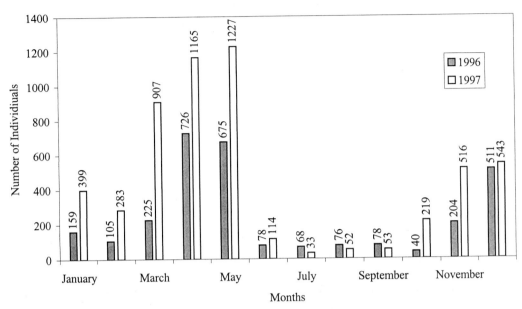

Total female Brown-headed Cowbirds killed from all traps by month for the years 1996 and 1997.

FIGURE 2. Relationship between Black-capped Vireo brood parasitism rate and number of female Brown-headed Cowbirds removed from the landscape study area population during the 1 Mar–30 June breeding season from 1987 to 1997, Fort Hood, Texas. ($r_s = -.952$, $P < 0.01$)

to access parasitism rates in the absence of cow-bird control (Robinson et al. 1995a).

The number of cowbirds removed from Fort Hood over the past 10 years has not decreased (Fig. 2). In a calendar year most cowbirds are caught in spring and fall migration (Fig. 3). The percentage of captured birds that are year round Fort Hood residents, migrants coming to Fort Hood to breed, migrants passing through Fort Hood, or birds wintering at Fort Hood from else-where is unknown. In an effort to learn more about the cowbird populations found at Fort Hood throughout the year, more than 2,000 males have been banded each year since 1991. Few band recoveries have been reported to date.

In addition to recaptures on Fort Hood and birds recovered in central Texas, three birds banded during spring migration have been recovered in Canada (Alberta and British Columbia). Two birds banded in January were recovered the fol-lowing spring in Paris, Tennessee, and Wilming-ton, North Carolina.

The sharp increase in females trapped in 1997 (3413) versus 1996 (1704) was probably a result of the accumulation of several factors. Trap cap-ture rates throughout the installation rose; how-ever, two factors may be significant—vandalism and slot width. In April 1996, vandals destroyed or severely damaged four traps, including two Mega traps, in the telemetry study area on the

TABLE 3. COMPARISON OF THE NUMBER OF FEMALE BROWN-HEADED COWBIRDS AND NON-TARGET INDIVIDUALS (IN PARENTHESES) CAPTURED IN MEGA STYLE TRAPS ON FORT HOOD, TEXAS, USING A SLOT WIDTH OF 2.9 CM IN 1996 VERSUS 3.2 CM IN 1997

	3OAK		OCMV		RORI		HENC	
	1996	1997	1996	1997	1996	1997	1996	1997
March	12 (0)	11 (36)	1 (0)	3 (0)	1 (0)	29 (1)	0 (0)	134 (0)
April	45 (1)	18 (0)	11 (0)	62 (0)	1 (0)	105 (2)	0 (0)	136 (16)
May	1 (1)	38 (1)	13 (0)	133 (13)	4 (0)	43 (0)	4 (0)	55 (22)
June	0 (0)	6 (0)	2 (0)	1 (0)	0 (0)	9 (0)	3 (0)	10 (0)

Note: Non-target species captured were House Finches (*Carpodacus mexicanus*), Red-winged Blackbirds (*Agelaius phoeniceus*), and Common Grackles (*Quiscalus quiscala*).

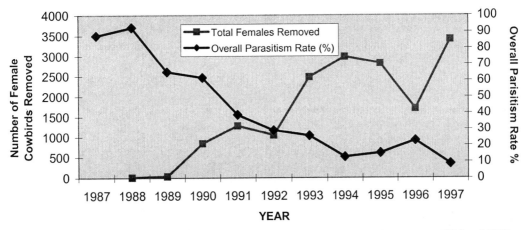

FIGURE 3.   Total numbers of female cowbirds killed from all traps by month for the years 1996 and 1997 at Fort Hood, Texas

east side of the installation. The vandalism released at least 200 female cowbirds, although many of these were likely migrants. Only one trap (a Mega) was repairable; thus, the potential captures of the other 3 traps were lost. There was no vandalism in that area in 1997. The increased capture rates of the four Mega traps with widened slots in 1997 probably lowered parasitism rates in nearby vireo breeding areas. However, other factors such as global population dynamics, drought, cattle movement, and military presence, may also be important.

SHOOTING

Sixty-seven female cowbirds were shot in 1997, representing 1.9% of all females removed during the breeding season. We believe selective shooting is an effective and efficient way to target females in breeding habitat as a complement to our trapping program since it has been conducted in conjunction with trap operation without requiring additional personnel. Having reviewed Fort Hood data from 1987–94, Hayden et al. (in press) state that more data are needed to assess if shooting in occupied habitat on a methodical basis is effective in reducing site-specific parasitism rates. In 1989 Fort Hood implemented routine shooting of female cowbirds in occupied vireo habitat in the expectation that parasitism would drop. Although 119 females were shot, parasitism rates were not appreciably affected (Tazik and Cornelius 1993). Tazik and Cornelius (1993) hypothesized that the overall cowbird population density on Fort Hood might have been too high to make shooting effective at that time. Shooting has been the only control measure used on WFH since 1994. Although traps were used on WFH in 1990, nest parasitism was 100% (N = 5). After improved trapping and random shooting the rate dropped to 25% (N = 8) in 1991. After all cowbird control was stopped in 1992, even in conjunction with cattle removal, parasitism rose to 42.9% (N = 21). Resumption of trapping in 1993 did not reduce parasitism. The parasitism rate reached 60% (N = 34) while the installation-wide rate dropped to the lowest recorded level (25.8%, N = 67) to that date (Table 2). After removing all traps and instituting a rigid, methodical shooting program, parasitism changed to 11.8% (15 females shot) in 1994, 6.9% (22 females shot) in 1995, 15.4% (21 females shot) in 1996, and 11.3% (15 females shot) in 1997. We do not know the threshold at which the landscape-scale cowbird population density drops low enough to make shooting females in breeding habitat an effective management tool.

CONCLUSIONS

Brood parasitism in situations similar to ours (a large area with widely dispersed endangered bird habitat) can be limited by a landscape approach to cowbird control that combines effective cowbird trapping with a methodical shooting program. We recommend the use of predation-resistant, easy-to-fabricate traps such as the Fort Hood Hybrid and Mega trap designs. Information on these traps may be obtained from John Cornelius, Fort Hood Natural Resources Branch (254) 287-2885, e-mail: corneliusj@ hood-emh3.army.mil. These traps should be placed in primary cowbird feeding areas, usually near cattle concentrations, to reduce the overall cowbird population. To complement the trapping program, we suggest a shooting program in breeding habitat to eliminate specific territorial females. Although trapping at cowbird feeding sites and a shooting program in breeding habitat have proved to be highly effective at Fort Hood, other strategies for removing cowbirds may be equally or more effective in other landscapes. For example, Griffith and Griffith (in press) report that cowbird numbers in a large southern California landscape were reduced effectively with extensive trapping in breeding habitats and with no shooting program.

While the Fort Hood cowbird control effort and other successful programs have demonstrated that an endangered avian species can be protected from brood parasitism, trapping and shooting do not correct land management practices that ultimately cause the problem. Cowbird control is a never-ending management option requiring scarce money and time. Further studies are necessary to address the questions of species recovery in terms of cowbird control, habitat loss and fragmentation, cattle grazing, urbanization, and cost effectiveness of various land management alternatives.

ACKNOWLEDGMENTS

We thank the staff of The Nature Conservancy Fort Hood Field Office for constructive comments on drafts of this manuscript. Special thanks go to John Cornelius, Dennis Herbert, and other personnel of the Fort Hood Natural Resources Branch. This project has been funded by the Department of Defense through a contract with Egan McAlister and Associates, TDL-0053 and Prime Contract N00140-95-C-H026, as well as cooperative agreement DPW-ENV97-A-0001 between The Nature Conservancy and Department of Defense and Fort Hood, Texas.

Studies in Avian Biology No. 18:275–281, 1999.

THE EFFECTS OF PRESCRIBED BURNING AND HABITAT EDGES ON BROWN-HEADED COWBIRD PARASITISM OF RED-WINGED BLACKBIRDS

Ethan D. Clotfelter, Ken Yasukawa, and Richard D. Newsome

Abstract. We studied the effects of prescribed burning and habitat edges on brood parasitism by Brown-headed Cowbirds (*Molothrus ater*) of a prairie-nesting population of Red-winged Blackbirds (*Agelaius phoeniceus*) in southern Wisconsin. A year-level analysis (1984–1996) revealed that spring versus fall burns, time elapsed since the study area was last burned, the area burned, and the quality of the burn had no significant effects on the proportion of nests in the population that were parasitized per year nor on the total number of cowbird eggs laid. In addition, these variables had no effect on the proportion of red-wing nests in the population that successfully fledged red-wing young, nor on the number of nests constructed. A nest-level analysis (1988–1996) revealed that the probability that a nest was parasitized increased as the distance to the nearest habitat edge or the nearest road decreased. The probability of parasitism also increased with increasing distance from the perimeter of the burn. Parasitism was unrelated to the quality of the burn or the time elapsed since the last burn. Parasitized nests containing multiple cowbird eggs were not significantly closer to roads or edges than were parasitized nests containing one cowbird egg. However, there was a trend for nests in burned units to have fewer cowbird eggs in them than nests in unburned units. The nest-level analysis also showed that success of Red-winged Blackbird nests increased with increasing distance from the burn perimeter. Nest success and the number of red-wing offspring produced were unrelated to the other burn-related and edge-related variables. Our results suggest that prescribed burning reduces cowbird parasitism of red-wings, but the mechanism responsible for this effect is not known.

Key Words: *Agelaius phoeniceus,* brood parasitism, Brown-headed Cowbird, edge effects, *Molothrus ater,* nest success, prescribed burning, Red-winged Blackbird.

Fire has been an important factor in the maintenance of grassland ecosystems for thousands of years (Daubenmire 1968). As a consequence of European settlement of central North America, grasslands were largely replaced with intensive agriculture and natural fires were suppressed. This was especially true of the tallgrass prairie ecosystem in central North America, of which less than 1% currently remains. In the near absence of natural fires, prescribed burning has become an important management tool in protecting native prairie remnants and in restoring native biodiversity to reclaimed agricultural lands. The effects of prescribed burning on grassland plant communities include removal of woody invaders, an increase in overall productivity, and reduction of litter, though these effects vary depending on the season in which burns are conducted (Hurlbert 1988, Bragg 1995). Despite the ubiquitous practice of prescribed burning, there is little agreement as to which burn season or which burn rotation best mimics natural processes (Howe 1994).

The impacts of prescribed burning on grassland bird populations are highly variable. Galliform birds, Upland Sandpipers (*Bartramia longicauda*), and some sparrows show consistent increases following burns (Cannon 1979, Kantrud 1981, Huber and Steuter 1984, Pylypec 1991, Zimmermann 1992). Many other sparrows typically decrease in abundance following a burn (Best 1979, Huber and Steuter 1984, Pylypec 1991, Zimmermann 1992, Herkert 1994a). Meadowlarks (*Sturnella* spp.), Grasshopper Sparrows (*Ammodramus savannarum*), and Savannah Sparrows (*Passerculus sandwichensis*) show geographically variable short-term responses to burning (Tester and Marshall 1961, Huber and Steuter 1984, Johnson and Temple 1986, Pylypec 1991, Zimmerman 1992, Herkert 1994a, Swengel 1996). Finally, species such as Bobolinks (*Dolichonyx oryzivorus*) show negative short-term responses to burning but thrive 2–3 years after a burn (Cody 1985). With several exceptions (e.g., Higgins 1986, Johnson and Temple 1986, Kruse and Piehl 1986, Vickery et al. 1992), few studies have examined the effects of fire on reproductive success of grassland birds, focusing instead on species abundance and diversity.

A subject that has received even less attention in the literature is the relationship between fire and brood parasitism by the Brown-headed Cowbird (*Molothrus ater*). Brown-headed Cowbirds are generalist brood parasites native to the grasslands of central North America, and thus have a long history of exposure to natural fire. However, we know very little of the dynamics of parasitism following prescribed burns. With increased fragmentation of natural grassland communities, a growing dependence on prescribed burning to maintain these fragments, and a concomitant decrease in grassland bird populations, it is important that we understand this relationship (Herkert 1994b, Howe 1994, Knopf 1994). The little information available suggests that burning has a negative effect on cowbird parasitism (Best 1979, Johnson and Temple 1990). However, neither of these studies examined the effects of multiple burns on the same study area to control for year and habitat differences. In the current study, we describe the effects of multiple prescribed burns over a 13-year period on cowbird parasitism of a prairie-nesting population of Red-winged Blackbirds (*Agelaius phoeniceus*).

The second objective of this study was to examine the importance of proximity to habitat edges in predicting patterns of cowbird parasitism on Red-winged Blackbirds. Numerous studies have suggested that passerine species suffer reduced reproductive success along habitat edges as a result of increased predation and brood parasitism (Gates and Gysel 1978, Chasko and Gates 1982, Brittingham and Temple 1983, Temple and Cary 1988). However, other studies report no such declines along habitat edges, calling into question the universal importance of edge effects (reviewed in Paton 1994). This may be because the mechanisms that cause edge effects can vary at different spatial scales (Donovan et al. 1997). In addition, the majority of studies has focused on edge effects on woodland-nesting birds, with relatively few studies of edges in grassland habitats (Paton 1994). In the current study, we examine the importance of habitat edges and roads in predicting patterns of cowbird parasitism in the same prairie-nesting population of Red-winged Blackbirds.

STUDY AREA

The study area was Newark Road Prairie (NRP), an isolated 13-ha wet-mesic prairie located in southern Wisconsin (42° 32′ N, 89° 08′ W). The dominant plant species over much of the prairie were cordgrass (*Spartina pectinata*), reed canary grass (*Phalaris arundinacea*), and various sedges (*Carex* spp.), with other areas dominated by a mixture of forbs and grasses of several species. The site is bounded on three sides by agricultural fields and woodlots (hereafter habitat edges) and on one side by a two-lane paved road. NRP has been managed by Beloit College with some supervision by The Nature Conservancy since 1977. Since then, prescribed burns have been conducted on at least a biennial basis. Originally, only spring burns (1 April–15 May) were employed. During the period of this study (1984–1996), however, fall burns (15 October–15 November) were conducted nearly as frequently as spring burns (Ta-

TABLE 1. SUMMARY OF PRESCRIBED BURNS AND RED-WINGED BLACKBIRD NESTING ON NEWARK ROAD PRAIRIE (NRP), 1984–1996

Year	Spring burn	Fall burn	Total nests (% successful)	% parasitized
1984	X	X	42 (38.1)	19.0
1985			57 (35.1)	3.5
1986	X	X	41 (51.2)	2.4
1987	X	X	62 (41.9)	12.9
1988		X	82 (45.1)	8.5
1989			58 (51.7)	10.3
1990		X	92 (33.7)	9.8
1991			126 (14.3)	19.1
1992	X		119 (34.5)	18.5
1993	X		90 (34.4)	10.0
1994	X	X	72 (19.4)	15.3
1995			87 (20.7)	23.0
1996	X		39 (23.1)	17.9

ble 1). Burns were attempted each year, but weather conditions dictated the season (if any) in which they succeeded. In some years, both spring and fall burns were successful (Table 1). Burn units of NRP 2–8 ha in size were burned in a rotating cycle. The primary management objective of these burns was the reduction of woody vegetation (*Salix* spp., *Cornus* spp.) and the restoration of native herbaceous vegetation.

METHODS

The Red-winged Blackbirds of NRP have been studied by K. Yasukawa and his colleagues since 1984 (see references in Searcy and Yasukawa 1995). In each year, 30–130 nests were found (mean $\pm$ SE; $\bar{x}$ = 74.1 $\pm$ 7.8 nests) and their fates monitored by daily nest visits. Nesting usually began in early May ($\bar{x}$ = 7 May $\pm$ 1.6 days) and peaked 1–2 weeks later. Therefore, relatively few nests were directly affected by spring burns. The majority of nests were located during nest construction or egg-laying (Yasukawa et al. 1990), so it is reasonable to assume that the proportion of nests found parasitized represents an accurate estimate of the parasitism rate of all nests. In addition, most red-wings in the study population were individually color-banded, which allowed us to attribute nests to individual pairs and minimized the possibility that females constructed nests without our knowledge. In 1987, a system of markers was installed on NRP, dividing it into a grid of 20 × 20 m squares. Beginning in 1988, the location of each nest was recorded using these grid markers.

Cowbird eggs were removed from all parasitized nests on NRP 2–24 h after they were laid. As part of a separate study, we allowed cowbird eggs to hatch in red-wing nests on a neighboring prairie (Diehls Prairie) to quantify the impact of cowbird parasitism on Red-winged Blackbird reproductive success. Consistent with other studies of red-wings (Weatherhead 1989, Røskaft et al. 1990), clutch size and fledgling production were reduced in parasitized nests as a consequence of egg removal by cowbirds (Clotfelter 1998a).

As is true in many grassland areas, the bird community of NRP is relatively species-poor (Wiens 1974, Knopf 1994). In addition to Red-winged Blackbirds, the most abundant potential cowbird hosts of NRP were Song Sparrows (*Melospiza melodia*), Swamp Sparrows (*M. georgiana*), Bobolinks, Eastern Meadowlarks (*Sturnella magna*), Common Yellowthroats (*Geothlypis trichas*), Yellow Warblers (*Dendroica petechia*), and Northern Cardinals (*Cardinalis cardinalis*). We located nests of these species opportunistically, but did not study them in a systematic fashion. The most abundant potential predators in the area were bullsnakes (*Pituophis melanoleucus*), raccoon (*Procyon lotor*), mink (*Mustela vison*), Sedge Wrens (*Cistothorus platensis*), and American Crows (*Corvus brachyrhynchos*).

STATISTICAL ANALYSES: GENERAL

In the current study, we conducted two levels of analysis. First, we examined the effects of differences in burn treatment on parasitism and nest success among years using linear regression (year-level analysis) (Draper and Smith 1981). Second, we used logistic regression (Kleinbaum et al. 1988) to examine the effects of differences in burn treatment and proximity to edges among nests within years (nest-level analysis). In addition, we used ANOVA and linear regression to examine the effects of burn treatment and distance to edges on the number of cowbird eggs laid per red-wing nest. SYSTAT 7.0 (Wilkinson 1997) was used to perform regressions, ANOVAs, and *t*-tests. All tests are two-tailed and differences were considered significant at P < 0.05. Means and regression coefficients are presented ± SE.

STATISTICAL ANALYSES: YEAR-LEVEL ANALYSIS

We performed stepwise forward multiple regressions (P = 0.15 to enter model) to determine the independent variables that were associated with (1) the proportion of red-wing nests parasitized by cowbirds, (2) the total number of cowbird eggs laid, and (3) the proportion of red-wing nests that succeeded in fledging at least one red-wing offspring across all 13 years. We used the angular transformation for proportions before analysis (Sokal and Rohlf 1981). The independent variables considered in these models included two dummy variables for spring (0,1)

and fall (0,1) burning; the total area of the prairie burned (to nearest 100 m^2); the quality of spring and fall burns; the time elapsed since the last burn (6–24 mo); the study year (1984–1996); and the total number of red-wing nests. Burn quality was ranked on an ordinal scale (0–5) based on a combination of the following factors: number and size of unburned patches, extent of burn on woody vegetation, how well the fire carried itself as a back-burn, and the extent to which short-distance head fires were necessary.

STATISTICAL ANALYSES: NEST-LEVEL ANALYSIS

We constructed logistic models to predict the probability of two dichotomous outcomes, cowbird parasitism (parasitized or unparasitized) and red-wing nest success (successful or failed), for all nests in the 1988–1996 period. Data from 1984–1987 were excluded because exact locations of these nests were unavailable until the grid was established in 1988. We defined a successful nest as one producing at least one fledgling. We included the following independent variables in the full models: a dummy variable for whether the nest was in an unburned unit or a unit burned that spring; the time since the nest site was last burned for nests in unburned units (6–24 mo; nests in burned units were given a score of 0); the distance to the burn perimeter for nests in unburned units (m; nests in burned units were given a score of 0); the quality of the burn for nests in burned units (nests in unburned units were given a score of 0); the distance between the nest and the nearest habitat edge; the distance between the nest and the road; the Julian date on which the nest was initiated; and the study year. Second-order variables and interaction terms were also included as variables in the logistic models. Because study year was a categorical variable, the stepwise procedure took the highest value first (1996) and then entered all other years into the model as separate variables (see Tables 2, 4). If no spring burn was conducted in a given year, nests in that year were assigned a distance to burn perimeter of 1000 m (exceeds greatest distance possible if burn had been conducted). Burn quality was measured as described above. Distance to nearest habitat edge was the linear distance between the nest and the nearest woodlot or agricultural field. If the road was also the nearest edge to a given nest, then that distance was used for both variables. Distances to the burn perimeter, the nearest habitat edge, and the road were all estimated ± 10 m on a map of the study area.

To determine how burn treatment and habitat edges were associated with the number of cowbird eggs laid per red-wing nests (0–4) and the

TABLE 2.   STEPWISE LOGISTIC REGRESSION MODEL OF THE RELATIONSHIP OF BURN-RELATED AND EDGE-RELATED VARIABLES TO PARASITISM OR NO PARASITISM OF RED-WINGED BLACKBIRD NESTS, 1988–1996 (N = 698 NESTS)

Variable	Coefficient ± SE	t statistic	P-value
Constant	2.48 ± 1.34	1.85	0.065
Distance to edge	−0.016 ± 0.005	−3.36	0.001
Distance to road	−0.006 ± 0.002	−3.93	<0.001
Nest initiation date	−0.024 ± 0.008	−3.08	0.002
Year (1988)	−22.45 ± 8.88	−2.53	0.011
Year (1989)	−22.23 ± 8.88	−2.51	0.012
Year (1990)	−22.22 ± 8.86	−2.51	0.012
Year (1991)	−21.42 ± 8.86	−2.42	0.016
Year (1995)	−21.04 ± 8.84	−2.38	0.017
[Distance to burn]^2	1E-04 ± 1E-04	2.41	0.016

number of red-wing offspring fledged per nest (0–4), we used stepwise forward multiple regression (P = 0.15 to enter model). We used the same independent variables described above in these regressions.

RESULTS

YEAR-LEVEL ANALYSIS

The proportion of red-wing nests parasitized by cowbirds between 1984–1996 varied by an order of magnitude (Table 1). Parasitized nests with ≥ 2 cowbird eggs accounted for 17.2 % of all parasitized nests found on NRP. The multiple linear regressions showed that none of the burn-related variables had significant relationships to the proportion of red-wing nests parasitized each year (adj. R^2 < 0.001, $F_{3,9}$ = 1.01, P = 0.56), nor to the total number of cowbird eggs laid per year (adj. R^2 = 0.23, $F_{3,9}$ = 1.4, P = 0.43). In addition, the burn-related variables were not related to the proportion of nests that successfully fledged offspring (adj. R^2 < 0.001, $F_{3,9}$ = 0.95, P = 0.58). Spring burns were not related to the onset of red-wing nesting. The dates of first nesting attempts in spring burn years were no different than in non-burn years (t = 0.15, df = 10, P = 0.89) as were the dates of the first cowbird eggs (t = −0.094, df = 10, P = 0.93). A separate multiple regression showed that none of the burn-related variables were related to the total number of red-wing nests constructed on NRP (adj. R^2 < 0.001, $F_{4,8}$ = 0.51, P = 0.81).

NEST-LEVEL ANALYSIS

The reduced logistic regression model for cowbird parasitism obtained using the forward stepwise procedure is shown in Table 2 (log-likelihood for reduced model = −270.6, χ^2_{12} = 66.9, P < 0.001). The probability of cowbird parasitism increased with decreasing distance to the nearest habitat edge and the nearest road, and increased with increasing distance away from the burn perimeter. The date and year in which a nest was initiated were also significant predictors of cowbird parasitism. None of the other burn-related variables remained in the reduced model.

The multiple regression model showed that the number of cowbird eggs laid per red-wing nest increased with decreasing nest initiation date, distance to nearest edge, and distance to road (adj. R^2 = 0.05, $F_{3,694}$ = 12.62, P < 0.001; Table 3). However, when distances to nearest edges and distances to road were compared among unparasitized nests, parasitized nests with one cowbird egg, and parasitized nests with ≥ 2 cowbird eggs, it was apparent that this relationship was primarily the result of differences between parasitized and unparasitized nests (ANOVA$_{Edge}$: $F_{2,695}$ = 12.74, P < 0.001; ANOVA$_{Road}$: $F_{2,695}$ = 8.33, P < 0.001). In other words, nests with multiple cowbird eggs were not significantly closer to edges or roads than were nests parasitized only once (Figs. 1, 2). To determine whether the number of cowbird eggs in

TABLE 3.   STEPWISE MULTIPLE REGRESSION MODEL FOR THE NUMBER OF COWBIRD EGGS LAID PER RED-WINGED BLACKBIRD NEST, 1988–1996 (N = 698 NESTS)

Variable	Coefficient ± SE	t statistic	P-value
Constant	0.859 ± 0.182	4.71	<0.001
Nest initiation date	−0.094 ± 0.001	−2.53	0.012
Distance to edge	−0.157 ± 0.001	−4.21	<0.001
Distance to road	−0.123 ± 1.0E-04	−3.31	0.001

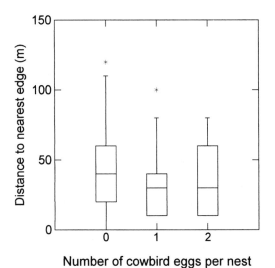

FIGURE 1. Differences in mean distance to habitat edge among unparasitized nests (N = 587), parasitized nests containing one cowbird egg (N = 89), and parasitized nests containing two or more cowbird eggs (N = 22) (ANOVA $F_{2,695}$ = 12.74, P < 0.001). Asterisks represent outside values.

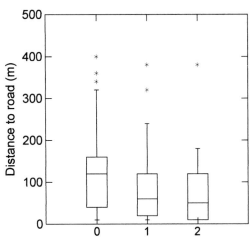

FIGURE 2. Differences in mean distance to road among unparasitized nests (N = 587), parasitized nests containing one cowbird egg (N = 89), and parasitized nests containing two or more cowbird eggs (N = 22) (ANOVA $F_{2,695}$ = 8.33, P < 0.001). Asterisks represent outside values.

red-wing nests differed between nests on burned versus unburned units, we compared the residuals from the linear regression in Table 3. Nests on unburned units of NRP tended to have more cowbird eggs in them than nests on burned units of NRP (t = 1.88, df = 696, P = 0.061). In other words, when edge effects were statistically controlled, parasitism was less intense on burned units than on unburned units.

The logistic regression model for red-wing nest success showed that the probability of success increased depending on study year, nest initiation date, and distance to burn perimeter (Table 4; log-likelihood for reduced model = −402.0, χ^2_{11} = 69, P < 0.001). The multiple regression results showed that the number of fledglings produced was affected only by nest initiation date (adj. R^2 = 0.03, $F_{1,696}$ = 25.73, P < 0.001). When residuals from this regression were compared between burned and unburned units of NRP, we found no significant differences in the number of red-wing offspring fledged (t = 0.79, df = 696, P = 0.43).

DISCUSSION

In general, prescribed burning on Newark Road Prairie appeared to have little direct impact on Red-winged Blackbirds. Spring burns did not delay the start of the breeding season nor affect the total number of nests constructed. In fact, the annual variation in number of red-wings nesting on NRP remains largely unexplained. Previous

studies examining the responses of red-wings to prescribed burns have reported mixed results. Huber and Steuter (1984) observed no difference between burned and unburned treatments in June, but a significant decline in red-wing abundance in July. Zimmerman (1992), however, found that red-wing numbers increased twofold on burned units compared with unburned units (see also Westemeier and Buhnerkempe 1983). However, these studies measured red-wing abundance and not nest success.

In the year-level analysis, we found no effect of prescribed burning on the proportion of red-wing nests parasitized by cowbirds, the number of cowbird eggs laid, or the proportion of those nests that successfully produced at least one red-wing fledgling. In the nest-level analysis, however, we found some evidence that prescribed burning had a negative impact on cowbird parasitism. Nests in burned units had fewer cowbird eggs in them than nests in unburned units, and nests near the burn perimeter were significantly less likely to be parasitized than nests far from the burn perimeter. These results generally support those of Best (1979), who reported that a spring burn reduced cowbird parasitism of a population of Field Sparrows (*Spizella pusilla*) in Illinois. We found no evidence that burn interval (or time elapsed since last burn) had a significant effect on cowbird parasitism, as Johnson and Temple (1990) did in their study of several host species (*S. pallida, Passerculus*

TABLE 4. STEPWISE LOGISTIC REGRESSION MODEL OF THE RELATIONSHIP OF BURN-RELATED AND EDGE-RELATED VARIABLES TO SUCCESS OR FAILURE OF RED-WINGED BLACKBIRD NESTS, 1988–1996 (N = 698 NESTS)

Variable	Coefficient ± SE	t statistic	P-value
Constant	24.46 ± 8.94	2.74	0.006
Year (1988)	−14.63 ± 6.12	−2.39	0.017
Year (1989)	−14.16 ± 6.12	−2.31	0.021
Year (1990)	−15.30 ± 6.12	−2.50	0.013
Year (1991)	−16.19 ± 6.12	−2.64	0.008
Year (1995)	−15.81 ± 6.13	−2.58	0.010
Nest initiation date	−0.32 ± 0.17	−2.75	0.006
[Nest initiation date]^2	0.001 ± 1E-04	2.57	0.010
[Distance to burn]^2	1E-04 ± 1E-04	2.52	0.012

sandwichensis, Ammodramus savannarum, Dolichonyx oryzivorus, and *Sturnella neglecta*) in the tallgrass prairie of Minnesota.

We found that the distance to habitat edge and distance to road were highly significant predictors of parasitism, although the number of cowbird eggs per parasitized nest did not increase with increasing proximity to edges or to the road. These results are important because relatively few studies have examined edge effects in grassland areas (Best 1978, Johnson and Temple 1990, Burger et al. 1994). However, we saw no indication of increased predation, which accounts for 70% of failed nests (Yasukawa et al. 1990), along habitat edges in the current study. We found that the distances to habitat edges and to roads were not significant predictors of nest success nor of the number of red-wing offspring fledged per nest. Annual variation in nest success is likely due to factors such as predator abundance and food availability (see references in Searcy and Yasukawa 1995), which were not measured in the current study. Therefore, although proximity of nests to habitat edges or to roads may increase the probability that Red-winged Blackbirds are parasitized, it does not have a serious impact on their reproductive success per se. Edge effects are likely to be more pronounced in grassland species that suffer greater losses from cowbird parasitism than do red-wings.

There are several potential explanations for the relationship between prescribed burning and cowbird parasitism. First, burns may reduce the density of potential cowbird hosts nesting on the burned units (e.g., sparrows; see references above). If cowbirds search for host nests in areas of high host density (Gates and Gysel 1978) then burned units would theoretically receive fewer cowbird visits. We found no such relationship for cowbird parasitism of Red-winged Blackbirds. The number of red-wing nests constructed each year was unrelated to the overall proportion of nests parasitized (year-level analysis), sug-

gesting that cowbird parasitism was density-independent. Arcese et al. (1992) found similar results in an island population of Song Sparrows. It is possible, however, that prescribed burning affects dispersion of red-wing nests, which has been shown to be related to cowbird parasitism in a neighboring prairie (Clotfelter 1998a). Because we did not monitor the responses of other species to prescribed burns, however, we cannot rule out the hypothesis that burning reduced cowbird parasitism on red-wings by reducing overall host density.

Second, prescribed burns may alter the vegetative structure in a way that deters parasitism. Late in the season, for example, nests may have greater cover in burned units than in unburned units, making them less conspicuous to cowbirds (Herkert 1994a). However, the evidence that nest cover is an important predictor of parasitism is equivocal (Brittingham and Temple 1996, Barber and Martin 1997, Burhans 1997, Clotfelter 1998b). Another way that fire might affect vegetation structure and reduce parasitism is through the exposure of woody vegetation. Many studies of cowbirds have found that proximity to trees or tall perches is a significant predictor of parasitism (Freeman et al. 1990, Romig and Crawford 1995, Clotfelter 1998b). Because burned trees leaf out later in the spring than unburned trees, they may be more exposed and less useful to cowbirds as surveillance perches. However, the proximity of host nests to leafless snags has been shown to be an important predictor of parasitism in some cases (Anderson and Storer 1976). Given the apparent importance of trees to female cowbirds, this hypothesis merits further investigation.

Finally, if food abundance increases following a burn, then hosts in burned units may be more capable of deterring parasitism because they are able to feed near their nests (Herkert 1994a). This was demonstrated experimentally by Arcese and Smith (1988), who observed a decrease in cowbird parasitism of Song Sparrows following food supplementation. Past studies have shown that some insect populations respond positively to prescribed burning (Rice 1932, Knutson and Campbell 1976, Seastedt 1984), suggesting that this hypothesis needs further attention.

In conclusion, we found that both prescribed burning and habitat edges affected parasitism levels, but to varying degrees. From this observation, we can make two general statements. First, we urge further study of this interesting relationship between prescribed burning and cowbird parasitism to determine if it holds true for species of conservation concern. If it does, wildlife managers should consider shorter burn intervals in grassland habitats where these hosts are severely affected by cowbird parasitism. However, it is important to determine first how robust a host species is to fire disturbance. In this regard, Red-winged Blackbirds may not be an ideal model species because they showed virtually no response to spring burns. Species such as Grasshopper Sparrows and Bobolinks, for example, seem to have greater success in grass-lands with longer burn intervals (Cody 1985, Johnson and Temple 1990, Swengel 1996). Second, we found that proximity to edge was a highly significant predictor of cowbird parasitism, and that this effect was much stronger than that of prescribed burning. This again illustrates one of the effects of habitat fragmentation, and should serve to remind us that the ultimate goal in the management of grassland birds is to protect large areas of grassland habitat free from woody or agricultural edges.

ACKNOWLEDGMENTS

We are grateful to The Nature Conservancy for their purchase of Newark Road Prairie and to Beloit College for their stewardship of the prairie and for allowing us to conduct our research there. Financial support was provided by National Science Foundation Grants IBN95–28346 to E.D.C. and BNS86–16572, BNS89–19298, and IBN93–06620 to K.Y. We would also like to thank numerous undergraduates from Beloit College, some of whom were supported by funding from the Pew Charitable Trusts and the Howard Hughes Medical Institute. Comments by J. Baylis, D. Curson, L. Hall, T. Manolis, D. Sample, and an anonymous reviewer greatly improved previous versions of this paper.

Studies in Avian Biology No. 18:282–289, 1999.

COWBIRD TRAPPING IN REMOTE AREAS: ALTERNATIVE CONTROL MEASURES MAY BE MORE EFFECTIVE

KIRSTEN J. WINTER AND SHARON D. MCKELVEY

Abstract. Brown-headed Cowbirds *(Molothrus ater)* were trapped on the Cleveland National Forest from 1992 to 1997 in an attempt to increase the reproductive success of the endangered Least Bell's Vireo *(Vireo bellii pusillus)* and Southwestern Willow Flycatcher *(Empidonax traillii extimus)* on National Forest lands. Over this time period the flycatcher population has been stable, while two of three vireo populations have declined. We postulate that the remote locations of vireo populations made cowbird trapping an ineffective tool for reducing the impact of brood parasitism. The lack of road and trail access to these areas limits both the number of traps that can be employed and the selection of trap locations. Where these conditions exist, our data suggest that nest monitoring and cowbird egg removal may be more effective and less costly than cowbird trapping.

Key Words: brood parasitism, Brown-headed Cowbird, *Empidonax traillii extimus,* Least Bell's Vireo, *Molothrus ater,* Southwestern Willow Flycatcher, *Vireo bellii pusillus.*

The Least Bell's Vireo *(Vireo bellii pusillus)* is federally-listed as endangered (U.S. Fish and Wildlife Service [USFWS] 1986). Major threats to this subspecies include loss of riparian habitat and brood parasitism by Brown-headed Cowbirds *(Molothrus ater)* (Goldwasser et al. 1980). The Southwestern Willow Flycatcher *(Empidonax traillii extimus)* is also federally-listed as endangered (USFWS 1995) and faces similar threats. In San Diego County, California, Cleveland National Forest personnel manage habitat for these species. A large population of Southwestern Willow Flycatchers nests along the upper San Luis Rey River, within the Cleveland National Forest. Several smaller populations of Least Bell's Vireos nest along Santa Ysabel, Pine, and Cottonwood creeks. To minimize the effects of cowbird parasitism, the Forest conducted cowbird trapping from 1992–1997. Here we report the results of this cowbird trapping and compare these with data on population trends and reproductive success of vireos and flycatchers on our study areas.

STUDY AREA

Our study included four riparian areas in the foothill regions of the Laguna and Palomar mountains, in San Diego County: Pine Creek, Cottonwood Creek, Santa Ysabel Creek, and the upper San Luis Rey River (Fig. 1). All of the study areas are located on National Forest lands. The breeding habitat for vireos and flycatchers in these areas consists of mixed riparian forest, varying from early successional to mature stands of arroyo willow *(Salix lasiolepis)*, cottonwood *(Populus fremontii)*, sycamore *(Platanus racemosa)*, and coast live oak *(Quercus agrifolia)*. Surrounding land uses include wilderness areas, agriculture, grazing, and rural residential development.

Pine Creek is located within the Pine Creek Wilderness Area, and Cottonwood and Santa Ysabel Creeks are in rugged, remote areas that are 2 to 3 km (by air) from the nearest road (Fig. 1). Cottonwood Creek is at the southern edge of the Hauser Canyon Wilderness Area. All of these creeks are located in narrow, steep-sided canyons where the dominant vegetation type is dense chaparral. The primary access is by hiking through the riparian areas; vireo territories are 1.5 to 6.5 kilometers from the nearest road. The San Luis Rey River is adjacent to state Highway 76.

METHODS

Over the past six years, Cleveland National Forest staff have conducted cowbird trapping in the four study areas. We began a pilot trapping effort at Santa Ysabel Creek and the San Luis Rey River in 1992, and fully implemented the program in 1993 with an additional trapping effort at Pine Creek to increase the reproductive success of vireo and flycatcher. Standard trapping methods, as described in Robinson et al. (1992), were employed. The design was modeled on the Australian Crow trap and the trap size was $2 \times 2.5 \times 1.5$ m. In 1992, one trap was placed at Santa Ysabel Creek and one trap at the San Luis Rey River. Beginning in 1993, three to five traps were placed at the San Luis Rey River, three or four traps at Santa Ysabel Creek, and two traps at Pine and Cottonwood Creeks. (Pine Creek is a tributary to Cottonwood Creek; traps were placed near their confluence.)

The number of traps placed at each site was based on the number of suitable trap locations that were reasonably accessible for monitoring. At the San Luis Rey River, traps were placed at 0.8 km intervals in the riparian habitat. Due to the lack of road access to Pine and Cottonwood

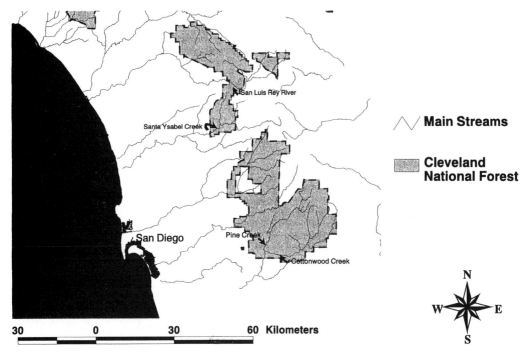

FIGURE 1.   Least Bell's Vireo and Southwestern Willow Flycatcher study sites, Cleveland National Forest, CA, 1992–1997.

Creeks, traps were placed near Barrett Lake where these creeks converge; this was the only area in which road access was available. At Santa Ysabel Creek, there is road access to the riparian habitat only at a point where a road crosses the riparian area, about 1.5 kilometers from the nearest vireo territory. Traps were placed in three areas in the adjoining Pamo Valley, which is the primary cowbird foraging area.

The trapping season was approximately April 1 through July 15. Each trap had 'bait birds,' typically two male cowbirds and three female cowbirds, to entice additional cowbirds to enter the trap. Traps were checked daily and the number, age and sex of trapped cowbirds were recorded. Excess cowbirds and non-target bird species were released and cowbirds were humanely destroyed. Water and food were provided within the trap and were replenished daily.

Population monitoring and nest monitoring of Least Bell's Vireos and Southwestern Willow Flycatchers fluctuated between years as a function of funding and staffing levels. For Least Bell's Vireo, nest and population surveys were conducted in 1993, 1994, and 1997 between April 1 and July 15. In 1995 and 1996 no surveys were conducted (US Forest Service, unpubl. reports). For Southwestern Willow Flycatcher, intensive population monitoring was

conducted from 1994 through 1997, between May 1 and August 15 (J. T. Griffith and J. C. Griffith unpubl. report, W. E. Haas unpubl. report).

Population surveys consisted of walking through the study area in the morning hours, typically between 0600 and 1100 hrs. Taped playbacks of Least Bell's Vireo and Southwestern Willow Flycatcher songs were occasionally used to elicit responses. Nest monitoring was conducted by observing Least Bell's Vireo and Southwestern Willow Flycatcher behavior for more extended periods. The observer would determine whether birds were paired and would locate nests. Once nest locations had been determined, the observer would monitor nests at 7–10 day intervals to determine the rate of brood parasitism and number of successful fledglings. In 1997, cowbird trapping at Cottonwood Creek was supplemented with nest checks and cowbird egg removal. Five Least Bell's Vireo pairs were monitored.

RESULTS

The Santa Ysabel Creek and San Luis Rey River trap arrays were most effective at capturing large numbers of cowbirds (Fig. 2). An average of 59 cowbirds (SD = 23) were trapped annually at Santa Ysabel Creek and 79 (SD =

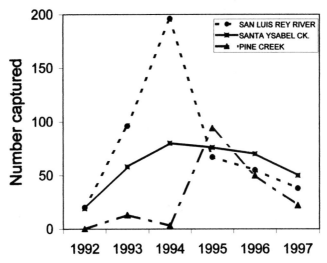

FIGURE 2.   Cowbird trapping results Cleveland National Forest, CA, 1992–1997. Note that in 1994, cowbird shooting was substituted for cowbird trapping at Pine Creek and Cottonwood Creek.

63) at San Luis Rey River. However, the trapping effort was complicated by a few factors. For example, one trap at the San Luis Rey River was constantly vandalized with consequent release of cowbirds, and one trap at Santa Ysabel Creek was a favorite feeding area for predators, making it difficult to maintain the target number of bait birds in the trap. The presumed predators were Cooper's Hawks *(Accipiter cooperi)* and raccoons *(Procyon lotor)*. It appeared that predators grabbed cowbirds and pulled them through the mesh enclosing the trap.

The cowbird traps at Pine Creek and Cottonwood Creek caught an average of 45 (SD = 36) cowbirds per year (Fig. 2). In 1994 cowbird shooting was substituted for trapping and three cowbirds were shot. The trapping in this area was complicated by the frequent capture of large numbers of non-target species, particularly Redwinged Blackbirds *(Agelaius phoeniceus)*. At all locations the number of cowbird captures per year decreased slightly from 1995 to 1997.

BELL'S VIREOS

The Least Bell's Vireo population at Pine Creek declined over the course of the study (Fig. 3). The Pine Creek population was at its highest level in 1994 with a total of five pairs reported (U.S. Forest Service, unpubl. Report), and at its lowest level in 1997 with no Least Bell's Vireos found (Wells and Turnbull 1998). The Least Bell's Vireo population at Santa Ysabel Creek declined from four pairs in 1992 to a single territorial male in 1997 (Fig. 3). The Cottonwood Creek population of Least Bell's Vireo fluctuated from 1990 to 1997, but has been generally increasing since 1993 (Fig. 3). In 1990, before the initiation of cowbird trapping, five pairs of vireos were detected, and in 1997 six pairs were observed at Cottonwood Creek (Wells and Turnbull 1998).

In 1997, we detected no breeding activity at Pine Creek, and in 1994 and 1997, no activity at Santa Ysabel Creek due to the absence of paired vireos (Fig. 4). At Cottonwood Creek (Fig. 4), the Least Bell's Vireo population has been able to maintain itself over the years, and in fact experienced its best year ever in 1997.

Five vireo pairs were monitored at Cottonwood Creek in 1997. They made a total of eight nesting attempts. Four nests failed due to predation, and cowbird brood parasitism affected three out of eight attempts, for a parasitism rate of 37.5%. However, cowbird eggs were removed from the parasitized nests, allowing the three parasitized broods to successfully fledge a total of seven young (Wells and Turnbull 1998).

For reference purposes, additional pre-trapping data from the years 1985–1990 are summarized here. At Santa Ysabel Creek, a brood parasitism rate of 50% was observed (N = 6 nests detected, 3 parasitized) at Pine Creek, a parasitism rate of 10% (N = 10), and at Cottonwood Creek, a parasitism rate of 30% (N = 10) (U.S. Forest Service, unpubl. report).

WILLOW FLYCATCHERS

The Southwestern Willow Flycatcher population at the upper San Luis Rey River was monitored between 1994 and 1997 (J. T. Griffith and J. C. Griffith, unpubl. report; W.E. Haas, pers. comm.). This population appeared to be stable

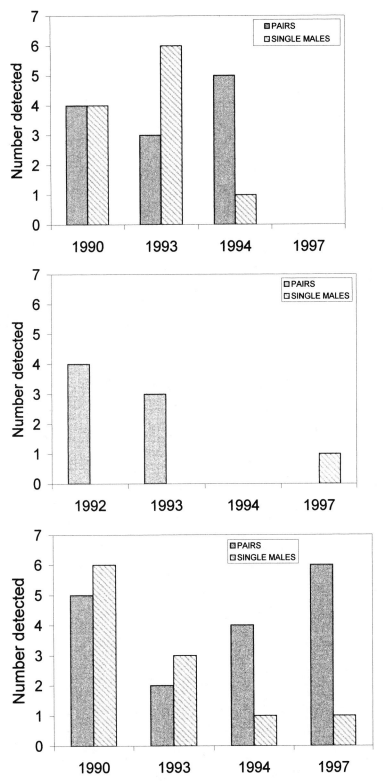

FIGURE 3. Least Bell's Vireo population, Cleveland National Forest, CA, 1992–1997. Top, Pine Creek; middle, Santa Ysabel Creek; bottom, Cottonwood Creek.

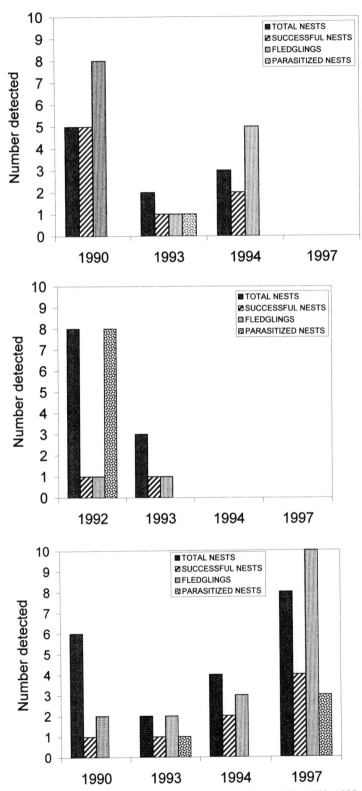

FIGURE 4. Least Bell's Vireo reproduction, Cleveland National Forest, CA, 1992–1997. Top, Pine Creek; middle, Santa Ysabel Creek; bottom, Cottonwood Creek.

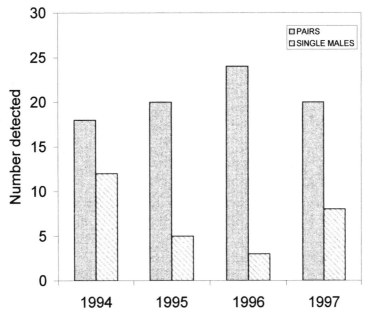

FIGURE 5.   Southwestern Willow Flycatcher population, San Luis Rey River, Cleveland National Forest, CA, 1994–1997.

over this time period (Fig. 5). A total of 18 pairs was reported in 1994; the population was at its peak in 1996 at 24 pairs. In 1997, 20 pairs were detected.

No cowbird parasitism of Southwestern Willow Flycatcher nests was noted in 1994–1996. Two out of 27 nests were parasitized in 1997 (7.4%), although both of the affected pairs subsequently re-nested and successfully fledged young (W. E. Haas, pers. comm.). This flycatcher population has had a high rate of reproductive success over the last four years, with a total of 64.6% of detected nests (53/82) successfully fledging young (Fig. 6).

DISCUSSION

On the Cleveland National Forest, cowbird trapping was undertaken as a management technique. This work was not intended to be a research project. Based on trapping results from elsewhere in San Diego County, we expected that trapping would be successful in reducing cowbird parasitism rates. In retrospect, it is clear that we should have placed more emphasis on monitoring the effectiveness of trapping. The data that we do have shows that trapping has had mixed results.

At the San Luis Rey River, cowbird trapping appears to have been effective in controlling cowbird numbers, thereby limiting brood parasitism on the Southwestern Willow Flycatcher. J. T. Griffith and J. C. Griffith (unpubl. report)

concluded that the 0% brood parasitism and the 64% nest success rate they observed along the San Luis Rey River in 1994 demonstrated the effectiveness of the cowbird trapping program. However, since there is no information on the pre-trapping rates of brood parasitism for this area it is not possible to determine whether cowbird trapping had any effect.

The consistently high rates of nest success and extremely low rates of cowbird brood parasitism appear to be unique to the San Luis Rey River population. Even with cowbird trapping in place, the Southwestern Willow Flycatcher population at the Kern River, in the southern Sierra Nevada of California, experienced nest success rates of 47.8% and brood parasitism rates of 15.6% in 1993 and 1994 (Whitfield and Strong 1995). Populations of Southwestern Willow Flycatcher at the Grand Canyon, where there is no cowbird trapping, experienced average nest success rates of 18% and brood parasitism rates of 47% between 1992–1996 (Sogge et al. 1997).

In the Pine Creek, Cottonwood Creek, and Santa Ysabel Creek areas, the lack of road and trail access limited both the number of traps that could be employed and the selection of trap locations. In these areas we have observed brood parasitism rates of Least Bell's Vireo populations as high as 100% and the extirpation of two local vireo populations even with cowbird trapping in place. In 1997, the addition of nest monitoring and cowbird egg removal in the Cotton-

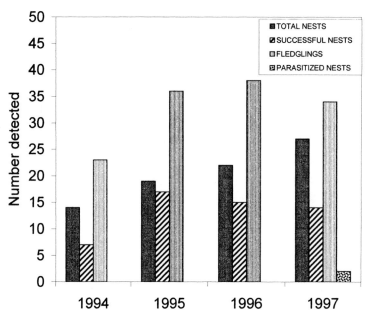

FIGURE 6.   Southwestern Willow Flycatcher reproduction, San Luis Rey River, Cleveland National Forest, CA, 1994–1997.

wood Creek area apparently allowed parasitized vireo pairs to successfully fledge young.

In southern California, cowbird trapping has frequently been prescribed as the preferred method for control of cowbird brood parasitism on endangered species (USFWS unpubl. reports). In many areas cowbird trapping has proven to be an effective tool for managing cowbird populations, and Least Bell's Vireo and Southwestern Willow Flycatcher populations have stabilized or increased. For example, at Camp Pendleton, the number of vireo pairs increased from 68 pairs in 1986 to over 900 pairs in 1997, and at the Tijuana River, the number of vireo pairs increased from 5 pairs in 1990 to over 100 pairs in 1997 (USFWS 1998). Range-wide, the Least Bell's Vireo increased from about 300 pairs in 1986 to over 1600 pairs in 1996 (L. Hays, pers. comm.) This increase is largely attributed to an increase in fecundity resulting from cowbird trapping. At the Kern River in the southern Sierra Nevada, a Southwestern Willow Flycatcher population stabilized 2 years after cowbird trapping was initiated (Whitfield and Strong 1995).

The Cleveland National Forest study shows a different pattern. For Least Bell's Vireos, observed rates of brood parasitism remained high, even with cowbird trapping in place. A 100% parasitism rate was observed at Santa Ysabel Creek in 1992 and a 37.5% parasitism rate was observed at Cottonwood Creek in 1997 (Wells and Turnbull 1998). These rates are higher than

observed pre-trapping parasitism rates of 50% and 30% respectively. This suggests that cowbird trapping was not effective in reducing brood parasitism in these areas, probably due to the remote locations of vireo breeding habitat. Due to the rugged terrain and lack of road access, cowbird traps at Santa Ysabel, Cottonwood, and Pine Creeks were a minimum of 1.5 km and a maximum of 6.5 km from vireo nesting areas. The effectiveness of individual traps in breeding areas often extends less than 0.8 km from the trap (Robinson et al. 1992).

Nest monitoring in the Cottonwood Creek area in 1997 resulted in the removal of cowbird eggs from three parasitized nests, allowing seven additional vireo fledglings to be produced. Nest checks at 7–10 day intervals can be effective in managing brood parasitism (Wells and Turnbull 1998), whereas cowbird trapping must be completed on a daily basis throughout the breeding season (J. T. Griffith and J. C. Griffith, unpubl. report). Even allowing for the greater technical knowledge required, and the higher pay rates needed to support nest monitoring, we have found that the cost for daily monitoring of cowbird traps is at least twice as much as the cost of nest monitoring for small vireo populations (U.S. Forest Service, unpubl. report). Our data suggest that in rugged, remote areas, nest monitoring and cowbird egg removal may be more effective and less costly than cowbird trapping.

ACKNOWLEDGMENTS

Many thanks to all of the people who have contributed to the cowbird trapping program, Least Bell's Vireo monitoring, and Southwestern Willow Flycatcher monitoring over the years. Thanks to L. S. Hall and T. Manolis for their review and comments, which greatly improved this manuscript. Special thanks to J. Wells and J. Turnbull for their excellent work with Least Bell's Vireo, and J. Stephenson for his contributions to the cowbird trapping. Southwestern Willow Flycatcher data for the years 1995–1997 were graciously provided by W. E. Haas of Varanus Biological.

Studies in Avian Biology No. 18:290–291, 1999.

GOLDEN-CHEEKED WARBLER FATALITY IN A COWBIRD TRAP

KRISTIN K. TERPENING

Abstract. Management for the federally endangered Black-capped Vireo (*Vireo atricapillus*) and Golden-cheeked Warbler (*Dendroica chrysoparia*) in Travis County, Texas, has included Brown-headed Cowbird (*Molothrus ater*) trapping since the mid-1980s. In June of 1997, remains of a Golden-cheeked Warbler were found inside a cowbird trap two days after a Golden-cheeked Warbler was observed bringing food to a juvenile Brown-headed Cowbird inside the trap. The trapping protocol for Travis County has been modified to require immediate removal of any juvenile cowbirds from traps to minimize the possibility of any further such incidents.

Key Words: Brown-headed Cowbird, cowbird trapping, *Dendroica chrysoparia*, Golden-cheeked Warbler, host species, *Molothrus ater*, non-target species, parasitism.

Trapping of Brown-headed Cowbirds (*Molothrus ater*) has been used as a management tool for the conservation of endangered songbird species for more than a decade (Kepler et al. 1996, Griffith and Griffith in press, Hayden et al. in press; W. Armstrong, pers. comm.). As information has been assimilated, modifications to trap size, design, and placement have been made to maximize capture success and minimize non-target captures. Decreasing trap entrance slot size has resulted in a decrease of the total number of non-target species captured on Fort Hood, Texas (J. Cornelius, pers. comm.). Other modifications have included replacing poultry wire with half-inch hardware cloth to minimize predator impacts and cowbird escapes.

Cowbird trapping has been used in central Texas for management of the federally endangered Black-capped Vireo (*Vireo atricapillus*) and Golden-cheeked Warbler (*Dendroica chrysoparia*). Trapping locations include Fort Hood Military Reservation, probably the best-known trapping program in the central United States; Kerr Wildlife Management Area; Balcones Canyonlands National Wildlife Refuge; and Balcones Canyonlands Preserve (BCP). Managed by five different conservation entities, the BCP is a network of preserve units established by the Balcones Canyonlands Conservation Plan (BCCP) to protect habitat for the Black-capped Vireo and Golden-cheeked Warbler, six federally endangered karst invertebrates, and 27 Species of Concern. Due to the increasing destruction of songbird habitat in this rapidly urbanizing area, coupled with an increase in habitat edge, cowbird trapping is considered an essential management technique for the Black-capped Vireo (USFWS 1991, Grzybowski 1995) and, to a lesser extent, the Golden-cheeked Warbler (USFWS 1992).

Cowbird trapping has been conducted in Travis County since the mid-1980s. A private consulting company conducted the first trapping for the BCCP in 1989. Texas Animal Damage Control operated the traps from 1990 to 1996. In 1997, Travis County Transportation and Natural Resources Department operated the trapping program.

In 1997, efforts were made to minimize non-target fatalities by limiting the trap entrance size to a 3.2 cm wide slot, and by checking traps at least three times a week in the early part of the trapping season, and daily in the latter part of the season. Traps were situated in the immediate vicinity of Black-capped Vireo habitat and, in some cases, also in the vicinity of Golden-cheeked Warbler habitat (these vegetation types may be contiguous). Vireos breed in shrubby forest-grassland ecotones of mostly deciduous species of irregular height and distribution with vegetative cover from 0 to 3 m tall (Graber 1961, Grzybowski 1995). Given the opportunity to mature, many sites with vireo habitat may eventually produce warbler habitat. Both these songbirds nest in association with Ashe juniper (*Juniperus ashei*). While many of the same plant species are present in each bird's breeding habitat, the structure of the vegetation is quite different. Unlike the vireo, the warbler requires mature junipers at least 4.5 m tall with shedding bark from which the warbler constructs its nest (Pulich 1976, USFWS 1992, Campbell 1995).

In 1997 a new trap location (CC1) was established in a small open area surrounded by mature live oaks (*Quercus virginiana*) and second growth Ashe juniper. This trap location was the closest available access point to the largest existing Black-capped Vireo population in the county. Although not considered habitat for either songbird, the location was 2.75 km from the vireo colony and within 600m of warbler habitat, well within the 6.7 km commuting distance for Brown-headed Cowbirds reported by Rothstein et al. (1984).

On June 2, 1997, during a routine check of traps, I observed a female Golden-cheeked Warbler feeding a juvenile Brown-headed Cowbird through the trap wire of CC1. The same feeding behavior was observed the following day. No Golden-cheeked Warbler was observed attempting to enter the trap. However, on June 5, the remains of a Golden-cheeked Warbler were found on the trap floor along with a dead juvenile cowbird and three dead adult male cowbirds. Presumably the host bird entered the trap to feed the juvenile cowbird, was unable to find an exit, and died. The cause of death for the birds was not determinable. By the time of discovery, red imported fire ants (*Solenopsis invicta*) had consumed most of the warbler and some of the remains of the cowbirds.

Golden-cheeked Warblers have been observed feeding Brown-headed Cowbird fledglings through cowbird traps at Fort Hood (T. Cook, pers. comm.) and in Travis County (D. Lyter, pers. comm.). A male Kirtland's Warbler (*Dendroica kirtlandii*) was observed entering and exiting a trap to feed a young Brown-headed Cowbird in Michigan (M. DeCapita, pers. comm.). I know of no other instance of a host bird entering a trap to feed cowbirds (W. Armstrong, pers. comm.; A. Averill, pers. comm.; J. C. Griffith, pers. comm.; S. Rothstein, pers. comm.).

In the effort to protect rare species through management techniques such as cowbird trapping, the possibility always exists that control methods could negatively impact the very species these efforts are designed to protect. Admittedly, the capture of host species in cowbird traps appears to be extremely rare. However, measures taken to lessen the likelihood of repeat incidents may be worthwhile for the survival of all non-target species. Modifications to the Travis County cowbird trapping program to minimize non-target captures and fatalities, especially of host species, include daily trap monitoring throughout the trapping season and prompt removal of juvenile cowbirds. In addition, efforts will be made to relocate traps from host breeding sites to cowbird foraging areas. Such foraging sites may include open shortgrass areas with grazing cattle or horses, large lawn areas such as golf courses, and residential areas with numerous bird feeders, all within commuting distance for cowbirds (Verner and Ritter 1983, Rothstein et al. 1984, Airola 1986, Coker and Capen 1995).

ACKNOWLEDGMENTS

Travis County Transportation and Natural Resources provided funding for the 1997 cowbird trapping program. Thanks to S. L. Breslin of the Texas Parks and Wildlife Department for her review of this manuscript.

Studies in Avian Biology No. 18:292–312, 1999.

LITERATURE CITED

AGENBROAD, L. D. 1978. Buffalo jump complexes in Owyhee County, Idaho. Plains Anthropologist 23: 213–221.

AHLERS, D., AND L. WHITE. 1995. 1995 Southwestern Willow Flycatcher survey results: selected sites along the Rio Grande from Velarde, New Mexico, to the headwaters of Elephant Butte Reservoir. Technical Service Center, Bureau of Reclamation, Denver, CO.

AIROLA, D. A. 1986. Brown-headed Cowbird parasitism and habitat disturbance in the Sierra Nevada. Journal of Wildlife Management 50:571–575.

ALLEN, J. A. 1877. History of the American bison, *Bison americanus.* Annual Report of the U.S. Geological and Geographical Surveys of the Territories 9:443–587.

ALVAREZ, F. 1993. Proximity of trees facilitates parasitism by Cuckoos *Cuculus canorus* on Rufous Warblers *Cercotrichas galactotes.* Ibis 135:331.

ALVERSON, W. S., W. KUHLMANN, AND D. M. WALLER. 1994. Wild forests: conservation biology and public policy. Island Press, Washington, D.C.

ANDERSON, B. W., AND R. D. OHMART. 1986. Vegetation. Pp. 639–659 *in* A. Y. Cooperrider, R. J. Boyd, and H. R. Stuart (editors). Inventory and monitoring of wildlife habitat. U.S. Bureau of Land Management Service Center, Denver, CO.

ANDERSON, W. L., AND R. W. STORER. 1976. Factors influencing Kirtland's Warbler nesting success. Jack-Pine Warbler 54:105–115.

ANKNEY, C. D., AND D. M. SCOTT. 1980. Changes in nutrient reserves and diet of breeding Brown-headed Cowbirds. Auk 97:684–696.

ANONYMOUS. No date. Forest land distribution data for the United States [online]. Available: http://www.epa.gov/docs/grd/forest_inventory/ [1998, September 13].

ANTHONY, A. W. 1893. Birds of San Pedro Martir, Lower California. Zoe 4:228–247.

ANTHONY, A. W. 1895. Birds of San Fernando, Lower California. Auk 12:134–143.

ARCESE, P., AND J. N. M. SMITH. 1988. Effects of population density and supplemental food on reproduction in Song Sparrows. Journal of Animal Ecology 57:119–136.

ARCESE, P., AND J. N. M. SMITH. In press. Impacts of nest depredation and brood parasitism on the productivity of North American passerines. *In* N. Adams and R. Slotow (editors). Proceedings of the 22nd International Ornithological Congress. University of Natal, Durban, South Africa.

ARCESE, P., J. N. M. SMITH, AND M. I. HATCH. 1996. Nest predation by cowbirds and its consequences for passerine demography. Proceedings of the National Academy Science (USA) 93:4608–4611.

ARCESE, P., J. N. M. SMITH, W. M. HOCHACHKA, C. M. ROGERS, AND D. LUDWIG. 1992. Stability, regulation and the determination of abundance in an insular Song Sparrow population. Ecology 73:805–822.

ARMSTRONG, D. M. 1972. Distribution of mammals in Colorado. Monograph of the University of Kansas Museum of Natural History 3:1–415.

ARNOLD, K. A. 1983. Annual adult survival rates for Brown-headed Cowbirds wintering in southeast Texas. Wilson Bulletin 95:150–153.

ARNQVIST, G., AND D. WOOSTER. 1995. Meta-analysis: synthesizing research findings in ecology and evolution. Trends in Evolution and Ecology 10:236–240.

ASKINS, R. A. 1995. Hostile landscapes and the decline of migratory birds. Science 67:1956–1957.

ASKINS, R. A., J. F. LYNCH, AND R. GREENBERG. 1990. Population declines in migratory birds in eastern North America. Current Ornithology 7:1–57.

AVERILL, A. 1996. Brown-headed cowbird parasitism of neotropical migrant songbirds in riparian areas along the lower Colorado River. M.S. thesis. University of Arizona, Tucson, AZ.

BAICICH, P. J., AND C. J. O. HARRISON. 1997. A guide to the nests, eggs, and nestlings of North American birds, 2nd ed. Academic Press, San Diego, CA.

BAILEY, F. M. 1923. Birds recorded from the Santa Rita Mountains in southern Arizona. Pacific Coast Avifauna No. 15. Cooper Ornithological Club, Berkeley, CA.

BAIRD, S. F. 1858. Explorations and surveys for a railroad route from the Mississippi River to the Pacific Ocean. Volume IX: Birds. Part II—General report upon the zoology of the several Pacific railroad routes. Beverley Tucker (printer), Washington, D.C.

BALAZS, I. J., M. BAIRD, M. CLYNE, AND E. MEADE. 1989. Human population genetic studies of five hypervariable DNA loci. American Journal Human Genetics 44:182–190.

BALAZS, I. J., A. CHIMERA, D. EISENBERG, D. ENDEAN, R. GILES, J. LATELY, S. MAGUIRE, B. SCHALL, A. TURCK, AND R. MCKEE. 1990. Accuracy, precision, and site-to-site reproducibility in analysis of DNA polymorphisms for identity testing. Pp. 54–56 *in* H. F. Polesky and W. R. Mayr (editors). Advances in forensic haemogenetics 3. Springer-Verlag, Berlin, Germany.

BANKS, A. J. 1997. Variation among host species in probability of parasitism by Brown-headed Cowbirds: the role of everyday host activity. M. S. thesis. University of Montana, Missoula, MT.

BARBER D. R., AND T. E. MARTIN. 1997. Influence of alternate host densities on Brown-headed Cowbird parasitism rates in Black-capped Vireos. Condor 99: 595–604.

BARLOW, J. C. 1962. Natural history of the Bell's Vireo, *Vireo bellii* Audubon. University of Kansas Publications of the Museum of Natural History 12:241–296.

BEAL, F. E. L. 1900. Food of the bobolink, blackbirds, and grackles. U.S. Department of Agriculture, Biological Survey Bulletin 13.

BEEDY, E. C., AND S. L. GRANHOLM. 1985. Discovering Sierra Birds. Yosemite Natural History Association.

BEEZLEY, J. A., AND J. P. RIEGER. 1987. Least Bell's Vireo management by cowbird trapping. Western Birds:55–61.

BEHLE, W. H., E. D. SORENSON, AND C. M. WHITE. 1985. Utah Birds: a revised checklist. Utah Museum of Natural History, University of Utah, Salt Lake City, UT.

BEIDLEMAN, R. G. 1955. An altitudinal record for bison

in northern Colorado. Journal of Mammalogy 36: 470–471.

BENEDICT, J. B. 1993. Excavations at Bode's Draw, a women's work area in the mountains near Estes Park, Colorado. Research Report, Center for Mountain Archeology 6:1–42.

BENSON R. H., AND K. L. P. BENSON. 1990. Estimated size of Black-capped Vireo populations in Coahuila, Mexico. Condor 92: 777–779.

BENT, A. C. 1958. Life histories of North American blackbirds, orioles, tanagers, and allies. U.S. National Museum Bulletin No. 211, Washington, D.C.

BENT, A. C. 1968. Life histories of North American cardinals, grosbeaks, buntings, towhees, finches, sparrows, and allies. U.S. National Museum Bulletin No. 237 (parts 1 and 2), Washington, D.C.

BERGER, A. J. 1951. The cowbird and certain host species in Michigan. Wilson Bulletin 63:26–34.

BERGIN, T. M., L. B. BEST, AND K. E. FREEMARK. 1997. An experimental study of predation on artificial nests in roadsides adjacent to agricultural habitats in Iowa. Wilson Bulletin 109:437–448.

BERGTOLD, W. H. 1929. Bison in Colorado. Journal of Mammalogy 10:107.

BEST, L. B. 1978. Field Sparrow reproductive success and nesting ecology. Auk 95:9–22.

BEST, L. B. 1979. Effects of fire on a Field Sparrow population. American Midland Naturalist 101:434–442.

BEST, L. B., AND D. F. STAUFFER. 1980. Factors affecting nesting success in riparian bird communities. Condor 82:149–158.

BEYER, D. E. 1987. Population and habitat management of elk in Michigan. Ph.D. dissertation. Michigan State University, East Lansing, MI.

BIERMANN, G. C., W. B. MCGILLIVRAY, AND K. E. NORDIN. 1987. The effect of cowbird parasitism on Brewer's Sparrow productivity in Alberta. Journal of Field Ornitholgy 58: 350–354.

BLINCOE, B. J. 1935. A cowbird removes a robin's egg. Wilson Bulletin 47:158.

BLONDEL, J., C. FERY, AND B. FROCHOT. 1981. Point counts with unlimited distance. Studies in Avian Biology 6:414–420.

BOCK, C. E., V. A. SAAB, T. D. RICH, AND D. S. DOBKIN. 1993. Effects of livestock grazing on neotropical migratory landbirds in Western North America. Pp. 296–309 in D. M. Finch and P. W. Stangel (editors). Status and management of neotropical migratory birds. USDA Forest Service Gen. Tech. Rep. RM-229. USDA Forest Service, Rocky Mountain Forest and Range Experimental Station, Ft. Collins, CO.

BÖHNING-GAESE, K., M. L. TAPER, AND J. H. BROWN. 1993. Are declines in North American insectivorous songbirds due to causes on the breeding range? Conservation Biology 7:76–86.

BONHAM, C. D. 1989. Measurements for terrestrial vegetation. John Wiley and Sons, New York, NY.

BRADEN, G. T., R. L. MCKERNAN, AND S. M. POWELL. 1997a. Association of within-territory vegetation characteristics and fitness components of California Gnatcatchers. Auk 114:601–609.

BRADEN, G. T., R. L. MCKERNAN, AND S. M. POWELL. 1997b. Effects of nest parasitism by the Brown-headed Cowbird on nesting success of the California Gnatcatcher. Condor 99:858–865.

BRAGG, T. B. 1995. The physical environment of Great Plains grasslands. Pp. 49–81 in A. Joern and K. H. Keeler (editors). The changing prairie: North American grasslands. Oxford University Press, New York, NY.

BRAULT, S., AND H. CASWELL. 1993. Pod-specific demography of killer whales (Orcinus orca). Ecology 74:1444–1454.

BRAWN, J. D., AND S. K. ROBINSON. 1996. Source-sink dynamics may complicate the interpretation of long-term census data. Ecology 77:3–11.

BRAY, O. E., J. W. DEGRAZIO, J. L. GUARINO, AND R. G. STREETER. 1974. Recoveries of Brown-headed Cowbirds banded at Sand Lake, South Dakota. Inland Bird Banding News 46:204–209.

BRISKIE, J. V., AND S. G. SEALY. 1990. Evolution of short incubation periods in the parasitic cowbirds, Molothrus spp. Auk 107:789–794.

BRISKIE, J. V., S. G. SEALY, AND K. A. HOBSON. 1990. Differential parasitism of Least Flycatchers and Yellow Warblers by the Brown-Headed Cowbird. Behavioral Ecology and Sociobiology 27:403–410.

BRISKIE, J. V., S. G. SEALY, AND K. A. HOBSON. 1992. Behavioral defenses against brood parasitism in sympatric and allopatric host populations. Evolution 46:334–340.

BRITTINGHAM, M. C., AND S. A. TEMPLE. 1983. Have cowbirds caused forest songbirds to decline? BioScience 33:31–35.

BRITTINGHAM, M. C., AND S. A. TEMPLE. 1996. Vegetation around parasitized and non-parasitized nests within a deciduous forest. Journal of Field Ornithology 67:406–413.

BROCKNER, W. W. 1984. Brown-headed Cowbird parasitizing Mountain Chickadee nest. C. F. O. [Colorado Field Ornithologists] Journal 18:109–110.

BROOKER, M. G., AND L. C. BROOKER. 1989a. The comparative breeding behaviour of two sympatric cuckoos, Horsfield's Bronze-Cuckoo Chrysococcyx basalis and the Shining Bronze-Cuckoo C. lucidus, in Western Australia: a new model for the evolution of egg morphology and host specificity in avian brood parasites. Ibis 131:528–547.

BROOKER, M. G., AND L. C. BROOKER. 1989b. Cuckoo hosts in Australia. Australian Zoological Reviews 2: 1–67.

BROOKER, M. G., AND L. C. BROOKER. 1992. Evidence for individual female host specificity in two Australian Bronze-Cuckoos (Chrysococcyx spp.). Australian Journal of Zoology 40:485–493.

BROWN, B. T. 1988. Breeding ecology of a Willow Flycatcher population in Grand Canyon, Arizona. Western Birds 19: 25–33.

BROWN, B. T. 1994. Rates of brood parasitism by Brown-headed Cowbirds on riparian passerines in Arizona. Journal of Field Ornithology 65: 160–168.

BROWN, H. 1903. Arizona bird notes. Auk 20:43–50.

BROWN, J. L. 1975. The evolution of behavior. W.W. Norton and Co., New York, NY.

BROWNING, M. R. 1993. Comments on the taxonomy of Empidonax traillii (Willow Flycatcher). Western Birds 24:241–257.

BUCKLAND, S. T., D. R. ANDERSON, K. P. BURNHAM,

AND J. L. LAAKE. 1996. Distance sampling. Chapman and Hall, New York, NY.

BUECH, R. R. 1982. Nesting ecology and cowbird parasitism of Clay-colored, Chipping, and Field sparrows in a Christmas tree plantation. Journal of Field Ornithology 53:363–369.

BURGER, L. D., L. W. BURGER, JR., AND J. FAABORG. 1994. Effects of prairie fragmentation on predation on artificial nests. Journal of Wildlife Management 58:249–254.

BURGHAM, M. C. J., AND J. PICMAN. 1989. Effect of Brown-headed Cowbirds on the evolution of Yellow Warbler anti-parasite strategies. Animal Behavior 38:298–308.

BURGMAN, M. A., S. FERSON, AND H. R. AKÇAKAYA. 1993. Risk assessment in conservation biology. Chapman and Hall, New York, NY.

BURGMAN, M. A., AND V. A. GERARD. 1990. A stage-structured, stochastic population model for the giant kelp Macrocystis pyrifera. Marine Biology 105:15–23.

BURHANS, D. E. 1997. Habitat and microhabitat features associated with cowbird parasitism in two forest edge cowbird hosts. Condor 99:866–872.

BURHANS, D. E. In press. Dawn nest arrivals in cowbird hosts: their role in aggression, cowbird recognition, and response to parasitization. In J. N. M. Smith, T. L. Cook, S. I. Rothstein, S. K. Robinson, and S. G. Sealy (editors). The biology and management of cowbirds and their hosts. University of Texas Press, Austin, TX.

BURKE, T., N. B. DAVIES, M. W. BRUFORD, AND B. J. HATCHWELL. 1989. Parental care and mating behavior of polyandrous dunnocks (Prunella modularis) related to paternity by DNA fingerprinting. Nature 338:249–251.

BURNHAM, K. P., D. R. ANDERSON, AND J. L. LAAKE. 1980. Estimation of density from line transect sampling of biological populations. Wildlife Monographs 72:1–202.

BUTCHER, G. S. (CHAIR), AND CORRESPONDENTS. 1992. Needs assessment: monitoring neotropical migratory birds. Partners in Flight. Cornell University, Ithaca, NY.

BUTLER, R. B. 1978. Bison hunting in the desert west before 1800: the paleo-ecological potential and the archaeological reality. Plains Anthropologist 23:107–112.

CAMPBELL, L. 1995. Endangered and threatened animals of Texas—their life history and management. Texas Parks and Wildlife Press, Austin, TX.

CANNON, R. W. 1979. Lesser Prairie Chicken responses to range fires at the booming ground. Wildlife Society Bulletin 7:44–46.

CAROTHERS, S. W. 1974. Population structure and organization of southwestern riparian birds. American Zoologist 14:97–108.

CARTER, M. D. 1986. The parasitic behavior of the Bronzed Cowbird in south Texas. Condor 88:11–25.

CASWELL, H. 1989. Matrix population models. Sinauer Associates, Inc., Sunderland, MA.

CAVALCANTI, R. B. 1981. Nest desertion: theory and tests of its adaptive significance in birds. Ph.D. dissertation. McGill University, Montreal, PQ.

CHACE, J. F. 1995. The factors affecting the reproductive success of the Solitary Vireo (Vireo solitarius plumbeus) in Colorado. M.A. thesis. University of Colorado, Boulder, CO.

CHACE, J. F. AND A. CRUZ. 1996. Knowledge of the Colorado host relations of the parasitic Brown-headed Cowbird. C. F. O. [Colorado Field Ornithologists] Journal 30:67–81.

CHACE, J. F. AND A. CRUZ. 1998. Range of the Brown-headed Cowbird in Colorado—past and present. Great Basin Naturalist 58:245–249.

CHACE, J. F., A. CRUZ, AND R. E. MARVIL. In press. Reproductive interactions of the Brown-headed Cowbird and Solitary Vireo in Colorado. In J. N. M. Smith, T. L. Cook, S. I. Rothstein, S. K. Robinson, and S. G. Sealy (editors). The biology and management of cowbirds and their hosts. University of Texas Press, Austin, TX.

CHASKO, G. G., AND E. J. GATES. 1982. Avian habitat suitability along a transmission-line corridor in an oak-hickory forest region. Wildlife Monographs 82:1–41.

CHRISTMAN, G. M.. 1971. The mountain bison. American West 8:44–47.

CHRISTY, B. H. 1925. Summer birds of Huron Mountain, Michigan. Wilson Bulletin 37:208–215.

CLARK, K. L., AND R. J. ROBERTSON. 1979. Spatial and temporal multi-species nesting aggregations in birds as anti-parasite and anti-predator defenses. Behavioral Ecology and Sociobiology 5:359–371.

CLARK, K. L., AND R. J. ROBERTSON. 1981. Cowbird parasitism and evolution of anti-parasite strategies in the Yellow Warbler. Wilson Bulletin 93:249–258.

CLOTFELTER, E. D. 1998a. Impact of Brown-headed Cowbird brood parasitism on Red-winged Blackbirds and factors influencing patterns of parasitism. Ph.D. dissertation. University of Wisconsin, Madison, WI.

CLOTFELTER, E. D. 1998b. What cues do Brown-headed Cowbirds use to locate Red-winged Blackbird host nests? Animal Behaviour 55:1181–1189.

CLOTFELTER, E. D., AND T. BRUSH. 1995. Unusual parasitism by the Bronzed Cowbird. Condor 97:814–815.

CODY, M. L. 1985. Habitat selection in grassland and open-country birds. Pp. 191–226 in M. L. Cody (editor). Habitat selection in birds. Academic Press, Orlando, FL.

COHEN, J. 1988. Statistical power analysis for the behavioral sciences, 2nd ed. Academic Press, New York, NY.

COKER, D. R., AND D. E. CAPEN. 1995. Landscape-level habitat use by Brown-headed Cowbirds in Vermont. Journal of Wildlife Management 59:631–637.

COKER, D. R., AND D. E. CAPEN. In press. Distribution and habitat associations of Brown-headed Cowbirds in the Green Mountains of Vermont. In J. N. M. Smith, T. L. Cook, S. I. Rothstein, S. K. Robinson, and S. G. Sealy (editors). The biology and management of cowbirds and their hosts. University of Texas Press, Austin, TX.

COLLAR, N. J., M. J. CROSBY, AND A. J. STATTERSFIELD. 1994. Birds to watch 2: the world list of threatened birds. BirdLife International, Cambridge, U.K.

COLLAR, N. J., L. P. GONZAGA, N. KRABBE, A. MADRONO NIETO, L. G. NARANJO, T. A. PARKER, III, AND

D. C. WEGE. 1992. Threatened birds of the Americas: the ICBP/IUCN Red Data Book. International Council for Bird Preservation, Cambridge, U.K.

COLLINS, C. T., L. R. HAYS, A. DAVENPORT, AND D. WILLICK. 1988. Status and management of Least Bell's Vireo within the Prado Basin, California. Report submitted to State of California, Dept. of Transportation, District 8, San Bernardino, CA.

COOK, T. L., J. A. KOLOSZAR, M. D. GOERING, AND L. L. SANCHEZ. 1998. The spatial and temporal response of Brown-headed Cowbirds (Molothrus ater) to cattle removal. Pp. 76–96 in The Nature Conservancy, Summary of 1997 Research Activities. Texas Conservation Data Center, The Nature Conservancy, Fort Hood, Texas.

COOKE, W. W. 1897. The birds of Colorado. Bulletin of the State Agriculture Collection 37 (Technical Series) 2:1–224.

COOPER, C. A. 1996. Summary of 1995 Surveys for Willow Flycatchers in New Mexico. Contract #96–516.51. New Mexico Department of Game and Fish, Santa Fe, NM.

COOPER, C. A. 1997. Summary of 1996 Surveys for Willow Flycatchers in New Mexico. Contract #96–516.81. New Mexico Department of Game and Fish, Santa Fe, NM.

COOPER, J. G. 1861. New California animals. Proceedings of the California Academy of Science 2:118–123.

COX, G. W. 1990. Laboratory manual of general ecology, 6th ed. Wm. C. Brown Publishers, Dubuque, IA.

CROUSE, D. T., L. B. CROWDER, AND H. CASWELL. 1987. A stage-based population model for loggerhead sea turtles and implication for conservation. Ecology 68:1412–1423.

CRUZ, A., W. POST, J. W. WILEY, C. P. ORTEGA, T. K. NAKAMURA, AND J. W. PRATHER. 1998. Potential impacts of cowbird range expansion in Florida. Pp. 313–336 in S. I. Rothstein and S. K. Robinson (editors). Parasitic birds and their hosts. Oxford University Press, Oxford, U.K.

CUNNINGHAM, R. 1993. The cowbird peril: a resources management problem and an interpretive story. Internal report of the National Park Service, Western Regional Office, San Francisco, CA.

CURSON, D. R. 1996. Nest predation and brood parasitism of passerine birds in pinyon-juniper woodland in northeast New Mexico. M.S. thesis. University of Wisconsin, Madison, WI.

DARLEY, J. A. 1971. Sex ratio and mortality in the Brown-headed Cowbird. Auk 88:560–566.

DARLEY, J. A. 1983. Territorial behavior of the female Brown-headed Cowbird (Molothrus ater). Canadian Journal of Zoology 61:65–69.

DAUBENMIRE, R. F. 1968. Ecology of fire in grasslands. Advances in Ecological Research 5:209–266.

DAUBENMIRE, R. F. 1988. Steppe vegetation of Washington. Washington State University, Pullman, WA.

DAVIES, N. B., AND M. DE L. BROOKE. 1988. Cuckoos versus reed warblers: adaptations and counteradaptations. Animal Behaviour 36: 262–284.

DAVIS, S. K., AND S. G. SEALY. In press. Cowbird parasitization and predation in grassland fragments of southwestern Manitoba. In J. N. M. Smith, T. L.

Cook, S. I. Rothstein, S. K. Robinson, and S. G. Sealy (editors). The biology and management of cowbirds and their hosts. University of Texas Press, Austin, TX.

DAVIS, W. B. 1935. Mammals of the Ross Expedition (1824) in Idaho. Murrelet 16:7–10.

DAVISON, W. 1998. Starvation and nestling ejection as sources of mortality in parasitized Lazuli Bunting nests. Great Basin Naturalist 58:285–288.

DECAPITA, M. E. In press. Brown-headed Cowbird control on Kirtland's Warbler nesting areas in Michigan, 1972–1995. In J. N. M. Smith, T. L. Cook, S. I. Rothstein, S. K. Robinson, and S. G. Sealy (editors). The biology and management of cowbirds and their hosts. University of Texas Press, Austin, TX.

DELLASALA, D. A. 1985. The Yellow Warbler in southeastern Michigan: factors affecting its productivity. Jack-Pine Warbler 63:52–60.

DELLASALA, D. A., D. M. OLSON, S. E. BARTH, S. L. CRANE, AND S. A. PRIMM. 1995. Forest health: moving beyond rhetoric to restore healthy landscapes in the inland Northwest. Wildlife Society Bulletin 23:346–356.

DESANTE, D. F., AND T. L. GEORGE. 1994. Population trends in the landbirds of western North America. Studies in Avian Biology 15:173–190.

DHONDT, A. A. 1979. Summer dispersal and survival of juvenile Great Tits in southern Sweden. Oecologia 42:139–157.

DOAK, D. F., AND L. S. MILLS. 1994. A useful role for theory in conservation. Ecology 75:615–626.

DOBKIN, D. S. 1994. Conservation and management of neotropical migrant landbirds in northern Rockies and Great Plains. University of Idaho Press, Moscow, ID.

DOBKIN, D. S., AND B. A. WILCOX. 1986. Analysis of natural forest fragments: riparian birds in the Toyabe Mountains, Nevada. Pp. 293–299 in J. Verner, M. L. Morrison, and C. J. Ralph (editors). Wildlife 2000: modeling habitat relationships of terrestrial vertebrates. University of Wisconsin Press, Madison, WI.

DOBLER, F. C., J. EBY, C. PERRY, S. RICHARDSON, AND M. VANDER HAEGEN. 1996. Status of Washington's shrubsteppe ecosystem: extent, ownership, and wildlife/vegetation relationships. Research Report. Washington Department of Fish and Wildlife, Olympia, WA.

DOLBEER, R. A. 1982. Migratory patterns for age and sex classes of blackbirds and starlings. Journal of Field Ornithology 53:28–46.

DONOVAN, T. M., P. W. JONES, E. M. ANNAND, AND F. R. THOMPSON, III. 1997. Variation in local-scale edge effects: mechanisms and landscape context. Ecology 78:2064–2075.

DONOVAN, T. M., R. H. LAMBERSON, F. R. THOMPSON, III, AND J. FAABORG. 1995a. Modeling the effects of habitat fragmentation on source and sink demography of neotropical migrant birds. Conservation Biology 9:1396–1407.

DONOVAN, T. M., F. R. THOMPSON, III, AND J. FAABORG. In press. Ecological trade-offs and the influence of scale on Brown-headed Cowbird distribution. In J. N. M. Smith, T. L. Cook, S. I. Rothstein, S. K. Robinson, and S. G. Sealy (editors). The biology and management of cowbirds and their hosts. University of Texas Press, Austin, TX.

DONOVAN, T. M., F. R.. THOMPSON, III, J. FAABORG, AND J. R. PROBST. 1995b. Reproductive success of migratory birds in habitat sources and sinks. Conservation Biology 9:1380–1395.

DRAPER, N. R., AND H. SMITH. 1981. Applied regression analysis. John Wiley & Sons, New York, NY.

DRAWE, D. L., A. D. CHAMRAD, AND T. W. BOX. 1978. Plant communities of the Welder Wildlife Refuge, 2nd ed. Welder Wildlife Foundation, Sinton, TX.

DRENT, R. H., AND S. DAAN. 1980. The prudent parent: energetic adjustments in avian breeding. Ardea 68: 225–252.

DREW, F. M. 1885. On the vertical range of birds in Colorado. Auk 2:16.

DRILLING, N. E., AND C. F. THOMPSON. 1988. Natal and breeding dispersal in House Wrens (*Troglodytes aedon*). Auk 105:480–491.

DUFTY, A. M., JR. 1982a. Movements and activities of radio-tracked Brown-headed Cowbirds. Auk 99: 316–327.

DUFTY, A. M., JR. 1982b. Responses of Brown-headed Cowbirds to simulated conspecific intruders. Animal Behavior 30:1043–1052.

DUFTY, A. M., JR. 1983. Variation in the egg markings of the Brown-headed Cowbird. Condor 85:109–111.

DUNN, J. D., AND K. L GARRETT. 1997. A field guide to the warblers of North America. Houghton Mifflin, Boston, MA.

DUNNING, J. B., JR. 1993. CRC handbook of avian body masses. CRC Press, Boca Raton, FL.

EATON, S. W. 1958. A life history study of the Louisiana Waterthrush. Wilson Bulletin 70:211–236.

EDWARDS, T. C., JR., E. T. DESHLER, D. FOSTER, AND G. G. MOISEN. 1996. Adequacy of wildlife habitat relation models for estimating spatial distribution of terrestrial vertebrates. Conservation Biology 10: 263–270.

EHRLICH, P. R., D. S. DOBKIN, AND D. WHEYE. 1988. The birder's handbook: a field guide to the natural history of North American Birds. Simon and Shuster, New York, NY.

EHRLICH, P. R., D. S. DOBKIN, AND D. WHEYE. 1992. Birds in jeopardy. Stanford University Press, Stanford, CA.

ELLIOT, P. F. 1978. Cowbird parasitism in the Kansas tallgrass prairie. Auk 95:161–167.

EVANS, D. R., AND J. E. GATES. 1997. Cowbird selection of breeding areas: the role of habitat and bird species abundance. Wilson Bulletin 109:470–480.

EVANS, H. E. 1997. The natural history of the Long expedition to the Rocky Mountains 1819–1820. Oxford University Press, New York, NY.

FANKHAUSER, D. P. 1971. Survival rates of blackbirds and starlings. Bird-Banding 42:36–42.

FERNANDEZ-DUQUE, E., AND C. VALEGGIA. 1994. Meta-analysis: a valuable tool in conservation research. Conservation Biology 8:555–561.

FERSON, S. 1994. RAMAS/stage: generalized stage-based modeling for population dynamics (version 1.4). Applied Biomathematics, Setauket, NY.

FERSON, S., AND H. R. AKÇAKAYA. 1991. RAMAS/age: modeling fluctuations in age-structured populations. Exeter Software, Setauket, NY.

FIGGINS, J. D. 1933. The bison of the western area of the Mississippi Basin. Proceedings of the Denver Museum of Natural History 12:16–33.

FINCH, D. M. 1983. Brood parasitism of the Abert's Towhee: timing, frequency, and effects. Condor 85: 355–359.

FINCH, D. M. 1991. Population ecology, habitat requirements, and conservation of neotropical migratory birds. USDA Forest Service Gen. Tech. Rep. RM-205. USDA Forest Service, Rocky Mountain Forest and Range Experiment Station, Fort Collins, CO.

FISHER, A. K. 1893a. Report on the ornithology of the Death Valley Expedition of 1891. North American Fauna 7:7–158.

FISHER, A. K. 1893b. The Death Valley expedition: a biological survey of parts of California, Nevada, Arizona, and Utah. U.S. Government Printing Office, Washington, D.C.

FLEISCHER, R. C. 1985. A new technique to identify and assess the dispersion of eggs of individual brood parasites. Behavioral Ecology and Sociobiology 17: 91–99.

FLEISCHER, R. C., AND S. I. ROTHSTEIN. 1988. Known secondary contact and rapid gene flow among subspecies and dialects in the Brown-headed Cowbird. Evolution 42:1146–1158.

FLEISCHER, R. C., S. I. ROTHSTEIN, AND L. S. MILLER. 1991. Mitochondrial DNA variation indicates gene flow across a zone of known secondary contact between two subspecies of the Brown-headed Cowbird. Condor 93:185–189.

FLEISCHER, R. C., A. P. SMYTH, AND S. I. ROTHSTEIN. 1987. Temporal and age-related variation in the laying rate of the parasitic Brown-headed Cowbird in the eastern Sierra Nevada, California. Canadian Journal of Zoology 65: 2724–2730.

FLESHMAN, C., AND D. S. KAUFMAN. 1984. The South Fork (Kern River) Wildlife Area: will the commitment be forgotten? Pp. 482–494 in R. E. Warner and K. M. Hendrix (editors). California riparian systems: ecology, conservation and productive management. University of California Press, Berkeley, CA.

FONDELL, T. F. 1997. Nest density and nest success of ground-nesting grassland birds relative to grazing in western Montana. M. S. thesis. University of Montana, Missoula, MT.

FORD, R., Z. MA, S. BARSNESS, AND R. REDMOND. 1997. Rule-based aggregation of classified imagery. Proceedings of the 1997 ACSM/ASPRS Convention and Exposition 3:115–123.

FRAGA, R. M. 1985. Host-parasite interactions between Chalk-browed Mockingbirds and Shiny Cowbirds. Ornithological Monographs 36:829–844.

FRANZREB, K. E. 1989a. Ecology and conservation of the endangered least Bell's vireo. U.S. Fish and Wildlife Service, Biological Report 89(1). U.S. Fish and Wildlife Service Publications Unit, Washington, D.C.

FRANZREB, K. E. 1989b. Ecology and conservation of the Least Bell's Vireo (Vireo bellii pusillus) in California. Western Birds 18:43–49

FRANZREB, K. E. 1990. An analysis of options for reintroducing a migratory, native passerine, the endangered Least Bell's Vireo *Vireo bellii pusillus* in the

Central Valley, California. Biological Conservation 53:105–123.

FREEMAN, S. D., F. FORI, AND S. ROHWER. 1990. Red-winged Blackbirds and Brown-headed Cowbirds: some aspects of a host-parasite relationship. Condor 92:336–340.

FRIEDMANN, H. 1928. The origin of host specificity in the parasitic habit in the Cuculidae. Auk 45:33–38.

FRIEDMANN, H. 1929. The cowbirds: a study in the biology of social parasitism. Charles C. Thomas, Springfield, IL.

FRIEDMANN, H. 1963. Host relations of the parasitic cowbirds. U.S. National Museum Bulletin 233:1–276.

FRIEDMANN, H. 1967a. Alloxenia in three sympatric African species of Cuculus. Proceedings of the United States National Museum 124:1–14.

FRIEDMANN, H. 1967b. Evolutionary terms for parasitic species. Systematic Zoology 16:175.

FRIEDMANN, H. 1971. Further information on the host relations of the parasitic cowbirds. Auk 88:239–255.

FRIEDMANN, H., AND L. F. KIFF. 1985. The parasitic cowbirds and their hosts. Proceedings of the Western Foundation of Vertebrate Zoology 2: 226–304.

FRIEDMANN, H., L. F. KIFF, AND S. I. ROTHSTEIN. 1977. A further contribution to the knowledge of the host relations of the parasitic cowbirds. Smithsonian Contributions in Zoology 235:1–75.

FRYXELL, F. M. 1926. A new high altitude limit for the American bison. Journal of Mammalogy 7:102–109.

FRYXELL, F. M. 1928. The former range of the American bison in the Rocky Mountains. Journal of Mammalogy 9:129–139.

FULLER, W. A. 1962. The biology and management of the bison of Wood Buffalo National Park. Wildlife Management Bulletin, Canadian Wildlife Service Series 1, 16:1–52.

GAILLARD, J., M. FESTA-BIANCHET, AND N. G. YOCCOZ. 1998. Population dynamics of large herbivores: variable recruitment with constant adult survival. Trends in Ecology and Evolution 13:58–63.

GAINES, D. 1974. A new look at the nesting riparian avifauna of the Sacramento Valley, California. Western Birds 5:61–80.

GAINES, D. 1977. Birds of the Yosemite Sierra: a distributional survey. California Syllabus, Oakland, CA.

GAINES, D. 1988. Birds of Yosemite and the East Slope. Artemisia Press, Lee Vining, CA.

GALBRAITH, D. A., P. T. BOAG, H. L. GIBBS, AND B. N. WHITE. 1991. Sizing bands on autoradiograms: a study of precision for scoring DNA fingerprints. Electrophoresis 12: 210–220.

GARDALI, T., A. M. KING, AND G. R. GEUPEL. 1998. Cowbird parasitism and nest success of the Lazuli Bunting in the Sacramento Valley. Western Birds 29: 174–179.

GARRETT, K. L., AND J. D. DUNN. 1981. Birds of southern California: status and distribution. The Artesian Press, Los Angeles, CA.

GATES, J. E., AND N. R. GIFFEN. 1991. Neotropical migrant birds and edge effects at a forest-stream ecotone. Wilson Bulletin 103:204–217.

GATES, J. E., AND L. W. GYSEL. 1978. Avian nest dispersion and fledging success in field-forest ecotones. Ecology 59:871–883.

GAVIN, T. A. 1991. Why ask "why": the importance of evolutionary biology in wildlife science. Journal of Wildlife Management 55:760–766.

GEORGES, M., A. S. LEQUARRE, M. CASTILLI, R. HANSET, AND G. LESSART. 1988. DNA fingerprinting in domestic animals using four different microsatellite probes. Cytogenetic and Cellular Genetics 47: 127–131.

GILL, F. B. 1990. Ornithology. W. H. Freeman and Co., New York, NY.

GILL, S. A., P. M. GRIEEF, L. M. STAIB, AND S. G. SEALY. 1997. Does nest defense deter or facilitate cowbird parasitism? A test of the nesting-cue hypothesis. Ethology 103: 56–71.

GILPIN, M. E., AND I. HANSKI (EDITORS). 1991. Metapopulation dynamics: empirical and theoretical investigations. Academic Press, London, U.K.

GLITZENSTEIN, J. S., C. D. CANHAM, M. J. MCDONNELL, AND D. R. STRENG. 1990. Effects of environment and land-use history on upland forests of the Cary Arboretum, Hudson Valley, New York. Bulletin of Torrey Botanical Club 117:106–122.

GOCHFELD, M. 1979. Brood parasite and host coevolution: interactions between Shiny Cowbirds and two species of meadowlarks. American Naturalist 113:855–870.

GOGUEN, C. B., AND N. E. MATHEWS. 1996. Nest desertion by Blue-gray Gnatcatchers in association with Brown-headed Cowbird parasitism. Animal Behaviour 52:613–619.

GOGUEN, C. B., AND N. E. MATHEWS. 1998. Songbird community composition and nesting success in grazed and ungrazed pinyon-juniper woodlands. Journal of Wildlife Management 62:474–484.

GOLDWASSER, S., D. A. GAINES, AND S. R. WILBUR. 1980. The Least Bell's Vireo in California: a de facto endangered race. American Birds 34:742–745.

GOOSSEN, J. P., AND S. G. SEALY. 1982. Production of young in a dense nesting population of Yellow Warblers, Dendroica petechia, in Manitoba. Canadian Field-Naturalist 96:189–199.

GOTMARK, F. 1992. The effects of investigator disturbance on nesting birds. Current Ornithology 9:63–104.

GOWATY, P. A. 1996. Field studies of parental care in birds: new data focus questions on variation among females. Advances in the Study of Behavior 25:477–531.

GRABER, J. W. 1961. Distribution, habitat requirements, and life history of the Black-capped Vireo (Vireo atricapilla). Ecological Monographs 31:313–336.

GRAHAM, D. S. 1988. Responses of five host species to cowbird parasitism. Condor 90:588–591.

GRANT, P. R., AND P. T. BOAG. 1980. Rainfall on the Galápagos and the demography of Darwin's finches. Auk 97:227–244.

GRAY, M. V., AND J. GREAVES. 1984. Riparian forest as habitat for the Least Bell's Vireo. Pp. 605–611 in R. E. Warner and K. M. Hendrix (editors). California riparian systems: ecology, conservation and productive management. University of California Press, Berkeley, CA.

GREENE, E., V. MUEHTER, AND W. DAVISON. 1996. Lazuli Bunting (*Passerina amoena*). *In* A. Poole and F. Gill (editors). The birds of North America, no. 232. Academy of Natural Sciences, Philadelphia, PA, and American Ornithologists' Union, Washington, D.C.

GREENLAND, S. 1988. On sample-size and power calculations for studies using confidence intervals. American Journal of Epidemiology 128:231–237.

GREENLAW, J. S. 1996. Spotted Towhee (*Pipilo maculatus*). *In* A. Poole and F. Gill (editors). The birds of North America, no. 263. Academy of Natural Sciences, Philadelphia, PA, and American Ornithologists' Union, Washington, D.C.

GREENWOOD, P. J. AND P. H. HARVEY. 1982. The natal and breeding dispersal of birds. Annual Review of Ecology and Systematics 13:1–21.

GRIFFITH, J. T., AND J. C. GRIFFITH. In press. Cowbird control and the endangered Least Bell's Vireo: a management success story. *In* J. N. M. Smith, T. L. Cook, S. I. Rothstein, S. K. Robinson, and S. G. Sealy (editors). The biology and management of cowbirds and their hosts. University of Texas Press, Austin, TX.

GRINNELL, J. 1914. An account of the mammals and birds of the lower Colorado River Valley with especial reference to the distributional problems presented. University of California Publications in Zoology 12:51–294.

GRINNELL, J., AND A. H. MILLER. 1944. The distribution of the birds of California. Pacific Coast Avifauna No. 27. Cooper Ornithological Club, Berkeley, CA.

GRINNELL, J., AND T. I. STORER. 1924. Animal life in Yosemite. University of California Press, Berkeley, CA.

GRINNELL, J., AND H. S. SWARTH. 1913. An account of the birds and mammals of the San Jacinto area of southern California. University of California Publications in Zoology 10:197–406.

GROENEVELD, D. P., AND T. E. GRIEPENTROG. 1985. Interdependence of groundwater, riparian vegetation, and streambank stability: a case study. Pp. 44–48 *in* R. R. Johnson, C. D. Ziebell, D. R. Patton, and others (technical coordinators). Riparian ecosystems and their management: reconciling conflicting uses. USDA Forest Service Gen. Tech. Rep. RM-120. USDA Forest Service, Rocky Mountain Forest and Range Experimental Station, Fort Collins, CO.

GRYZBOWSKI, J. A. 1991. Survivorship, dispersal, and population structure of the Black-capped Vireo at the Kerr Wildlife Management Area, Texas. Resource Protection Division, Texas Parks and Wildlife Department, Austin, TX.

GRZYBOWSKI, J. A. 1995. Black-capped Vireo (*Vireo atricapillus*). *In* A. Poole and F. Gill (editors). The birds of North America, no. 181. Academy of Natural Sciences, Philadelphia, PA, and American Ornithologists' Union, Washington, D.C.

GRZYBOWSKI, J. A., R. B. CLAPP, AND J. T. MARSHALL, JR. 1986. History and current population status of the Black-headed Vireo in Oklahoma. American Birds 40:1151–1161.

GRZYBOWSKI, J. A., AND C. M. PEASE. In press. Comparing the relative effects of brood parasitism and nest predation on seasonal fecundity in passerine birds. *In* J. N. M. Smith, T. L. Cook, S. I. Rothstein, S. K. Robinson, and S. G. Sealy (editors). The bi-

ology and management of cowbirds and their hosts. University of Texas Press, Austin, TX.

GUREVITCH, J., AND L. V. HEDGES. 1993. Meta-analysis: combining the results of independent experiments. Pp. 378–398 *in* S.M. Scheiner and J. Gurevitch (editors). Design and analysis of ecological experiments. Chapman and Hall, New York, NY.

GUSTAFSSON, L., AND W. J. SUTHERLAND. 1988. The costs of reproduction in the Collared Flycatcher *Ficedula albicollis*. Nature 335:813–815.

GUTZWILLER, K. J., AND S. H. ANDERSON. 1992. Interception of moving organisms: influences of patch shape, size, and orientation on community structure. Landscape Ecology 6:293–303.

GYSEL, L. W., AND L. J. LYON. 1980. Habitat analysis and evaluation. Pp. 305–327 *in* S. D. Schemnitz (editor). Wildlife management techniques manual. The Wildlife Society, Washington, D.C.

HAHN, D. C., AND R. C. FLEISCHER. 1995. DNA fingerprint similarity between female and juvenile Brown-headed Cowbirds trapped together. Animal Behavior 49:1577–1580.

HAHN, D. C., AND J. S. HATFIELD. 1995. Parasitism at the landscape scale: cowbirds prefer forests. Conservation Biology 6:1415–1424.

HAHN, D. C., AND J. S. HATFIELD. In press. Host selection in the forest interior: cowbirds target ground-nesting species. *In* J. N. M. Smith, T. L. Cook, S. I. Rothstein, S. K. Robinson, and S. G. Sealy (editors). Ecology and management of cowbirds and their hosts. University of Texas Press, Austin, TX.

HAIG, S. M., J. D. BALLOU, AND N. J. CASNA. 1994. Identification of kin structure in Guam Rails: analysis of pedigrees and DNA profiles. Molecular Ecology 3:109–119.

HAIG S. M., J. D. BALLOU, AND N. J. CASNA. 1995. Genetic identification of kin in Micronesian Kingfishers. Journal of Heredity 86: 423–431.

HALL, L. S., M. L. MORRISON, AND W. M. BLOCK. 1997. Songbird status and roles. Pp. 69–88 *in* W. M. Block and D. M. Finch (editors). Songbird ecology in southwestern ponderosa pine forests: a literature review. USDA Forest Service Gen. Tech. Rep. RM-292. USDA Forest Service, Rocky Mountain Forest and Range Experiment Station, Fort Collins, CO.

HAMILTON, W. J., III, AND G. H. ORIANS. 1965. Evolution of brood parasitism in altricial birds. Condor 67:361–382.

HANEY, J. C., D. S. LEE, AND M. WALSH-MCGEHEE. 1998. A quantitative analysis of winter distribution and habitats of Kirtland's Warblers in the Bahamas. Condor 100:201–217.

HANKA, L. R. 1985. Recent altitudinal range expansion by the Brown-headed Cowbird in Colorado. Western Birds 16:183–184.

HANN, H. W. 1937. Life history of the Oven-bird in southern Michigan. Wilson Bulletin 49:145–237.

HANN, W. J., J. L. JONES, M. G. KARL, P. F. HESSBURG, R. E. KEANE, D. G. LONG, J. P. MENAKIS, C. H. MCNICOLL, S. G. LEONARD, R. A. GRAVENMIER, AND B. G. SMITH. 1997. Landscape dynamics of the basin. Volume II. Pp. 337–1055 *in* T. M. Quigley and S. J. Arbelbide (technical editors). An assessment of ecosystem components in the Interior Columbia Basin and portions of the Klamath and Great Basins.

USDA Forest Service Gen. Tech. Rep. PNW-405. USDA Forest Service Pacific Northwest Research Station, Portland, OR.

HANNA, W. C. 1928. Notes on the Dwarf Cowbird in southern California. Condor 30:161–162.

HANSEN, P. L., R. D. PFISTER, K. BOGGS, B. J. COOK, J. JOY, AND D. K. HINCKLEY. 1995. Classification and management of Montana's riparian and wetland sites. Montana Forest and Conservation Experiment Station, Miscellaneous Publication No. 54. University of Montana, Missoula, MT.

HANSKI, I. 1982. Dynamics of regional distribution: the core and satellite species hypothesis. Oikos 38:210–221.

HARRIS, J. H. 1991. Effects of brood parasitism by Brown-headed Cowbirds on Willow Flycatcher nesting success along the Kern River, California. Western Birds 22:13–26

HARRIS, J. H., S. D. SANDERS, AND M. A. FLETT. 1987. Willow Flycatcher surveys in the Sierra Nevada. Western Birds 18:27–36.

HARRISON, S. 1991. Local extinction in a metapopulation context: an empirical evaluation. Biological Journal of the Linnean Society 42:73–88.

HARRISON, S., AND J. F. QUINN. 1989. Correlated environments and the persistence of metapopulations. Oikos 56:293–298.

HAUFLER, J. B. 1998. A strategy for bird research in forested ecosystems of the western United States. Pp. 219–229 in J. M. Marzluff and R. Sallabanks (editors). Avian conservation: research and management. Island Press, Washington, D.C.

HAYDEN, T. J., AND D. J. TAZIK. 1991. Project status report: 1991 field studies of two endangered species (the Black-capped Vireo and the Golden-cheeked Warbler) and the cowbird control program on Fort Hood, Texas. Report submitted to HQ III Corps and Fort Hood, DEH, Fort Hood, Texas.

HAYDEN, T. J., D. J. TAZIK, R. H. MELTON, AND J. D. CORNELIUS. In press. Cowbird control program at Fort Hood, Texas: lessons for mitigation of cowbird parasitism on a landscape scale. In J. N. M. Smith, T. L. Cook, S. I. Rothstein, S. K. Robinson, and S. G. Sealy (editors). The biology and management of cowbirds and their hosts. University of Texas Press, Austin, TX.

HAYWARD, C. L. 1941. Notes on the nesting habits some mountain-dwelling birds in Utah. Great Basin Naturalist 2:1–8.

HAYWARD, C. L. 1945. Biotic communities of the southern Wasatch and Unita Mountains, Utah. Great Basin Naturalist 6:1–124.

HAYWARD, C. L., C. COTTAM, A. M. WOODBURY, AND H. H. FROST. 1976. Birds of Utah. Great Basin Naturalist Memoirs 1:1–229.

HEINSOHN, R. G. 1987. Age-dependent vigilance in winter aggregations of cooperatively breeding White-winged Choughs (Corcorax melanoramphos). Behavioral Ecology and Sociobiology 20:303–306.

HEINSOHN, R. G. 1991. Slow learning of foraging skills and extended parental care in cooperatively breeding White-winged Choughs. American Naturalist 137:864–881.

HEJL, S. J. 1992. The importance of landscape patterns to bird diversity: a perspective from the Northern Rocky Mountains. Northwest Environmental Journal 8:119–137.

HEJL, S. J. 1994. Human-induced changes in bird populations in coniferous forests in western North America during the past 100 years. Studies in Avian Biology 15:232–246.

HEJL, S. J., R. L. HUTTO, C. R. PRESTON, AND D. M. FINCH. 1995. Effects of silvicultural treatments in the Rocky Mountains. Pp. 220–244 in T. E. Martin and D. M. Finch (editors). Ecology and management of neotropical migratory birds. Oxford University Press. New York, NY.

HEJL, S. J., AND L. C. PAIGE. 1994. A preliminary assessment of birds in continuous and fragmented forests of western red-cedar/western hemlock in northern Idaho. Pp. 189–197 in D. M. Baumgartner and J. E. Lotan (editors). Proceedings of a symposium on interior cedar-hemlock-white pine forests: ecology and management. Washington State University Cooperative Extension, Pullman, WA.

HEJL, S. J., AND R. E. WOODS. 1991. Bird assemblages in old-growth and rotation-aged Douglas-fir/ponderosa pine stands in the northern Rocky Mountains: a preliminary assessment. Pp. 93–100 in D. M. Baumgartner and J. E. Lotan (editors). Proceedings of a symposium on interior Douglas-fir: the species and its management. Washington State University Cooperative Extension, Pullman, WA.

HENDERSON, A. B. 1870. Narrative of a prospecting expedition to the east fork and Clark's fork of the Yellowstone. In M. Meagher, The bison of Yellowstone National Park. 1973 National Park Service Science Monograph 1:1–161.

HENSHAW, H. W. 1875. Chapter III. Report upon the ornithological collections made in portions of Nevada, Utah, California, Colorado, New Mexico, and Arizona during the years 1871, 1872, 1873, and 1874. U.S. Government Printing Office, Washington, D.C.

HENSLER, G. L. 1985. Estimation and comparison of functions of daily nest survival probabilities using the Mayfield method. Pp. 289–301 in B. J. T. Morgan and P. M. North (editors). Statistics in ornithology. Springer-Verlag, New York, NY.

HENSLER, G. L., AND J. D. NICHOLS. 1981. The Mayfield method of estimating nesting success: a model, estimators and simulation results. Wilson Bulletin 93:42–53.

HERGENRADER, G. L. 1962. The incidence of nest parasitism by the Brown-headed Cowbird (Molothrus ater) on roadside nesting birds in Nebraska. Auk 79:85–88.

HERKERT, J. R. 1994a. Breeding bird communities of midwestern prairie fragments: the effects of prescribed burning and habitat area. Natural Areas Journal 14:128–135.

HERKERT, J. R. 1994b. The effects of habitat fragmentation on midwestern grassland bird communities. Ecological Applications 4:461–471.

HIGGINS, K. F. 1986. A comparison of burn season effects on nesting birds in North Dakota mixed-grass prairie. Prairie Naturalist 18:219–228.

HILBORN, R., AND M. MANGEL. 1997. The ecological detective: confronting models with data. Princeton University Press, Princeton, NJ.

HILL, D. P., AND S. G. SEALY. 1994. Desertion of nests parasitized by cowbirds: have Clay-coloured Sparrows evolved an anti-parasite defense? Animal Behaviour 48:1063–1070.

HILL, R. A. 1976. Host-parasite relationships of the Brown-headed Cowbird in a prairie habitat of west-central Kansas. Wilson Bulletin 88:555–565.

HOBSON, K. A., P. PERRINE, E. B. ROBERTS, M. L FOSTER, AND P. WOODIN. 1985. A breeding bird survey of Salt Marsh Yellowthroats, Geothlypis trichas sinuosa, in the San Francisco Bay Region. San Francisco Bay Bird Observatory. U.S. Fish and Wildlife Service Contract No. 84–57. U.S. Fish and Wildlife Service, Sacramento, CA.

HOBSON, K. A., AND S. G. SEALY. 1989. Responses of Yellow Warblers to the threat of cowbird parasitism. Animal Behavior 38:510–519.

HOCHACHAKA, W. 1990. Seasonal decline in reproductive performance of Song Sparrows. Ecology 71:1279–1288.

HOFSLUND, P. B. 1957. Cowbird parasitism of the northern Yellow-Throat. Auk 74:42–48.

HOFSLUND, P. B. 1959. A life history study of the Yellowthroat, Geothlypis trichas. Proceedings of the Minnesota Academy of Sciences 27:144–174.

HOLFORD, K. C., AND D. D. ROBY. 1993. Factors limiting fecundity of captive Brown-headed Cowbirds. Condor 95:536–545.

HOLMES, B. 1993. An avian arch-villain gets off easy. Science 262:1514–1515.

HOLMES, N. D., D. S. SMITH, AND A. JOHNSTON. 1979. Effect of grazing by cattle on the abundance of grasshoppers on fescue grasslands. Journal of Range Management 32:310–311.

HOLMES, R. T., AND T. W. SHERRY. 1992. Site fidelity of migratory warblers in temperate breeding and neotropical wintering areas: implications for population dynamics, habitat selection, and conservation. Pp 563–575 in J. M. Hagan, III, and D. W. Johnston (editors). Ecology and conservation of neotropical migrant landbirds. Smithsonian Institution Press, Washington, D.C.

HOOVER, J. P., AND M. C. BRITTINGHAM. 1993. Regional variation in brood parasitism of Wood Thrushes. Wilson Bulletin 105:228–238.

HOOVER, J. P., M. C. BRITTINGHAM, AND L. J. GOODRICH. 1996. Effects of forest patch size on nesting success of Wood Thrushes. Auk 112:146–155.

HORN, H. S., AND D. I. RUBENSTEIN. 1984. Behavioral adaptations and life history. Pp. 279–300 in J. Krebs and N. B. Davies (editors). Behavioral ecology: an evolutionary approach. Blackwell, Oxford, U.K.

HOSMER, D. W., JR., AND S. LEMESHOW. 1989. Applied logistic regression. Wiley Series in Probability and Statistics. John Wiley and Sons, New York, NY.

HOWE, H. F. 1994. Managing species diversity in tallgrass prairie: assumptions and implications. Conservation Biology 8:691–704.

HOWE, W. H., AND F. L. KNOPF. In press. The role of vegetation on cowbird parasitism on Yellow Warblers. In J. N. M. Smith, T. L. Cook, S. I. Rothstein, S. K. Robinson, and S. G. Sealy (editors). The biology and management of cowbirds and their hosts. University of Texas Press, Austin, TX.

HOY, G., AND J. OTTOW. 1964. Biological and oological studies of the molothrine cowbirds (Icteridae) of Argentina. Auk 81:186–203.

HUBER, G. E., AND A. A. STEUTER. 1984. Vegetation profile and grassland bird response to spring burning. Prairie Naturalist 16:55–61.

HUNT, J. 1991. Status of black-capped vireos on Fort Hood, Texas. Preliminary report submitted to U.S. Army Construction Engineering Laboratories, Champaign, IL.

HUNTER, W. C., R. D. OHMART, AND B. W. ANDERSON. 1988. Use of exotic saltcedar (Tamarix chinensis) by birds in arid riparian systems. Condor 90:113–123.

HURLBERT, L. C. 1988. Causes of fire effects in tallgrass prairie. Ecology 69:46–58.

HUTTO, R. L. 1995a. Composition of bird communities following stand-replacement fires in northern Rocky Mountain (U.S.A.) conifer forests. Conservation Biology 9:1041–1058.

HUTTO, R. L. 1995b. USFS Northern Region Songbird Monitoring Program: Distribution and Habitat Relationships. USDA Forest Service Report R1–95–05. (Also available at www.umt.edu/biology/dbs/landbird.html).

HUTTO, R. L., S. M. PLETSCHET, AND P. HENDRICKS. 1986. A fixed radius point count method for non-breeding and breeding season use. Auk 103:593–602.

IMMELMANN, K. 1971. Ecological aspects of periodic reproduction. Pp. 342–489 in D. S. Farner and J. R. King (editors). Avian biology. Vol 1. Academic Press, New York, NY.

INGOLD, D. J. 1996. Delayed nesting decreases reproductive success in Northern Flickers: implications for competition with European Starlings. Journal of Field Ornithology 67:321–326.

INTERNATIONAL BIRD CENSUS COMMITTEE. 1970. An international standard for a mapping method in bird census work recommended by the International Bird Census Committee. Audubon Field Notes 24:722–726.

JACKSON, N. H., AND D. D. ROBY. 1992. Fecundity and egg-laying patterns of captive yearling Brown-headed Cowbirds. Condor 94:585–589.

JAMES, F. R., AND C. E. McCULLOCH. 1990. Multivariate analysis in ecology and systematics: panacea or Pandora's box. Annual Review of Ecology and Systematics 21:129–166.

JAMES, F. C., AND H. H. SHUGART, JR. 1970. A quantitative method of habitat description. Audubon Field Notes 24:727–736.

JEPSON-INNES, K., AND C. E. BOCK. 1989. Response of grasshoppers (Orthoptera:Acrididae) to livestock grazing in southeastern Arizona: differences between seasons and subfamilies. Oecologia 78:430–431.

JETTE, L. A., T. J. HAYDEN, AND J. D. CORNELIUS. 1998. Demographics of the Golden-cheeked Warbler (Dendroica chrysoparia) on Fort Hood, Texas. USACERL Technical Report 98/52. U.S. Army Construction Engineering Laboratories, Champaign, IL.

JOHNSON, M., AND M. SOGGE. 1995. Cowbird concentrations at livestock corrals in Grand Canyon National Park. Pp. 275–284 in C. Van Riper (editor). Proceedings of the second biennial conference on research in Colorado Plateau National Parks. National Park Service Proceedings NPS/NRNAU/NRTP-95/11. Flagstaff, AZ.

JOHNSON, R. G., AND S. A. TEMPLE. 1986. Assessing habitat quality for birds nesting in fragmented tallgrass prairies. Pp. 245–250 *in* J. Verner, M. L. Morrison, and C. J. Ralph (editors). Wildlife 2000: modeling habitat relationships of terrestrial vertebrates. University of Wisconsin Press, Madison, WI.

JOHNSON, R. G., AND S. A. TEMPLE. 1990. Nest predation and brood parasitism of tallgrass prairie birds. Journal of Wildlife Management 54:106–111.

JOHNSON, R. R., AND L. T. HAIGHT. 1984. Riparian problems and initiatives in the American southwest: a regional perspective. Pp. 404–411 *in* R. E. Warner and K. M. Hendrix (editors). California riparian systems: ecology, conservation and productive management. University of California Press, Berkeley, CA.

JOHNSON, R. R., L. T. HAIGHT, AND J. M. SIMPSON. 1977. Endangered species vs. endangered habitats: a concept. Pp. 68–79 *in* R. R. Johnson and D. A. Jones (technical coordinators). Importance, preservation and management of riparian habitat: a symposium. USDA Forest Service Gen. Tech. Rep. RM-166. USDA Forest Service, Rocky Mountain Forest and Range Experiment Station, Fort Collins, CO.

KANTRUD, H. A. 1981. Grazing intensity effects on the breeding avifauna of North Dakota native grasslands. Canadian Field-Naturalist 95:404–417.

KANTRUD, H. A., AND R. L. KOLOGOWSKI. 1982. Effects of soils and grazing on breeding birds of uncultivated upland grasslands of the Northern Great Plains. U.S. Fish and Wildlife Service Research Report No.15, Washington, D.C.

KEELER-WOLF, T., V. KEELER-WOLF, AND W. A. CALDER. 1972. Bird fauna of the vicinity of the Rocky Mountain Biological Laboratory. Colorado Field Ornithology 15: 22–25.

KELLY, S. T., AND M. E. DECAPITA. 1982. Cowbird control and its effect on Kirtland's Warbler reproductive success. Wilson Bulletin 94:63–365.

KEPLER, C. B., W. G. IRVINE, M. E. DECAPITA, AND J. WEINRICH. 1996. The conservation and management of Kirtland's Warbler *Dendroica kirtlandii.* Bird Conservation International 6:11–22

KING, A. P. 1979. Variables affecting parasitism in the North American cowbird (*Molothrus ater*). Ph.D. dissertation. Cornell University, Ithaca, NY.

KLAAS, E. E. 1975. Cowbird parasitism and nesting success in the Eastern Phoebe. Occasional Papers of the Kansas Museum of Natural History 41:1–18.

KLEINBAUM, D. G., L. L. KUPPER, AND K. E. MULLER. 1988. Applied regression analysis and other multivariable methods. Duxbury Press, Belmont, CA.

KNAPTON, R. W. 1978. Breeding ecology of the Clay-colored Sparrow. Living Bird 17:137–158.

KNOPF, F. L. 1985. Significance of riparian vegetation to breeding birds across an altitudinal cline. Pp. 105–111 in R. R. Johnson, C. D. Ziebell, D. R. Patton, P. F. Ffolliot and R. H. Hamre (editors). Riparian ecosystems and their management: reconciling conflicting uses. USDA Forest Service Gen. Tech. Rep. RM-120. USDA Forest Service, Rocky Mountain Forest and Range Experimental Station, Fort Collins, CO.

KNOPF, F. L. 1994. Avian assemblages on altered grasslands. Studies in Avian Biology 15:247–257.

KNOPF, F. L., R. R. JOHNSON, T. RICH, F. B. SAMSON, AND R. C. SZARO. 1988. Conservation of riparian ecosystems in the United States. Wilson Bulletin 100:272–282.

KNOPF, F. L., AND F. B. SAMSON. 1994. Scale perspectives on avian diversity in western riparian ecosystems. Conservation Biology 8:669–676.

KNOPF, F. L., J. A. SEDGWICK, AND R. W. CANNON. 1988. Guild structure of a riparian avifauna relative to seasonal cattle grazing. Journal of Wildlife Management 52:280–290.

KNUTSON, H., AND J. B. CAMPBELL. 1976. Relationships of grasshoppers (Acrididae) to burning, grazing, and range sites of native tallgrass prairie in Kansas. Proceedings of the Tall Timbers Conference on Ecology of Animal Control by Habitat Management 6:107–120.

KOFORD, R. R., B. S. BOWEN, J. T. LOKEMOEN, AND A. D. KRUSE. In press. Cowbird parasitism in grassland and cropland in the northern Great Plains. *In* J. N. M. Smith, T. L. Cook, S. I. Rothstein, S. K. Robinson, and S. G. Sealy (editors). The biology and management of cowbirds and their hosts. University of Texas Press, Austin, TX.

KOLOSZAR, J. A. 1998. 1997. Field studies of the Black-capped Vireo (*Vireo atricapillus*) on Fort Hood, Texas. Pp. 7–27 *in* The Nature Conservancy, Summary of 1997 Research Activities. Texas Conservation Data Center, The Nature Conservancy of Texas, Fort Hood, Texas.

KOZLOVIC, D. R. In press. Cowbird parasitism and productivity of House Finch hosts. Canadian Journal of Zoology.

KOZLOVIC, D. R., R. W. KNAPTON, AND J. C. BARLOW. 1996. Unsuitability of the House Finch as a host of the Brown-headed Cowbird. Condor 98:253–258.

KREBS, J., AND N. B. DAVIES. 1993. An introduction to behavioral ecology. Blackwell Scientific Publications, Cambridge, MA.

KRUSE, A. D., AND J. L. PIEHL. 1986. The impact of prescribed burning on ground-nesting birds. Pp.153–156 *in* G. K. Clambey and R. H. Pemble (editors). The prairie—past, present, and future. North Dakota State University, Fargo, ND.

KUEHL, R. O. 1994. Statistical principles of research design and analysis. Duxbury Press, Belmont, CA

LAAKE, J. L., S. T. BUCKLAND, D. R. ANDERSON, AND K. P. BURNHAM. 1993. DISTANCE User's Guide. Colorado Cooperative Fish and Wildlife Research Unit, Colorado State University, Fort Collins, CO.

LANGEN, T. A., D. T. BOLGER, AND T. J. CASE. 1991. Predation on artificial bird nests in chaparral fragments. Oecologia 86:395–401.

LANTZ, G. 1976. Compartment prescription and environmental analysis report. USDA Forest Service, 2410-1, Harrisville, MI.

LARISON, B. 1996. Avian responses to riparian restoration. M.S. thesis. San Francisco State University, San Francisco, CA.

LARISON, B., S. A. LAYMON, P. L. WILLIAMS, AND T. B. SMITH. 1998. Song Sparrows vs. cowbird brood parasites: impacts of forest structure and nest-site selection. Condor 100:93–101.

LAWTON, J. H., J. R. BEDDINGTON, AND R. BONSER. 1974. Switching in invertebrate predators. Pp. 141–158 *in* M. B. Usher and M. H. Williamson (editors). Ecological stability. Chapman and Hall, London, U.K.

LAYMON, S. A. 1987. Brown-headed cowbirds in California: historical perspectives and management opportunities in riparian habitats. Western Birds 18:63–70.

LAYMON, S. A. 1988. Ecology of the Spotted Owl in the central Sierra Nevada, California. PhD dissertation. University of California, Berkeley, CA.

LAYMON, S. A., P. L. WILLIAMS, M. D. HALTERMAN, AND S. D. ROWE. 1996. Monitoring of riparian habitat restoration sites at the South Fork Kern River, California: breeding birds and habitat characteristics, 1988 to 1995. Nature Conservancy Report. Kern River Research Center, Weldon, CA.

LAYMON, S. A., P. L. WILLIAMS, M. D. HALTERMAN, AND S. D. ROWE. 1997. Riparian restoration at the Kern River Preserve: 1996 bird monitoring results. Nature Conservancy Report. Kern River Research Center, Weldon, CA.

LEVIN, S. 1974. Dispersion and population interactions. American Naturalist 108:207–228.

LINDSDALE, J. M. 1936. The birds of Nevada. Pacific Coast Avifauna No. 23. Cooper Ornithological Club, Berkeley, CA.

LITTELL, R. C., G. A. MILLIKEN, W. W. STROUP, AND R. D. WOLFINGER. 1996. SAS System for Mixed Models. SAS Institute, Inc., Cary, NC.

LOSENSKY, B. J. 1993. Historical vegetation in Region One by climatic section. USDA Forest Service, Draft Report for the Northern Region, P. O. Box 7669, Missoula, MT 59807.

LOWTHER, P. E. 1979. Nest selection by Brown-headed Cowbirds. Wilson Bulletin 91:118–122.

LOWTHER, P. E. 1993. Brown-headed Cowbird (*Molothrus ater*). *In* A. Poole and F. Gill (editors). The birds of North America, no. 47. Academy of Natural Sciences, Philadelphia, and American Ornithologists' Union, Washington, D.C.

LOWTHER, P. E. 1995. Bronzed Cowbird (*Molothrus aeneus*). *In* A. Poole and F. Gill (editors). The birds of North America, no. 144. Academy of Natural Sciences, Philadelphia, PA, and American Ornithologists' Union, Washington, D.C.

LYMAN, R. L., AND S. D. LIVINGSTON. 1983. Late Quaternary mammalian zoogeography of eastern Washington. Quaternary Research 20: 360–373.

LYNCH, M. 1988. Estimation of relatedness by DNA fingerprinting. Molecular Biology and Evolution 5: 584–599.

LYNCH, M. 1990. The similarity index and DNA fingerprinting. Molecular Biology and Evolution 7: 478–484.

MA, Z. 1995. Using a rule-based merging algorithm to eliminate "salt-pepper" and small regions of classified images. Proceedings of the Ninth Annual Symposium on Geographic Information Systems 11: 834–837.

MAJOR, R. E. 1990. The effect of human observers on the intensity of nest predation. Ibis 132:608–612.

MANN, C. 1990. Meta-analysis in the breech. Science 249:476–480.

MARTIN, T. E. 1987. Artificial nest experiments: effects of nest appearance and type of predator. Condor 89: 925–928.

MARTIN, T. E. 1988. On the advantage of being different: nest predation and the coexistence of bird species. Proceedings of the National Academy of Science (USA) 85:2196–2199.

MARTIN, T. E. 1992. Breeding productivity considerations: what are the appropriate habitat features for management? Pp. 455–473 *in* J. M. Hagan, III, and D. W. Johnston (editors). Ecology and conservation of neotropical migrant landbirds. Smithsonian Institution Press, Washington, D.C.

MARTIN, T. E. 1993. Nest predation among vegetative layers and habitat types: revising the dogmas. American Naturalist 141: 897–913.

MARTIN, T. E., AND G. R. GEUPEL. 1993. Nest-monitoring plots: methods for locating nests and monitoring success. Journal of Field Ornithology 64:507–519.

MARTIN, T. E., W. M. HOCHACHKA, C. J. CONWAY, AND J. W. JENKINS. 1996. BBIRD field protocol. Montana Cooperative Wildlife Research Unit. University of Montana, Missoula, MT.

MARTIN, T. E., C. R. PAINE, C. J. CONWAY, W. M. HOCHACHKA, P. ALLEN, AND J. W. JENKINS. 1997. BBIRD field protocols [online]. Available: http://pica.wru.umt.edu/bbird/protocol/protocol.htm [1998, September 13].

MARTIN, T. E., AND J. J. ROPER. 1988. Nest predation and nest-site selection of a western population of the Hermit Thrush. Condor 90:51–57.

MARVIL, R. E., AND A. CRUZ. 1989. Impact of Brown-headed Cowbird parasitism on the reproductive success of the Solitary Vireo. Auk 106:276–480.

MASON, P. 1986. Brood parasitism in a host generalist, the Shiny Cowbird: I. The quality of different species as hosts. Auk 103:52–60.

MATSUOKA, S. M., C. M. HANDEL, AND D. D. ROBY. 1997. Nesting ecology of Townsend's Warblers in relation to habitat characteristics in a mature boreal forest. Condor 99:271–281.

MAY, R. M., AND S. K. ROBINSON. 1985. Population dynamics of avian brood parasitism. American Naturalist 126:475–494.

MAYFIELD, H. F. 1960. The Kirtland's Warbler. Cranbrook Institute of Science, Bloomfield Hills, MI.

MAYFIELD, H. F. 1961. Nesting success calculated from exposure. Wilson Bulletin 73:255–261.

MAYFIELD, H. F. 1965. The Brown-headed Cowbird, with old and new hosts. Living Bird 4:13–28.

MAYFIELD, H. F. 1975. Suggestions for calculating nest success. Wilson Bulletin 87:456–466.

MAYFIELD, H. F. 1977. Brown-headed cowbird: agent of extinction? American Birds 31:107–113.

MAYNARD, W. R. 1994. Summary of 1994 survey efforts in New Mexico for Southwestern Willow Flycatchers (*Empidonax traillii extimus*). Contract #94–516–69. New Mexico Department of Game and Fish, Albuquerque, NM.

McCULLAGH, P., AND J. A. NELDER. 1983. Generalized linear models. Chapman and Hall, New York, NY.

McCUNE, B. 1983. Fire frequency reduced two orders of magnitude in the Bitterroot Canyons, Montana. Canadian Journal of Forest Research 13:212–218.

MCDONALD, D. B., AND H. CASWELL. 1993. Matrix methods for avian demography. Current Ornithology 10:139–185.

MCDONALD, J. N. 1981. North American bison: their classification and evolution. University of California Press, Berkley, CA.

MCGARIGAL, K., AND B. J. MARKS. 1995. FRAGSTATS: spatial pattern analysis program for quantifying landscape structure. USDA Forest Service Gen. Tech. Rep. PNW-351. USDA Forest Service Pacific Northwest Research Station, Portland, OR.

MCGEEN, D. S. 1972. Cowbird-host relationships. Auk 89:360–380.

MCMASTER, D. G., AND S. G. SEALY. 1997. Host-egg removal by Brown-headed Cowbirds: a test of the host incubation limit hypothesis. Auk 114:212–220.

MEAGHER, M. 1976. Winter weather as a population-regulating influence on free-ranging bison in Yellowstone National Park. Research in the Parks: transactions of the National Centennial Symposium 1:29–38.

MEAGHER, M. 1986. *Bison bison.* Mammalian Species 266:1–8.

MEANEY, C. A., AND D. VAN VUREN. 1993. Recent distribution of bison in Colorado west of the Great Plains. Proceedings of the Denver Museum Natural History, Series 3, 4:1–10.

MEHTA, C., AND N. PATEL. 1995. StatXact 3, User manual. Cytel Software Corporation, Cambridge, MA.

MENG, A., R. E. CARTER AND D. T. PARKIN. 1989. The variability of DNA fingerprints in three species of swan. Heredity 64:73–80.

MERRILL, J. C. 1876. Notes on Texan birds. Bulletin of the Nuttall Ornithological Club 1:88–89.

MICHIGAN WEATHER SERVICE. 1974. Climate of Michigan bystations. Michigan Department of Agriculture Cooperating with NOAA—National Weather Service. U.S. Department of Commerce, East Lansing, MI.

MIDDLETON, A. L. A. 1977. Effect of cowbird parasitism on American Goldfinch nesting. Auk 94:304–307.

MIDDLETON, A. L. A. 1991. Failure of Brown-headed Cowbird parasitism in nests of the American Goldfinch. Journal of Field Ornithology 62:200–203.

MILLS, G. S., J. B. DUNNING, JR., AND J. M. BATES. 1991. The relationship between breeding bird density and vegetation volume. Wilson Bulletin 103:468–479.

MILLS, L. S., D. F. DOAK, AND M. J. WISDOM. In press. The reliability of conservation actions based on elasticity analysis of matrix models. Conservation Biology.

MINNICH, R. A. 1985. Evolutionary convergence or phenotypic plasticity? Responses to summer rain by California chaparral. Physical Geography 6:272–287.

MORRIS, D. L., AND F. R. THOMPSON, III. 1998. Effects of habitat and invertebrate density on abundance and foraging behavior of Brown-headed Cowbirds. Auk 115:376–385.

MORRISON, M. L., AND B. G. MARCOT. 1995. An evaluation of resource inventory and monitoring program used in national forest planning. Environmental Management 19:147–156.

MORSE, D. H. 1988. American warblers: an ecological and behavioral perspective. Harvard University Press, Cambridge, MA.

MORSE, S., AND S. K. ROBINSON. In press. Nesting success of a neotropical migrant in a multiple-use forested landscape. Conservation Biology.

MORTON, E. S., L. FORMAN, AND M. BRAUN. 1990. Extrapair fertilizations and the evolution of colonial breeding in Purple Martins. Auk 107:275–283.

MORTON, M. L. 1992. Effects of sex and birth date on premigration biology, migration schedules, return rates and natal dispersal in the Mountain White-crowned Sparrow. Condor 94:117–133.

MOSCONI, S. L., AND R. L. HUTTO. 1982. The effects of grazing on land birds of a western Montana riparian habitat. Pp. 221–223 in J. M. Peek and P. D. Dalke (editors). Wildlife-livestock relationships symposium. University of Idaho, Forest, Wildlife, and Range Experiment Station, Moscow, ID.

MUIZNIEKS, B. D., T. E. CORMAN, S. J. SFERRA, M. K. SOGGE, AND T. J. TIBBITTS. 1994. Arizona Partners in Flight 1993 Southwestern Willow Flycatcher survey. Nongame and Endangered Wildlife Program Tech. Rpt. 52. Arizona Game and Fish Department, Phoenix, AZ.

MUMFORD, R. E. 1952. Bell's Vireo in Indiana. Wilson Bulletin 64:224–233.

NAKAMURA, T. K., AND A. CRUZ. In press. The ecology of egg puncture by the Shiny Cowbird (*Molothrus bonariensis*) in southwestern Puerto Rico. *In* J. N. M. Smith, T. L. Cook, S. I. Rothstein, S. K. Robinson, and S. G. Sealy (editors). The biology and management of cowbirds and their hosts. University of Texas Press, Austin, TX.

NATIONAL OCEANIC AND ATMOSPHERIC ADMINISTRATION. 1994. Climatological data annual summary, Arizona. Vol. 97, No. 13. US Department of Commerce, Ashville, NC.

NERNEY, N. J. 1958. Grasshopper infestation in relation to range conditions. Journal of Range Management 3:308–315.

NEUDORF, D. L., AND S. G. SEALY. 1992. Reactions of four passerine species to threats of predation and cowbird parasitization: enemy recognition or generalized response? Behaviour 123:84–105.

NEUDORF, D. L., AND S. G. SEALY. 1994. Sunrise nest attentiveness in cowbird hosts. Condor 96:162–169

NEWMAN, G. A. 1970. Cowbird parasitism and nesting success of Lark Sparrows in southern Oklahoma. Wilson Bulletin 82:304–309.

NEWTON, I. (EDITOR). 1989. Lifetime reproduction in birds. Academic Press, London, U.K.

NEWTON, S. F., AND A. V. NEWTON. 1997. The effect of rainfall and habitat on abundance and diversity of birds in a fenced protected area in the central Saudi Arabian desert. Journal of Arid Environments 35:715–735.

NICE, M. M. 1937. Studies in the life history of the song sparrow. I. Transactions of the Linnean Society of New York 4:1–247.

NICE, M. M. 1954. Problems of incubation periods in North American birds. Condor 56:173–197.

NOLAN, V., JR. 1978 The ecology and behavior of the Prairie Warbler, *Dendroica discolor.* Ornithological Monographs 26:1–595.

NOON, B. R. 1981. Techniques for sampling avian habitats. Pp. 42–52 in D. E. Capen (editor). The use of multivariate statistics in the studies of wildlife habitat. USDA Forest Service Gen. Tech. Rep. RM-87. USDA Forest Service, Rocky Mountain Forest and Range Experimental Station, Fort Collins, CO.

NORMAN, R. F., AND R. J. ROBERTSON. 1975. Nest-searching behavior in the Brown-headed Cowbird. Auk 92:610–611.

NORRIS, R. T. 1947. The cowbirds of Preston Frith. Wilson Bulletin 59:83–103.

NUR, N. 1988. The cost of reproduction in birds: an examination of the evidence. Ardea 76: 155–168.

O'LEARY, J. F. 1990. Coastal sage scrub: general characteristics and consideration for biological conservation. Pp. 24–41 in A. A. Schoenherr (editor). Endangered plant communities of southern California. Southern California Botanists Special Publication No. 3.

OBERHOLSER, H. C. 1974. The birdlife of Texas. Vol. 2. University of Texas Press, Austin, TX.

O'CONNER, R. J., AND J. FAABORG. 1992. The relative abundance of the Brown-headed Cowbird (Molothrus ater) in relation to exterior and interior edges in forests of Missouri. Transactions of the Missouri Academy of Sciences 26:1–9.

OHMART, R. D. 1994. The effects of human-induced changes on the avifauna of western riparian habitats. Studies in Avian Biology 15:273–285.

ORIANS, G. H., E. RØSKAFT, AND L. D. BELETSKY. 1989. Do Brown-headed Cowbirds lay their eggs at random in the nests of Red-winged Blackbirds? Wilson Bulletin 101:599–605.

ORING, L. W., K. P. ABLE, D. W. ANDERSON, L. F. BAPTISTA, A. S. GAUNT, F. B. GILL, AND J. C. WINGFIELD. 1988. Guidelines for the use of wild birds in research. Auk (supplement) 105:1A–14A.

ORING, L. W., R. C. FLEISCHER, J. M. REED, AND K. MARSDEN. 1992. Cuckoldry via sperm storage in the polyandrous Spotted Sandpiper. Nature 359:631–633.

ORR, R. T., AND J. MOFFITT. 1971. Birds of the Lake Tahoe region. California Academy of Sciences, San Francisco, CA.

ORTEGA, C. P., AND A. CRUZ. 1988. Mechanisms of egg acceptance by marsh-dwelling blackbirds. Condor 90: 349–358.

ORTEGA, C. P., AND A. CRUZ. 1991. A comparative study of cowbird parasitism in Yellow-headed Blackbirds and Red-winged Blackbirds. Auk 108: 16–24.

ORTEGA, C. P., J. C. ORTEGA, AND A. CRUZ. 1994. Use of artificial cowbird eggs as a potential management tool in deterring parasitism. Journal of Wildlife Management 58:488–492.

OTT, L. 1988. An introduction to statistical methods and data analysis. PWS-Kent Publishing Co., Boston, MA.

PATON, P. W. C. 1994. The effect of edge on avian nest success: how strong is the evidence? Conservation Biology 8:17–26.

PATTIE, D. L., AND N. A. M. VERBEEK. 1966. Alpine birds of the Beartooth Mountains. Condor 68:167–176.

PATTIE, D. L., AND N. A. M. VERBEEK. 1967. Alpine mammals of the Beartooth Mountains. Northwest Science 41:110–117.

PAYNE, R. B. 1973. The breeding season of a parasitic bird, the Brown-headed Cowbird. Condor 75: 80–89.

PAYNE, R. B. 1976. The clutch size and numbers of eggs of Brown-headed Cowbirds: effects of latitude and breeding season. Condor 78:337–342.

PAYNE, R. B. 1977. The ecology of brood parasitism in birds. Annual Review of Ecology and Systematics 8:1–28.

PAYNE, R. B. 1989. Indigo Bunting. Pp. 153–172 in I. Newton (editor). Lifetime reproduction in birds. Academic Press, London, U.K.

PAYNE, R. B. 1992. Indigo Bunting. In A. Poole and F. Gill (editors). The birds of North America, no. 4. Academy of Natural Sciences, Philadelphia, PA, and American Ornithologists' Union, Washington, D.C.

PAYNE, R. B. 1997. Avian brood parasitism. Pp. 338–369 in D. H. Clayton and J. Moore (editors). Host-parasite evolution: general principles and avian models. Oxford University Press, Oxford, U.K.

PAYNE, R. B. 1998. Brood parasitism in birds: strangers in the nest. BioScience 48:377–386.

PAYNE, R. B., AND K. PAYNE. 1967. Cuckoo hosts in southern Africa. Ostrich 38:135–143.

PAYNE, R. B., AND L. L. PAYNE. 1998. Brood parasitism by cowbirds: risks and effects on reproductive success and survival in Indigo Buntings. Behavioral Ecology 9:64–73.

PEASE, C. M., AND J. A. GRYBOWSKI. 1995. Assessing the consequences of brood parasitism and nest predation on seasonal fecundity in passerine birds. Auk 112:343–363.

PECK, G. K., AND R. D. JAMES. 1987. Breeding birds of Ontario. Nidiology and distribution, Vol. 2. Passerines. Life Sciences Miscellaneous Publications, Royal Ontario Museum, Toronto, ON.

PEER, B. D. 1998. An experimental investigation of egg rejection behavior in the grackles (Quiscalus). Ph.D. dissertation. University of Manitoba, Winnipeg, MB.

PEER, B. D., AND E. K. BOLLINGER. 1997. Explanations for the infrequent cowbird parasitism on Common Grackles. Condor 99:151–161.

PEER, B. D., AND E. K. BOLLINGER. In press. Why do female Brown-headed Cowbirds remove host eggs? A test of the incubation efficiency hypothesis. In J. N. M. Smith, T. L. Cook, S. I. Rothstein, S. K. Robinson, and S. G. Sealy (editors). The biology and management of cowbirds and their hosts. University of Texas Press, Austin, TX.

PEER, B. D., AND S. G. SEALY. 1999. Laying time of the Bronzed Cowbird. Wilson Bulletin. 111:138–140.

PERRINS, C. M. 1965. Population fluctuations and clutch-size in the Great Tit, Parus major. Journal of Animal Ecology 34:601–647.

PERRINS, C. M. 1970. The timing of birds' breeding seasons. Ibis 112:242–255.

PERRINS, C. M., AND R. H. MCCLEERY. 1989. Laying dates and clutch size in the Great Tit. Wilson Bulletin 101:236–253.

PETERJOHN, B. G., J. R. SAUER, AND S. SCHWARTZ. In press. Temporal and geographic patterns in population trends of Brown-headed Cowbirds. *In* J. N. M. Smith, T. L. Cook, S. I. Rothstein, S. K. Robinson, and S. G. Sealy (editors). The biology and management of cowbirds and their hosts. University of Texas Press, Austin, TX.

PETIT, L. J. 1991. Adaptive tolerance of cowbird parasitism by Prothonotary Warblers: a consequence of nest-site limitation? Animal Behaviour 41:425–432.

PETIT, L. J., AND D. R. PETIT. In press. Brown-headed Cowbird parasitism of migratory birds: effects of forest area and surrounding landscape. *In* J. N. M. Smith, T. L. Cook, S. I. Rothstein, S. K. Robinson, and S. G. Sealy (editors). The biology and management of cowbirds and their hosts. University of Texas Press, Austin, TX.

PETIT, L. J., D. R. PETIT, AND T. E. MARTIN. 1995. Landscape-level management of migratory birds: looking past the trees to see the forest. Wildlife Society Bulletin 23:420–429.

PETRINOVICH, L., AND T. L. PATTERSON. 1978. Cowbird parasitism on the White-crowned Sparrow. Auk 95: 415–417.

PETRINOVICH, L., AND T. L. PATTERSON. 1983. The White-crowned Sparrow: reproductive success (1975–1980). Auk 100:811–825.

PHILLIPS, R. S. 1951. Nest location, cowbird parasitism, and nesting success of the Indigo Bunting. Wilson Bulletin 63:206–207.

PICMAN, J. 1992. Egg destruction by Eastern Meadowlarks. Wilson Bulletin 104:520–525.

PLISSNER, J. H., AND P. A. GOWATY. 1996. Patterns of natal dispersal, turnover, and dispersal costs in Eastern Bluebirds. Animal Behavior 51:1307–1322.

PLUMB, G. E., AND J. L. DODD. 1993. Foraging ecology of bison and cattle on a mixed prairie: implications for natural area management. Ecological Applications 3:631–643.

POST, W., A. CRUZ, AND D. B. MCNAIR. 1993. The North American invasion pattern of the Shiny Cowbird. Journal of Field Ornithologists 64:32–41.

POST, W., AND J. W. WILEY. 1977. Reproductive interactions of the Shiny Cowbird and the Yellow-shouldered Blackbird. Condor 79:176–184.

PRICE, J., S. DROEGE, AND A. PRICE. 1995. The summer atlas of North American birds. Academic Press, New York, NY.

PULICH, W. M. 1976. The Golden-cheeked Warbler—a bioecological study. Texas Parks and Wildlife Press, Austin, TX.

PULLIAM, H. R. 1988. Sources, sinks, and population regulation. American Naturalist 137:550–566.

PURCELL, K. L. 1997. Use of a fiberscope for examining cavity nests. Journal of Field Ornithology 68: 283–286.

PYLE, P., S. N. G. HOWELL, R. P. YUNICK, AND D. DESANTE. 1987. Identification guide to North American passerines. Slate Creek Press, Bolinas, CA.

PYLYPEC, B. 1991. Impacts of fire on bird populations in a fescue prairie. Canadian Field-Naturalist 105: 346–349.

QUIGLEY, T. M., AND S. J. ARBELBIDE (TECHNICAL EDITORS). 1997. An assessment of ecosystem components in the interior Columbia basin and portions of the Klamath and Great Basins. Vol. 2. USDA Forest Service Gen. Tech. Rep. PNW-405. USDA Forest

Service, Pacific Northwest Research Station, Portland, OR.

RAIM, A. In press. Spatial patterns of breeding female cowbirds on an Illinois site. *In* J. N. M. Smith, T. L. Cook, S. I. Rothstein, S. K. Robinson, and S. G. Sealy (editors). The biology and management of cowbirds and their hosts. University of Texas Press, Austin, TX.

RALPH, C. J., S. DROEGE, AND J. R. SAUER. 1995. Managing and monitoring birds using point counts: standards and applications. Pp. 161–175 *in* C. J. Ralph, J. R. Sauer, and S. Droege (editors). Monitoring bird populations by point counts. USDA Forest Service Gen. Tech. Rep. PSW-149. USDA Forest Service Pacific Southwest Research Station, Albany, CA.

RALPH, C. J., G. R. GEUPEL, P. PYLE, T. E. MARTIN, AND D. F. DESANTE. 1993. Handbook of field methods for monitoring landbirds. USDA Forest Service Gen. Tech. Rep. PSW-144. USDA Forest Service Redwood Sciences Laboratory, Arcata, CA.

REDMOND, R. L., AND M. L. PRATHER. 1996. Mapping existing vegetation and land cover across western Montana and northern Idaho. Executive summary. Wildlife Spatial Analysis Lab, Montana Cooperative Wildlife Research Unit. University of Montana, Missoula, MT.

REDMOND, R. L., AND WILDLIFE SPATIAL ANALYSIS LAB. 1996. Mapping existing vegetation and land cover across western Montana and northern Idaho. Final Report. USDA Forest Service, Northern Regional Office, Missoula, MT.

REEVES, B. O. K. 1978. Bison killing in the southwestern Alberta Rockies. Plains Anthropologist 23: 63–78.

REGOSIN, J. V. 1994. Scissor-tailed Flycatchers eject Brown-headed Cowbird eggs. Journal of Field Ornithology 65:508–511.

REYNOLDS, R. T., J. M. SCOTT, AND R. A. NUSSBAUM. 1980. A variable circular-plot method for estimating bird numbers. Condor 82:309–313.

REYNOLDS, T. D. 1981. Nesting of the Sage Thrasher, Sage Sparrow and Brewers Sparrow in southeast Idaho. Condor 83: 61–64.

REYNOLDS, T. D., AND C. H. TROST. 1981. Grazing, crested wheatgrass, and bird populations in southeastern Idaho. Northwest Science 55:225–234.

RICE, L. 1932. The effect of fire on prairie animal communities. Ecology 13:392–401.

RICH, A. C., D. S. DOBKIN, AND L. J. NILES. 1994. Defining forest fragmentation by corridor width: the influence of narrow forest-dividing corridors on forest-nesting birds in southern New Jersey. Conservation Biology 8:1109–1121.

RICH, T. D. 1978. Cowbird parasitism of Sage and Brewers sparrows. Condor 80:438.

RICH, T. D., AND S. I. ROTHSTEIN. 1985. Sage Thrashers reject cowbird eggs. Condor. 87:561–562.

RICKLEFS, R. E. 1969. An analysis of nesting mortality in birds. Smithsonian Contributions in Zoology 9:1–48.

RICKLEFS, R. E. 1973. Fecundity, mortality, and avian demography. Pp. 366–435 *in* D. S. Farner (editor). Breeding biology of birds. National Academy of Sciences, Washington, D.C.

RIDGWAY, R. 1880. Report of the geological exploration of the fortieth parallel made by order of the Secretary of War according to acts of Congress of March 2, 1867, and March 3, 1869, under the direction of A. A. Humphreys, Chief of Engineers. Part III: Ornithology. U.S. Government Printing Office, Washington, D.C.

RISCH, N. J., AND B. DEVLIN. 1992. On the probability of matching DNA fingerprints. Science 255:717–720.

ROBBINS, C. S., J. R. SAUER, R. S. GREENBERG, AND S. DROEGE. 1989. Population declines in North American birds that migrate to the neo-tropics. Proceedings of the National Academy of Sciences (USA) 86:7658–7662.

ROBERTSON, R. J., AND R. F. NORMAN. 1976. Behavioral defenses to brood parasitism by potential hosts of the Brown-headed Cowbird. Condor 78: 166–173.

ROBERTSON, R. J., AND R. F. NORMAN. 1977. The function and evolution of aggressive host behavior towards the Brown-headed Cowbird (*Molothrus ater*). Canadian Journal of Zoology 55:508–518.

ROBINSON, S. K. 1990. Effects of forest fragmentation on nesting songbirds. Illinois Natural History Reports 296:1–2

ROBINSON, S. K. 1992. Population dynamics of breeding neotropical migrants in a fragmented Illinois landscape. Pp. 408–418 *in* J. M. Hagan, III, and D. W. Johnston (editors). Ecology and conservation of neotropical migrant landbirds. Smithsonian Institute Press, Washington, D.C.

ROBINSON, S. K., J. A. GRYZBOWSKI, S. I. ROTHSTEIN, M. C. BRITTINGHAM, L. J. PETIT, AND F. R. THOMPSON, III. 1993. Management implications of cowbird parasitization on neotropical migrant songbirds. Pp. 93–102 *in* D. M. Finch and P. W. Stangel (editors). Status and management of neotropical migratory birds. USDA Forest Service Gen. Tech. Rep. RM-229. USDA Forest Service, Rocky Mountain Forest and Range Experiment Station, Fort Collins, CO.

ROBINSON, S. K., J. HOOVER, J. R. HERKERT, AND R. JACK. In press. Cowbird parasitism in a fragmented landscape: effects of tract size, habitat, and abundance of cowbirds and hosts. *In* J. N. M. Smith, T. L. Cook, S. I. Rothstein, S. K. Robinson, and S. G. Sealy (editors). The biology and management of cowbirds and their hosts. University of Texas Press, Austin, TX.

ROBINSON, S. K., S. I ROTHSTEIN, M. C. BRITTINGHAM, L. J. PETIT, AND J. A. GRZYBOWSKI. 1995a. Ecology of cowbirds and their impact on host populations. Pp. 428–460 *in* T. E. Martin and D. M. Finch (editors). Ecology and management of neotropical migratory birds. Oxford University Press, New York, NY.

ROBINSON, S. K., AND J. N. M. SMITH. In press. Cowbird parasitization at multiple spatial scales. *In* J. N. M. Smith, T. L. Cook, S. I. Rothstein, S. K. Robinson, and S. G. Sealy (editors). The biology and management of cowbirds and their hosts. University of Texas Press, Austin, TX.

ROBINSON, S. K., F. R. THOMPSON III, T. M. DONOVAN, D. R. WHITEHEAD AND J. FAABORG. 1995b. Forest fragmentation and the regional population dynamics of songbirds. Science 267:1987–1990.

ROBINSON, S. K., AND D. S. WILCOVE. 1994. Forest fragmentation in the temperate zone and its effects on migratory songbirds. Bird Conservation International 4:233–249.

RODENHOUSE, N. L., T. W. SHERRY, AND R. T. HOLMES. 1997. Site-dependent regulation of population size: a new synthesis. Ecology 78:2025–2042.

ROE, F. G. 1970. The North American buffalo, 2nd ed. University of Toronto Press, Toronto, ON.

ROGERS, C. M., M. J. TAITT, J. N. M. SMITH, AND G. J. JONGEJAN. 1997. Nest predation and cowbird parasitism create a population sink in a wetland breeding population of Song Sparrows. Condor 99:622–633.

ROHWER, S., AND C. D. SPAW. 1988. Evolutionary lag versus bill-size constraints: a comparative study of the acceptance of cowbird eggs by old hosts. Evolutionary Ecology 2:27–36.

ROMIG, G. P., AND R. D. CRAWFORD. 1995. Clay-colored Sparrows in North Dakota parasitized by Brown-headed Cowbirds. Prairie Naturalist 27:193–203.

ROSA, S. M., AND M. T. MURPHY. 1994. Trade-offs and constraints on Eastern Kingbird parental care. Wilson Bulletin 106:668–678.

ROSENBERG, K. V., A. A. DHONDT, AND J. D. LOWE. 1996. Lessons from the landscape. Birdscope 10:1–3.

ROSENBERG, K. V., R. D. OHMART, W. C. HUNTER, AND B. W. ANDERSON. 1991. Birds of the lower Colorado River Valley. University of Arizona Press, Tucson, AZ.

ROSENBERG, K. V., AND M. G. RAPHAEL. 1986. Effects of forest fragmentation on vertebrates in Douglas-fir forests. Pp. 263–272 *in* J. Verner, M. L. Morrison, and C. J. Ralph (editors). Wildlife 2000: modeling habitat relationships of terrestrialvertebrates. University of Wisconsin Press, Madison, WI.

RØSKAFT, E., G. H. ORIANS, AND L. D. BELETSKY. 1990. Why do Red-winged Blackbirds accept eggs of Brown-headed Cowbirds? Evolutionary Ecology 4:35–42.

RØSKAFT, E., S. ROHWER, AND C. D. SPAW. 1993. Cost of puncture ejection compared with costs of rearing cowbird chicks for Northern Orioles. Ornis Scandinavica 24:28–32.

ROTENBERRY, J. T., AND J. A. WIENS. 1980. Temporal variation in habitat structure and shrubsteppe bird dynamics. Oecologia 47:1–9.

ROTH, R. R., M. S. JOHNSON, AND T. J. UNDERWOOD. 1996. Wood Thrush (*Hylocichla mustelina*). *In* A. Poole and F. Gill (editors). The birds of North America, no. 246. Academy of Natural Sciences, Philadelphia, PA, and American Ornithologists' Union, Washington, D.C.

ROTH, R. R., AND R. K. JOHNSON. 1993. Long-term dynamics of a Wood Thrush population breeding in a forest fragment. Auk 110:37–48.

ROTHSTEIN, S. I. 1975a. An experimental and teleonomic investigation of avian brood parasitism. Condor 77:250–271.

ROTHSTEIN, S. I. 1975b. Evolutionary rates and host defenses against avian brood parasitism. American Naturalist 109:161–176.

ROTHSTEIN, S. I. 1976. Cowbird parasitism of the Cedar Waxwing and its evolutionary implications. Auk 93:498–509.

ROTHSTEIN, S. I. 1976. Experiments on defenses Cedar Waxwings use against cowbird parasitism. Auk 93: 675–691.

ROTHSTEIN, S. I. 1977. Cowbird parasitism and egg recognition of the Northern Oriole. Wilson Bulletin 89:21–32.

ROTHSTEIN, S. I. 1978. Geographical variation in the nestling coloration of parasitic cowbirds. Auk 95: 152–160.

ROTHSTEIN, S. I. 1982. Successes and failures in avian egg and nestling recognition with comments on the utility of optimality reasoning. American Zoologist 22:547–560

ROTHSTEIN, S. I. 1990. A model system for coevolution: avian brood parasitism. Annual Review of Ecology and Systematics 21:481–508.

ROTHSTEIN, S. I. 1994. The cowbird's invasion of the Far West: history, causes and consequences experienced by host species. Studies in Avian Biology 15: 301–315

ROTHSTEIN, S. I. AND T. L. COOK. In press. Cowbird management, host population regulation and efforts to save endangered species. In J. N. M. Smith, T. L. Cook, S. I. Rothstein, S. K. Robinson, and S. G. Sealy (editors). The biology and management of cowbirds and their hosts. University of Texas Press, Austin, TX.

ROTHSTEIN, S. I. AND S. K. ROBINSON. 1994. Conservation and coevolutionary implications of brood parasitism by cowbirds. Trends in Ecology and Evolution 9:162–164.

ROTHSTEIN, S. I., AND S. K. ROBINSON (EDITORS). 1998. Parasitic birds and their hosts. Oxford University Press, Oxford, U.K.

ROTHSTEIN, S. I., J. VERNER, AND R. C. FLEISCHER. 1986a. Social dominance, mating and spacing systems, female fecundity, and vocal dialects in captive and free-ranging Brown-headed Cowbirds. Current Ornithology 3:127–185.

ROTHSTEIN, S. I., J. VERNER, AND E. STEVENS. 1980. Range expansion and diurnal changes in dispersion of the Brown-headed Cowbird in the Sierra Nevada. Auk 97:253–267.

ROTHSTEIN, S. I., J. VERNER, AND E. STEVENS. 1984. Radio-tracking confirms a unique diurnal pattern of spatial occurrence in the parasitic Brown-headed Cowbird. Ecology 65:77–88.

ROTHSTEIN, S. I., J. VERNER, E. STEVENS, AND L. V. RITTER. 1987. Behavioral differences among sex and age classes of the Brown-headed Cowbird and their relation to the efficacy of a control program. Wilson Bulletin 99:322–337.

ROTHSTEIN, S. I., D. A. YOKEL, AND R. C. FLEISCHER. 1986b. Social dominance, mating and spacing systems, female fecundity, and vocal dialects in captive and free-ranging Brown-headed Cowbirds. Current Ornithology 3:127–185.

SAAB, V. A., C. E. BOCK, T. D. RICH, AND D. S. DOBKIN. 1995. Livestock grazing effects in western North America. Pp 311–353 in T. Martin and D. Finch (editors). Ecology and management of neotropical migrant birds. Oxford University Press, New York, NY.

SAAB, V. A., AND C. R. GROVES. 1992. Idaho's migratory landbirds: description, habitats and conservation. Idaho Department of Fish and Game, Nongame Wildlife Leaflet No. 10.

SAAB, V. A., AND T. D. RICH. 1997. Large-scale conservation assessment for neotropical migratory land birds in the interior Columbia River Basin. USDA Forest Service Gen. Tech. Rep. PNW-399. USDA Forest Service, Pacific Northwest Research Station, Portland, OR.

SABADELL, J. E. 1982. Desertification in the United States. U.S. Bureau of Land Management, Washington, D.C.

SAETHER, B.-E. 1990. Age-specific variation in reproductive performance of birds. Current Ornithology 7:251–283.

SAS INSTITUTE. 1985. SAS/STAT user's guide, Release 6.03. SAS Institute, Inc., Cary, NC.

SAS INSTITUTE. 1997. SAS/STAT software: changes and enhancements through Release 6.12. SAS Institute, Inc., Cary, NC.

SAUER, J. R., AND S. DROEGE. 1992. Geographic patterns in population trends of neotropical migrants in North America. Pp. 26–42 in J. M. Hagan, III, and D. W. Johnston (editors). Ecology and conservation of neotropical migrant landbirds. Smithsonian Institution Press, Washington, D.C.

SAUER, J. R., J. E. HINES, G. GOUGH, I. THOMAS, AND B. G. PETERJOHN. 1997. The North American Breeding Bird Survey: results and analysis. Version 96.4 (http://www.mbr.nbs.gov/bbs/). Patuxent Wildlife Research Center, Laurel, MD.

SAUNDERS, A. A. 1921. A distributional list of the birds of Montana. Pacific Coast Avifauna 14. Cooper Ornithological Club, Berkeley, CA.

SCHMIEGELOW, F. K. A., C. S. MACHTANS, AND S. J. HANNON. 1997. Are boreal birds resilient to forest fragmentation? An experimental study of short-term community responses. Ecology 78:1914–1932.

SCHROEDL, G. F. 1973. The archaeological occurrence of bison in the southern plateau. Washington State University Laboratory of Anthropolgy, Reports of Investigations 51. Washington State University, Pullman, WA.

SCHULZ, T. T., AND W. C. LEININGER. 1991. Nongame wildlife communities in grazed and ungrazed montane riparian sites. Great Basin Naturalist 51:286–292.

SCLATER, W. L. 1912. A history of the birds of Colorado. Witherby and Co., London, U.K.

SCOTT, D. M. 1963. Changes in the reproductive activity of the Brown-headed Cowbird within the breeding season. Wilson Bulletin 75:123–129.

SCOTT, D. M. 1977. Cowbird parasitism on the Gray Catbird at London, Ontario. Auk 94:18–27.

SCOTT, D. M., AND C. D. ANKNEY. 1979. Evaluation of a method for estimating the laying rate of Brown-headed Cowbirds. Auk 96:483–488.

SCOTT, D. M., AND C. D. ANKNEY. 1980. Fecundity of the Brown-headed Cowbird in southern Ontario. Auk 97:677–683.

SCOTT, D. M., AND C. D. ANKNEY. 1983. The laying cycle of Brown-headed Cowbirds: passerine chickens? Auk 100:583–592.

SCOTT, D. M., AND R. E. LEMON. 1996. Differential reproductive success of Brown-headed Cowbirds with Northern Cardinals and three other hosts. Condor 98:259–271.

SCOTT, P. E., AND B. R. MCKINNEY. 1994. Brown-headed cowbird removes Blue-grey Gnatcatcher nestlings. Journal of Field Ornithology 65:363–364.

SCOTT, T. W. 1979. Growth and age determination of nestling Brown-headed Cowbirds. Wilson Bulletin 91:464–466.

SCURLOCK, D., AND D. M. FINCH. 1997. A historical review. Pp. 43–68 in W. M. Block and D. M. Finch (editors). Songbird ecology in southwestern ponderosa pine forests: a literature review. USDA Forest Service Gen. Tech. Rep. RM-292. USDA Forest Service, Rocky Mountain Forest and Range Experiment Station, Fort Collins, CO.

SEALY, S. G. 1992. Removal of Yellow Warbler eggs in association with cowbird parasitism. Condor 94:40–54.

SEALY, S. G. 1994. Observed acts of egg destruction, egg removal, and predation on nests of passerine birds at Delta Marsh, Manitoba. Canadian Field-Naturalist 108:41–51.

SEALY, S. G. 1996. Evolution of host defenses against brood parasitization: implications of puncture-ejection by a small passerine. Auk 113:346–355.

SEALY, S. G., AND R. C. BAZIN. 1995. Low frequency of observed cowbird parasitism on eastern kingbirds: host rejection, effective nest defense, or parasite avoidance? Behavioral Ecology 6:140–145.

SEALY, S.G., J. E. SÁNCHEZ, R. G. CAMPOS, AND M. MARIN. 1997. Bronzed Cowbird hosts: new records, trends in host use, and cost of parasitism. Ornitologia Neotropical 8:175–184.

SEARCY, W. A., AND K. YASUKAWA. 1995. Polygyny and sexual selection in Red-winged Blackbirds. Princeton University Press, Princeton, NJ.

SEASTEDT, T. R. 1984. Belowground macroarthropods of annually burned and unburned tallgrass prairie. American Midland Naturalist 11:405–407.

SEDGWICK, J. A., AND F. L. KNOPF. 1988. A high incidence of Brown-headed Cowbird parasitism of Willow Flycatchers. Condor 90:253–256.

SERENA, M. 1982. The status and distribution of the Willow Flycatcher (Empidonax traillii) in selected portions of the Sierra Nevada, 1982. California Department of Fish and Game, Wildlife Management Branch Administrative Report 82–5.

SFERRA, S. J., T. E. CORMAN, C. E. PARADZICK, J. W. ROURKE, J. A. SPENCER, AND M. W. SUMNER. 1997. Arizona Partners in Flight Southwestern Willow Flycatcher survey: 1993–1994. Nongame and Endangered Wildlife Program Tech. Rep. 113. Arizona Game and Fish Department, Phoenix, AZ.

SFERRA, S. J., R. A. MEYER, AND T. E. CORMAN. 1995. Arizona Partners in Flight 1994 Southwestern Willow Flycatcher survey. Nongame and Endangered Wildlife Program Tech. Rep. 69. Arizona Game and Fish Department, Phoenix, AZ.

SHAKE, W. F. AND J. P MATTSON. 1975. Three years of cowbird control: an effort to save the Kirtland's Warbler. Jack-Pine Warbler 53:48–53.

SHARP, B. E. 1995. Brown-headed Cowbirds and grazing on National Forests in the Pacific Northwest. Northwestern Naturalist 76:121–126.

SHAW, J., AND T. S. CARTER. 1990. Bison movements in relation to fire and seasonality. Wildlife Society Bulletin 18:426–430.

SHEPPARD, J. M. 1996. Nestling Kentucky Warblers and cowbird attacked by Brown-headed Cowbird. Journal of Field Ornithology 67:384–386.

SHERRY, T. W., AND R. T. HOLMES. 1992. Population fluctuations in a long-distance neotropical migrant: demographic evidence for the importance of breeding season events in the American Redstart. Pp. 431–442 in J. M. Hagan, III, and D. W. Johnston (editors). Ecology and conservation of neotropical migrant landbirds. Smithsonian Institution Press, Washington, D.C.

SIMPSON, T. B., P. E. STUART, AND B. V. BARNES. 1990. Landscape ecosystems and cover types of the reserve area and adjacent lands of the Huron Mountain Club. Occasional Papers of the Huron Mountain Wildlife Foundation. No. 4.

SKAGGS, R. W. 1996. Population size, breeding biology, and habitat of Willow Flycatchers in the Cliff Gila Valley, New Mexico. New Mexico Dept. Game and Fish, Santa Fe, NM

SLACK, R. D. 1976. Nest guarding behavior by male gray catbirds. Auk 93:292–300.

SMITH, C. C. 1940. The effect of overgrazing and erosion upon the biota of the mixed grass prairie of Oklahoma. Ecology 21:381–397.

SMITH, J. N. M., T. L. COOK, S. I. ROTHSTEIN, S. K. ROBINSON, AND S. G. SEALY (EDITORS). In press. The biology and management of cowbirds and their hosts. University of Texas Press, Austin, TX.

SMITH, J. N. M. 1981. Cowbird parasitism, host fitness, and age of the host female in an island Song Sparrow population. Condor 83:152–161.

SMITH, J. N. M., AND P. ARCESE. 1994. Brown-headed Cowbird and an island population of Song Sparrows: a 16-year study. Condor 96:916–934.

SMITH, J. N. M., AND J. R. MERKT. 1980. Development and stability of single-parent family units in the Song Sparrow. Canadian Journal of Zoology 58:1869–1875.

SMITH, J. N. M., AND I. H. MYERS-SMITH. 1998. Spatial variation in parasitization of song sparrows by Brown-headed Cowbirds. Pp. 296–312 in S. I. Rothstein and S. K. Robinson (editors). Parasitic birds and their hosts. Oxford University Press, Oxford, U.K.

SMITH, J. N. M., M. J. TAITT, C. M. ROGERS, P. ARCESE, L. F. KELLER, A. L. E. V. CASSIDY, AND W. M. HOCHACHKA. 1996. A metapopulation approach to the population biology of the Song Sparrow. Ibis 138:120–128.

SOGGE, M. K., T. J. TIBBITTS, AND J. R. PETTERSON. 1997. Status and breeding ecology of the Southwestern Willow Flycatcher in the Grand Canyon. Western Birds 28:142–157.

SOKAL, R. R., AND F. J. ROHLF. 1981. Biometry, 2nd ed. W. H. Freeman and Co., New York, NY.

SOKAL, R. A., AND F. J. ROHLF. 1995. Biometry, 3rd ed. W. H. Freeman and Co., New York, NY.

SOLER, M. 1990. Relationships between the Great Spotted Cuckoo Clamator glandarius and its corvid hosts in a recently colonized area. Ornis Scandinavica 21:212–223.

SOLER, M., J. J. SOLER, AND J. G. MARTINEZ. 1997.

Great Spotted Cuckoos improve their reproductive success by damaging magpie host eggs. Animal Behaviour 54:1227–1233.

SOLER, M., J. J. SOLER, J. G. MARTINEZ, AND A. P. MØLLER. 1995. Magpie host manipulation by Great-Spotted Cuckoos: evidence for an avian *mafia*? Evolution 49:770–775.

SOULÉ, M. E., A. C. ALBERTS, AND D. T. BOLGER. 1992. The effects of fragmentation on chaparral plants and vertebrates. Oikos 63:39–47.

SOULÉ, M. E., D. T. BOLGER, A. C. ALBERTS, J. WRIGHT, M. SORICE, AND S. HILL. 1988. Reconstructed dynamics of rapid extinctions of chaparral-requiring birds in urban habitat islands. Conservation Biology 2:75–92.

SOUTHERN, W. E. 1958. Nesting of the Red-eyed Vireo in the Douglas Lake region, Michigan. Jack-Pine Warbler 36:105–130, 185–207.

SPENCER, J. A., S. J. SFERRA, T. E. CORMAN, J. W. ROURKE AND M. W. SUMNER. 1996. Arizona Partners in Flight 1995 Southwestern Willow Flycatcher survey. Nongame and endangered Wildlife Program Tech. Rep. 97. Arizona Game and Fish Department, Phoenix, AZ.

SPENCER, R. A. 1985. Brown-headed Cowbird feeding incidents. C. F. O. [Colorado Field Ornithologists] Journal 19:39.

SPSS. 1992. SPSS/PC+ advanced statistics, version 5.0. SPSS Inc., Chicago, IL.

SPSS. 1996. SPSS Base 7.0 for Windows users guide. SPSS Inc., Chicago, IL.

SPSS. 1997. Sigmaplot 4.0 for Windows Users Manual. SPSS Inc., Chicago, IL.

STAAB, C. A. 1995. Host and nest selection by Brown-Headed cowbirds within a riparian area in central Arizona. M.S. thesis. University of Arizona, Tucson, AZ.

STAMPS, J. 1994. Territorial behavior: testing the assumptions. Advances in the Study of Behavior 23:173–232.

STANSBURY, H. 1852. Exploration and survey of the valley of Great Salt Lake of Utah. Lippincott, Grambo and Co., Philadelphia, PA.

STARFIELD, A. M. 1997. A pragmatic approach to modeling for wildlife management. Journal of Wildlife Management 61:261–270.

STEELE, B. M., J. C. WINNE, AND R. L. REDMOND. 1998. Estimation and mapping of misclassification probabilities for thematic land cover maps. Remote Sensing of Environment. 66:192–202.

STEIDL, R. J., J. P. HAYES, AND E. SCHAUBER. 1997. Statistical power analysis in wildlife research. Journal of Wildlife Management 61:270–279.

STEVENS, D. R. 1980. The deer and elk of Rocky Mountain National Park: a 10 year study. Report to Rocky Mountain National Park, ROMO-N-13.

STEWART, R. E. 1953. A life study history of the Yellowthroat. Wilson Bulletin 65:99–115.

STEWART, R. M., R. P. HENDERSON, AND K. DARLING. 1977. Breeding ecology of the Wilson's Warbler in the high Sierra Nevada, California. Living Bird 16:83–102.

STOLESON, S. H., M. J. WHITFIELD, AND M. K. SOGGE. In press. Demography of the Southwestern Willow Flycatcher. Chapter 7 *in* D. M. Finch, R. Perriman,

S. H. Stoleson, S. J. Sferra, and M. J. Whitfield (editors). Southwestern Willow Flycatcher conservation assessment. Final report. USDA Forest Service, Rocky Mountain Research Station, Albuquerque, NM.

STRAUSBERGER, B. M., AND M. V. ASHLEY. 1997. Community-wide patterns of parasitization of a host "generalist" brood-parasitic cowbird. Oecologia 112:254–262.

STRIBLEY, J. M. 1993. Factors influencing cowbird distributions in forested landscapes of northern Michigan. M.S. thesis. Michigan State University, East Lansing, MI.

STUTCHBURY, B. 1997. Effects of female cowbird removal on reproductive success of Hooded Warblers. Wilson Bulletin 109:74–81.

STUTCHBURY, B., J. M. RHYMER, AND E. S. MORTON. 1994. Extra-pair paternity in the Hooded Warbler. Behavioral Ecology 5:384–339.

SULLIVAN, K. A. 1988. Ontogeny of time budgets in Yellow-eyed Juncos: adaptations to ecological constraints. Ecology 69:118–124.

SWARTH, H. S. 1914. A distributional list of the birds of Arizona. Pacific Coast Avifauna No. 10. Cooper Ornithological Club, Hollywood, CA.

SWENGEL, S. R. 1996. Management responses of three species of declining sparrows in tallgrass prairie. Bird Conservation International 6:241–253.

SYKES, P. W., JR., AND M. H. CLENCH. 1998. Winter habitat of Kirtland's Warbler: an endangered nearctic-neotropical migrant. Wilson Bulletin 110:244–261.

SZARO, R. C. 1989. Riparian forest and scrubland community types of Arizona and New Mexico. Desert Plants 9:70–138.

TATE, J., JR. 1967. Cowbird removes nestling warbler from nest. Auk 84:822.

TAYLOR, D. M. 1986. Effects of cattle grazing on passerine birds nesting in riparian habitat. Journal of Range Management 39:254–258.

TAYLOR, D. M., AND C. D. LITTLEFIELD. 1986. Willow Flycatcher and Yellow Warbler response to cattle grazing. American Birds 40:1169–1173.

TAZIK, D. J., AND J. D. CORNELIUS. 1993. Status of the Black-capped Vireo population at Fort Hood, Texas. Volume III: Population and nesting ecology. USA-CERL Technical Report EN-94/01, Vol III. U.S. Army Construction Engineering Laboratories, Champaign, IL.

TAZIK, D. J., J. D. CORNELIUS, AND C. A. ABRAHAMSON. 1993. Status of the Black-capped Vireo at Fort Hood, Texas. Volume I: Distribution and abundance. USACERL Technical Report EN-94/01, Vol I. U.S. Army Construction Engineering Laboratories, Champaign, IL.

TEATHER, K. L., AND R. J. ROBERTSON. 1985. Female spacing patterns in Brown-headed Cowbirds. Canadian Journal of Zoology 63:218–222.

TELFAIR, R. C., II. 1994. Cattle Egret (*Bubulcus ibis*). *In* A. Poole and F. Gill (editors). The birds of North America, no. 113. Academy of Natural Sciences, Philadelphia, PA, and American Ornithologists' Union, Washington, D.C.

TELFER, E. S. AND J. P. KELSALL. 1984. Adaptations of

some large North American mammals for survival in snow. Ecology 65:1828–1834.

TEMPLE, S. A., AND J. R. CARY. 1988. Modeling dynamics of habitat-interior bird populations in fragmented landscapes. Conservation Biology 2:340–347.

TERBORGH, J. 1989. Where have all the birds gone? Princeton University Press, Princeton, NJ.

TESTER, J. R., AND W. H. MARSHALL. 1961. A study of certain plant and animal interrelationships on a prairie in northwestern Minnesota. University of Minnesota, Minneapolis, MN.

TEWKSBURY, J. J., S. J. HEJL, AND T. E. MARTIN. 1998. Breeding productivity does not decline with increasing fragmentation in a western landscape. Ecology 79:2890–2903.

THOMAS, J. W., C. MASER, AND J. E. REDOIK. 1979. Riparian zones. Pp. 40–47 in J. W. Thomas (editor). Wildlife habitats in managed forests: the Blue Mountains of Oregon and Washington. Agricultural Handbook No. 553. USDA Forest Service, Washington, D.C.

THOMAS, L. 1997. Retrospective power analysis. Conservation Biology 11:276–280.

THOMPSON, C. F., AND V. NOLAN, JR. 1973. Population biology of the Yellow-breasted Chat (*Icteria virens* L.) in southern Indiana. Ecological Monographs 43:145–171.

THOMPSON, F. R., III. 1993. Simulated response of a forest-interior bird population to forest management options in central hardwoods forests of the United States. Conservation Biology 7:325–333.

THOMPSON, F. R., III. 1994. Temporal and spatial pattern of breeding in Brown-headed Cowbirds in the midwestern United States. Auk 111:979–990.

THOMPSON, F. R., III, AND W. D. DIJAK. In press. Differences in movements, home range, and habitat preferences of female Brown-headed Cowbirds in three midwestern landscapes. In J. N. M. Smith, T. L. Cook, S. I. Rothstein, S. K. Robinson, and S. G. Sealy (editors). The biology and management of cowbirds and their hosts. University of Texas Press, Austin, TX.

THOMPSON, F. R., III, W. D. DIJAK, T. G. KULOWIEC, AND D. A. HAMILTON. 1992. Breeding bird populations in Missouri Ozark forests with and without clearcutting. Journal of Wildlife Management 56:23–30.

THOMPSON, F. R., III, S. K. ROBINSON, T. M. DONOVAN, J. FAABORG, AND D. R. WHITEHEAD. In press. Biogeographic, landscape, and local factors affecting cowbird abundance and host parasitism levels. In J. N. M. Smith, T. L. Cook, S. I. Rothstein, S. K. Robinson, and S. G. Sealy (editors). The biology and management of cowbirds and their hosts. University of Texas Press, Austin, TX.

TONHASCA, A., JR., AND D. N. BYRNE. 1994. The effects of crop diversification on herbivorous insects: a meta-analysis approach. Ecological Entomology 19:239–244.

TRAIL, P. W. 1992. Nest invaders. Pacific Discovery Summer 1992: 32–37.

TRAIL, P. W., AND L. F. BAPTISTA. 1993. The impact of Brown-headed Cowbird parasitism on populations of the Nuttall's White-crowned Sparrow. Conservation Biology 7:309–315.

TRAUTMAN, M. B. 1940. The birds of Buckeye Lake, Ohio. Miscellaneous Publications of University of Michigan Museum of Zoology 44:1–466.

TRINE, C. L. 1998. Wood Thrush population sinks and implications for the scale of regional conservation strategies. Conservation Biology 12:576–585.

TRINE, C. L. In press. Effects of multiple parasitism on cowbird and Wood Thrush nesting success. In J. N. M. Smith, T. L. Cook, S. I. Rothstein, S. K. Robinson, and S. G. Sealy (editors). The biology and management of cowbirds and their hosts. University of Texas Press, Austin, TX.

TRINE, C. L., W. D. ROBINSON, AND S. K. ROBINSON. 1998. Consequences of Brown-headed Cowbird brood parasitization for host population dynamics. Pp. 273–295 in S. I. Rothstein and S. K. Robinson (editors). Parasitic birds and their hosts. Oxford University Press, Oxford, U.K.

TUCKER, K., S. P. RUSHTON, R. A. SANDERSON, E. B. MARTIN, AND J. BLAIKLOCK. 1997. Modelling bird distributions—a combined GIS and Bayesian rule-based approach. Landscape Ecology 12:77–93.

TULJAPURKAR, S. D., AND S. H. ORZACK. 1980. Population dynamics in variable environments I. Long-run growth rates and extinction. Theoretical Population Biology 18:314–342.

TWOMEY, A. C. 1945. The bird population of an elm-maple forest with special reference to aspection, territorialism, and coactions. Ecological Monographs 15:173–205.

U.S. DEPARTMENT OF COMMERCE. 1979. Climate atlas of the United States. National Oceanic and Atmospheric Administration, Washington, D.C.

U.S. FISH AND WILDLIFE SERVICE. 1973. Building and operating a decoy trap for live-capturing cowbirds and other birds. Report AC-211. U.S. Fish and Wildlife Service, Twin Cities, MN.

U.S. FISH AND WILDLIFE SERVICE. 1984. Starling control with live traps. Report GPO 794–791. U.S. Fish and Wildlife Service, Olympia, WA.

U.S. FISH AND WILDLIFE SERVICE. 1986. Final rule determining endangered status for the Least Bell's Vireo. Federal Register 51(85):16474–16482.

U.S. FISH AND WILDLIFE SERVICE. 1991. Black-capped Vireo (*Vireo atricapillus*) recovery plan. U.S. Fish and Wildlife Service, Austin, TX.

U.S. FISH AND WILDLIFE SERVICE. 1992. Golden-cheeked Warbler recovery plan. U.S. Fish and Wildlife Service, Albuquerque, NM.

U.S. FISH AND WILDLIFE SERVICE. 1993a. Biological opinion. U.S. Fish and Wildlife Service, Austin, TX.

U.S. FISH AND WILDLIFE SERVICE. 1993b. Proposed Rule to list the Southwestern Willow Flycatcher as endangered with critical habitat. Federal Register 58:39495–39522.

U.S. FISH AND WILDLIFE SERVICE. 1995. Final rule determining endangered status for the Southwestern Willow Flycatcher. Federal Register 60(38):10694–10715.

U.S. FISH AND WILDLIFE SERVICE. 1998. Draft recovery plan for the Least Bell's Vireo. U.S. Fish and Wildlife Service, Portland, OR.

UNITT, P. 1987. *Empidonax traillii extimus*: an endangered subspecies. Western Birds 18:137–162.

UYEHARA, J. C., AND P. M. NARINS. 1995. Nest defense by Willow Flycatchers to brood-parasitic intruders. Condor 97: 361–368.

UYEHARA, J. C., AND M. J. WHITFIELD. In press. Cowbird parasitism and vegetative cover in territories of Southwestern Willow Flycatchers. *In* J. N. M. Smith, T. L. Cook, S. I. Rothstein, S. K. Robinson, and S. G. Sealy (editors). The biology and management of cowbirds and their hosts. University of Texas Press, Austin, TX.

UYEHARA, J. C., M. J. WHITFIELD, AND L. GOLDWASSER. In press. The ecology of Brown-headed Cowbirds and their effects on Southwestern Willow Flycatchers. Chapter 8 *in* D. M. Finch, R. Perriman, S. H. Stoleson, S. J. Sferra, and M. J. Whitfield (editors). Southwestern Willow Flycatcher conservation assessment. Final report. USDA Forest Service Rocky Mountain Research Station, Albuquerque, NM.

VAN TIENDEREN, P. H. 1995. Life cycle trade-offs in matrix population models. Ecology 76:2482–2489.

VAN VUREN, D. 1983. Group dynamics and summer home range of bison in southern Utah. Journal of Mammalogy 64:329–332.

VAN VUREN, D., AND M. P. BRAY. 1985. The recent geographic distribution of *Bison bison* in Oregon. Murrelet 66:56–58.

VAN VUREN, D., AND M. P. BRAY. 1986. Population dynamics of bison in the Henry Mountains, Utah. Journal of Mammalogy 67:503–511.

VERHULST, S., J. H. VAN BALEN, AND J. M. TINBERGEN. 1995. Seasonal decline in reproductive success of the Great Tit: variation in time or quality. Ecology 76: 2392.

VERNER, J. 1985. Assessment of counting techniques. Current Ornithology 2:247–302.

VERNER, J. 1988. Optimizing the duration of point counts for monitoring trends in bird populations. USDA Forest Service Res. Note PSW-395. USDA Forest Service, Pacific Southwest Research Station, Berkeley, CA.

VERNER, J., AND A. S. BOSS. 1980. California wildlife and their habitats: western Sierra Nevada. USDA Forest Service Gen. Tech. Rep. PSW-37. USDA Forest Service Pacific Southwest Research Station, Berkeley, CA.

VERNER, J., AND L. V. RITTER. 1983. Current status of the Brown-headed Cowbird in the Sierra National Forest. Auk 100:355–368.

VERNER, J., AND S. I. ROTHSTEIN. 1988. Implications of range expansion into the Sierra Nevada by the parasitic Brown-headed Cowbird. Pp. 92–98 *in* D. Bradley (editor). Proceedings, State of the Sierra Symposium 1985–1986. Pacific Publications, San Francisco, CA.

VICKERY, P. D., M. L. HUNTER, JR., AND J. V. WELLS. 1992. Evidence of incidental nest predation and its effects on nests of threatened grassland birds. Oikos 63:281–288.

VILLARD, M.-A., K. FREEMARK, AND G. MERRIAM. 1989. Metapopulation theory and neotropical migrant birds in temperate forests: an empirical investigation. Pp. 474–482 *in* J. M. Hagan, III, and D. M. Johnston (editors). Ecology and conservation of neotropical migrant birds. Smithsonian Institution Press, Washington D.C.

WALKINSHAW, L. H. 1972. Kirtland's Warbler—endangered. American Birds 26:3–9.

WALKINSHAW, L. H. 1983. Kirtland's Warbler: the natural history of an endangered species. Cranbrook Institute of Science, Bloomfield Hills, MI.

WALTERS, C. 1986. Adaptive management of renewable resources. Macmillan, New York, NY.

WARD, D., AND J. N. M. SMITH. 1998. Morphological differentiation of Brown-headed Cowbirds in the Okanagan Valley, British Columbia. Condor 100: 1–7.

WARREN, E. R. 1906. Mammals of Colorado. Colorado College Publications, General Series, 19 (Science Series, 46):225–274.

WARREN, E. R. 1927. Altitude limit of bison. Journal of Mammalogy 8:60–61.

WEATHERHEAD, P. J. 1989. Sex ratios, host-specific reproductive success, and impacts of Brown-headed Cowbirds. Auk 106:358–366.

WEBSTER, M. S., AND D. F. WESTNEAT. 1998. The use of molecular markers to study kinship in birds: techniques and questions. Pp. 7–35 *in* R. DeSalle and B. Schierwater (editors). Molecular approaches to ecology and evolution. Birkhauser Verlag, Boston, MA.

WEINBERG, H. J., T. J. HAYDEN, AND J. D. CORNELIUS. 1998. Local and installation-wide Black-capped Vireo dynamics on the Fort Hood, Texas, Military Reservation. USACERL Technical Report 98/54. U.S. Army Construction Engineering Laboratories, Champaign, IL.

WELLS, J., AND J. TURNBULL. 1998. Sensitive species survey results for Pine Creek and Hauser Canyon Wilderness Areas. Cleveland National Forest, San Diego, CA.

WESTEMEIER, R. L., AND J. E. BUHNERKEMPE. 1983. Responses of nesting wildlife to prairie grass management on prairie chicken sanctuaries in Illinois. Pp. 36–46 *in* R. Brewer (editor). Proceedings of the Eighth North American Prairie Conference. Western Michigan University, Kalamazoo, MI.

WESTMAN, W. E. 1981. Diversity relationships and succession in California coastal sage scrub. Ecology 62: 170–184.

WESTMAN, W. E. 1983. Xeric Mediterranean-type shrubland associations of Alta and Baja California and the community/continuum debate. Vegetatio 52: 3–19.

WESTNEAT, D. F. 1990. Genetic parentage in Indigo Buntings: a study using DNA fingerprinting. Behavior Ecology and Sociobiology 27:67–76.

WHITE, J. M. 1973. Breeding biology and feeding patterns of the Oregon Junco in two Sierra Nevada habitats. Ph.D. dissertation. University of California, Berkeley, CA.

WHITFIELD, M. J. 1990. Willow Flycatcher reproductive response to Brown-headed Cowbird parasitism. M.S. thesis. California State University, Chico, CA.

WHITFIELD, M. J. In press. Results of a Brown-headed Cowbird program for the Southwestern Willow Flycatcher. *In* J. N. M. Smith, T. L. Cook, S. I. Rothstein, S. K. Robinson, and S. G. Sealy (editors). The biology and management of cowbirds and their hosts. University of Texas Press, Austin, TX.

WHITFIELD, M. J., AND K. M. ENOS. 1996. A Brown-headed Cowbird control program and monitoring for the Southwestern Willow Flycatcher, South Fork Kern River, California, 1996. Report: U.S. Army Corps of Engineers, Sacramento District, Environmental Resources Division. Purchase order DACW05-96-P-0900.

WHITFIELD, M. J., AND C. M. STRONG. 1995. A Brown-headed Cowbird control program and monitoring for the Southwestern Willow Flycatcher, South Fork Kern River, CA, 1995. California Department of Fish and Game Bird and Mammal Conservation Program, Report 95–4.

WIEDENFELD, D. A. In press. Cowbird population changes and their relationship to changes in some host species. In J. N. M. Smith, T. L. Cook, S. I. Rothstein, S. K. Robinson, and S. G. Sealy (editors). The biology and management of cowbirds and their hosts. University of Texas Press, Austin, TX.

WIENS, J. A. 1963. Aspects of cowbird parasitism in southern Oklahoma. Wilson Bulletin 75:130–138.

WIENS, J. A. 1974. Climatic instability and the "ecological saturation" of bird communities in North American grasslands. Condor 76:385–400.

WIENS, J. A. 1992. The ecology of bird communities. Vol. 2: processes and variations. Cambridge University Press, Cambridge, U.K.

WILCOVE, D. 1985. Nest predation in forest tracts and the decline of migratory songbirds. Ecology 66: 1211–1214.

WILKINSON, L. 1997. SYSTAT: the system for statistics. SYSTAT Inc., Evanston, IL.

WINTERNITZ, B. L., AND D. W. CRUMPACKER (EDITORS). 1985. Species of special concern. Unpubl. Rep., Colorado Wildlife Workshop, Denver, CO.

WISDOM, M. J., AND L. S. MILLS. 1997. Using sensitivity analysis to guide population recovery: prairie chickens as an example. Journal of Wildlife Management 61:302–312.

WITTENBERGER, J. F. 1981. Animal social behavior. Duxbury Press, Boston, MA.

WOLF, L. 1987. Host-parasite interactions of Brown-headed Cowbirds and Dark-eyed Juncos in Virginia. Wilson Bulletin 99:338–350.

WOODBURY, A. M., AND N. H. RUSSELL, JR. 1945. Birds of the Navajo Country. University of Utah, Salt Lake City, UT.

WOODWARD, P. W. 1983. Behavioral ecology of fledgling Brown-headed Cowbirds and their hosts. Condor 85:151–163.

WOODWARD, P. W., AND J. C. WOODWARD. 1979. Survival of fledgling Brown-headed Cowbirds. Bird Banding 50:66–68.

WOODWORTH, B. L. 1997. Brood parasitism, nest predation, and season-long reproductive success of a tropical island endemic. Condor 99:605–621.

WOOTTON, J. T. 1996. Purple Finch (Carpodacus purpureus). In A. Poole and F. Gill (editors). The birds of North America, no. 208. Academy of Natural Sciences, Philadelphia, PA, and American Ornithologists' Union, Washington, D.C.

WOOTON, J. T., AND D. A. BELL. 1992. A metapopulation model of the Peregrine Falcon in California: viability and management strategies. Ecological Applications 2:307–321.

YAHNER, R. H., AND C. A. DeLONG. 1992. Avian predation and parasitism on artificial nests and eggs in two fragmented landscapes. Wilson Bull. 104: 162–168.

YAMASAKI, M., T. M. McLELLAN, R. M. DeGRAAF, AND C. A. COSTELLO. In press. Effects of land-use and management practices on the presence of Brown-headed Cowbirds in the White Mountains of New Hampshire and Maine. In J. N. M. Smith, T. L. Cook, S. I. Rothstein, S. K. Robinson, and S. G. Sealy (editors). The biology and management of cowbirds and their hosts. University of Texas Press, Austin, TX.

YASUKAWA, K., J. L. McCLURE, R. A. BOLEY, AND J. ZANOCCO. 1990. Provisioning of nestlings by male and female Red-winged Blackbirds, Agelaius phoeniceus. Animal Behaviour 40:153–166.

YOKEL, D. A. 1989. Intrasexual aggression and mating behavior of Brown-headed Cowbird. Condor 91:43–51.

YOUNG, B. E. 1991. Annual molts and interruption of the fall migration for molting in Lazuli Buntings. Condor 93: 236–250.

ZAHAVI, A. 1979. Parasitism and nest predation in parasitic cuckoos. American Naturalist 113:157–159.

ZAR, J. H. 1984. Biostatistical analysis, 2nd ed. Prentice Hall, Englewood Cliffs, NJ.

ZIMMERMAN, J. L. 1983. Cowbird parasitism of Dickcissels in different habitats and at different nest densities. Wilson Bulletin 95:7–22.

ZIMMERMAN, J. L. 1992. Density-independent factors affecting the avian diversity of the tallgrass prairie community. Wilson Bulletin 104:85–94.